WHAREKAUHAU

LODGE AND COUNTRY ESTATE NEW ZEALAND | TASTE AND FLAVOUR

WHAREKAUHAU

LODGE AND COUNTRY ESTATE NEW ZEALAND | TASTE AND FLAVOUR

PHANTOM
HOUSE

PHOTOGRAPHS BY **GRANT SHEEHAN**

ACKNOWLEDGEMENTS

Thanks to: Robert Cullen, Kristy & Nico de Lange, David Walsh, Joe Houghton and the Wharekauhau farm animals that kindly co-operated in the making of this book.
Karen Hermon, Marty Hunt and Duncan Galletly for their input.
Helipro for assistance with aerial photography shoots, and Kirkcaldie & Stains Ltd for accessories.

Published for Wharekauhau Lodge and Country Estate by Phantom House Books

First Edition 2007

Printed by Toppan Print Ltd
Designed by typeface ltd - www.typeface.co.nz

Photography by Grant Sheehan ©
Text by Shelley-Maree Cassidy ©
Recipes by Robert Cullen ©

ISBN 978-0-9582838-1-6

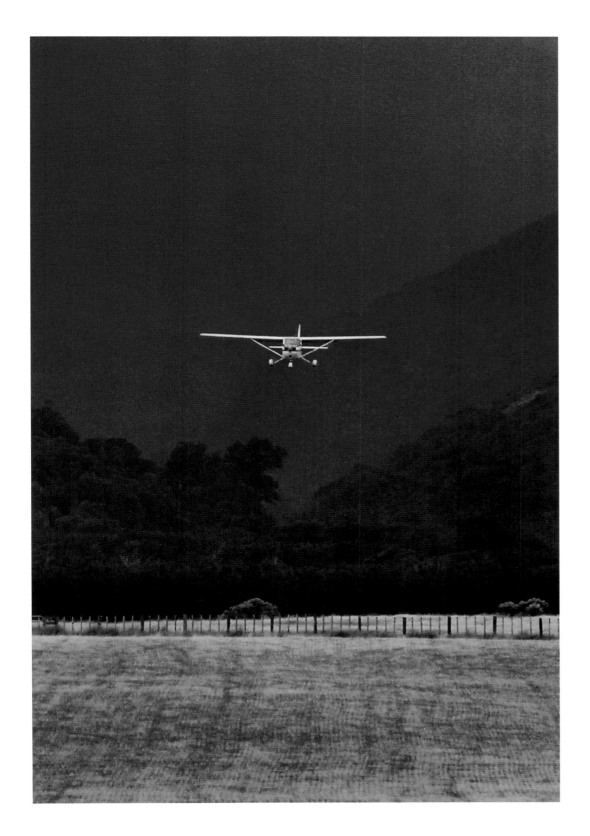

CONTENTS

< Coming in to Wharekauhau land

WHAREKAUHAU

A PLACE APART

Yet in the middle of somewhere

Backed by mountains and hills, bordered by a rugged coast and rolling seas, in a place that is rural in character, temperate in climate, and in a region favoured with wines and foods to rival anywhere, Wharekauhau Lodge and Country Estate is a true hideaway, its setting surely one of the most spectacular in the world.

"Give me land, lots of land and starry skies above..."

Overview of the Lodge at Wharekauhau, a grand country house in bravura scenery. >

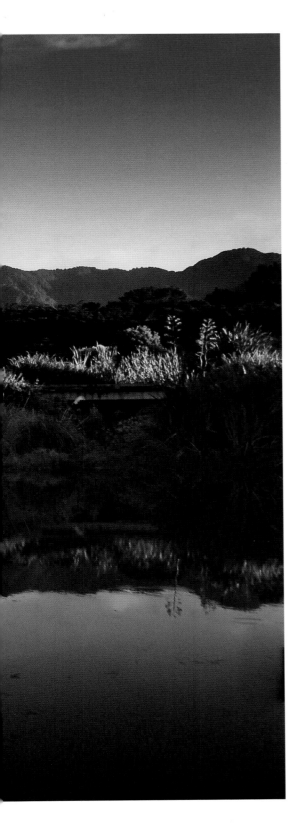

There are two ways in and out of Wharekauhau: by helicopter or private plane, or by car.

Land on the lawn in front of the house after just a few minutes flight time from New Zealand's capital city Wellington; an ideal choice if your visit is brief or you cannot tolerate a car trip of one and a half hours. The drive over the Rimutaka Hills from Wellington is on a high and winding stretch of road; snaking through a mountain pass much loved by motorcyclists and fast car owners. The road drops down to the valley of the Wairarapa below, and then curves back around the coast along a back road to Wharekauhau. Either way, your arrival is after a journey over and across impressive terrain.

Wharekauhau is a grand country house, in an equally grand setting. Rugged hills rise behind it. Thick native forest flanks it. The sea rolls out before it. From the Lodge, the long view is out over a wide expanse of grass, to reed-lined wetlands, across broad paddocks to a wide curving bay. The often-wild water that crashes on to the coast below the tablelands is the Pacific Ocean; this is the southern tip of the North Island.

There is a luxury of space in both the lodge and the cottages; the sweeping views outside are matched by generous interiors. Inside the Lodge there are ample rooms with nooks and crannies to settle yourself into, with a good book to read – or to write.

Guests gather in the large living room for drinks in the evening, meeting in front of the fire if the weather warrants it, or on the terrace on a fine clear evening. Although there is a formal dining room where dinner is most often served, other rooms can be set for a smaller and more secluded dinner.

ᵛ   The entrance hall and main living room of the Lodge   >

After a hearty breakfast – the proper way to start a day on the farm – in the Lodge's chic country kitchen, there is work to be done. It's more how you will choose to occupy yourself than real work, of course. You can watch others at work, by touring the farm. Or take a leisurely walk around the acres of private land or more actively along the coast or into the bush. Farm quad bikes and horses are a way to cover more ground.

< The Palliser Room at Wharekauhau,
  a grand location for relaxing or dining

The estate's cottages are separate from the lodge house, only a short walk away. Each one looks out to the ocean. And each is surrounded by native bush and an almost unnatural quiet. There is a pastoral symphony to be heard. The soft lowing of cattle; sometimes the distant and brief barking of the farm's sheep dogs moving the flock to new grazing ground; to the sound of roaring winds in the pines or the soft rattle of bronze flax leaves and cabbage tree fronds stirred by a sea-breeze.

Cottage comforts are such that you can stay in your room if you prefer, you will not feel bound by its size to leave it. Sheep are allowed inside – but not real ones. Metal models stand guard by the fireplace. These are dual-purpose sheep in the best New Zealand tradition, not for their meat and wool, but for their decorative and useful nature. They double as candleholders. You can buy one or more to take home; more manageable than a real sheep and easier to fit into a city life.

Views of the spacious and simply luxurious cottage interior >

The letter from English admiral Sir Hugh Palliser, dated August 30th 1773, acknowledges His Majesty King George's granting of the 'dignity of a Baronet of the Kingdom' to him and his male heirs. He sets out his pedigree for record in the College of Arms, for ratification of his family's arms and crest. From 1770 to 1776, Palliser was the Controller of the British Royal Navy, responsible for procurement and supply.

During his term, he helped outfit several voyages of exploration, including those of Captain James Cook. Before he became the famous explorer of the Pacific and Southern Oceans, Cook had served as Master's Mate on HMS Eagle, a ship captained by Palliser. On one of his journeys around New Zealand, Cook named Cape Palliser and the bay after "his worthy friend."

The Palliser name lives on in the Wairarapa, as a geographical reminder of Captain Cook.

These are remote rural pastures. Far from the bright lights of the city, Wharekauhau Lodge and Country Estate is a classic New Zealand sheep station albeit on a grander scale than most.

From its pioneer beginnings in 1840, it has grown to over 5000 acres. Although Edwardian in style, the main house is a good deal more recent. But it is as grand as the Edwardian country mansions were, and with many more luxurious and contemporary accessories than the early farmers had. Playing croquet or tennis, swimming in the pool, or being pampered in the spa would have not been on their daily agenda.

The homestead is impressive, the guest lodgings far more comfortable and stylish than farm cottages ever were, and the standard of food greater than most farm cooks ever put on the table, yet Wharekauhau is all the same a working farm, with sheep and cattle that must earn their keep.

The farm animals are outside, free ranging and exposed to the elements, whether temperate or tempestuous, as it can often be here. This is no soft English meadow transposed to a tropical climate, as the early European settlers soon found out. Lured here by claims of lush farmland, they had to come to grips with a far more demanding landscape.

For the indigenous Maori, this area was considered to be a place of learning. In pre-European times it was where their **tohunga** – the wise – came, sent away to study their craft. You can see why this challenging place, high above the immense sweep of Palliser Bay, should be chosen for such initiation.

In the Maori language, Wharekauhau means place of knowledge. The keepers of this place have learnt much about farming at least, since its early days. It was one of the first sheep stations in the remote region, and is the second oldest Romney sheep stud in New Zealand.

The distinctive Wharekauhau brand has a practical history, much like the nation and its people. When the farm first began exporting wool to Britain over 150 years ago, the wool had to be taken out by longboat, launched from the beach below, and rowed through thunderous breakers to a ship waiting at anchor beyond the surf. Just as this was being attempted for the first time, an observant farmhand spotted that the wool bales had no markings identifying them with Wharekauhau. Once on the ship, there would be no way of knowing where they came from; and more importantly, who should be paid for the wool they contained.

With quick thinking and a handy pot of paint, the longboat's rowlock was put to work as a branding iron. There on the beach it became the Wharekauhau brand. It is still in use today.

The principal flock of sheep on the estate is Romney, a versatile and hardy breed that originated in Britain. The few ancestors of today's many flocks were imported here in the 1870s. New Zealand had similar land and weather conditions so the Romney adapted easily to its new home. It became quickly established and remains the predominant sheep breed. In most flocks, Romney ewes regularly produce twins, sometimes triplets, in spring. A versatile breed, it is a dual-purpose sheep, producing quality lean meat and lustrous white wool under diverse climate conditions and on variable land.

Recently a much newer breed, the Texel, has been added to the farm's livestock. Its first home was the island of Texel, above Holland; those that came to New Zealand were sourced from Denmark and Finland. Their meat is sought after for its lean character and succulent taste, and is an exclusive feature on the Wharekauhau menu.

< Farm manager David Walsh expertly shears the wool from a Romney sheep

Wharekauhau means place of knowledge; this character is the current keeper of the knowledge about the estate and its evolution.

All at Wharekauhau agree that Joe embodies the place.

One fine day with sheep many years ago, with a young Joe at right.   ∨

His familiarity with and affection for this place is such that he might well be branded, spiritually at least, with the Wharekaukau logo. He was almost born and definitely bred here, arriving as a baby when his father came to trap rabbits, the bane of every sheep farmer. Joe has taken root here, much like the trees he has helped plant and seen grow on the land he knows like the back of his hand. He is familiar with the farm's contours, its seasons and its all weather moods. After a half-century of life here as farm hand, builder, landscaper, shepherd and now chief farm tour guide, he still roams its hills and bush. He knows where to find the great rimu trees, massively tall, hidden deep in the dark native forest, which of the mushrooms growing on logs in the undergrowth can be safely taken back to the chef, the streams where eels lurk waiting to be fed, the best places for catching fish. He has lived most of his life here, walking, riding and driving along every track and paddock, through the bush, up and over the hills, down to the beach and around the coast, and now shares the history of the land and the Lodge with guests who take the farm tour. Joe has a repertoire of yarns about the farm, its people and animals – ask him about the wild boars that once roamed here – and is on hand for a range of visitor entertainment, from taking tours to clay target shooting, archery and jet boating across the bay.

Joe Houghton in front of a native hinau tree – Joe's tree – in the Hinau Field at Wharekauhau   >

Black Angus and Charolais breeds make up the Wharekauhau cattle herd, seen here being encouraged by example to cross a river at the foot of the Rimutaka Mountains, on the coast of Palliser Bay.

Horse whispering while waiting to take guests riding on the estate.

One of the most often seen buildings in the rural landscape of New Zealand is the woolshed. Its simple architectural style has influenced contemporary building design in towns and cities. Wharekauhau's woolshed is where the sheep are shorn every eight months, and the fleece sorted and pressed for sale, continuing a long-established tradition.

On most farms, the quad bike has replaced the horse for shepherding. There's room on a four-wheeler for the dogs to hitch a ride too, until it is time for them to follow orders and move the stock.

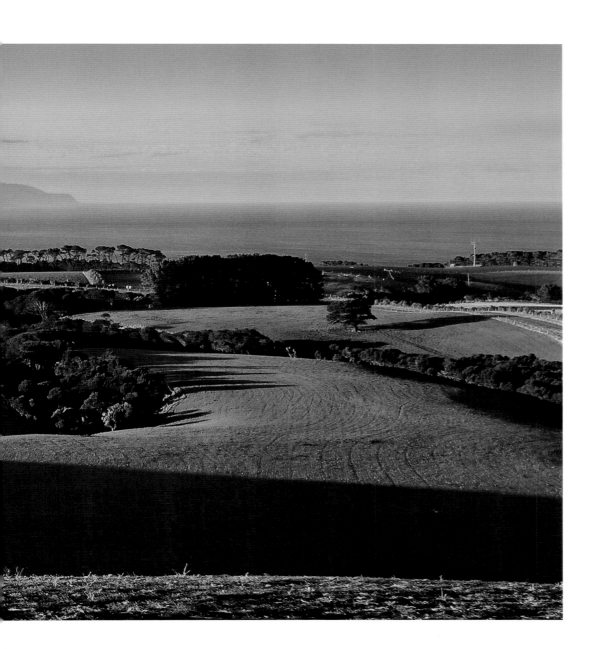

A panoramic view from up high on the farm, looking across the bay on a clear and calm winter's morning to Cape Palliser in the distance.

FLAVOUR

RECIPES FROM THE LODGE

The food philosophy at Wharekauhau is simple: what's fresh, in season and in the neighbourhood. Dishes are largely created from the Lodge gardens, the farm and the region, wherever possible.

The signature style is European contemporary, with New Zealand twists that make it special to the place and unique for its visitors. Ingredients only found in this country – a garnish of green and crunchy native fern shoots, iconic and prized whitebait, much-loved and traditional hokey pokey ice-cream – play an important part in adding extra and original flavour to the Wharekauhau fare. The cuisine celebrates the Wairarapa region that guests will experience, as well as acknowledging the European antecedents that were seminal in carving out a distinct New Zealand style. The Antipodean nation has long been known for its exhilarating outdoor activities, now it has a growing and deserved reputation for its cuisine.

The Lodge food is partnered with complementary New Zealand wines, most from the bountiful region Wharekauhau is part of. Wairarapa is famous for its young vibrant wines, especially its signature grape – pinot noir.

The food at Wharekauhau has evolved from the great farm kitchens of traditional country estates, a heritage spanning from grand English manors to the large sheep stations of colonial New Zealand. In those days, cooks worked around the clock to feed the landowner's family and farm workers, who sat down to table to hearty, simple food that gave them energy and nourishment for the working day ahead and rewarded their labours at the close of day.

Today, sustenance and style combine in the modern menu devised, prepared and served under the direction of Executive Chef Robert Cullen, a professional who has travelled the world working in many of its best restaurants. Now that he has returned to his native New Zealand, the Lodge guests are the focus of his abilities.

Robert believes in letting the main ingredients speak for themselves, in keeping dishes simple so that the real taste shines through. Clear flavours and clever texture contrasts are important elements. There are often a touch of mystery added, so that 'food detective' guests can wonder and try to guess just what is the underlying herb, spice or piquant oil that makes the taste so intriguing.

In the country tradition, it is hearty food, filling, flavoursome and tasty, yet mindful of modern palates and dietary preferences. Being out in the fresh country air usually makes most appetites keen and guests coming back from day trips and tours find they are ready to do justice to the gourmet dinner put before them.

Much of what is served at the lodge's dining table is grown on the estate or within a few miles radius of Wharekauhau. From the lodge gardens, the chefs harvest salad herbs, tomatoes, asparagus and strawberries; foraging in native bush on the farm yields wild honeycomb and mushrooms; clear running streams are the source of fresh green watercress. New Zealand lamb is an iconic dish that guests look forward to sampling, and the special breed of Texel lamb raised on the farm is a recent and valuable asset to the Lodge larder.

Chef Robert Cullen is more than a cook; he is literally a hunter, gatherer and collector of produce that provide him with resources for his recipes. "Food is what inspires me; for me it is science and art combined", he says. A key ingredient of his inspiration comes from a diverse range of local growers. He seeks out and encourages those who can meet the high standards set for the Lodge food. His regular travels around the region take him from farmers' markets and individual growers, from fishermen to olive oil makers: those who can offer the best and will work him to develop his ideas. Some of those contributors are featured in the next pages.

The recipes that follow are a taste of Wharekauhau Lodge and the Wairarapa; recipes that highlight the variety and flavours of the seafood and fish, meat and game, vegetables, fruits and herbs of this richly resourced region and country. Food that is matched by the wealth of New Zealand wines; tastes to be savoured at the Lodge and at home.

∧ Robert Cullen, executive chef and committed forager

Wharekauhau Native Bush Salad with Venison Bacon

Ingredients

16	piko piko – tender young fern fronds native to New Zealand	50 gm	straw mushrooms
1 bunch	baby watercress	200 gm	venison bacon lardons
4	fresh ruby figs	100 ml	fennel-infused olive oil
1	lemon – zest only	30 ml	lemon juice
		Salt and pepper to season	

Method

Clean the piko piko and blanch in boiling water for 10 seconds. Refresh in ice water and pat dry with a paper towel. Place in a bowl and mix together with the watercress, mushrooms and lemon zest, then season with salt, pepper and fennel oil.

To serve, sauté venison bacon, quarter the figs and add to the salad. Just before serving, spray the salad with the lemon juice.

Chef's Note

Piko Piko is a native fern tip that is high in vitamin E. The fern shoots can be found growing in damp shady areas of New Zealand's native bush. There are 312 different varieties but only seven are edible. They are pale green in colour with brown specks and are picked before the leaves unfold.

Pistachio nuts or sliced macadamia nuts also go very well with this dish, and for a bit more of a crunch, try adding some garlic croutons.

SERVES 4

WINE SUGGESTION: Nga Waka Martinborough Sauvignon Blanc

Milk-Braised Cauliflower Soup with Caviar

Ingredients

1 lt	full cream milk	Extra virgin olive oil
500 gm	cauliflower florets	Salt and pepper to season
20 gm	caviar	

Method

Place the cauliflower florets in a medium pot and cover with milk, bring to the boil, remove from heat and cover until cool.

Blend the cauliflower and pass through a sieve, season to taste and garnish with milk froth – made in a cappuccino hand blender -and olive oil, with caviar served on the side.

Chef's Note

You may prefer to place the caviar on top of the milk froth, or use skim milk instead of full cream milk. If you don't have any caviar, try smoked salmon or even bacon lardons; this soup is very adaptable.

SERVES 4

Salmon Gravlax with Pickled Fennel and Hemp Oil

SALMON GRAVLAX

Ingredients

1-1.5 kg	salmon fillet skinned and pin bones removed
150 gm	sea salt
50 gm	sugar
100 gm	wild honeycomb, melted, wax removed
75 gm	Dijon mustard
50 ml	lemon juice
350 gm	fresh dill, roughly chopped

Method

Mix the sea salt and sugar then spread half of this mixture over the base of a dish large enough to hold the salmon fillet. Place the fillet over the mixture then cover it with the remaining half. Cover closely with cling film and and refrigerate for 24 hours. Next, wash the fillet free from the salt and sugar cure and pat dry. Rub the Dijon mustard over the fillet and pour over the melted and cooled honeycomb syrup. Then add the dill and finally the lemon juice. Cover the salmon and leave for a further 12 hours before serving.

PICKLED FENNEL

Ingredients

500 gm	fennel bulb
100 ml	lime juice
Sea salt to season	

Method

Shave the fennel bulb into fine slices and season with salt and lime juice. Leave for 30 minutes before serving. Drain off the lime juice.

To serve this wonderful fresh-tasting dish, slice the salmon thinly on an angle. Serve with the pickled fennel and seasonal salad leaves dressed with hemp oil.

The gravlax is excellent for sandwiches, antipasto platters or even tossed in a salad; very versatile and healthy. It will last for up to two weeks if refrigerated well.

SERVES 10-15

Poached Koura with Herbs and Caviar Fregola

Ingredients

500 gm	freshwater koura tails – baby crayfish	75 ml	lemon-infused olive oil
		1 bunch	chives
200 gm	Fregola pasta	20	baby piko piko tips
10 gm	caviar	1 lt	fish stock for poaching
25 gm	salmon roe		

Method

Poach the koura – baby crayfish found in New Zealand freshwater lakes – in simmering fish stock for 2-3 minutes, remove and blanch in cold water and drain. Remove meat from shell and refrigerate.

Pour the pasta into 2 litres of boiling salted water and stir, continuously, for 12 minutes. Drain well. Season the pasta with lemon oil then add the koura meat, chopped chives and caviar. Season to taste with sea salt and black pepper. Garnish with piko piko tips.

SERVES 4

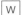

Salmon Consommé with Crayfish Ravioli

SALMON CONSOMMÉ

Ingredients

2.5 kg	salmon heads and bones
1 kg	mirepoix (vegetable and herb mix)
5 lt	water
7	egg whites
225 gm	salmon meat

Salt and pepper to season

Method

Rinse the salmon heads under cold water to clean, discard the gills then transfer to a pot and cover with water. Bring to the boil and skim, add the mirepoix, return to the boil and skim again. Leave to simmer, uncovered, for about an hour.

Strain the stock into another pot and leave to cool.

Mix together the salmon meat and egg whites, and whisk into the stock slowly. Bring to the boil, season with salt and pepper then turn down the heat making sure the egg whites have formed a crust-like topping to clear the stock, and leave simmering for about 30 minutes.

Strain the consommé through muslin, being careful not to break the crust. Leave to cool.

CRAYFISH MOUSSE

Ingredients

325 gm	crayfish meat
1	egg white
125 ml	cream

Sea salt to season

Method

Blend the crayfish with the egg white until the mixture is smooth in consistency. Pass the mixture through a fine sieve and into a bowl.

Place the bowl on a bowl of ice, stir in the cream then add the salt a little at a time, making sure not to over-salt. The mixture will thicken, then cover it and leave to rest in the refrigerator.

CONTINUED OVERLEAF

Salmon Consommé with Crayfish Ravioli

...CONTINUED

SQUID INK PASTA FOR RAVIOLI

Ingredients

3 tsp	squid ink
500 gm	strong flour
2	whole eggs
3	egg yolks
50 ml	extra virgin olive oil

Water to combine

Salt to season

Method

Place flour, eggs and squid ink in a food processor and mix together. Add the olive oil then slowly add the water until the dough starts to form. Remove and knead the mixture for 10 minutes. Cover with cling film and refrigerate to leave to rest for about 20 minutes before rolling.

To make the ravioli, roll the dough in a pasta machine until it is your preferred thickness. Cut into 20 discs around 10cm across. Place a dessert spoonful of crayfish mousse in the centre of each disc. Brush egg wash around the mousse and cover it with another disc of pasta. With your fingers, pinch lightly around the pasta disc to remove any trapped air and to seal in the mousse.

Blanch the ravioli in boiling salted water and oil for about 4 minutes or until the pasta is cooked al dente. Immediately place in ice-cold water, then remove and carefully pat dry with a paper towel. Brush with olive oil, if not serving immediately.

To serve

Gently heat up the salmon consommé – taking care not to boil it, as this will make the consommé go cloudy – add the ravioli for 4 minutes to heat through. Ladle into bowls and garnish with salmon pearls and crayfish oil.

SERVES 8-10

Pipi and Cockle Chowder

Ingredients

500 gm	pipis		300 gm	potato, diced
500 gm	cockles or clams		1	bay leaf
60 ml	grapeseed oil		250 ml	fish stock
60 gm	smoked bacon lardons		1 lt	full cream milk
3	shallots, chopped		6	chives, snipped
1	garlic clove, crushed			Salt and pepper to season

Method

Place the pipis and cockles in a tub of water overnight, then drain and rinse again with clear water to remove all grit. Place a pot over a medium high heat, sauté the garlic and shallots in the grapeseed oil until translucent. Add pipis and cockles then the fish stock. Cover for about 2-3 minutes until the shells open, then remove from heat and strain. Place the stock to one side.

Place the potatoes in the milk and bring to a simmer until cooked, add the bay leaf and remove once you can smell its fragrance. Season the milk.

Add fish stock and bring to the boil skimming off any impurities. Next, add the shellfish and re-heat to a simmer. Do not boil. Season to taste and garnish with sautéed bacon lardons and snipped chives.

Chef's Note

Do not boil otherwise the pipis and cockles will go rubbery.

SERVES 6-8

Watercress and Redcurrant Salad with Granny Smith Apple Sorbet

Ingredients

500 ml	Granny Smith apple	60 gm	dried redcurrants
100 ml	lime juice	8-10	dried apple crisps
175 ml	stock syrup		Fennel-infused olive oil to season salad
1 bunch	fresh watercress		

Method

Peel and core the apple and place through a juicer, to combine with the lime juice in the juice container. Once the apple juice has been extracted, add stock syrup and churn in an ice-cream machine. Freeze.

Wash and pick over the watercress, pat dry with a paper towel removing excess water. Toss in a bowl with dried redcurrants and season with fennel oil. To serve, place salad in a bowl, add apple crisp followed by the apple sorbet. Garnish with an apple crisp and serve immediately.

Chef's Note

If you do not have an ice cream machine, place the mixture in a large tray and freeze. Before serving, scrape with a fork and place on top of the salad.

Make the effort to go out and pick your own watercress if you can, or buy it from the local farmers' market – then you know it's fresh and wild. The chefs at the lodge have their favourite sites where they like to go and pick watercress, making sure the water is not contaminated and the creeks are clean and running. Going that 'extra mile' adds adventure and character to the dish.

MAKES ABOUT 8 – 10 PORTIONS

Green Lip Mussels with Chorizo

Ingredients

2 kg	green lip mussels in shells, cleaned	250 gm	tomato, diced
150 gm	chorizo sausage	50 ml	sunflower oil
75 gm	haricot beans, blanched	100 gm	unsalted butter
1	clove garlic, diced	200 ml	dry white wine
50 gm	shallots, diced	1 sprig	Italian parsley, chopped

Method

Take a large pot and place over a medium high heat, add oil and butter and sauté shallots and garlic but do not colour. Add the chorizo and haricot beans, then the mussels, and once the heat increases, add the white wine and cover with a lid.

Once the mussels have opened, toss the tomato and parsley in the pot and mix well. Serve straight away, lightly dressed with broth. Keep the remainder of the mussel broth as the stock is a good base for risotto or chowders.

Chef's Note

When you are cleaning mussels, submerge them in a sink full of water and remove any that float to the top. And any mussels that do not open during cooking must not be eaten.

SERVES 4

Coffee-rubbed Wharekauhau Texel Lamb Loin with Butternut Purée, Smoked Vanilla and Sauce Syrah

Ingredients

4	trimmed lamb loins	80 ml	olive oil
50 gm	fresh finely ground coffee	260 ml	Syrah wine
100 ml	cream	350 ml	beef stock
2	eggs	2	smoked vanilla pods, soaked in white cocoa liqueur
100 gm	unsalted butter		
275 gm	butternut		Cocoa nibs, sea salt, ground pepper and smoked sea salt to season

Method

Slice butternut in half and de-seed. Fill each half with butter, wrap in tin foil and bake in the oven at 180⁰c until flesh is tender. Remove skin, blend flesh to a purée, season to taste and pass through a sieve.

Rub the lamb with coffee, then quickly sear the loins in a pan to colour, then remove. Roast the lamb in a preheated 180⁰c oven until medium rare and leave to rest, keeping it warm.

Sauce Syrah: Deglaze the pan with the wine and cook until the liquid is reduced by half. Pour in the beef stock, bring to the boil, skim, reduce heat and leave to simmer for 10-15 minutes. Season to taste and pass through a muslin cloth or fine sieve to serve. Add the split vanilla pods to the cream and reduce by half, simmering gently, then whisk in the egg yolks with a teaspoon of the vanilla-infused white cocoa liqueur and leave to one side.

To serve, slice the lamb. Serve on butternut purée, with sauce Syrah and smoked vanilla cream, garnished with cocoa nibs, ground pepper and smoked sea salt.

SERVES 4

WINE SUGGESTION: Vidal Joseph Soler Cabernet Sauvignon

Braised Venison Shank with Haricot Beans, Stuffed Savoy Cabbage and Sauce Paysanne

BRAISED VENISON

Ingredients

5 kg	venison shanks	3 lt	beef stock
1.5 kg	mirepoix	60 ml	canola oil
500 ml	cabernet sauvignon	12 slices	prosciutto

Method

In a large roasting dish, sear the venison shanks and remove. Sauté the mirepoix until coloured, place the shanks into the mixture, cover with red wine and reduce until thick and syrupy. Add the stock and bring to the boil, skim, reduce the heat to a low simmer and cover dish with foil. Place in a preheated 120⁰c oven at and bake 6-8 hours until the meat is falling off the bone.

Strain, keeping the braising stock to the side. Cool the shanks, then remove the meat and place in a bowl.

Lay out a couple of sheets of tin foil, then on top of each sheet place a layer of cling film. Place the pre-sliced prosciutto on top, to form an interleaved mat.

Correct the seasoning of the venison, moisten with a little of the braising stock and mix together. Arrange the meat on top of the prosciutto down the centre. Roll up tightly into a firm sausage and refrigerate.

CONTINUED OVERLEAF

Braised Venison Shank with Haricot Beans, Stuffed Savoy Cabbage and Sauce Paysanne

...CONTINUED

STUFFED SAVOY CABBAGE

Ingredients

8	savoy cabbage leaves	60 gm	butter
80 gm	raw corn kernels		Salt and pepper to season
1	garlic clove, crushed		

Method

Take 6 leaves and blanch in boiling water. Refresh in ice cold water and leave to drain. Finely shred the other two leaves and sauté in a buttered pan with the crushed garlic and sweet corn until the cabbage starts to caramelize. Remove from heat, season to taste and place the mixture in the whole leaves. Wrap each leaf in cling film and tie a knot.

HARICOT BEANS

Ingredients

250 gm	pre-soaked haricot beans	175 ml	chardonnay
1	garlic clove, crushed	125 ml	cream
1 lt	dark chicken stock		Sea salt to season

Method

Place the beans in the chicken stock and bring to the boil. Skim, then simmer until beans are al dente.

Meanwhile, reduce wine by half, add cream and garlic and infuse until aromatic. Remove the garlic, add beans and simmer, just before serving.

...CONTINUED

SAUCE PAYSANNE OF VEGETABLES AND ROSEMARY

Ingredients

50 gm	carrots, diced	25 gm	shallots, diced
30 gm	parsnip, diced	1 sprig	rosemary
30 gm	leeks, diced	60 ml	olive oil
40 gm	zucchini, diced	75 gm	unsalted butter
1	garlic clove, diced	300 ml	pinot noir
1 tsp	truffle paste	300 ml	beef stock

Method

Sauté the vegetables in olive oil, add red wine and reduce by half. Then add the stock, bring to the boil and skim, add the rosemary and infuse until fragrant. Remove rosemary. Season to taste, and just before serving whisk in the butter.

To serve

Unwrap and slice the venison. Place in a preheated oven with the reserved braising stock and reheat at 180°c making sure not to over-bake.

Meanwhile, reheat the cabbage balls in boiling water and carefully unwrap.

Serve the venison on the seasoned haricot beans, top with the stuffed cabbage balls and spoon over the sauce paysanne.

SERVES 6

Ngawi Crayfish and Jerusalem Artichoke Salad

Ingredients

2	crayfish tails	120 ml	Muscatel hollandaise
350 gm	jerusalem artichokes	8	cherry tomatoes
4 portions	mesclun salad leaves	1 lt	fish stock for poaching
60 ml	fennel-infused olive oil	60 gm	crispy shallots
120 ml	Romesco sauce	20 ml	lime juice

Method

Poach the tails in stock for about 10-12 minutes depending on the size. Refresh in an ice bath, remove and drain excess water. Split the tails in half, removing the vein, and slice into half inch pieces.

Peel and thickly slice the artichokes, season with olive oil and sea salt, then sauté in a frying pan until coloured. Roast them on a tray in the oven until cooked, then remove from tray and place on paper to drain.

For the crispy shallots, peel and finely slice shallots, place in a deep fat fryer or wok until golden in colour and drain on paper towels to remove excess oil.

CONTINUED OVERLEAF

Ngawi Crayfish and Jerusalem Artichoke Salad ...CONTINUED

ROMESCO SAUCE

Ingredients

3	red capsicum
1	red chilli
2	garlic clove
1 tsp	paprika
100 ml	olive oil
20 ml	lime juice

Sea salt to season

Method

Roast the capsicum, chilli and garlic whole until soft, then peel. Deseed the capsicum and chilli. Purée in a blender with the olive oil, add paprika and lime juice, season to taste with sea salt.

MUSCATEL HOLLANDAISE

Ingredients

3	egg yolks
20 ml	lemon juice
30 ml	Muscatel vinegar
125 gm	clarified unsalted butter

Salt to season

Method

Place the egg yolks, lemon juice and vinegar in a stainless steel bowl over a medium heat and whisk until the mixture begins to thicken. Slowly add the clarified butter, season to taste and strain through muslin cloth before serving.

To serve, toss the mesclun leaves in lime juice. Sauté the crayfish tails in butter to reheat and transfer to plates. Add artichokes and mix with mesclun leaves. Drizzle with fennel oil and season to taste with sea salt, garnish with cherry tomatoes and crispy shallots. Serve with Romesco sauce and muscatel hollandaise.

Chef's note

If the hollandaise mixture is too thick, add a little water to dilute.

SERVES 4

Confit Hemp Salmon with Celeriac

Ingredients

4	serving size pieces of salmon	125 gm	cream
100 ml	hemp oil	50 gm	unsalted butter
1	garlic clove, crushed	250 ml	full cream milk
425 gm	celeriac	Sea salt and pepper to taste	

Method

Place the salmon in a sealable bag, add the hemp oil and garlic, season with salt and pepper, seal, and leave to infuse.

Peel and dice the celeriac and poach in milk until soft; remove and strain. Place the cream in a pot and bring to the boil, add the butter and celeriac, simmer until the celeriac is just tender. Blend the mixture and pass through a sieve, season to taste.

Place the sealed bag in simmering hot water and poach the salmon for about 3-5 minutes, depending on the size of the fillets and how you like your salmon cooked. Remove from the bag, strain off the oil and serve with celeriac puree. Garnish with salmon roe and crisp-fried salmon skin ring.

Chef's note

I also like to garnish this dish with beetroot crisps and a sherry reduction seasoning; sun dried olives and tomatoes go really well with it too.

Hemp oil contains healthy omegas 6&3, and is rich, nutty and delicate in flavour. However, if you can't find hemp oil, use olive oil.

SERVES 4

Wild Boar Sausages with Creamed Potatoes (Bangers and Mash)

WILD BOAR SAUSAGES
WITH CREAMED POTATOES

Ingredients

8	wild boar sausages
500 gm	Agria potatoes
300 ml	cream
100 gm	butter
200 ml	onion gravy

Sea salt and pepper to season

Method

Boil the unpeeled potatoes in salted water until tender, strain and leave to dry. Meanwhile, place the cream in a pot and bring to the boil. Once the potatoes are dry, peel and place them in a blender with the cream and blend carefully. Add the diced butter a little at a time; season to taste and remove. Make sure not to over-blend the mixture to avoid it turning to paste. Alternatively, use a mouli.

ONION GRAVY

Ingredients

1 kg	brown onions, finely sliced
80 ml	olive oil
100 gm	unsalted butter
1 lt	beef stock
350 ml	port
350 ml	red wine

Method

Take a large pan, add oil and butter and over a medium heat, sauté the onions slowly until they are golden, not burnt, and caramelized. Add port and reduce by half, then add the red wine and reduce by half. Finally add the beef stock and reduce by half again. Season to taste.

To serve

Place grilled sausages on the potato puree, surround with onion gravy, garnish with cracked pepper and sea salt.

SERVES 4

WINE SUGGESTION: Schubert Cabernet Sauvignon/Merlot

Peppered Venison with Roast Parsnip Purée

PEPPERED VENISON

Ingredients

1	Venison loin rack
1tsp	white peppercorns
1tsp	black peppercorns
1/2tsp	red peppercorns
1 Tbsp	Dijon mustard
Sea salt to season	
800 gm	parsnip puree
60 ml	olive oil
4	stuffed courgette flowers
200 ml	game jus

Method

Trim and tidy up the venison rack. Sear the loin and rub it with mustard, crush the peppercorns with a little salt in a mortar and pestle and rub on the loin.

Place in a preheated oven of 180°c for 18-25 minutes, and once cooked, leave to rest in a warm place for 3-5 minutes before slicing and serving.

PARSNIP PURÉE

Ingredients

1.5 kg	parsnips
300 ml	cream
100 gm	butter
60 ml	porcini-infused olive oil
Sea salt and pepper to season	

Method

Trim and peel the parsnips, toss lightly in olive oil and roast in a preheated 180°c oven until tender. Remove and cut into pieces. Place the cream in a pot and bring to the boil, remove and pour into a blender with the chopped parsnips. Blend with the porcini oil until smooth. Pass through a sieve, and add seasoning. Stir in butter just before serving.

STUFFED COURGETTE FLOWERS

Ingredients

4	baby courgettes with flowers
60 ml	olive oil
60 gm	shallots, diced
1	garlic clove, chopped
325 gm	mushrooms, assorted, finely chopped
150 ml	dry white wine
125 ml	cream
30 gm	Dijon mustard
1 sprig	parsley
Sea salt and cracked pepper to season	

Method

Over a medium heat in a saucepan, add oil and gently sauté garlic and shallots until fragrant and transparent. Add mushrooms and sauté until the moisture has nearly evaporated, then add wine and reduce by half. Next, add the mustard, then the cream and reduce until a thick consistency. Season to taste and leave to cool.

Stuff the courgette flower with this mixture. Wrap the flower end in foil, and just before serving, roast in a 180°c preheated oven for 3-5 minutes depending on the size of the courgette.

To serve, slice venison, place on a bed of parsnip purée and roasted mushroom-stuffed courgette flower. At the Lodge we sauce this dish with a game jus, and garnish it with parsnip crisps.

Crispy Wild Caught Prawns with Mint-spiced Sorbet

CRISPY WILD CAUGHT PRAWNS

Ingredients

8	fresh prawns, shelled & deveined	60 ml	hemp oil
1	Agria potato, peeled		Seaweed salt
4 scoops	mint-spiced sorbet		Mesclun leaves to garnish
4	sweet corn cakes		

Method

Wrap the prawns in thin strands of potato – you can do this by using a peeler and slicing the potatoes lengthways with a knife. Place the wrapped prawns in a preheated deep fryer at 180⁰c until golden, and finish in the oven.

MINT-SPICED SORBET

Ingredients

1 cup	Vietnamese mint	100 gm	glucose
1/2 cup	garden mint	225 gm	caster sugar
60 ml	lime juice	1 lt	Water
1tsp	paprika		

Method

Place glucose, caster sugar and water in a pot and bring to the boil until sugar has dissolved. Remove from the heat and leave to cool. Add the freshly picked mint and paprika and blend for 3-5 minutes with a stick blender. Pass through a sieve, add lime juice and churn in an ice cream machine and freeze.

SWEET CORN CAKES

Ingredients

250 gm	sweet corn whole kernels
250 gm	sweet corn purée
1	garlic clove, smashed
1	whole egg
80 gm	flour to bind
	Salt and pepper to season

Method

Combine all the ingredients and place in 4 ramekins lined with cling film to prevent the mixture from sticking to the mould. Place the ramekins in a preheated bain-marie (water bath) and cover. Place over a medium heat for 3-5 minutes depending on the size of the moulds, then remove from the heat and unmould. Pan fry in butter and olive oil until golden.

To serve, place the prawns on the sweet corn cakes and season with hemp oil and seaweed salt. Place a spoonful of the sorbet alongside, on a serving of Mesclun leaves.

SERVES 4

Porcini Dusted Mountain Thar with Potato Vanilla Brulée

PORCINI DUSTED MOUNTAIN THAR

Ingredients

4	thar loins	2	vanilla pods
50 gm	porcini powder	Sea salt and pepper to season	
200 ml	port wine and beet jus		

Method

Rub the loins in porcini powder, sauté in a hot frying pan. Once the meat has been sealed, season and place in a preheated oven at 200°c for about 8-10 minutes depending on the size of the loin. Once the loins are cooked, leave to rest for 2-3 minutes before slicing.

POTATO VANILLA BRULÉE

Ingredients

500 gm	floury potatoes, peeled & diced	100 ml	full cream milk
2	egg yolks	200 ml	cream
1	egg	60 ml	clarified butter
50 gm	Parmagiano butter	Sea salt and olive oil to season	

Method

Simmer the potatoes, milk and cream in a pot over a moderate heat until the potatoes are cooked. Put the potato mixture into a blender, blend until smooth. Add the rest of the ingredients, blend and season to taste, then pour the mixture in buttered moulds. Set the moulds in a saucepan with hot water and cover, cook over a moderate heat for 3-4 minutes. Remove the pan from heat but keep it covered for another minute before removing. To serve, remove potato from the moulds and season with salt and a drizzle of olive oil.

PORT WINE AND BEET JUS

Ingredients

250 ml	beetroot juice
100 ml	balsamic vinegar
300 ml	port wine
500 ml	beef stock
80 gm	unsalted butter
1 sprig	rosemary
Sea salt to season	

Method

Place a saucepan over a moderate heat, add balsamic and reduce by half, then add the port wine and reduce by half; next, the beetroot juice and again reduce by half. Add beef stock and rosemary, and once the stock has become fragrant with the herb, remove it and reduce stock until it is the consistency of cream. Before serving, whisk in butter and season to taste.

Serve the meat with the port wine, beet jus, and the brulée, garnished with milk froth and half a vanilla pod.

Chef's note

Just before garnishing the plate with the vanilla pod, place the pod in the oven for 30 seconds to release the aromas. Your guests will be greeted with a vanilla perfumed dish, a great talking point at the table.

WINE SUGGESTION: Schubert Pinot Noir

SERVES 4

Wharekauhau Texel Lamb Rack with Sauce Forestière

WHAREKAUHAU TEXEL LAMB

Ingredients

2	French trimmed Texel Lamb racks
800 gm	olive-crushed potato
60 ml	olive oil
200 ml	Sauce Forestière
120 ml	cèpe froth
4 portions	mixed baby vegetables
Sea salt and pepper to season	

Method

In a hot frying pan seal off the lamb racks. Season and place in a preheated 180°c oven and cook for about 15-18 minutes, depending on how you like meat cooked. Leave to rest in a warm place for 3-4 minutes before serving.

OLIVE CRUSHED POTATOES

Ingredients

1 kg	Agria potatoes
150 ml	extra virgin olive oil
Sea salt to season	

Bake the potatoes in their skins. Once cooked, peel and leave to dry. Place in a bowl and gently crush with your hand, stir in the oil and season to taste. When making this dish, ensure the potatoes are dry so as to let the potato absorb the oil. Do not mash.

CONTINUED OVERLEAF

Wharekauhau Texel Lamb Rack with Sauce Forestière   ...CONTINUED

SAUCE FORESTIÈRE

Ingredients

500 ml	mushroom stock	1 sprig	thyme	20 gm	wood ear mushrooms
500 ml	beef stock	1	bay leaf		
1	garlic clove, diced	50 gm	girolles	60 ml	olive oil
60 gm	shallots, diced	35 gm	morelles	60 gm	unsalted butter
100 ml	red wine	40 gm	field mushrooms	Sea salt and cracked	
100 ml	brandy	20 gm	straw mushrooms	pepper to season	

Method

In a large saucepan, add mushroom stock, bring to the boil and reduce by half. Pour in the beef stock and again reduce by half. Ignite brandy and red wine mixture, and when the flames die out add to stock and reduce by half. Infuse the stock with bay leaf and thyme until scented and remove, then skim the stock. Pass through muslin cloth 3-4 times until the stock has a lovely sheen.

In another pan, sauté garlic and shallots in olive oil and butter until fragrant and transparent. Next, toss in the field mushrooms, girolles, wood ear, morelles and lastly the straw mushrooms, and quickly sauté on high heat, making sure not to let the mushrooms stew in their own juices. Season to taste and place mushrooms in the stock, ready to be served with the lamb.

CÈPE FOAM

Ingredients

10 gm	dried cèpes	60 ml	full cream milk
100 ml	hot water	Sea salt to season	

Method

Place the cèpes in a pot of hot water and leave to infuse for 20 minutes. Place the pot over a simmering heat and reduce the stock by three-quarters. Strain the stock and leave to cool, then pour the stock into the milk and bring to the boil. Remove and blend with a stick blender.

To serve, mould crushed potatoes on plates, add lamb, sauce and cèpe foam.

SERVES 4-6

Classic Whitebait Fritter

Ingredients

125 gm	fresh West Coast whitebait
2	eggs
30 gm	salted butter
10 ml	lemon juice

Salt and pepper to season

Seasonal salad leaves

Method

Lightly beat the eggs and stir in the whitebait, season with salt and pepper and pour the mixture into a medium non-stick frying pan over the melted butter. Cook until lightly coloured. Remove from the pan and serve with salad leaves drizzled with lemon juice.

Chef's note

This is a simple treatment of one of New Zealand's most sought-after delicacies.

SERVES ONLY ONE,
THIS IS NOT FOR SHARING…

WINE SUGGESTION:
Dry Riesling, Pinot Gris, a glass of champagne…

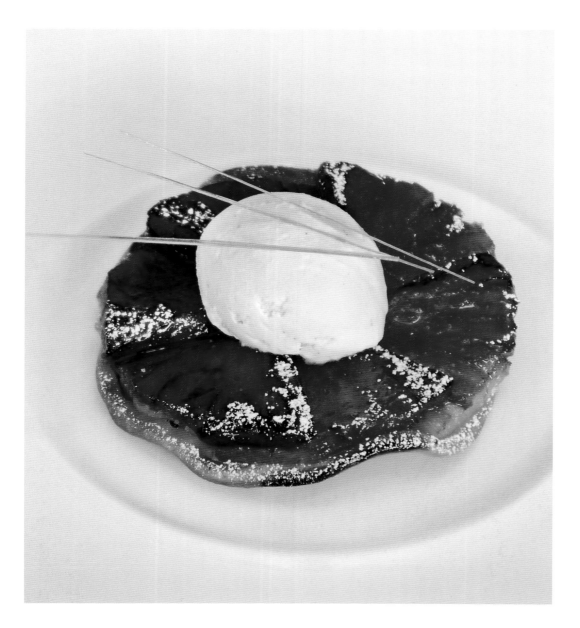

Pineapple Tarte Tatin

Ingredients

400 gm	fresh pineapple, sliced
100 gm	caster sugar
100 gm	butter
4	paté brisé discs cut about same size as pineapple slices
4	scoops of crème fraiche ice-cream

Icing sugar for dusting

Method

Rub the inside of a non-stick pan with about 25 gm of butter. Cover with about 25 gm sugar and place the pineapple slices on top, then put the pastry discs over the pineapple. Place over a medium heat until the pineapple starts to caramelize – you will see the juices caramelize around the side of the pan. Once the juice is golden brown, place in the oven for about 4-5 minutes at 180⁰c or until the pastry is golden in colour. Quickly invert the tarte tartin over a serving plate and lift out of the pan. Dust with icing sugar and serve immediately, with crème fraiche ice cream.

SERVES 4

WINE SUGGESTION:
Ata Rangi Kahu Botrytis Riesling

Hokey Pokey Soufflé

Ingredients

50 gm	Hokey Pokey
320 ml	crème patissiere
4	egg whites
30 gm	caster sugar
1tsp	cornflour

To coat the dishes

60 gm	unsalted butter
75 gm	ground macadamia nuts
60 gm	caster sugar

Method

Crush the hokey pokey into the crème patissiere and mix in well. Whisk the egg whites and slowly add the sugar until soft peaks form. Add 1 teaspoon of cornflour and beat for a further minute, then fold half this mixture into the hokey pokey mixture until well blended. Then lightly fold in the remaining half of egg whites. Pre-butter 6 ramekins and coat with sugar and ground macadamia nuts. Add the mixture to the ramekins, smooth the top of the mixture with a palate knife and run a tea towel or knife around the inside of the rim to make a groove. Bake at 220°c for about 9-10 minutes, or until the soufflés have risen and are golden brown. Dust with icing sugar and serve immediately.

Chef's note

When making soufflés, make sure your utensils are spotlessly clean and that the oven is preheated. Serve the cooked soufflés immediately.

SERVES 6

Chocolate and Macadamia Fondant with Hokey Pokey Ice Cream

CHOCOLATE AND MACADAMIA FONDANT

Ingredients

140 gm	unsalted butter		125 gm	caster sugar
175 gm	Manjari chocolate		30 gm	flour
4	eggs		30 ml	Amaretto liqueur
3	egg yolks		60 gm	ground macadamia nuts

Method

Lightly grease 4 or 6 dariole moulds with butter and lightly coat insides with ground macadamia nuts and refrigerate.

Melt the unsalted butter and chocolate together. Lightly whisk the eggs, egg yolks and caster sugar together with the Amaretto, and then stir in the warm chocolate mixture. Add the flour and stir until combined, then pour the mixture into the prepared moulds and refrigerate overnight.

Preheat the oven to 220⁰c and bake the fondant for about 8-10 minutes or until the centre has nearly set. Once cooked, leave to rest for two minutes before removing from the mould.

To serve

Place a scoop of hokey pokey ice cream on top and serve immediately.

Chef's note

This dessert goes well with berries and citrus fruits, in order to cut the richness of the chocolate. Valrhona's Manjari chocolate comes from the north of the island of Madagascar.

SERVES 4-6, OR LESS – IT ALL DEPENDS ON HOW CHOCOHOLIC THE RECIPIENTS ARE.

HOKEY POKEY ICE CREAM

Ingredients

75 gm	Hokey Pokey
1.5 lt	vanilla crème anglaise
100 ml	cream
300 gm	sugar
50 gm	honey or golden syrup
110 gm	glucose
1 tsp	baking soda

Method

Put sugar, glucose and honey into a pot and heat gently until the sugar has dissolved, stirring constantly. Bring to the boil, stirring occasionally for about a minute or two to prevent burning, add the baking soda and stir quickly until mixture foams up. Pour onto greaseproof paper and leave to cool before breaking into pieces.

Place the crème anglaise in the ice cream machine and churn, crumble in the hokey pokey. Just before churning has finished, add the cream for a smoother texture. Freeze.

Leave for a day so the caramel can infuse into the vanilla ice cream.

Chef's note

This is New Zealand's iconic ice cream and my personal favourite, so I have added a generous amount of hokey pokey.

WINE SUGGESTION: Martinborough Late Harvest Riesling

Basics

STOCK DESSERT SYRUP

Ingredients

500 ml	water
100 gm	glucose
225 gm	caster sugar

Method

Combine the ingredients in a pot, place over heat, boil until the sugar has dissolved; remove from heat and leave to cool.

PATE BRISÉ

Ingredients

200 gm	flour	1	egg yolk
100 gm	unsalted butter	2 tbsp	water
45 gm	caster sugar		

Method

Sift flour, add softened butter and mix together. Add the rest of the ingredients, work together and refrigerate; leave to rest for an hour before using.

CRÈME FRAICHE ICE CREAM

Ingredients

1 lt	full cream milk	400 gm	caster sugar
16	egg yolks	800 gm	crème fraiche
1	vanilla pod		

Method

Bring milk to the boil, add split vanilla pod, combine yolks and sugar and whisk in hot milk. Cook the anglaise and strain, cool over ice. Once the mixture is at room temperature, whisk in crème fraiche slowly and churn in an ice-cream maker. Be careful not to over-churn or this will turn grainy, or into butter.

FREGOLA

Italian small macaroni pasta made from 100% durum wheat semolina.

MIREPOIX

A mixture of diced carrot, celery, leek, garlic and onion, sautéed in butter with herbs, and used to enhance the flavour of meats, fish, shellfish dishes and sauces.

CRÈME PATISSIERE

Ingredients

500 ml	milk	6	egg yolks
30 gm	flour	120 gm	caster sugar
15 gm	cornflour		

Method

Whisk egg yolks and sugar together until thick and pale, stir in flour and cornflour. Bring the milk to boil then whisk milk into egg mixture. Pour back into pan, bring to boil over a medium heat and cook the mixture on simmer for about five minutes.

VEAL STOCK

Ingredients

3 kg	veal bones	10 lt	water
1 kg	mirepoix	1 sprig	thyme
120 ml	olive oil	1	bay leaf
250 ml	Madeira	12	black peppercorns
120 gm	tomato paste		

Method

Roast veal bones in oil until golden in colour. Cover the bones in water and bring to the boil, skim and leave to simmer. In a separate saucepan sauté the mirepoix until golden in colour, add tomato paste. Cook the tomato and mirepoix until soft, making sure not to burn, add to veal stock. Deglaze pan with Madeira, reduce by half and add to the stock.

BEEF STOCK

Ingredients

6	shallots	750 ml	red wine
3	garlic cloves	1 lt	veal stock
60 ml	clarified butter	50 gm	tomato purée
50 ml	sherry vinegar	2 sprigs	parsley
50 ml	cognac	2 sprigs	tarragon
100 ml	port		

Method

Sweat shallots and garlic in butter until caramelized, deglaze pan with sherry vinegar and cook until almost glacé. Add cognac and reduce, add port and bring to the boil, add red wine and bring to the boil again. Reduce by half, then add veal stock, tarragon, parsley and fresh tomato purée and bring back to the boil. Simmer for 30 minutes, skim and pass through a muslin cloth 7 times.

FISH STOCK

Ingredients

1.5 kg	turbot bones	60 ml	olive oil
2	leeks – whites only	200 ml	white wine
1	celery stalk	6	white peppercorns
250 gm	brown onion	1 sprig	parsley stalks
250 gm	fennel bulb	2 lt water	
3	garlic cloves		

Method

Wash the fish bones in running water to remove any blood, sauté the chopped vegetables and garlic in oil without colouring, add fish bones and white wine. Reduce the wine by a third, add water and bring to the boil. Remove from the heat and skim. Add white peppercorns and parsley stalks and simmer for 20 minutes, then strain and leave to cool.

EXTRA FLAVOUR...

< ROGER, MURRAY AND
THE SHOC-OLATE FACTORY...

A historic Greytown cottage is home to alchemists and authors, Roger Simpson and Murray Langham, often up to their white gloves in chocolate. They make, and help, chocoholics. Schoc is a treatment for tastebuds and eyes. There are currently 58 varieties to dither over. Lime chilli is the front-runner in sales; Cuba, with its rich cigar-smoke aftertaste an intriguing dark horse.

Their book **Chocolate Therapy**, subtitled **'dare to discover your inner centre'** might help you decide. It illustrates what the chocolate you choose says about you.

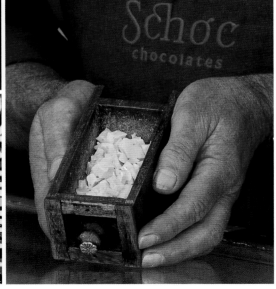

GIVE US OUR DAILY BREAD… >

And often in the Wairarapa that bread is from the French Baker: Moïse Cerson. Born in Brittany, he has travelled from cosmopolitan Paris to settle in rural Greytown – a homecoming for his wife whose hometown this is, and a bonus for the locals when he opened his stylish bakery and espresso bar in their neighbourhood. Take-out or stay-in, for authentic French bread and pastries, this is a committed foodie's compulsory stop, for residents and visitors to the picturesque small town.

< THE GOOD OIL...

Pressing matters brought Helen Meehan and her family to Martinborough – olives and their oil. Nearly a thousand trees make up the silvery peaceful grove of Olivo, set on eight acres near the vineyards. This is the oldest commercial olive grove in the Wairarapa. First planted in 1991 by pioneers of the olive industry in this region and New Zealand, Olivo began producing awarding-winning extra virgin olive oil in 2001. Its infused olive oils range from classic lemon and tangerine, to porcini, fennel and smoked chilli.

FRUIT AND VEG...   >

The business name sums it up, for fruit and vegetables, this is the Lodge chef's favourite other garden – Greytown Fresh. It is just a short drive from Wharekauhau to one of the region's most attractive towns. Its growing reputation for its food makes it a magnet for visitors from Wellington and further afield. Just through the town, at their roadside store, Paul and Marilyn Mason and Wendy Williams stand behind and in front of their produce. If it is fresh, good and interesting, it will be here.

∧ MEAT MATTERS...

Along from the candlestick-maker, and very near the baker is the butcher, just like the old nursery rhyme. This was the first shop in Greytown's Main Street. It opened in 1873, and still purveys the classic cuts of beef and lamb. Now it offers the gourmet sausages, game and meats that current tastes – and chefs – demand. One of the house specialities here at the Greytown Butcher is the exclusive Wharekauhau-bred Texel lamb, a lean yet finely marbled meat, succulent with a unique flavour.

∨ SALAD DAYS....

Knowing from personal experience what chefs are looking for gives Trevor Bell a head start.

He is a chef and cookery tutor who has turned to cultivation. Belle Gourmet Produce, his growing business, has a clean green philosophy of freshness. From his grow tunnel, using spray-free hydroponics, and in his potager gardens, he plants and nurtures organic salad greens, lettuces, herbs, baby capsicums and hot, hot 'gringo killer" chillis. Shoppers at the weekend farmers' market in Masterton, and restauranteurs are regular customers of his greens.

SAY CHEESE....   >

Steven and Valda Scheckter are the big cheeses of On Trays Emporium, a food cave stacked high and wide. These people are serious hoarders of a vast range of speciality gourmet products. Over the hill in the harbour city of Wellington, within easy striking distance of the chef, their warehouse takes regular delivery of imported foodstuffs from all points of the globe. You can take a tasting tour of the world of cheese here. The shelves are laden with chef-attracting ingredients from the Middle East, Europe and Africa.

WAIRARAPA

IN THE MIDDLE OF SOMEWHERE

Wairarapa translates from Maori to mean 'land of glistening waters'. From the great sweep of Palliser Bay, part of the Pacific Ocean, to its two lakes – Lake Ōnoke and Lake Wairarapa – and its rivers and streams, water is a constant presence in the often spectacular landscape. Wine is too; this is one of New Zealand's prime wine regions.

<   Horses race along
     Castlepoint Beach (Previous page)

The dramatic White Rock,   >
north of Cape Palliser

The distinctive red and white Cape Palliser lighthouse was built in 1896-7, with all the construction materials brought in to its site by sea. There was no road to it until 1941. Its now automatic light warns ships and boats of the rocky coast below. The 18 metre lighthouse sits on a hill 80 metres above sea level.

Palliser Bay on a tranquil day, beautiful in good weather but bleak in a storm. It was the original entry point to the Wairarapa for the first European settlers. In those pre-lighthouse days, many sailing ships were driven onto the rocks by southerly storms.

The glistening waters of Lake Ōnoke, on the road to Wharekauhau, are a refuge for a rich variety of bird life from shags to kingfishers, and mirror the skies above, dramatic sunrises and sunsets that are a feature of the region. In the early mornings at Wharekauhau, dozens of pukekos, native indigo-coloured birds with lipstick-red beaks, stalk about on long legs in the rushes near the wetland, going over the lawn outside the cottages with minute care and attention, feeding themselves on insects in the grass.

Vintage tractors are brought out and put though their paces in an annual ploughing competition near Gladstone. More contemporary models work the farmlands on a daily basis.

The beerstand in the garden of the Lake Ferry Hotel, the Shed, has proud and permanent product placement in any photograph for one of New Zealand's best-known and oldest breweries. Based in Northern Wairarapa, it bears the name and emblem of one of the most beautiful native songbirds. Coast tours often stop at the hotel for lunch; fish and chips are a favourite on the menu here.

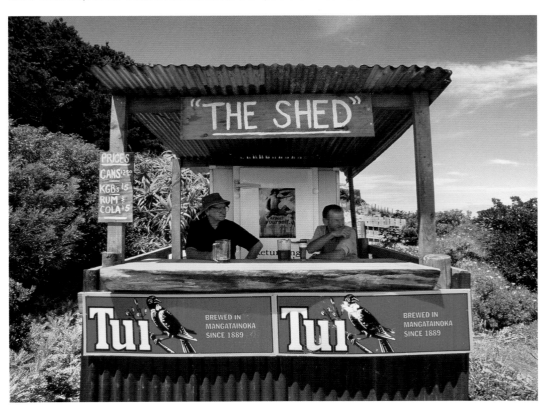

One of the many restored Victorian buildings that make Greytown architecturally interesting, the Heart of Glass in Greytown's Main Street was originally called Kouka (Cabbage Tree) Cottage. It was built around 1868, and restored by the Greytown Community Trust. Its present occupiers design and make traditional and modern stained glass.

Tekoteko, carved figures of ancestors, stand guard on the perimeter of the Papawai Pa, just east of Greytown. Traditionally these face outwards, at Papawai they face inwards, a decision made by a past chief who decided there was no longer any need to guard from attacks from outside. Papawai Pa is a centre of Maori culture in the Wairarapa.

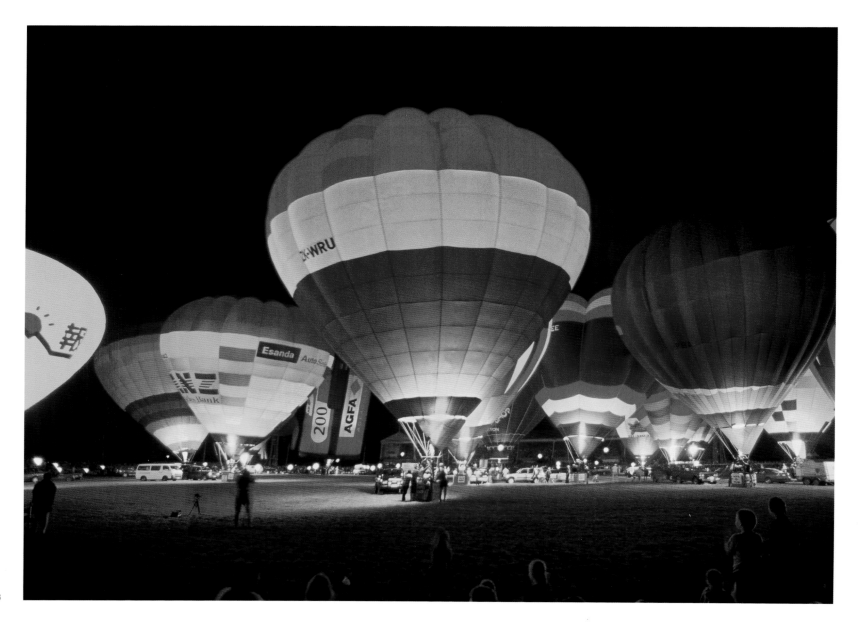

Buildings and businesses with character and personality are found all over the Wairarapa; from old and recently restored hotels like the Royal to the collectables store, both in Featherston just before the turn off to Wharekauhau, places to fossick in or pop into for a beer or two.

At left, the Night Glow parade lights up the opening ceremony of the Hot Air Balloon Fiesta in Masterton. Temperatures and wind currents make the region ideal for gliding, parachuting and ballooning. Weather permitting, the balloons are seen in Wairarapa skies for several days each March.

Vineyards run their straight lines across the Wairarapa landscape. At its heart, many rows radiate out from the wine village of Martinborough – and it is Martinborough Vineyard's Pinot Noir that is the area's signature wine. Pinot noir is its star, but there are other varietals to taste and savour, like merlot, pinot gris, gewutztraminer, reisling, chardonnay, sauvignon blanc and more. Plenty of sunshine is one of the key ingredients behind Wairarapa's wine-growng success. At left, the sun rises on the Martinborough Vineyard and below, nets protect the grapes from birds.

Olive groves are now a familiar sight in the Wairarapa.

Many boutique vineyards are in walking and tasting distance of the centre of Martinborough village. The annual wine and food festival attracts thousands to the town and its surrounding vineyards every November. Capitalising on low rainfall, a temperate climate with hot summers and dry autumns, Martinborough's boutique wine industry has built an international reputation in less than two decades.

Most of the region's wines are represented and can be compared in this one location, the Martinborough Wine Centre. Its café serves wine too, of course.

The fishing village of Ngawi is on the coast near the tip of Cape Palliser. There is no harbour at Ngawi, so tractors pull the fishing boats in and out of the sea. The main catch is crayfish.

Near here, further along the coast, is one of New Zealand's largest breeding colonies of protected fur seals.

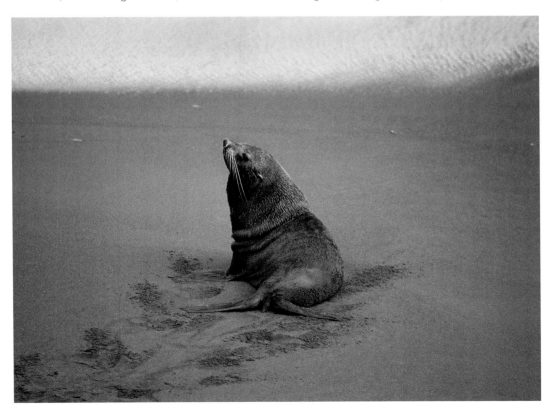

Autumn colours the valley. Its plains are bounded in the West by the Tararuas, hills that are part of the North Island's great mountain chain, and a favourite of trampers and hunters.

There is an evident enthusiasm for trees in this part of the country; many have been planted along fence lines, in paddocks and around homesteads.

The Putangirua Pinnacles at Cape Palliser, spectacular and beautiful. Severe erosion in the last 7000 years has produced a cathedral of soaring rock pillars and elaborate flutings.   ∨

A vivid sunset, seen from the beach below Wharekauhau, lights up the Kaikouras, the mountain range at the top of the South Island. There are often magical skies over the Wairarapa, with majestic north-west arches and an infinite array of cloud patterns.

Palliser Bay, at the southern tip of the North Island, has a dramatic and rugged coastline that was used as a location in the movie trilogy **Lord of the Rings.** Reviewing that trilogy, one movie critic wrote, "If Oscars were awarded for locations, New Zealand would scoop the lot."

< View across Lake Wairarapa at sunset.

Burnside Church, built in the late 1870s from local timber milled near Greytown, stands alone inland from Palliser Bay, north of Pirinoa, and is one of a myriad of attractive old churches in the region.

Back on the Wharekauhau estate, sheep are on the move. Pastoral landscape is combined with native bush and stands of native and exotic trees, often sculpturally shaped by the prevailing winds.

A richly coloured sky as the sun sets behind the lodge and over the rugged Rimutakas, the hills that separate the Wairarapa from Wellington. As night blankets out the land and sea, the stars shine brighter above this place apart.

Pukeko on the prowl.　>

Other programs in **Strong Kids**™:
A Social & Emotional Learning Curriculum

> *Strong Kids—Grades 3–5:*
> *A Social & Emotional Learning Curriculum*
>
> *Strong Kids—Grades 6–8:*
> *A Social & Emotional Learning Curriculum*
>
> *Strong Teens—Grades 9–12:*
> *A Social & Emotional Learning Curriculum*

STRONG START

Grades K–2

A Social & Emotional Learning Curriculum

by

Kenneth W. Merrell, Ph.D.
University of Oregon

Danielle M. Parisi
University of Oregon

and

Sara A. Whitcomb
University of Oregon

·P A U L·H·
BROOKES
PUBLISHING Cᴑ ®

Baltimore • London • Sydney

Paul H. Brookes Publishing Co.
Post Office Box 10624
Baltimore, Maryland 21285-0624

www.brookespublishing.com

Typeset by Barton Matheson Willse & Worthington, Baltimore, Maryland.
Manufactured in the United States of America by
Versa Press, Inc., East Peoria, Illinois.

Library of Congress Cataloging-in-Publication Data
Merrell, Kenneth W.
    Strong start : a social and emotional learning curriculum / by Kenneth W. Merrell,
    Danielle M. Parisi, and Sara A. Whitcomb.
          p.   cm.
    Vols. 2–4 have the title: Strong kids
    Vols. 2–4 authored by Kenneth W. Merrell alone.
    Includes bibliographical references.
    ISBN-13: 978-1-55766-929-2 (v. 1 : layflat (paper)
    ISBN-10: 1-55766-929-5 (v. 1 : layflat (paper)
    ISBN-13: 978-1-55766-930-8 (v. 2 : layflat (paper)
    ISBN-10: 1-55766-930-9 (v. 2 : layflat (paper)
    [etc.]
    1. Affective education.   2. Social learning.   3. Child development.   4. Emotional intelligence.
    5. Education—Social aspects.   I. Parisi, Danielle M.   II. Whitcomb, Sara A.   III. Title.
    IV. Title: Strong kids.

LB1072.M47 2007
370.15'34—dc22   2007015480

British Library Cataloguing in Publication data are available from the British Library.

Contents

Contents of the Accompanying CD-ROM

Lesson 7

Supplement 7.1: Basic Feelings

Strong Start Bulletin

Lesson 8

Supplement 8.1: What Does a Good Friend Do?

Strong Start Bulletin

Lesson 9

Supplement 9.1: The Stop, Count, In, Out Strategy

Supplement 9.2: The ABCs of Positive Thinking

Strong Start Bulletin

Lesson 10

Supplement 10.1: About *Strong Start*

Supplement 10.2: Basic Feelings

Supplement 10.3: The Stop, Count, In, Out Strategy

Supplement 10.4: The ABCs of Positive Thinking

Strong Start Bulletin

Appendix A

Supplement A.1: *Strong Start* Feelings Bingo

Supplement A.2: *Strong Start* Feelings Bingo

Supplement A.3: *Strong Start* Feelings Bingo

Supplement A.4: *Strong Start* Feelings Bingo

Supplement A.5: *Strong Start* Feelings Bingo

About the Authors

Kenneth W. Merrell, Ph.D., is a professor of school psychology in the Department of Special Education and Clinical Sciences at the University of Oregon. He has served as School Psychology Program Director and Co-director as well as Department Head. Dr. Merrell received his Ph.D. in school psychology from the University of Oregon in 1998 and held tenured faculty positions at the University of Iowa and Utah State University before returning to the University of Oregon in 2001. In addition to his academic experience, he worked for 3 years as a school psychologist for a public school district and has extensive additional experience in providing psychological services and consultation in schools.

Dr. Merrell's research and scholarly work in social-emotional assessment and intervention in schools has been published widely in the field of school psychology, and he has been recognized in three separate studies as one of the 20 most influential scholars in the field over the past two decades. His peers have acknowledged his impact by electing him a fellow in the American Psychological Association's Division of School Psychology and Society for Clinical Child and Adolescent Psychology. His research studies have been published in *School Psychology Review, School Psychology Quarterly, Psychology in the Schools, Journal of Psychoeducational Assessment,* and elsewhere, and he has been interviewed for articles appearing in popular media, including *U.S. News & World Report, Family Circle,* and other national publications.

In addition to authoring more than 85 journal articles, Dr. Merrell has authored eight books and several assessment tools. Currently, Dr. Merrell serves as editor of Guilford Press's influential *Practical Intervention in the Schools* book series and is a member of the editorial advisory board for *School Psychology Review.* He is also a member of the Board of Directors at the Oregon Social Learning Center in Eugene.

Danielle M. Parisi is a doctoral candidate in school psychology at the University of Oregon and will earn a concurrent master's degree in special education. She received her bachelor's degree in psychology from the University of Chicago. Her professional interests include improving academic and social outcomes for students through promotion of systems-level prevention and early intervention efforts. As a doctoral student, Ms. Parisi has experience in assessment, teaching, planning interventions, and consultation around both individual student and systems-level issues.

Sara A. Whitcomb, Ed.M., received her master's degree from the Harvard Graduate School of Education's Risk and Prevention Program, and she is currently a doctoral candidate in school psychology at the University of Oregon. Ms. Whitcomb collaborates in curriculum development and research efforts with the Oregon Resiliency Project, and she supervises graduate students seeking licensure in special education. Her professional interests include promoting mental health and positive behavioral support systems in schools and consulting with teachers. Prior to attending the University of Oregon, Ms. Whitcomb spent 6 years as a teacher in special education, kindergarten, and first-grade settings.

Foreword

Since the 1990s, there has been an intense national focus on the mental health needs of children and youth. Increasing numbers of school-age youth are experiencing serious stress, anxiety, and depressive disorders. It is currently estimated that approximately 20%–25% of today's youth have mental health conditions that would result in a diagnosable mental disorder; yet, only about 20% of these youth will actually gain access to mental health services to address their problems. Furthermore, about 75% of these services will be obtained through the public schools.

It is clear that the ability of traditional mental health systems and their delivery mechanisms to solve this continuing problem is inadequate. We urgently need to find ways to promote and provide quality mental health–type services that are universal in nature, low cost, feasible, and easily accessible and that provide effective tools.

The development of the field of *social-emotional learning* offers great promise for addressing this set of issues within the context of schooling. This specialty shows that social-emotional learning processes are of parallel importance as academic learning processes and that they can have a powerful impact on both academic and social-emotional outcomes. I regard the Strong Kids™ curriculum (which includes *Strong Start, Strong Kids—Grades 3–5, Strong Kids—Grades 6–8,* and *Strong Teens*) as a model exemplar of effective social-emotional learning practices in teaching critical social-emotional concepts and coping skills, including self-regulation.

The Strong Kids curriculum is *practical, easy-to-use, low cost,* and *teacher friendly.* Perhaps of equal importance, it fits well into the normal routines of schooling and thus does not disrupt the instructional scope and sequence of most classrooms. This program is evidence based and of proven effectiveness.

The Strong Kids program is also highly flexible in that it targets both universal prevention goals and outcomes and also provides more intensive, targeted procedures for individual students who do not respond well to the program's classwide instructional approach. The Strong Kids curriculum is developmentally sequenced into four levels—Grades K–2, Grades 3–5, Grades 6–8, and Grades 9–12—thus covering the full K–12 age range. The Strong Kids program can also be used as part of a tier 3, tertiary-level comprehensive intervention program for students with the most severe mental health involvements.

I am impressed with the evidence so far of the Strong Kids program's efficacy. A series of recently completed studies document high levels of consumer satisfaction, social validity, and increases in social-emotional knowledge among students who have been exposed to it.

I strongly recommend this program for use in K–12 schools to address the social-emotional and mental health needs of today's students—many of whom bring serious, unsolved problems with them from outside the school setting, which can powerfully affect their in-school performance and behavior. These problems are not of the schools' making, but educators can play a very important role in addressing and ameliorating their more deleterious effects. I think the Strong Kids curriculum is a seminal contribution to the field in improving our collective ability to intervene and prevent many of these problems.

Hill M. Walker, Ph.D.
Director, Center on Human Development
University of Oregon

Introduction and Overview

About *Strong Start*

Strong Kids™: A Social and Emotional Learning Curriculum consists of four brief and practical social and emotional learning (SEL) programs that have been designed for the purpose of promoting the SEL of children in kindergarten through twelfth grade. The *Strong Start* curriculum, the first volume in the Strong Kids curriculum, is for children in kindergarten through second grade. Because *Strong Start* is designed to be both a prevention and an early intervention program, it has a wide range of applications and may be used effectively with high-functioning, typically developing, or at-risk children as well as children with emotional disturbance. It can be used in a variety of settings.

We designed *Strong Start* to target each of the five pathways to wellness advocated by Cowen (1994). Moreover, we created this curriculum as a companion to the proven *Strong Kids—Grades 3–5*, *Strong Kids—Grades 6–8*, and *Strong Teens* programs, which are based on similar premises as *Strong Start* but were designed for use with older children and adolescents. We view *Strong Start* as a carefully designed SEL program intended to prevent the development of certain mental health problems and promote social and emotional wellness among young children.

Strong Start is not the right program for *all* problems or purposes. We especially targeted emotional and mental health problems (e.g., depression, anxiety, social withdrawal, somatic problems) and the promotion of what we term *social and emotional resiliency and competence* in designing this program: We never intended *Strong Start* (or its companion programs for older children) to be a comprehensive program for preventing school violence or antisocial behavior, even though it may play a role in supporting these aims as part of a comprehensive program of effective behavior support.

In addition, we specifically designed *Strong Start* as a low-cost, low-technology program that can be implemented in a school or related educational setting with minimal professional training and resources. It is not necessary to be a licensed mental health professional in order to learn and implement this curriculum. The curriculum can also be taught in a self-contained manner within a specific environment and does not require expensive community wrap-around services or mandatory parent training groups. The advantage of this programming approach is that *Strong Start* is brief, efficient, skill-based, portable, and focused.

There are several appropriate settings for use of this curriculum, including, but not limited to, general and special education K–2 classrooms, group counseling, and youth treatment facilities that have an educational component. A wide range of professionals may appropriately serve as group leaders or instructors for this curriculum. General and special education teachers, speech-language pathologists, school counselors, social workers, psychologists, early interventionists, and other education or mental health professionals may all serve as effective group leaders.

This curriculum was developed with both time feasibility and ease of implementation as high priorities. Even an exceptionally strong intervention program will never make much of an impact if its time requirements and difficulty of implementation result in few people being able to use it within the time and training constraints of a school system or other youth-serving agency. Thus, the maximum duration of the curriculum is 10 weeks (if lessons are taught once per week), and the expected length of each lesson is approximately 45 minutes.

One of the advantages of the Strong Kids curriculum is that it is designed to support academic skills and to be implemented seamlessly within an instructional program. The skills needed to effectively teach students academic and pre-academic skills are the same skills needed to deliver these curricula effectively. You do not need to be a mental health specialist or therapist to use *Strong Start*. The activities in this curriculum not only promote SEL and resiliency but also support literacy, language development, listening skills, memory skills, and self-expression skills. Our experience in delivering this curriculum in kindergarten and primary grade settings has shown that teachers have effectively used the program within their regular curriculum and that mental health professionals can use the curriculum effectively as a "pull-out" program for targeted students.

Strong Start is a highly structured and partially scripted curriculum designed to cover very specific objectives and goals. We developed the objectives and goals for each lesson, as well as the implementation guidelines, based on current research findings in education and psychology, aiming for a prevention and intervention program that is built on a solid base of empirical evidence. Each lesson follows a similar format. The lessons provide optional scripts to aid concept delivery, sample scenarios and examples to better illustrate the concept, and opportunities for guided and independent practice. Group leaders can follow the script and examples directly or modify the lessons to utilize creativity. Each lesson relies heavily on the use of appropriate children's literature, Think/Pair/Share activities, drawing or other creative activities, and a handout or letter for parents and families (i.e., the *Strong Start* Bulletin) to help enrich the basic delivery of lesson content.

PROMOTING CHILDREN'S MENTAL HEALTH

The primary mission of schools has traditionally been viewed as promoting the development of academic skills, but there is no question that most educators, parents, and the general public support and expect a broader mission for schools. Some examples of this expanded agenda include character education, developing good work habits, promoting citizenship, developing social and emotional competence, and promoting healthy and productive lifestyles. Commenting on the need for this broader agenda, Greenberg and his colleagues stated

> High-quality education should teach young people to interact in socially skilled and respectful ways; to practice positive, safe, and healthy behaviors; to contribute ethically and responsibly to their peer group, family, school, and community; and to possess basic competencies, work habits, and values as a foundation for meaningful employment and citizenship . . . . We consequently assert that school-based prevention programming—based on coordinated social, emotional, and academic learning—should be fundamental to preschool through high school education (2003, pp. 466–467).

We agree with this statement. We also propose that teaching children positive social, emotional, and behavioral skills is a critical challenge facing our society in the 21st century. As many researchers, writers, and public officials have noted, changes in the structure of society and families have resulted in an increasing percentage of children and families who are "at risk" for developing a variety of behavioral, social, and mental health problems (e.g., Doll & Lyon, 1998; Farmer & Farmer, 1999). Examples of these social changes include a larger percentage of young children living in poverty than was true in the past few decades and increasing percentages of young children who do not live with or have the support of both of their parents. In addition, young children who are being raised by parents who are under great socioeconomic stress, involved in substance abuse, or have mental health problems are at increased risk because their parents may be unable to provide a stable and consistent family environment.

The numbers of children and youth affected by these problems are surprisingly high. Greenberg, Domitrovich, and Bumbarger (2001) asserted that between 12% and 22% of children and adolescents younger than age 18 experience mental health problems of sufficient severity to be in need of mental health services. These percentages represent a staggering figure of up to one out of every five children and adolescents in some instances. Without question, effective responses to these problems, including mental health prevention and early intervention curricula in educational settings, must occur if these challenges are to be stemmed.

Despite sincere and well-meaning attempts to offer real solutions to the social, emotional, and mental health problems of students in school settings, many of the programs or interventions that have been implemented are simply ineffective. We recognize that educators who work on the front lines of serving children with significant mental health issues are often overworked and not provided with sufficient resources with which to make the impact they desire. Furthermore, some developers and publishers of mental health prevention programs tend to overwhelm educators and clinicians with claims of effectiveness, even when there is little or no supporting evidence. Worse yet are reactionary school policies, such as the perennial "get tough" approaches that are not only ineffective in the long term but contribute to the development of systems that are hostile, aversive, socially toxic, and incompatible with optimal development of academic skills and mental health (Skiba & Peterson, 1999).

Despite these problems and challenges, there is reason for optimism regarding our ability to positively affect the social and emotional health and resiliency of children, even those from very adverse life circumstances. One reason for this optimism is the accumulation of a large body of scientific evidence regarding what has been termed *developmental resilience* (Doll & Lyon, 1998). This notion concerns the ability of individuals to cope successfully with adversity, risk factors, and severe life stress and for young people to develop into competent and happy adults despite these problems.

Central to this notion of developmental resilience is the idea that some characteristics of resilience—the cognitive, behavioral, and affective skills that enable one to cope effectively with adversity—may be systematically taught and learned. Although some aspects of resiliency or developmental hardiness may be innate or biologically based, evidence shows that learning plays a crucial role in developing the ability to cope effectively with problems and challenges. Stated simply, the ability to be resilient and to cope effectively in the face of adverse circumstances and challenges in life is something that can be acquired in great measure through systematic and effective instruction in the critical requisite skills involved.

SOCIAL AND EMOTIONAL LEARNING

Another reason for optimism regarding our ability to positively affect the social and emotional health and resiliency of children is the emerging evidence in the area of SEL (Zins, Bloodworth, Weissberg, & Walberg, 2004). SEL has been defined as systematic, cohesive, and effective instructional programming designed to teach social and emotional skills to children and adolescents, to prevent mental health problems, and to provide effective early intervention for those problems that are beginning to emerge (Greenberg et al., 2003). There are many manifestations of SEL programs, ranging from simple training in social or other life skills to expansive, multipronged efforts to prevent antisocial behavior and conduct problems. Since about the early 1990s, an impressive array of evidence-based SEL programs has been developed and made available for use in education and mental health. These programs vary substantially in mode of instruction, time and resources required, target areas, and cost.

The specific type of SEL program selected will depend on the specific needs and requirements of an institution or community and the competencies and problems that are most important to target, but those efforts that are most successful tend to be implemented in a planned, cohesive manner within a system. Fragmented, uncoordinated efforts seldom produce more than superficial, short-term results. Emory Cowen (1994), a pioneer in the modern science of mental health prevention and wellness promotion, has argued that there are five main pathways to wellness:

1. Forming wholesome early attachments

2. Acquiring age-appropriate competencies

3. Being exposed to settings that favor wellness outcomes

4. Having the empowering sense of being in control of one's fate

5. Coping effectively with stress

It stands to reason then, that for optimal effectiveness and impact, any comprehensive SEL program should address most, if not all, of these critical pathways.

SOCIAL AND EMOTIONAL NEEDS OF KINDERGARTEN AND PRIMARY GRADE CHILDREN

The *Strong Start* curriculum is unique because it is an SEL program designed specifically to address the needs of kindergarten and primary grade children, or from about age 5 through about age 8. Although several very good SEL intervention programs have been developed and made available since the 1980s, very few are focused on the unique needs of this younger age range of students.

To be effective, a curriculum must be designed and implemented to be developmentally appropriate for the students for whom it is intended. For kindergarten and primary grade children, there are some unique cognitive, social, and emotional developmental needs that must be considered. Cognitively, almost all children in this age range are *concrete thinkers*, meaning that they have not yet developed the ability to think abstractly or symbolically. They usually have difficulty with tasks that require a great deal of interpersonal insight or self-reflection. In addition, many K–2 children have not yet learned to read at all or with great fluency. Therefore, any curriculum designed for this age group must be explicit and somewhat concrete, use examples with which the children are familiar, use repetition and review to help teach mastery of skills, require only minimal reading skills, and be short enough and interesting enough to maintain their attention.

Children in the kindergarten and primary grade levels are developing emotionally and experiencing many emotional changes. They experience many feelings and tend to understand the general notion of feelings or emotions, but they usually have a very limited vocabulary of words describing different emotions. For example, most primary grade children will understand the concepts of happy, sad, angry, and worried, but they will probably not be able to understand more sophisticated emotional words such as *thrilled, joyful, tense,* or *proud.* Some of the critical tasks for children in this age range, in terms of emotional development, include developing a sense of self-control, learning new emotional words, learning that what is "right" or "wrong" may be based on more than just the immediate consequences of the behavior, and learning that how something appears is not always how it is.

Socially, children in the K–2 age range are learning how to initiate effective social interactions with other children and how to develop friendships. They are in the process of learning how to engage socially with individuals outside of their family and are often surprised to learn that different families have different social rules and expectations, as well as emotional and behavioral climates. Some of the critical skills during this period include learning to negotiate and compromise, learning to be empathetic or understand the feelings and experiences of another person, learning how to effectively join groups and initiate conversations, and learning appropriate use of humor. Many of the friendships children develop at this age are not lasting, but they tend to be very important in terms of providing a situation in which children can learn the skills required to make friends and to be a good friend to others. Children who fail to acquire the empathy or social skills needed to be successful in making and keeping friends are at risk for a variety of social and emotional problems, ranging from isolation and peer rejection to loneliness, poor self-esteem, and even depression.

In sum, any SEL program designed for use with kindergarten and primary grade children must take into account the unique developmental needs of this age group if it is to be effective. The developmental needs that must be considered include cognitive, emotional, and social development, among other issues.

MODEL FOR PREVENTING BEHAVIORAL AND EMOTIONAL PROBLEMS

Educational researchers have adapted a public health prevention model for use in school systems (e.g., Merrell & Buchanan, 2006; U.S. Department of Education, 2004; Walker et al., 1996). We believe that this model (see Figure 1) has great importance for promoting SEL and for school-based promotion of children's mental health in general. Sometimes referred to as the "triangle," this model of prevention and intervention includes service delivery at three levels of prevention: students who currently are not experiencing learning or social/behavior difficulties (*primary prevention*); students who are considered to be at risk for the development of learning or social/behavior difficulties (*secondary prevention*); and students who currently are experiencing significant learning or social/behavior difficulties (*tertiary prevention*).

We can visualize this model and its three levels of prevention as a triangle. The entire triangle represents all students within a school setting, the majority of whom

Figure 1. The prevention triangle model, specifically adapted for how to make systems work for assessing, identifying, and serving students with behavioral, social, and emotional problems. (*Key:* IEP, individualized education program.)

are not experiencing difficulties (i.e., the bottom portion of the triangle), some of whom are at risk of developing significant problems (i.e., the middle portion), and an even smaller percentage who are currently experiencing significant difficulties (i.e., the top portion). Typical practice is to focus on those students who are at the top of the triangle—those who are currently experiencing significant learning and/or social-emotional difficulties. Practitioners tend to spend the majority of their time and effort providing tertiary prevention (i.e., individualized assessment and intervention services) to these students on a case-by-case basis. These students make up the smallest percentage of the school population, but because of the significance of their problems, they often require the majority of time and resources from school personnel (Walker et al., 1996).

Shifting to a systemwide prevention model requires that we look at the "big picture" by considering the needs of all students, not just those who are referred because they are experiencing significant difficulties. The foundation of a prevention approach is the use of universal interventions (i.e., primary prevention) designed to enhance the delivery of effective instruction and improve school climate to promote academic, social, and behavioral resilience of all students in the school. This idea requires that we begin to move some resources and energy toward those children and adolescents who are not currently experiencing significant difficulties in order to help them acquire skills to reduce the probability that they will eventually rise to the "top of the triangle." More specifically, primary prevention for students who are not currently experiencing learning and/or social/behavior difficulties is accomplished through schoolwide and classwide efforts that involve the consistent use of research-based effective practices, ongoing monitoring of these practices and student outcomes, and staff training and professional development. The goal of primary prevention is to create school and classroom environments that promote student learning and health and decrease the number of students at risk for learning or social/behavior problems.

As important as it is to focus on primary prevention, we also know that not all students respond similarly to these efforts. Thus, it is important to monitor student progress and to assess whether students are at risk (i.e., in need of secondary prevention efforts) or experiencing significant difficulties (i.e., in need of tertiary prevention efforts). Identifying students at risk for learning, social-emotional, and behavior difficulties is an important aspect to comprehensive prevention efforts. For students identified as at risk and in need of secondary prevention efforts, the focus is on the delivery of specialized interventions (often at a small-group level) to prevent the worsening of problems and to prevent the development of more significant concerns. The focus on early identification and early intervention is important.

With respect to mental health and social-emotional problems of children and adolescents, we believe that this prevention model is an ideal way to think about providing SEL programs and other services. Thinking in this way about the challenges we face in promoting social-emotional wellness and mental health among children and adolescents makes these challenges more manageable. Instead of waiting until students have developed severe problems and require extensive time and effort to simply be managed, we can continually focus a portion of our resources on prevention activities that will ultimately reduce the number of students at the top of the triangle.

REFERENCES

Cowen, E.L. (1994). The enhancement of psychological wellness: Challenges and opportunities. *American Journal of Community Psychology, 22,* 149–179.

Doll, B., & Lyon, M.A. (1998). Risk and resilience: Implications for the delivery of educational and mental health services in schools. *School Psychology Review, 27,* 348–363.

Farmer, E.M.Z., & Farmer, T.W. (1999). The role of schools in outcomes for youth: Implications for children's mental health services research. *Journal of Child and Family Studies, 8,* 377–396.

Greenberg, M., Domitrovich, C., & Bumbarger, B. (2001, March 30). The prevention of mental health disorders in school-age children: Current state of the field. *Prevention and Treatment, 4.* Retrieved November 19, 2005, from http://journals.apa.org/prevention/volume4/pre0040001a.html

Greenberg, M.T., Weissberg, R.P., O'Brien, M.U., Zins, J.E., Fredericks, L., Resnick, H., et al. (2003). Enhancing school-based prevention and youth development through coordinated social, emotional, and academic learning. *American Psychologist, 58,* 466–474.

Merrell, K.W., & Buchanan, R.S. (2006). Intervention selection in school-based practice: Using public health models to enhance systems capacity of schools. *School Psychology Review, 35,* 167–180.

Skiba, R., & Peterson, R. (1999). The dark side of zero tolerance: Can punishment lead to safe schools? *Phi Delta Kappan, 80,* 372–376, 381–382. Retrieved November 19, 2005, from http://www.pdkintl.org/kappan/kcur9910.htm

U.S. Department of Education, OSEP Center on Positive Behavioral Interventions and Supports (2004). *School-wide PBS.* Retrieved November 19, 2005, from http://www.pbis.org

Walker, H.M., Horner, R.H., Sugai, G., Bullis, M., et al. (1996). Integrated approaches to preventing antisocial behavior patterns among school-age children and youth. *Journal of Emotional and Behavioral Disorders, 4,* 194–209.

Zins, J.E., Bloodworth, M.R., Weissberg, R.P., & Walberg, H.J. (2004). The scientific base linking social and emotional learning to school success. In J. Zins, M. Wang, & H. Walberg (Eds.), *Building academic success and social-emotional learning: What does the research say?* New York: Teachers College Press.

An Evidence-Based Program

We applaud the current movement toward the use of scientifically based curricula and programs in education and mental health services. SEL programs that are built on good scientific principles of instruction and behavior change and that have demonstrated evidence of effectiveness to support them are a key to making the kind of impact that we believe is necessary to help prevent and remediate the broad range of social, emotional, and mental health problems that plague our society. Several professional organizations have developed standards for determining whether prevention/intervention programs have sufficient evidence behind them to be considered effective from a scientific standpoint. Some of the names that have been used for programs that meet these standards include *empirically validated treatment, empirically supported treatment*, and our own preference, the more generic term, *evidence-based program*.

Since the initial development of the Strong Kids curriculum (including *Strong Start, Strong Kids—Grades 3–5, Strong Kids—Grades 6–8*, and *Strong Teens*), we have made extensive efforts to experimentally test the effectiveness of this program. As of 2007, eight studies have been conducted on the effectiveness of various versions of the Strong Kids program, under a variety of conditions. Each of these studies conducted to date has found that groups of students who participated in *Strong Kids—Grades 3–5, Strong Kids—Grades 6–8*, and *Strong Teens* have showed significant gains in their knowledge of curriculum concepts of SEL. Some of the studies have shown significant reductions of problem emotional-behavioral symptoms as a result of participating in the programs. In addition, some of the studies have evaluated the social validity of the programs from teacher and student perspectives. These studies, without exception, showed a very high amount of satisfaction and confidence in the programs by both students and teachers.

We encourage interested curriculum users and others to read detailed descriptions of these studies on our web site at http://strongkids.uoregon.edu. As we have already noted, our research efforts with the Strong Kids curriculum are continuing, and we hope to greatly expand the available evidence in support of this program. We will post summaries and reports of research studies on the Strong Kids web site as they become available.

3

Preparing Your Lessons and Your Students

Strong Start is designed to be used primarily with children in kindergarten and the early primary grades, or grades K–2. This grade range translates to about age 5 through age 8. Obviously, there are important differences in the skills and developmental level of children at the two ends of the intended age or grade range. For this reason, we have included suggestions within the lessons for using them with younger or lower-performing students. By eliminating any need for reading by students, simplifying examples and language, and reducing some of the time or behavioral demands of different lesson components, *Strong Start* can be used effectively with children at the younger end of the intended grade and age range. Likewise, the curriculum can be made more relevant for typically developing and high-performing children at the higher end of the grade-age range by using components that require some basic reading skills, increasing the range and complexity of examples and language, and increasing the time and participation demands. As you prepare in advance to teach a *Strong Start* lesson, consider the developmental level of your children, and look carefully at the suggestions for adapting the lesson for younger children, if necessary.

Although the intended baseline or lower age/grade range for using *Strong Start* is kindergarten and about age 5, it may be appropriate to use the program with children slightly younger than this level, such as typically or higher-developing children ages 4 and 5 in Head Start and other preschool programs. To use the curriculum effectively with younger children, carefully identify the components of each lesson that can be adapted for simplification, and make appropriate developmental modifications.

MATERIALS NEEDED

To implement *Strong Start*, you should have access to an overhead projector, blank overhead transparency film sheets, a copy machine, chart paper, and a chalk or marker board. Many of the lessons provide templates for overhead transparencies. Although it is not essential to make overhead transparencies of these masters, we have found that doing so provides the advantage of being able to go over a graphic illustration or chart in front of the class while you introduce the critical concepts that are connected to them. Alternatively, some teachers and group leaders have found that they prefer to make paper copies of the overhead transparency masters and to provide each student with a copy of these materials rather than presenting the materials with an overhead projector. Some of the lessons also include reproducible templates for handouts or worksheets for students, and all of the lessons include a *Strong Start* Bulletin to be personalized, duplicated, and sent home to parents to reinforce the lesson goals. These items can also be found on the accompanying CD-ROM.

An important part of our lesson development throughout *Strong Start* is the use of a stuffed animal "mascot" for the curriculum. In the lessons, we have given the example of a stuffed bear by the name of Henry. You may follow our suggestion by locating a stuffed bear and naming it Henry, or you may use any type of stuffed animal and name that you think is most appropriate for your children. We have found that children especially enjoy this aspect of the curriculum. The mascot becomes not only a symbol for the program but a reminder to practice *Strong Start* skills and a welcome part of your classroom or group environment.

Some teachers who have assisted us in piloting the initial versions of *Strong Start* found that displaying the stuffed animal in a prominent place in the classroom served as a constant reminder of the program and the skills that were being taught and that their students often asked about the next lesson or previous activities by the prompt of this display. In addition, we recommend that you not only use the mascot when teaching *Strong Start* but also throughout the school year. Picking up the stuffed animal from time to time, weeks or months after completing *Strong Start*, can serve as a keen reminder of what was learned in the program and can help support continued practice and discussion of the critical concepts and skills that were taught.

SUPPLEMENTARY MATERIALS

Each *Strong Start* lesson includes one or more sheets of related or supplementary materials, which are found at the end of the lesson and on the accompanying CD-ROM. These materials are labeled throughout the text with a "reminder" symbol. For the sake of consistency, we refer to these materials as "supplements" and have titled them that way. These supplements include overhead transparency masters and the *Strong Start* Bulletins for parents and family members. As you prepare for each lesson, note the supplements for that lesson and how they should be used. Prior to teaching the lesson, make copies and transparency masters as needed. These supplements are all reproducible for users of the curriculum. Although we have made suggestions regarding how to use the supplementary materials, you should feel free to adapt them to your own needs and situation. For example, you might find it useful to enlarge some of the handouts or transparency masters into posters and to place them on the wall of the classroom to reinforce or visually prompt students as they learn and practice the skills promoted in *Strong Start*.

PROVIDING AN AGENDA

It is recommended that you inform your students before the class begins what the agenda or goals will be for that day's lesson. With children who can read, a written outline of the topics included in the curriculum may be useful as well as an agenda for the individual lesson. With children who are not yet skilled readers, a brief verbal overview will suffice.

STATING EXPECTED BEHAVIORS

Because of the nature of the lessons in *Strong Start*, behavior expectations for students or group members must be very clear. Some of the units revolve around sensitive issues, and every opportunity should be taken to provide instruction and subsequent reinforcement for appropriate behavior. Students should feel free to share their beliefs and feelings on the targeted topics but must not feel pressured into revealing anything that makes them feel uncomfortable. You should state expected behaviors prior to instruction, before modeling examples, and before the practice sections of lessons. In some cases, you may need to teach and reinforce behavioral expectations more frequently than these suggested times.

As a general recommendation for promoting appropriate behavior in school and related settings, we recommend that teachers and group leaders develop and teach a few simple rules for appropriate behavior. Rules should be stated *positively*, meaning that they should tell students what is expected rather than what to avoid. For example, *respect your classmates* is a positively stated rule, whereas *no fighting* is a negatively stated rule that does not tell students what specifically they should do. Rules should be simple and appropriate to the developmental level of the children for whom they are intended. In addition, the list of rules should be kept to a minimum. Usually, no more than five general rules are needed. You will find that rules are more effective when you teach them to students, then find frequent opportunities to reinforce the rules through reminders, examples, and so forth.

PLANNING FOR SMOOTH TRANSITIONS

Time is one of the most precious commodities in your classroom or center. In a brief curriculum such as *Strong Start*, the element of time is especially critical. To make the best use of your limited time in teaching the curriculum, use your transition time wisely prior to and during the *Strong Start* lessons. We recommend that you have all materials prepared and organized for easy distribution to students. Make sure that equipment is in working order before you start the lessons. *Explicitly state directions prior to and during transitions.* If possible, precorrect for any possible behavioral difficulties.

PHYSICAL ARRANGEMENTS

For the lessons in this curriculum, all students must have a clear view of you, the group leader. Forward facing seats or a horseshoe shape are both appropriate. For younger children, seating them in a semi-circle or horseshoe arrangement on the floor for parts of the lessons (e.g., the children's books, the demonstrations) may be appropriate. You may want to preassign students to groups of two or three because they will be required to separate into groups during the application sections in some of the lessons. This will not only save time but will also give you control of which students will be paired. Always use movement, voice level, and voice intonation to increase the interest of your students, and consequently increase active participation.

ADAPTATIONS FOR UNIQUE NEEDS

In many of the *Strong Start* lessons, you will be encouraged to create scenarios pertaining to a certain topic. To facilitate and encourage student participation, think of scenarios that would best reflect the interests, abilities, and level of understanding of the students in your class or group. You may choose to use current situations relevant to your classroom or school or even global current events to illustrate the concepts. The scenarios provided in the units should be considered examples and can be modified extensively to best fit the unique needs of your students. Making appropriate adaptations for the unique needs of your students will not only make the delivery of lessons go more smoothly but will aid with generalization and maintenance of new skills.

SUGGESTIONS FOR SUCCESS

As you teach the *Strong Start* lessons, you will increase your likelihood of success by observing and following a few additional suggestions for successful implementation of the curriculum:

- Be sure to give the children an *overview* of each lesson's purpose. Explain that a different topic/unit will be taught each week (or as frequently as possible) as students may come to expect a continuation of a certain topic as opposed to a new topic each lesson.

- Our experience has indicated that folders that are specifically designated for students to store their handouts, drawings, notes, and other materials related to *Strong Start* will help them to keep their materials organized and will reduce the amount of time needed by the teacher or group leader to start the weekly lessons. We suggest that you consider having all of your students keep a special *Strong Start folder* for this purpose.

- Ensure that you sufficiently *review the topics* from prior lessons and integrate concepts when at all possible.

- Introduce or reintroduce a *behavior management technique*, such as a token economy, to reinforce prosocial behaviors during the unit. Remind students of school and classroom rules as well as the rules associated with this curriculum.

- This curriculum involves teaching a wide range of skills in a relatively short period of time. In order to use your time most effectively, *directly teach these skills*. Place your priority on instruction, and keep discussion and activity time to a minimum.

- *Reinforce* any *Strong Start* skills that you might observe, both within and outside of the teaching setting. Make sure that parents, teachers, administrators, and other staff are aware of the skills you are instructing as your students will require frequent feedback in several settings in order for the skills to be durable and generalized.

- As a general practice, we suggest that you *do not add new students to a group once it has already started*. Particularly when the program is taught to small groups of students rather than entire classrooms, we have found that having new students join the group once it has started can be disruptive to the group process and may result in a slowing of the flow of training, as well as a reduction in the willingness of group members to participate.

- Look for opportunities to *use the Applying What We Learned* section found at the end of each lesson. These suggestions have been designed to facilitate the transfer of skills learned through the program across different settings and to help students maintain what they have learned over time. Again, the three areas we have included in Applying What We Learned include prompts for precorrecting errors in learning the expected skills, reminding students of the concepts being learned, and acknowledging students for demonstrating the skills that have been introduced and taught in the program.

- Use and personalize the *Strong Start Bulletins*, which are found at the end of each lesson and on the accompanying CD-ROM. These bulletins, which are in the form of a brief letter, are designed to inform parents and other family members regarding the objectives and activities of each lesson. If parents use the information from these bulletins to reinforce concepts from the lessons and praise their children for engaging in lesson-related skill development, increased generalization of skills across settings may result.

- Use the recommended *children's books*, and add your own titles as appropriate. Each lesson in *Strong Start* includes a 10- to 15-minute period designed to be used to read your students a book that reinforces the key concepts from that lesson. We have developed a short list of books for each lesson, and we encourage you to add and use other titles that you think are appropriate. We have a recommended list of discussion questions in each lesson that can be used with any relevant book.

- Our recommended *time allowance* for each of the lessons is approximately 45 minutes. Our experience (and the time breakdowns in the lesson plans) is based on this time length. These time allowances are only guidelines. If your children are very engaged in a particular activity and you are not under time pressure to finish it on schedule, you should feel free to let the activity continue. Likewise, if your children are having a particularly difficult time with one part of a lesson and you have additional time to spare, you should feel free to either continue beyond the time recommendation or to come back to the lesson later in the day.

- And, of course, *practice your lessons* before implementing them!

ADAPTATIONS FOR CULTURALLY AND LINGUISTICALLY DIVERSE LEARNERS

As our society becomes increasingly diverse, researchers and practitioners have recognized the need to address cultural issues in curriculum development and implementation. Efforts to address cultural issues have ranged from ignoring or dismissing the need for cultural adaptations to arguing the need for culture-specific research and curricula tailored for each cultural subgroup. Between these two extreme positions has emerged a set of criteria and recommendations for making cultural adaptations to existing curricula. The cultural adaptation approach retains the core assumptions and skill domains of the existing curriculum but recommends tailoring the teaching of these concepts to the specific needs of particular groups of interest. Research supports the success of making cultural adaptations to existing social and emotional curricula for specific groups (see Munoz, Penilla, & Urizar, 2002; Yu & Seligman, 2002).

We began the development of the *Strong Kids—Grades 3–5, Strong Kids—Grades 6–8,* and *Strong Teens* curricula—the predecessors to *Strong Start*—with the assumption that no single curriculum could meet the learning needs of all students. By focusing on teaching a set of key ideas related to SEL and resiliency, however, we believe that the curricula can successfully meet the needs of a wide range of students when appropriate adaptations are made. Some cultural variables that may require attention in curriculum adaptation processes include language, race/ethnicity, acculturation, socioeconomic status, sexual orientation, religion, gender, disability status, and nationality.

The "Big Ideas" of *Strong Start*

As we have noted, a successful curriculum adaptation process requires particular innovations and modifications to meet the needs of specific individuals and groups, but at the same time, these adaptations must retain the general concepts, or big ideas, on which the curriculum is based. With this notion in mind, we list the most important features of the *Strong Start* curriculum, with the hope that these ideas will be taken into account when making any type of adaptation to the curriculum. With the underlying goal of improving SEL and resiliency in kindergarten and primary grade children, these big ideas include the following:

- To help children to understand that social and emotional health, like physical health, requires attention and results from specific actions and situations
- To teach children to identify and understand their own feelings
- To teach children how to identify and understand other people's feelings
- To teach children appropriate ways to express a range of feelings
- To teach children to understand the link between how they think and behave and the way that they feel
- To teach children skills to appropriately monitor and modify their feelings, thoughts, and behaviors
- To help children approach their challenges in life with a realistic sense of optimism

- To help children to learn behavioral and affective techniques to relax and remain calm in the face of stress or worries

- To teach children problem-solving skills and effective communication skills (e.g., listening, using appropriate vocalization techniques)

- To help children to learn the skills needed to make friends and be a good friend

Specific Strategies for Making Cultural Adaptations

Keeping these big ideas in mind, the *Strong Start* curriculum may be adapted to better fit the needs of diverse children. For this purpose, we propose a few guidelines for making cross-cultural adaptations. These suggestions are based on our experiences in attempting to adapt *Strong Kids—Grades 3–5*, *Strong Kids—Grades 6–8*, and *Strong Teens* with specific cultural groups. They are also based in great measure on the premises of the American Psychological Association's Guidelines for Providers of Psychological Services to Ethnic, Linguistic, and Culturally Diverse Populations (available at http://www.apa.org).

1. Get to know your students.

   - Ask children about their cultural identities, activities, and rituals.

   - Reflect on the dominant cultural variables in your classroom and how these aspects of culture affect the way your students behave and think.

   - Identify common success and failure experiences, problem situations, and challenging life circumstances confronted by your students.

2. Get to know your students' community.

   - Visit the families and, as appropriate, the homes of children in your class or group.

   - Identify a cultural liaison (a parent or community member who identifies as a member of the target cultural group) to help you learn more about your students' culture.

   - Ask the cultural liaison to assist with the cultural adaptation process.

3. Deliver the curriculum in a manner that your students can understand.

   - Modify the language of each lesson so that your students can easily understand the key ideas.

   - Use examples and scenarios that match the lives of your students (e.g., change characters' names, include extended family, include children who use wheelchairs, use problem examples that your students have experienced).

4. Encourage tolerance.

   - Teach students ways to show respect for different cultural groups.

   - Encourage and reinforce children for respecting the examples and comments made by their peers.

   - Establish and enforce a classroom or group rule that teasing and name-calling are not allowed.

5. Become aware of variations within cultures.

- Do not assume too much about a child's culture or ethnicity.

- Avoid making overgeneralizations about cultural groups. Not all members of a culture act the same way.

- Examine your own values, assumptions, and worldviews and how these are the same and different from those of your students.

- Continually examine the accuracy and fairness of your assumptions about the beliefs and behaviors of different cultural groups.

6. Seek feedback.

- View the adaptation process as an ongoing process.

- Consult with children, your colleagues, and community members about the relevance and accuracy of the adaptation efforts.

- Ask the children how well the curriculum is matching their needs and life experiences.

In sum, adapting *Strong Start* or any other SEL curriculum for use with culturally and linguistically diverse learners may be challenging, but it is essential if the curricula are to have the most meaningful impact on the learners. The suggestions we have offered in this section may be useful as a guide to making the flexible *Strong Start* program appropriate for children and youth from a variety of cultural backgrounds.

REFERENCES

Munoz, R.F., Penilla, C., & Urizar, G. (2002, May 8). Expanding depression prevention research with children of diverse cultures. *Prevention and Treatment, 5.* Retrieved November 19, 2005, from http://www.journals.apa.org/prevention/volume5/pre0050013c.html

Yu, D.L., & Seligman, M.E.P. (2002). Preventing depressive symptoms in Chinese children. *Prevention and Treatment, 5.* Retrieved November 19, 2005, from http://www.journals. apa.org/prevention/volume5/pre0050009a.html

Overview of the Lessons

Strong Start consists of 10 carefully sequenced lessons, designed for maximum impact on cognitive, affective, and social functioning within a relatively brief period of time. Each of these lessons is overviewed in this section. You should read these descriptions carefully prior to preparing your first lesson so that you will understand the lesson sequencing and the "big ideas" behind *Strong Start*.

LESSON 1: THE FEELINGS EXERCISE GROUP

In the first lesson, The Feelings Exercise Group, students are introduced to the *Strong Start* curriculum, and the purpose, goals, and practices of the program are overviewed. A general overview of the big ideas of the curriculum and its individual lessons is provided so that students will understand what they can expect over the course of the instruction as well as behavioral expectations for their participation. Important terms are introduced, as is Henry, a stuffed animal that serves as the mascot for the curriculum and is used to help introduce key concepts. Students are made aware of the importance of this curriculum so that they are able to understand why appropriate behaviors such as respect for others, confidentiality of shared information, and adequate lesson preparation are integral parts of the experience.

LESSONS 2 AND 3: UNDERSTANDING YOUR FEELINGS

The second and third lessons, Understanding Your Feelings 1 and 2, are intended to improve the emotional vocabulary, awareness, and resiliency skills of students. Understanding and recognizing one's emotions is an important skill for everyone during all stages of life because people experience emotions at school, home, work, and play. Being able to recognize their emotions and react in an appropriate way, even when the emotion is not a good feeling, will allow your students to create and sustain positive relationships in school and throughout their lives.

In Understanding Your Feelings 1, students learn to identify different types of basic emotions and distinguish them as resulting in "good" or "not good" feelings. Students learn to recognize which situations might cause them to feel a certain way. The goal of this lesson is to apply the skills learned to different situations at different times and in different settings.

In Understanding Your Feelings 2, the feelings-identification skills are extended to include how one might express different feelings—both positive and negative—in an appropriate manner. Students learn that, although it is okay to have any feeling, there are appropriate and inappropriate ways of showing or expressing feelings. Given a way of expressing a feeling, students identify the way as "okay" or "not okay." Students then have the opportunity to apply their new skills in fun application exercises, making it more likely that they will be able to generalize the new skills to other situations.

LESSON 4: WHEN YOU'RE ANGRY

The fourth lesson, When You're Angry, teaches students that all people experience anger in their lives; however, many young children are not able to appropriately understand and deal effectively with their anger. Misunderstanding anger, and an inability to appropriately manage it, can often manifest itself in inappropriate behaviors such as arguments and fights, excessive sadness, and frustration. This lesson teaches students to understand the physical signs or manifestations of anger in their bodies, list synonyms for the emotion of anger, identify common situations that might lead people to feel angry, and determine if responses to anger are done in "Ways that Help" or "Ways that Hurt." Through activities and stories, a particular emphasis is placed on developing and practicing responses to anger that are Ways that Help.

LESSON 5: WHEN YOU'RE HAPPY

The fifth lesson, When You're Happy, teaches students how to understand and express the positive emotion of happiness and to understand the connection between this feeling and their thoughts and situations. Although virtually all kindergarten and primary grade students can identify the feeling of happiness, many or most have not yet learned the connection between this emotion and our thought processes and behaviors. This lesson focuses on identifying common physical or bodily sensations associated with feeling happy, actions and situations that are more likely to lead to this positive feeling, and developing synonyms for the word *happy*. In addition, students are taught a simple cognitive restructuring technique—the ABCs of Positive Thinking—that can help them cope with adverse situations in a positive way while being less likely to succumb to negative feelings such as sadness or anger.

LESSON 6: WHEN YOU'RE WORRIED

Learning appropriate techniques to manage stress, anxiety, and common worries is an important strategy to promote emotional resilience and prevent physical and emotional problems. In Lesson 6, When You're Worried, students are taught to apply specific behavioral, affective, and cognitive skills to situations that might cause them worry and anxiety. The same techniques that were taught for other specific feelings—understanding physical sensations, developing synonyms, and listing common situations in which the feeling might occur—are applied specifically to the emotion of worry or anxiety. Students again practice using the ABCs of Positive Thinking, and they are taught a new skill—the Stop, Count, In, Out strategy—that they can apply specifically to help cope with worries, fears, stress, and anxiety.

LESSON 7: UNDERSTANDING OTHER PEOPLE'S FEELINGS

The seventh lesson, Understanding Other People's Feelings, is a very basic form of empathy training, or teaching young children to discern and understand the feelings that other people experience. Many, if not most, kindergarten and primary grade students have not yet adequately learned to take the perspective of other people, so this lesson is an important step in beginning to acquire this critical people skill. Students are taught to identify common physical cues or clues to help understand how another person might be feeling and that different people can experience different feelings in the same situation. Through stories and fun activities, students are given practice in this skill to help increase the chance that they will maintain it and generalize it to other settings.

LESSON 8: BEING A GOOD FRIEND

The eighth lesson, Being a Good Friend, is a very basic social skills and interpersonal skills training module for young children. In this lesson, students are taught some of the most basic interpersonal communication skills and given opportunities to practice them in realistic situations. Skills such as using a nice voice, being a good listener, making appropriate eye contact, and using appropriate body language are emphasized. A particular focus is placed on skills that will help students make friends more easily and be good friends.

LESSON 9: SOLVING PEOPLE PROBLEMS

The ninth lesson, Solving People Problems, is designed to promote awareness of useful strategies for resolving conflict between and among peers. Interpersonal conflicts can begin early in life and, if they become a continual pattern, may provide a fertile breeding ground for depression, anxiety, and negative thinking. Thus, learning appropriate and effective ways to resolve these conflicts may be a strong preventive factor for deterring emotional as well as social problems. In this lesson, students define and describe situations in which conflicts with peers might commonly occur. Through a review of the previously taught skills for coping with anger and using the ABCs of Positive Thinking, students are taught to apply these strategies to help resolve peer problems. This lesson includes practice situations where students are expected to role-play and apply these important skills to a staged problem that they might potentially encounter with a peer.

LESSON 10: FINISHING UP!

The title of the final *Strong Start* lesson, Finishing UP!, has a double meaning. It implies that this lesson is the final one in the curriculum, but it also shows how we are striving to end on a positive or upbeat note, celebrating the accomplishments that have been made through involvement with the *Strong Start* curriculum. This lesson provides the opportunity for students to review key points and terms from the lessons presented throughout the previous several weeks. The specific *Strong Start* skills that students were taught in previous lessons—identifying okay and not okay feelings; defining Ways that Help and Ways that Hurt; and using the ABCs of Positive Thinking and the Stop, Count, In, Out strategy—are all reviewed one last time to ensure competency. Henry, the stuffed animal mascot, figures prominently in this lesson and will be available to students in the future as a tangible prompt regarding the things they learned and practiced in the *Strong Start* curriculum.

BOOSTER LESSONS

Appendices A and B include optional Booster Lessons for use with *Strong Start*. These Booster Lessons cover six and three *Strong Start* lessons, respectively. They are designed to be taught several weeks or months following the conclusion of the 10 *Strong Start* lessons, in order to help reteach and reinforce the main concepts from *Strong Start*. Although the Booster Lessons are optional components, we highly recommend them and urge teachers and group leaders to consider using them to make the curriculum optimally effective. We suggest that Booster Lesson 1 be taught at least 1 month after the conclusion of the 10 *Strong Start* lessons, and we also recommend using the Booster Lessons as two separate sessions, instead of combining them into one lesson. In addition to reteaching and reinforcing the critical components of *Strong Start*, your students will find the Booster Lessons to be fun. We have developed a game, Strong Start Feelings Bingo, for use specifically in the Booster Lessons, to help reteach the six basic emotions that are taught in *Strong Start*.

APPLYING WHAT WE LEARNED

As a teacher or group leader, you want your efforts in teaching *Strong Start* to result in the students continuing to use their new adaptive social-emotional skills over time and in other settings. In developing *Strong Start*, we specifically planned and programmed the curricula for optimal application by children across settings and over time. In technical terms, this sort of application is referred to as *maintenance and generalization*. Specifically, we have included suggestions and activities within each of the 10 *Strong Start* lessons that are aimed at promoting the application or generalization of new skills learned across settings other than the intervention setting (e.g., home, community, other school settings) and the maintenance of these skills over time.

At the end of each of the 10 lessons is a section titled Applying What We Learned. This brief section includes suggested activities and methods in the following three areas, which are based on literature on effective instructional approaches for teaching social-behavioral skills authored by Sugai and colleagues (e.g., Langland, Lewis-Palmer, & Sugai, 1998; Sugai, Bullis, & Cumblad, 1997):

- *Anticipate*—activities designed to help the instructor/group leader anticipate errors and difficulties that students may have in learning new skills, to maximize the efficacy in teaching new skills that are sequenced instructionally to previously taught skills

- *Remind*—suggestions for providing verbal or visual prompts to students that will help remind them of steps, sequences, skills, and actions that are needed to engage effectively in new skills as they are taught

- *Acknowledge*—prompts to provide acknowledgment or praise as students successfully approximate and perform the new skills they are taught in *Strong Start*

In addition to the suggestions in the Applying What We Learned sections, each lesson has, embedded within it, tips for instructors as they develop and model examples of new skills and help the students see the need for these skills. These suggestions are aimed at making the lessons relevant to students, thus increasing the potential effectiveness of each lesson. Appropriate activities are provided for each of the 10 lessons that are further designed to reinforce learning from the direct instructional part of the lessons. Each lesson also has a *Strong Start* Bulletin included as a supplement. These bulletins are important communication links to the home setting to help generalize new skills your students learn.

FINAL COMMENTS

Good luck as you prepare to use *Strong Start*. We have field-tested this curriculum with many teachers and mental health professionals in the United States and elsewhere and have made many improvements to it based on their feedback from experience using it with a large number of children and in a large variety of settings. Our efforts to create an effective, user-friendly, and practical mental health promotion program, coupled with the real-world experience and feedback we gained during 5 years of initial research and development, have convinced us that the Strong Kids curriculum has much to offer and can be a valuable tool for supporting SEL, promoting resilience, and teaching coping skills.

REFERENCES

Langland, S., Lewis-Palmer, T., & Sugai, G. (1998). Teaching respect in the classroom: An instructional approach. *Journal of Behavioral Education, 8*, 245–262.

Sugai, G., Bullis, M., & Cumblad, C. (1997). Provide ongoing skill development and support. *Journal of Emotional and Behavioral Disorders, 5*, 55–64.

The *Strong Start* Curriculum

The Feelings Exercise Group

TEACHER NOTES

⭐ **Purpose**

- To introduce students to the *Strong Start* curriculum

⭐ **Objectives**

- Students will identify the purpose of the *Strong Start* curriculum.

- Students will learn expected behaviors for participation in the program.

- Students will demonstrate an understanding of the concept of confidentiality.

MATERIALS NEEDED

- ❑ Henry (stuffed animal mascot)
- ❑ Supplement 1.1 (overhead transparency)
- ❑ Book from the literature list (or one of your choice)
- ❑ *Strong Start* Bulletin

5 minutes

Introduction

Communicate the lesson's purpose and objectives clearly. Explain to your students that they will be starting a new curriculum, *Strong Start*. Tell them how often it will be taught, and give examples of some of the topics that will be covered. Make it clear that the skills learned during this unit are skills that are vital to their social and emotional health and will be important during all phases of life.

 Throughout the lessons, we use a small stuffed bear named Henry as a class mascot. You may select a different stuffed animal or name if you wish. Introduce the children to Henry.

Sample Script

Today, we are going to begin a special class called Strong Start. In this class, we will be learning with a new friend. His name is Henry. In this class, Henry will help us understand our feelings and other people's feelings. He will also help us learn about being a good friend. We will be with Henry [once per week] for [one class period]. Every time we meet, we will do special exercises, except we won't be running around outside or lifting big, heavy weights. We will be working on growing strong on the inside, so we will call our group the Feelings Exercise Group. Everyone needs to be healthy—on the outside and on the inside. This class will help you to be healthy on the inside for your whole life.

 6 minutes

Defining Behavior Expectations

Explain to your students that they are now part of a special group with some special rules. It is helpful to present the rules one at a time and have your students help you to determine and demonstrate examples and nonexamples of each rule. The three rules for the group are as follows:

1. Be a good listener.
2. Keep a calm body.
3. Be a friend.

Sample Script

You are now part of a special group with some special rules. The first rule is "Be a good listener." What does a good listener do? (Expect answers like eyes on the person that is talking and lips zipped.) *The next rule is "Keep a calm body." What does a calm body look like?* (Expect answers like hands to ourselves and sitting on our bottoms.) *Why do you think it is important to have a calm body when we are in the Feelings Exercise Group? The last rule is "Be a good friend." What does it mean to be a good friend? How can you be a good friend?* (Expect answers like someone who listens to you and someone who is nice to you.)

6 minutes # Discuss the Concept of Confidentiality

Help your students understand the following ideas:

- They may be asked to share personal information during lessons.

- Participation is voluntary.

- They may speak to you individually if they feel uncomfortable sharing in a large group.

- When they share stories, they need not use specific names.

Have students demonstrate that they understand these concepts.

Sample Script

During this special class, you might be asked to share stories about times when you have been very happy, mad, or sad or have had other very strong feelings. You might also share stories about problems that you have had. If you want to share a story, you can raise your hand to let me know. When someone else is sharing a story, we will follow our special group rules—we will be good listeners, we will keep calm bodies, and we will be good friends. We can only talk about the things people share during our special group, and when we tell our stories, we do not need to use other people's names. If you start to feel like you don't want to share a story anymore, you can stop at any time. If you don't want to tell everyone your story, but you would still like to share it with me, you can talk to me after class.

Let's practice one of the important rules that we just talked about. If I say that I was angry because Sara was mean to me, is that okay? No, because I used Sara's name. How about if I say that I was angry because my friend was mean to me? Is that okay? Yes, because I didn't use someone's name.

10 minutes # Introduction to the Topics Covered in the Curriculum

Introduce the topics, and provide a brief explanation for each of the lessons using Supplement 1.1 as an overhead transparency.

15 minutes # Read a Book From the Literature List

Read a book from the following list of examples or choose your own book to share with students.

- *Feelings* by Aliki

- *The Way I Feel* by Janan Cain

- *Feelings* by Joanne Brisson Murphy

- *The Feelings Book* by Todd Parr
- *My Many Colored Days* by Dr. Seuss

Be sure to point out all of the actions or ways in which the characters behave when they are acting on their feelings. Use the following questions to guide your discussion:

- What was one of the feelings the character had?
- Do you think it was a good or not good feeling?
- What did the character do when he or she was feeling that way?

Closure

Gather your students together, and review the lesson's objectives.

Sample Script

Today, we talked about our new special class called the Feelings Exercise Group. We also talked about the rules of our group, which are 1) be a good listener, 2) keep a calm body, and 3) be a friend. It is important to remember that we can only talk about the things people share during our special group, and when we tell our stories, we do not need to use other people's names. This class will help us learn how to be healthy on the inside for the rest of our lives, and Henry is going to help us. I am excited to start this special class with you!

About Strong Start

We will learn about our feelings.

feeling *angry*   feeling *happy*   feeling *worried*

We will learn about other people's feelings.

We will learn about being a friend.

We will learn about solving problems.

And we will learn how to relax and feel calm.

Strong Start—Grades K–2: A Social and Emotional Learning Curriculum

Strong Start Bulletin

Dear Family,

Today, your child participated in the first lesson of **Strong Start**, a curriculum designed to boost the social and emotional development of young children. This curriculum includes 10 lessons that help children in recognizing and managing emotions, engaging in problem solving, and being a good friend. Your child was introduced to **Henry,** a stuffed bear who will serve as an important figure in the classroom community and in all lessons included in this curriculum. Today's lesson, entitled **The Feelings Exercise Group,** focused on helping children realize that it is just as important to be emotionally strong as it is to be physically strong. Below are examples of the vocabulary and pictures presented during today's lesson.

Strong Start's Objectives

To learn about our feelings

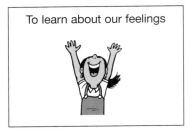

To learn about other people's feelings

To learn about being a friend

To learn about solving problems

And to learn how to relax and feel calm

Over the next several weeks, you will be receiving bulletins that detail the content of all of the *Strong Start* lessons. To help your child use the skills he or she learns, be sure to read the letters and try out the suggested strategies at home.

Thank you in advance for supporting your child as he or she learns about the important topics covered in *Strong Start.* If you notice your child using skills he or she has learned at school, be sure to applaud your child's efforts!

Strong Start—Grades K–2: A Social and Emotional Learning Curriculum
by Kenneth W. Merrell, Danielle M. Parisi, and Sara A. Whitcomb © 2007 University of Oregon. All rights reserved.

Understanding Your Feelings 1

TEACHER NOTES

★ Purpose

- To teach students to name basic feelings

★ Objectives

- Students will name feelings that make them feel good or not good on the inside.

- Students will apply the principles of this lesson to different situations.

MATERIALS NEEDED

- ❑ Henry (stuffed animal mascot)
- ❑ Blank overhead transparency or chart paper
- ❑ Supplement 2.1 (overhead transparency)
- ❑ Drawing paper
- ❑ Crayons
- ❑ Book from the literature list (or one of your choice)
- ❑ *Strong Start* Bulletin

2 minutes # Review

To activate prior knowledge, review and discuss previous topics and main ideas. Obtain 3–5 adequate ideas. Make sure to provide feedback.

Sample Script

During our last meeting, we introduced you to the Feelings Exercise Group. Raise your hand if you can tell me an important idea we learned during that lesson.

2 minutes # Introduction

Communicate the lesson's purpose and objectives clearly.

Sample Script

Today, Henry has come back to help us learn how to name our feelings. We will talk about all different kinds of feelings and how they make us feel good or not good on the inside.

11 minutes # Feelings Identification

Explain to students that you will be discussing feelings and labeling them as good or not good.

Sample Script

Let's talk about naming our feelings. No matter where we are, we always have feelings—at school, at home, and at play. If we know how to name our feelings and can talk about them, it will help us to know what to do even if the feeling makes us feel not good on the inside.

Use a piece of chart paper or a blank transparency and overhead projector to display the list of feelings generated from the following exercise.

1. Generate a list of feelings.

    *   State a basic emotion, such as happy or sad, and explain that this is a feeling.

    *   Give a second example, using a more complex emotion such as excited or worried. Write both of the chosen feelings on the chart paper or transparency.

    *   Ask students to generate other feelings, and write these feelings on the chart paper or transparency. (Basic emotions include happy, sad, angry, afraid, surprised, and disgusted.)

2. Identify feelings as good or not good.

    *   Model this skill using all of the feelings you and the students brainstormed in Step 1.

Sample Script

Happy is a good feeling. When I feel happy, I feel good, and I like to smile. Sad is not a good feeling. When I feel sad, I feel bad, and I may even cry.

- Go back to the start of your list, and have the students give you a thumbs-up for feelings that make people feel good on the inside and a thumbs-down for feelings that make people feel not good on the inside.

Sample Script

Another way you could show that feelings are good or not good is to give a thumbs-up or a thumbs-down. When I say a word from the list, I want you to give me a thumbs-up for a good feeling and a thumbs-down for a not good feeling.

3. Conduct a follow-up discussion.

- Ask students if they have ever had any feelings where it was hard to decide if the feeling made them feel good or not good on the inside. Give an example.

Sample Script

Have you ever had a feeling and it was hard for you to decide if you felt good or not good on the inside? Henry has. For example, one time I had a party for Henry, and he felt surprised. It was hard for him to decide if it was a good or a not good feeling. Give me some more examples of these kinds of feelings.

- Using examples students provide, further explain that not all feelings can be easily named as good or not good.

- Discuss these feelings with your students. Encourage them to pay attention to the feelings in their bodies, the expressions of their faces, and the thoughts in their minds to help them name feelings.

3 minutes

If You're Happy and You Know It

Encourage students to stand up and follow your lead in singing *If You're Happy and You Know It*. Use the following script as a guide, and add any additional feelings as you see fit. Display Supplement 2.1 if desired.

Sample Script

If you're happy and you know it, clap your hands.
If you're sad and you know it, say, "Boo hoo."
If you're afraid and you know it, take a breath.
If you're angry and you know it, use your words.
If you're surprised and you know it, say, "Wowee."
If you're disgusted and you know it, say, "Yucky."

15 minutes

How Do You Feel?

- Use this time to brainstorm examples of how people might feel at different times. Model examples of times when you felt happy or sad.

Sample Script

Now that we've named feelings and we know that feelings can make us feel good or not good on the inside, we are going to talk about when you might have those feelings. For instance, Henry feels happy when he goes to a birthday party. It makes him feel good on the inside. I feel happy when I'm playing outside.

- Engage in a Think/Pair/Share activity. Have students think about a time when they felt happy; then, have them turn to their neighbors and share their ideas.

- For each feeling that was brainstormed during Feelings Identification, describe a time when you felt that way. Then, have the students engage in the Think/ Pair/Share activity for some or all of the six feelings.

- Pass out drawing paper, and encourage students to draw a picture of one of their examples.

- At the conclusion, if appropriate and students are willing, invite two or three students to share their examples.

Read a Book from the Literature List

Read a book from the following list of examples or choose your own book to share with students.

- *Feelings* by Aliki
- *Everybody Has Feelings or Todos Tenemos Sentimientos* by Charles E. Avery
- *How Are You Peeling? Foods with Moods* by Saxton Freymann and Joost Elffers
- *On Monday When It Rained* by Cherryl Kachenmeister
- *Feelings* by Joanne Brisson Murphy
- *The Feelings Book* by Todd Parr
- *Lots of Feelings* by Shelley Rotner

Be sure to point out all of the actions or ways in which the characters behave when they are acting on their feelings. Use the following questions to guide your discussion:

- What was one of the feelings the character had?
- Do you think it was a good or not good feeling?
- What did the character do when he or she was feeling that way?

Closure

Gather your students together, and review the lesson objectives.

Sample Script

Today, we learned how to name our feelings. We learned how to name different kinds of feelings. We talked about how feelings make us feel good or not good on the inside, and we talked about times when we have different feelings. Everyone has feelings at school, at home, and at play. Being able to name our feelings is important because if we know how to name our feelings and can talk about them, it will help us to know what to do even if the feeling makes us feel not good on the inside.

Applying What We Learned

Anticipate

Tell your students to try to name the feelings they experience throughout the day. Once they identify or label the feelings they are experiencing, encourage them to investigate whether the feelings make them feel good or not good on the inside. This exercise might be particularly helpful on days that will likely include more intense emotions (e.g., field trips, assemblies, testing days).

Remind

If you notice students having difficulty expressing themselves in words (e.g., getting frustrated and showing it by rolling their eyes, feeling tired or upset and expressing it by putting their heads on the desk), remind them to tell you what they are feeling using the words or feelings labels that were learned in this lesson. Initially, it may be helpful to model use of such vocabulary (e.g., "It looks like you are feeling happy today. I can see that you have a big smile. Do you feel good on the inside?").

Acknowledge

Praise your students (or give them a small reward if you have a behavior management system in your classroom) if you notice them expressing a feeling or expressing that their feelings make them feel good or not good on the inside (e.g., "Sally called me a name, and it made me feel not good on the inside," or "My mom bought me a new toy, and it made me feel good on the inside.").

Basic Feelings

Happy

Sad

Afraid

Angry

Surprised

Disgusted

Strong Start—Grades K–2: A Social and Emotional Learning Curriculum

Strong Start Bulletin

Dear Family,

This week, our **Strong Start** lesson focused on identifying and understanding the **six basic feelings** reflected below. We reviewed the names of feelings and discussed that some make us feel **good** on the inside while others make us feel **not good**. We talked about situations that might trigger particular feelings, and we also drew pictures of ourselves experiencing one of the six feelings. Throughout the lesson, Henry helped us understand that it is natural for everyone to experience all feelings.

Basic Emotions

| Happy | Sad | Afraid | Angry | Surprised | Disgusted |

To better understand our feelings, we sang:
If you're happy and you know it, clap your hands.
If you're sad and you know it, say, "Boo hoo."
If you're afraid and you know it, take a breath.
If you're angry and you know it, use your words.
If you're surprised and you know it, say, "Wowee."
If you're disgusted and you know it, say, "Yucky."

At home encourage your child to
- Stop and name the feeling he or she is experiencing.
- Determine whether or not it is a good or not good feeling.

Thanks for supporting your child as he or she learns about identifying feelings. If you notice your child naming his or her feelings or expressing feelings that make him or her feel good or not good on the inside, be sure to acknowledge your child's efforts!

LESSON 3

Understanding Your Feelings 2

TEACHER NOTES

⭐ **Purpose**

- To teach students appropriate ways of expressing feelings

⭐ **Objectives**

- Students will be able to distinguish between okay and not okay ways of expressing feelings.
- Students will apply the principles of this lesson to different situations.

MATERIALS NEEDED

- ❑ Henry (stuffed animal mascot)
- ❑ Blank overhead transparency or chart paper
- ❑ Supplement 3.1 (overhead transparency)
- ❑ Supplement 3.2 (overhead transparency)
- ❑ Book from the literature list (or one of your choice)
- ❑ *Strong Start* Bulletin

2 minutes Review

To activate prior knowledge, review and discuss previous topics and main ideas. Prompt students to remember the six basic feelings: happy, sad, angry, afraid, surprised, and disgusted. Make sure to provide feedback.

Sample Script

During our last meeting, we learned to name our feelings. Raise your hand if you can remember a feeling that we learned about in our last class.

2 minutes Introduction

Communicate the lesson's purpose and objectives clearly.

Sample Script

Today, we are going to learn more about feelings. I have brought Henry to help us as we do this.

10 minutes Read a Book from the Literature List

Read a book from the following list of examples or choose your own book to share with students.

- *The Chocolate-Covered-Cookie Tantrum* by Deborah Blumenthal
- *Today I Feel Silly & Other Moods That Make My Day* by Jamie Lee Curtis
- *The Grumpy Morning* by Pamela Duncan Edwards
- *Chrysanthemum* by Kevin Henkes
- *Julius: The Baby of the World* by Kevin Henkes
- *Bye, Bye!* by Nancy Kaufmann
- *The Kissing Hand* by Audrey Penn
- *Sometimes I Like to Cry* by Elizabeth and Henry Stanton

Be sure to point out all of the actions or ways in which the characters behave when they are acting on their feelings. Use the following questions to guide your discussion:

- What was one of the feelings the character had?
- Do you think it was a good or not good feeling?
- What did the character do when he or she was feeling that way?
- Was it an okay or not okay way of showing the feeling?

5 minutes Identify Actions that Follow Feelings

Use one of the six basic feelings to identify common actions associated with that feeling.

Sample Script

Last time, we talked about feelings that are good and not good. Today, we're going to talk about what we do when we have good and not good feelings. Happy is a good feeling. When Henry feels happy, he smiles more, and he has fun playing and learning. Disgusted is not a good feeling. When Henry feels disgusted, his tummy hurts, and he makes a yucky face.

Convey the following main ideas to your students:

- Everyone has feelings, and it is okay to have any feeling.
- We have different feelings at different times.
- Sometimes we can have more than one feeling at the same time.
- It is important to talk about what we are feeling on the inside.
- There are different ways of showing feelings.
- Other people may not feel the same way I do about everything.

Sample Script

Everyone has feelings, and it is okay to have any feeling. We have different feelings at different times. For example, when Henry is playing outside, he is happy, but when he is taking a bath, he is sad. Sometimes, we also have more than one feeling at the same time. It is important to talk about what we are feeling on the inside, and there are different ways of showing our feelings. When I am angry, I am quiet, and I don't like to talk to anyone. When Henry is angry, he stomps his feet and has a frown on his face. Other people may not feel the same way that I do about everything. I am happy when it is time to get a haircut, but Henry is afraid of getting his hair cut.

2 minutes Having Multiple Feelings at Once

The following examples reflect situations when children may have more than one feeling at the same time. Use them to help further explain this concept to students.

- When Henry found out his grandma was coming to visit, he was happy because he wanted to see her, but he was also afraid because he didn't know her that well.
- When Henry had to go to the dentist, he was mad because he doesn't like to go to the dentist, but he was also happy because he likes getting a toy from the dentist's treasure chest.
- When Henry's mom had a surprise party for him, Henry was surprised because he didn't know about it. He was also angry because his mom didn't tell him, and he was happy because he got to see all of his friends.

Review and Mastery of Understanding Basic Emotions

- Revisit *If You're Happy and You Know It.*

- Present pictures of each of the six basic feelings using Supplement 3.1. Have students give examples of when they may experience these feelings. Write at least one response for each feeling on chart paper or a blank overhead transparency for use later.

Sample Script

This is a picture of disgust. Disgust is not a good feeling. Raise your hand if you can think of a time when you might feel disgust.

- *Note:* If a child mentions that eating broccoli makes him or her feel disgust, you could paraphrase and write "eating yucky foods" on chart paper.

Ways of Showing Feelings

Communicate to children that there are okay and not okay ways of showing feelings. Using the examples that the children provided in Review and Mastery of Understanding Basic Emotions, extend the examples to show okay and not okay ways of showing feelings. Be sure to provide examples and nonexamples for all six of the basic feelings.

Sample Script

Remember that there are different kinds of feelings. Now, let's talk about how we can show our feelings. We talked about how eating yucky foods might make us have a feeling of disgust. When Henry eats broccoli, he has a feeling of disgust. He chews it up and spits it out on the table. This is not an okay way of showing disgust because Henry wasn't showing good manners. Instead, when Henry's mom makes broccoli for dinner, Henry takes a small amount, chews, and swallows it. This is an okay way of showing disgust because Henry is showing good manners.

Okay and Not Okay Examples of Showing Other Feelings

The following additional examples may reflect similar situations that the children share. Use them to guide your thinking as you plan for this lesson.

Feeling	Example	Okay	Not okay
Sad	A pet runs away.	Telling a parent how you are feeling	Screaming and demanding a new pet
Angry	A friend borrows your bike without asking.	Taking a deep breath and using nice words to tell your friend how you are feeling	Pushing your friend off the bike
Surprised	You see your teacher at the grocery store.	Walking up to your teacher and saying hi	Pointing at the teacher but never saying hi
Afraid	You have to go to the doctor.	Telling your parents how you are feeling	Keeping it a secret

Practice Identifying Okay and Not Okay Ways of Showing Feelings

Read the examples provided in Supplement 3.2, Ways of Showing Feelings. Have students stand up if the example suggests an okay way of showing feelings and stay seated if the example is not an okay way of showing feelings.

Closure

Gather your students together, and review the lesson objectives.

Sample Script

We all have feelings. Today, we learned that there are okay and not okay ways of showing feelings. It is all right to have any feeling, but it is important that we show our feelings in okay ways. It is also important to remember that other people may not always feel the same way you do.

Applying What We Learned

Anticipate

Tell your students to remember to practice naming their feelings and using okay ways to show their feelings. It might be helpful to prompt them prior to potentially emotional times of day, such as recess period, lunch, or physical education.

Remind

Similar to the last lesson, if you notice students having difficulty expressing their feelings (e.g., getting bored and crying out, "This is boring! I hate this!"; feeling mad and yelling at a peer), remind them that these are not okay ways to express their feelings, and ask them to try it again in an okay way. Initially, you might have to model an okay way of expressing the particular feeling (e.g., "Watch me and listen. When you take that toy without asking, it makes me feel angry.").

Acknowledge

Praise your students for displaying okay ways of expressing their feelings. Some examples of okay ways could include students using "I feel" statements, talking (not yelling) about their issues with one another, or asking for help if they are getting frustrated.

Basic Feelings

Happy

Sad

Afraid

Angry

Surprised

Disgusted

★STRONG KIDS™ Ways of Showing Feelings

1. A boy feels angry because a friend calls him a bad name. He stops, counts to 10, and feels calm.

2. A girl feels happy because she did very well in math. She jumps up in the middle of class shouting, "Yippee!"

3. A boy is scared by a fire alarm at school and runs out of the building as quickly as he can.

4. A girl feels sad about leaving home on the first day of school. She lets her teacher know how she is feeling.

5. A boy is surprised to see that his mom has come to visit him at school. He smiles and laughs to himself.

6. A girl feels disgusted when she sees her friend sneeze all over the lunch table. She gets up and says, "Ewwwww!" very loudly.

Strong Start Bulletin

Dear Family,

This week, our **Strong Start** lesson extended ideas presented during last week's lesson. We reviewed the names of feelings: **happy, sad, angry, afraid, disgusted,** and **surprised.** We also reviewed those feelings that make us feel **good** or **not good.** Throughout the lesson, Henry helped us understand that it is natural for everyone to experience all feelings. He also helped us to know **okay** and **not okay** ways to act on our feelings. We defined situations that make us experience certain feelings and examples of okay and not okay ways for handling the situations. Some examples that we discussed are listed in the table.

Feeling	Example	Okay	Not okay
Sad	A pet runs away.	Telling a parent how you are feeling	Screaming and demanding a new pet
Angry	A friend borrows your bike without asking.	Taking a deep breath and using nice words to tell your friend how you are feeling	Pushing your friend off the bike

To better understand handling feelings, we read

_____ .

Following are great examples of relevant stories that you may want to read at home:
- *Chrysanthemum* by Kevin Henkes
- *The Chocolate-Covered-Cookie Tantrum* by Deborah Blumenthal
- *Today I Feel Silly & Other Moods That Make My Day* by Jamie Lee Curtis

At home, remind your child to
- Stop and identify the feeling he or she is experiencing.
- Determine whether or not it is a good or not good feeling.
- Choose an okay way to act on that feeling.

Thanks for helping your child to apply what he or she has learned about identifying feelings. Be sure to congratulate your child each time he or she chooses an okay way to handle a difficult situation.

When You're Angry

⭐ Purpose

- To teach students how to manage anger and helpful ways of handling anger

⭐ Objectives

- Students will accurately describe how their bodies feel when they are angry.

- Students will accurately list synonyms for the word *anger.*

- Students will identify situations that might make people angry.

- Students will understand Ways that Help and Ways that Hurt in handling their anger.

MATERIALS NEEDED

- ❑ Henry (stuffed animal mascot)
- ❑ Blank overhead transparency or chart paper
- ❑ Supplement 4.1 (overhead transparency)
- ❑ Supplement 4.2 (overhead transparency)
- ❑ Book from the literature list (or one of your choice)
- ❑ Drawing paper
- ❑ Crayons
- ❑ *Strong Start* Bulletin

2 minutes **Review**

To activate prior knowledge, review and discuss previous topics and main ideas. Make sure to provide feedback.

Sample Script

During our last meeting, we discussed how to understand our feelings and okay ways for showing them. Raise your hand if you can tell me an okay way of showing one of the feelings. How about a not okay way? We also learned about good and not good feelings. Raise your hand if you can remember a good feeling. How about a not good feeling?

2 minutes **Introduction**

Communicate the lesson's purpose and objectives clearly.

Sample Script

Today, we will talk about a feeling called anger. Anger is a normal feeling, and everybody feels angry sometimes. We will learn what anger looks like and when it might happen. We will also learn ways to deal with our anger so that we don't hurt ourselves or others.

10 minutes **Read a Book from the Literature List**

Read a book from the following list of examples or choose your own to share with students.

- *The Cranky Day, and Other Thomas the Tank Engine Stories* by W. Awdry
- *When Sophie Gets Angry—Really Really Angry* by Molly Bang
- *The Chocolate-Covered-Cookie Tantrum* by Deborah Blumenthal
- *Feeling Angry* by Althea Braithwaite
- *Mean Soup* by Betsy Everitt
- *If You're Angry and You Know It* by Cecily Kaiser
- *Andrew's Angry Words* by Dorothea Lachner
- *I Was So Mad* by Norma Simon
- *When I Feel Angry* by Cornelia Maude Spelman
- *Sometimes I'm Bombaloo* by Rachel Vail
- *Alexander and the Terrible, Horrible, No Good, Very Bad Day* by Judith Viorst

Be sure to point out all of the actions or ways in which the characters behave when they are acting on their feelings. Use the following questions to guide your discussion:

- Which character was angry?
- Do you think it was a good or not good feeling?

- What did the character look like when he or she was angry?
- What did the character do when he or she was angry?
- Did the character use a Way that Hurts or a Way that Helps to handle his or her anger?

Show and Define Anger

- Use Supplement 4.1 to show children pictures of different examples of angry faces.

  ### Sample Script

  This is angry. Angry is not a good feeling. What does angry look like in this picture? Raise your hand if you've ever felt angry. What did your body look or feel like?

- Have students share what their bodies felt like when they were angry. Examples include felt hot, had tight muscles, were shaky, or were teary.
- Engage in a Think/Pair/Share activity. Have students think about a time when they felt angry; then, have them turn to their neighbors and share their ideas.
- Reconvene and have two people who are willing share with the whole group.
- Using a blank overhead transparency or chart paper, have students help you generate a list of synonyms or words that make them think of anger. Examples include *angry*, *mad*, *furious*, and *upset*.

Ways of Handling Anger

Introduce the concept of Ways that Help and Ways that Hurt in handling anger.

Sample Script

Today, we've been talking about a feeling called anger. All people feel angry sometimes, and it's all right to feel angry. Most of the time, something happens to make us angry. This is called a spark. Something sparks our anger. Like the kind of sparks that start a fire, there are things we can do to stop anger and keep it from spreading, and there are things we can do that spread the anger and hurt ourselves and others. One time, Henry really wanted to go to his friend's house, but his mom said no. When this happened, his muscles got tight, and he began to feel hot. What sparked Henry's anger in this situation? How did his body feel? What do you think Henry did next?

After students have shared their ideas for what Henry did when he was angry, explain that there are two ways that you can deal with your anger: Ways that Help and Ways that Hurt. Use Supplement 4.2 to introduce Ways that Help.

Sample Script

Henry felt really angry when he couldn't go to his friend's house. Since this happened a long time ago, Henry didn't know about Ways that Help and

Ways that Hurt when handling his anger. In this situation, Henry stuck out his tongue, stomped his feet, and slammed the door to his room. When he was alone in the room, he kicked the wall. This kind of behavior is what I call Ways that Hurt. Henry stayed mad and wasn't acting nicely. When he got older and the same thing happened, he knew how to make himself feel better. He learned a special trick called Stop, Count, In, Out.

	Sample Script
STOP	When you feel a spark, **stop** what you are doing.
COUNT	**Count** to 10.
IN	Take a deep breath **in.**
OUT	Breathe **out.**

These steps are all Ways that Help.

Use the following examples to assess children's understanding of the concept of Ways that Hurt and Ways that Help in handling anger.

Spark	What Henry does	Is it a Way that Helps or a Way that Hurts?	How can Henry use a Way that Helps?
Henry's older brother wanted to play with his toys by himself for a while.	Henry took a deep breath and counted to 10.	It's a Way that Helps.	
Henry's pencil broke when he was doing his homework.	Henry stopped what he was doing and took a deep breath.	It's a Way that Helps.	
Henry missed his favorite TV show.	Henry kicked the wall.	It's a Way that Hurts.	Henry took a deep breath in and out.
Henry's favorite baseball team lost the game by one run.	Henry kicked the wall.	It's a Way that Hurts.	Henry stopped what he was doing and counted to 10.
Henry spilled red juice on his white T-shirt.	Henry stopped what he was doing, counted to 10, and took a deep breath in and out.	It's a Way that Helps.	
Henry didn't get to be his friend Robbie's partner on the field trip.	Henry wouldn't do his math work.	It's a Way that Hurts.	Henry stopped what he was doing and took a deep breath in and out.

8 minutes

Activities

Engage in a Think/Pair/Share activity. Have students think about how they handled their anger from the previous Think/Pair/Share. Then, have them briefly turn to a neighbor and discuss whether they handled their anger in a Way that Helps. Reconvene and have two students who are willing share their stories with the group.

Have students make a poster that shows a Way that Helps in handling anger. Display the posters when the students are finished. If time allows and students are willing, let some of the students describe their situation and the Way that Helps. Comment and reinforce appropriate situations.

Note: These activities can be completed later in the day if there is not time during the lesson.

1 minute

Closure

Gather your students together, and review the lesson objectives.

Sample Script

Everyone feels angry sometimes, and there are many ways that we can handle our anger. It is important to use a Way that Helps so that we don't hurt ourselves or others.

Applying What We Learned

Anticipate

Tell your students to use Ways that Help (the Stop, Count, In, Out strategy) if something sparks their anger. Prompting them prior to recess, lunch, physical education periods, and partner activities might be particularly helpful.

Remind

If you find that a student is not dealing with his or her anger properly, remind him or her to handle the anger with a Way that Helps. Some students might benefit from your modeling the Stop, Count, In, Out strategy ("Watch Me." Stop, count, breathe. "Your turn.").

Acknowledge

If you see your students using Ways that Help to handle their anger, provide them with specific praise, such as, "I like that you stopped and took a big, deep breath just then. I could tell that something had sparked your anger."

STRONG KIDS™ I'm Angry!

Strong Start—Grades K–2: A Social and Emotional Learning Curriculum
by Kenneth W. Merrell, Danielle M. Parisi, and Sara A. Whitcomb © 2007 University of Oregon. All rights reserved.

The Stop, Count, In, Out Strategy

STOP		When you feel a spark, **stop** what you are doing.
COUNT	1 2 3 4 6 5 9 7 8 10	**Count** to 10.
IN		Take a deep breath **in.**
OUT		Breathe **out.**

Strong Start—Grades K–2: A Social and Emotional Learning Curriculum
by Kenneth W. Merrell, Danielle M. Parisi, and Sara A. Whitcomb © 2007 University of Oregon. All rights reserved.

Strong Start Bulletin

Dear Family,
This week, our **Strong Start** lesson focused on teaching students helpful ways of handling anger. We discussed how our bodies feel when we are angry, and we also listed synonyms for the word **anger.** Throughout the lesson, Henry helped us understand **Ways that Help** and **Ways that Hurt** in dealing with situations that make us angry. We defined the kinds of situations that **spark** our anger and shared ideas for appropriately stopping our sparks from turning into big, angry fires. Below is one strategy we practiced:

The Stop, Count, In, Out Strategy

STOP	STOP	When you feel a spark, **stop** what you are doing.
COUNT	1 2 3 4 6 5 9 7 8 10	**Count** to 10.
IN		Take a deep breath **in.**
OUT		Breathe **out.**

To better understand handling anger, we read

_____.

Following are great examples of relevant stories that you may want to read at home:
- *When Sophie Gets Angry—Really Really Angry* by Molly Bang
- *If You're Angry and You Know It* by Cecily Kaiser
- *Andrew's Angry Words* by Dorothea Lachner
- *Alexander and the Terrible, Horrible, No Good, Very Bad Day* by Judith Viorst

When your child becomes angry at home, remind him or her to:
- Stop and identify the "spark."
- Count to 10, and breathe in and out.
- Act or behave in a Way that Helps.

Helping children to choose Ways that Help in handling anger is very important. If you see that your child is not making an appropriate choice for handling anger, help him or her to brainstorm a better way. If you notice your child making a great choice, be sure to praise his or her accomplishment (e.g., "I liked the way you took a breath when you started to get angry.").

Strong Start—Grades K–2: A Social and Emotional Learning Curriculum
by Kenneth W. Merrell, Danielle M. Parisi, and Sara A. Whitcomb © 2007 University of Oregon. All rights reserved.

LESSON 5

When You're Happy

TEACHER
NOTES

⭐ Purpose

- To teach students to feel happy and to use positive thinking

⭐ Objectives

- Students will accurately describe how their bodies feel when they are happy.

- Students will describe actions and situations that make them feel happy.

- Students will accurately list synonyms for the word *happy.*

- Students will understand the ABCs of Positive Thinking.

MATERIALS NEEDED

- ❏ Henry (stuffed animal mascot)
- ❏ Blank overhead transparency or chart paper
- ❏ Supplement 5.1 (overhead transparency)
- ❏ Supplement 5.2 (overhead transparency)
- ❏ Book from the literature list (or one of your choice)
- ❏ Drawing paper
- ❏ Crayons
- ❏ *Strong Start* Bulletin

2 minutes **Review**

To activate prior knowledge, review and discuss previous topics and main ideas. Make sure to provide feedback and refer to the steps of the Stop, Count, In, Out strategy.

Sample Script

During our last meeting, we discussed feeling angry. Raise your hand if you can tell me Ways that Help you feel better when you are angry. How about a Way that Hurts?

2 minutes **Introduction**

Communicate the lesson's purpose and objectives clearly.

Sample Script

Today, we will talk about feeling happy. Everyone feels happy sometimes. It is a good feeling. Today, we will talk about what our bodies and minds feel like when we are happy, and we will also talk about times that made us feel happy. We will think about how we can make ourselves feel happy when we are mad or sad.

10 minutes **Read a Book from the Literature List**

Read a book from the following list of examples or choose your own book to share with students.

- *Super Completely and Totally the Messiest* by Judith Viorst
- *I Like Me!* by Nancy Carlson
- *The Secret Remedy Book: A Story of Comfort and Love* by Karin Cates
- *Fun is a Feeling* by Chara M. Curtis
- *Today I Feel Silly & Other Moods That Make My Day* by Jamie Lee Curtis
- *A Bad, Bad Day* by Kirsten Hall

Be sure to point out all of the actions or ways in which the characters behave when they are acting on their feelings. Use the following questions to guide your discussion:

- Which character was happy?
- Do you think it was a good or not good feeling?
- What did the character look like when he or she was happy?
- What did the character do when he or she was happy?

Show and Define Happiness

- Use Supplement 5.1 to show children different examples of happy faces.

    Sample Script

    This is happy. Happy is a good feeling. What does happy look like in this picture? Raise your hand if you've ever felt happy. What did your body look or feel like?

- Have students describe what their bodies felt like when they were happy. Examples include felt comfortable, felt relaxed, and felt energetic.

- Engage in a Think/Pair/Share activity. Have students think about a time when they felt happy. Then, have them turn to their neighbors and share their ideas.

- Reconvene and have two students who are willing share their ideas with the whole group.

- Using a blank overhead transparency or chart paper, have students help you generate a list of synonyms or words that make them think of happiness. Examples include *glad, excited, pleased, joyful, cheerful, content,* and *delighted.*

Positive Thinking

Introduce the concept of Positive Thinking. Consider replacing the term *Positive Thinking* with *Happy Thinking* for younger children who may not understand the concept. As the concept of Positive or Happy Thinking requires a higher level of cognitive thought, it might be helpful to emphasize examples given through animated delivery and movement.

Sample Script

Today, we are also going to talk about Positive Thinking. We will learn what this is and how it can help us to feel better when we are sad or mad. Remember, it is always okay to have not good feelings like anger or sadness, but when we use Positive Thinking, we have the feeling that everything is going to be okay. Positive Thinking also helps us to feel better if we are experiencing feelings that are not good. Positive Thinking is like jogging or playing because the more we do it, the healthier we are. We are strong on the inside just as we are strong on the outside. When we don't use Positive Thinking, we might get stuck feeling sad or mad.

For example, Henry was not picked to be his teacher's special helper. This gave him feelings that were not good. He thought he'd never be able to be the helper. He was not using Positive Thinking. Instead, if Henry was using Positive Thinking, he would have made himself feel better by remembering that all of the students in the class get to take turns being the teacher's special helper and his turn would come soon.

Introduce the ABCs of Positive Thinking using Supplement 5.2 as a helpful tool to remember how to achieve positive thinking.

A	A problem	Whenever there's a problem . . .
B	Bad feelings	that gives you a not good feeling . . .
C	Comfort yourself	comfort yourself by thinking about it in a way that makes you feel better.

Use the following examples to assess children's understanding of the concept of Positive Thinking.

Problem	What Henry does	Is it Positive Thinking or Not Positive Thinking?	How can Henry use Positive Thinking?
Henry's older brother wanted to play with his toys by himself for a while.	Henry thought, "I hate my brother. I'll never be able to play with his toys ever."	It's Not Positive Thinking.	Henry found something else to do and realized he could play with his brother's toys another time.
Henry's pencil broke when he was doing his home-work.	Henry thought, "I'll never get my homework done."	It's Not Positive Thinking.	Henry knew he could sharpen his pencil or find another one that worked.
Henry missed his fa-vorite TV show.	Henry said, "I'll see it next week."	It's Positive Thinking.	
Henry's favorite baseball team lost the game by one run.	Henry knew they could win the next time.	It's Positive Thinking.	
Henry spilled red juice on his white T-shirt.	Henry began to cry and thought that he'd never wear the shirt again.	It's Not Positive Thinking.	Henry thought he could ask his mom to wash his shirt.
Henry didn't get to be his friend Robbie's partner in math class.	Henry thought, "That's okay. Maybe next time."	It's Positive Thinking.	

5 minutes

Activity

Have students draw a picture of a time when they had a problem and thought about it in a way that made them feel better or have younger children color a *happy badge* to remind them to think positively when they have problems.

Closure

Gather your students together, and review the lesson objectives.

Sample Script

Today, we learned about feeling happy and Positive Thinking. Everyone feels happy. It is a good feeling. If we use Positive Thinking, we can make ourselves feel happy even if we are having not good feelings.

Applying What We Learned

Anticipate

Encourage your students to use the ABCs of Positive Thinking when they are feeling badly. This may be particularly helpful before events that may cause negative feelings, such as partner activities, recess, and competitions.

Remind

If you find a student who is not using Positive Thinking, remind him or her to use the ABCs of Positive Thinking. The student may need help in determining ways to comfort (letter *C*) him- or herself.

Acknowledge

If you are able to observe students using Positive Thinking, be sure to applaud their application of this complex skill.

STRONG KIDS™ | I'm Happy!

Strong Start—Grades K–2: A Social and Emotional Learning Curriculum

The ABCs of Positive Thinking

A	A problem	Whenever there's a problem . . .
B	Bad feelings	that gives you a not good feeling . . .
C	Comfort yourself	comfort yourself by thinking about it in a way that makes you feel better.

Strong Start Bulletin

Dear Family,

This week, our **Strong Start** lesson focused on teaching students about **happiness.** We discussed how our bodies feel when we are happy and what actions or situations make us feel happy. We also listed synonyms for the word **happy.** In this lesson, Henry helped us understand **positive thinking.** We talked about how positive thinking can make us feel better when we are sad or mad. The **ABCs of Positive Thinking** is one strategy for positive thinking.

The ABCs of Positive Thinking

A	A problem	Whenever there's a problem . . .
B	Bad feelings	that gives you a not good feeling . . .
C	Comfort yourself	comfort yourself by thinking about it in a way that makes you feel better.

To better understand happiness, we read

_____.

Following are great examples of relevant stories that you may want to read at home:
- _Super Completely and Totally the Messiest_ by Judith Viorst
- _Fun is a Feeling_ by Chara M. Curtis
- _Today I Feel Silly & Other Moods That Make My Day_ by Jamie Lee Curtis

When your child becomes sad or mad at home, remind him or her to remember the ABCs of Positive Thinking noted above. The "comfort yourself" part can be hard, and your child might need your help to think about a problem in a better way. For example, if your child loses a baseball game, an example of Positive Thinking might be, "That's okay. I'll try again next game," rather than "I'll never win."

Thanks for all of your support in helping your child to be a positive thinker!

When You're Worried

TEACHER NOTES

★ **Purpose**

- To teach students to manage anxiety, worry, and fear

★ **Objectives**

- Students will accurately describe how their bodies feel when they are worried.
- Students will accurately list synonyms for the word *worried.*
- Students will identify situations that might make people worried.
- Students will apply the ABCs of Positive Thinking and the Stop, Count, In, Out strategy when they are worried.

MATERIALS NEEDED

- ❑ Henry (stuffed animal mascot)
- ❑ Book from the literature list (or one of your choice)
- ❑ Blank overhead transparency or chart paper
- ❑ Supplement 6.1 (overhead transparency)
- ❑ Supplement 6.2 (overhead transparency)
- ❑ *Strong Start* Bulletin

Review

To activate prior knowledge, review and discuss previous topics and main ideas. Make sure to provide feedback.

> **Sample Script**
>
> *During our last meeting, we learned about Positive Thinking. Raise your hand if you can tell me an important idea we learned from this lesson.*

 Introduction

Communicate the lesson's purpose and objectives clearly.

> **Sample Script**
>
> *Today, we will talk about feeling worried. Feeling worried is not good, but everyone feels worried sometimes. It's normal. Feeling worried is sometimes like feeling scared. We will learn how our bodies are when we are worried and think about when we might worry. We will also learn ways to deal with our worries so that we don't feel worried all the time.*

 Read a Book from the Literature List

Read a book from the following list of examples or choose your own to share with students.

- *Arthur's Baby* by Marc Brown
- *Will I Have a Friend* by Miriam Cohen
- *I'm Scared* by Elizabeth Crary
- *Mommy, Don't Go* by Elizabeth Crary
- *Even if I Did Something Awful* by Barbara Shook Hazen
- *Wemberly Worried* by Kevin Henkes
- *The Underbed* by Cathryn Clinton Hoellwarth
- *The Boy Under the Bed* by Preston McClear
- *The Kissing Hand* by Audrey Penn
- *The Good-Bye Book* by Judith Viorst

Be sure to point out all of the actions or ways in which the characters behave when they are acting on their feelings. Use the following questions to guide your discussion:

- Which character was worried?
- Do you think it was a good or not good feeling?
- What did the character look like when he or she was worried?
- What did the character do when he or she was worried?

Show and Define Worry

- Use Supplement 6.1 to show children different examples of worried faces.

    Sample Script

    This is worried. Worried can be a not good feeling. What does worried look like in this picture? Raise your hand if you've ever felt worried. What did your body look or feel like?

- Have students share what their bodies feel like when they are worried. Examples include stomachache, shaky hands and bodies, clenched fists, clenched teeth, and tightened muscles.

- Engage in a Think/Pair/Share activity. Have students think about a time when they felt worried; then, have them turn to their neighbors and share their ideas.

- Reconvene and have two people who are willing share with the whole group.

- Using a blank overhead transparency or chart paper, have students help you generate a list of synonyms or words that make them think of worry. Examples include bothered, troubled, concerned, nervous, and uneasy.

Letting Go of Worries

Explain to your students that you will be learning about what it is like to be worried and that Henry will help you with this.

Sample Script

Today, we've been talking about feeling worried. When we are worried, we often have a stomachache or maybe our muscles feel tight. When we feel this way, it can be hard to stop ourselves. We think about our worry all of the time. One time Henry felt very worried. His mom was supposed to pick him up from school, but she was not in the school office at the end of the day. Henry's stomach hurt, and he kept thinking, "Where could she be? Where could she be?" How do you think Henry could have comforted himself?

After students have shared their ideas for what Henry could have done, explain that there are helpful ways to let go of worries.

Display Supplement 6.2, and explain how the ABCs of Positive Thinking and the Stop, Count, In, Out strategy can be helpful tools for letting go of worries.

The ABCs of Positive Thinking

A	A problem	Whenever there's a problem . . .
B	Bad feelings	that gives you a not good feeling . . .
C	Comfort yourself	comfort yourself by thinking about it in a way that makes you feel better.

The Stop, Count, In, Out Strategy

STOP	When you feel a spark, **stop** what you are doing.
COUNT	**Count** to 10.
IN	Take a deep breath **in.**
OUT	Breathe **out.**

Sample Script

To comfort yourself, it is important to take time to think about what is bothering you. Once you can name your worry, it will be easier to use the ABCs of Positive Thinking to help you let go of your worry. For example, it might be helpful to talk to someone you trust about your worry or to realize that this is not the worst problem in the whole world, and it can be fixed. You could also think about a time when something like this happened before and turned out okay.

Use the following examples to assess children's understanding of Letting Go or Not Letting Go.

Problem	What Henry does	Is he Letting Go or Not Letting Go?	How can Henry Let Go?
Henry forgot to bring his signed permission slip for the field trip to school.	Henry took a deep breath, counted to 10, and remembered that he could bring it tomorrow.	He is Letting Go.	
Henry's parents got into an argument.	Henry found a quiet spot and remembered that his parents had argued before and they worked it out.	He is Letting Go.	
Henry forgot a note from his mom at home.	Henry thought about the note all day.	He is Not Letting Go.	Henry told his teacher about the note and asked her to call his mom.
Henry's dog ran away.	Henry's stomach began to hurt, and he kept looking out the window for his dog.	He is Not Letting Go.	Henry talked to his mom about his dog, and they looked for it together.

Problem	What Henry does	Is he Letting Go or Not Letting Go?	How can Henry Let Go?
Henry knew a substitute teacher was coming the next day and wasn't sure if he was ready for it.	Henry took a deep breath in and out and talked to his teacher about his worry.	He is Letting Go.	
Henry's dad was late picking him up from school.	Henry's hands got shaky, and he kept looking at the street for his dad's car.	He is Not Letting Go.	Henry found his teacher, and they waited for his dad together.
Henry was worried that his teacher would call on him, and he wouldn't have the right answer.	Henry's muscles got tight, and his body started to shake.	He is Not Letting Go.	Henry remembered that he could get the answer right, and even if he didn't, his teacher would just explain it to him.
Henry broke his mom's favorite vase and was worried that she would get angry.	Henry took a deep breath, counted to 10, and decided to tell his mom what happened.	He is Letting Go.	

5 minutes

Activity

Provide students with another strategy for letting go of worries.

Sample Script

Another way to help us let go of our worries is to focus on making our bodies feel better. We are going to practice a special exercise. It might feel silly at first, but if you follow all of my directions, your body will feel more calm.

- Have students find a quiet, comfortable place.

- Ask them to sit or lie quietly. Dim the lights if possible.

- Say, "Close your eyes. Take deep breaths. Breathe in and out slowly."

- Have students tighten their muscles, group by group. Then, ask them to loosen their muscles and make their bodies calm.

- Say, "Think about your favorite place, a place that makes you feel happy and calm."

- Say, "Sit quietly for a few minutes and continue breathing deeply and thinking about your happy place."

Closure

1 minute

Gather your students together, and review the lesson objectives.

Sample Script

Today, we talked about feeling worried. Everyone feels worried sometimes, and it does not feel good. If you're feeling worried, think about our ABCs of Positive Thinking and the Stop, Count, In, Out strategy. Try to comfort yourself and make your body feel calm.

Applying What We Learned

Anticipate

Whenever appropriate, remind students to identify times when their bodies may be showing them that they are feeling worried. Prior to situations that may cause worry, such as interruptions in daily routines, remind students to be on the lookout for body clues such as stomachaches, tense muscles, and shaky bodies. Remind them to use the ABCs of Positive Thinking and the Stop, Count, In, Out strategy to help let go of worries.

Remind

If you find a student who is showing physical signs of worry, remind the student to use strategies that will help his or her body to feel calm.

Acknowledge

When you observe students using the ABCs of Positive Thinking and the Stop, Count, In, Out strategy to help let go of worries or notice students trying to keep a calm body, specify the strategy and compliment them for using it.

★STRONG KIDS™ | I'm Worried!

Strong Start—Grades K–2: A Social and Emotional Learning Curriculum

The Stop, Count, In, Out Strategy

STOP		When you feel a spark, **stop** what you are doing.
COUNT	1 2 3 4 6 5 9 7 8 10	**Count** to 10.
IN		Take a deep breath **in.**
OUT		Breathe **out.**

Strong Start—Grades K–2: A Social and Emotional Learning Curriculum
by Kenneth W. Merrell, Danielle M. Parisi, and Sara A. Whitcomb © 2007 University of Oregon. All rights reserved.

STRONG START
LESSON 6

Strong Start Bulletin

Dear Family,

This week, our **Strong Start** lesson focused on teaching students helpful ways of **handling worries.** We discussed how our bodies feel when we are worried, and we also listed synonyms for the word **worry.** Throughout the lesson, Henry helped us understand strategies for letting go of our worries. He taught us to use **Positive Thinking** and the **Stop, Count, In, Out strategy** (outlined below) to make us feel better.

The Stop, Count, In, Out Strategy

STOP		When you feel a spark, **stop** what you are doing.
COUNT	1 2 3 4 6 5 9 7 8 10	**Count** to 10.
IN		Take a deep breath **in.**
OUT		Breathe **out.**

To better understand our worries, we read

_____.

Following are great examples of relevant stories that you may want to read at home:

- *The Kissing Hand* by Audrey Penn
- *The Good-bye Book* by Judith Viorst
- *Mommy, Don't Go* by Elizabeth Crary
- *I'm Scared* by Elizabeth Crary

When your child becomes worried at home, encourage him or her to let go by using the strategies above and taking time to

1. Name his or her worry.
2. Talk about it.
3. Understand that it is not necessarily the worst problem and can likely be fixed.
4. Think about a time when something like this happened before and turned out okay.

All children worry sometimes, and helping them to understand their worries is important. Thanks for your support in this endeavor!

LESSON 7

Understanding Other People's Feelings

TEACHER NOTES

_____
_____
_____
_____
_____
_____
_____
_____
_____
_____
_____
_____
_____
_____
_____
_____
_____
_____
_____

⭐ Purpose

- To teach students how to identify others' feelings

⭐ Objectives

- Students will learn to use physical cues to understand how someone else is feeling.
- Students will learn that different people have different feelings in the same situation.
- Students will apply the principles of this lesson to different situations.

MATERIALS NEEDED

- ❑ Henry (stuffed animal mascot)
- ❑ Blank overhead transparency or chart paper
- ❑ Supplement 7.1 (overhead transparency, in-class handout)
- ❑ Book from the literature list (or one of your choice)
- ❑ *Strong Start* Bulletin

Review

2 minutes

To activate prior knowledge, review and discuss previous topics and main ideas. Obtain 3–5 adequate ideas from the previous lesson. Make sure to provide feedback.

Sample Script

During our last meeting, we learned about using the ABCs of Positive Thinking and the Stop, Count, In, Out strategy when we are feeling worried. Raise your hand if you can tell me an important idea we learned from this lesson.

Introduction

2 minutes

Communicate the lesson's purpose and objectives clearly.

Sample Script

Today, we will learn about understanding how other people feel. To help us understand how other people feel, we will learn how to notice what other people's bodies and faces look like when they are feeling different ways. This will make it easier for us to make friends and solve problems.

Name and Define Skill

2 minutes

Convey the following main ideas to your students using your own words or the sample script provided.

- It might be possible to tell someone's feelings by looking for visual clues (like a detective).

- It is important to listen to others to find out how they are feeling.

Sample Script

Today, we're going to learn how we can be detectives and search for clues to help us figure out how other people are feeling. The first clue we can look at is a person's face. The second clue we can look at is the rest of the person's body.

Modeling

15 minutes

Model some feelings for the class. Begin by showing one of the six basic emotion faces from Supplement 7.1 and describing how it looks. Then, model and list body language tied to each feeling on a blank overhead transparency, chart paper, or board.

Sample Script

(Show picture of happy face.) *This is happy. A happy face shows a smile.* (Model some happy body clues, e.g., smile, open arms, stand up straight, walk with head high, laugh.) *What body clues show you that I am happy?*

(Show picture of sad face.) This is sad. A sad face is not smiling. A tear may be rolling down a sad person's cheek. (Model some sad body clues, e.g., frown, put head down, pull arms close to body, shuffle feet, cry.) What body clues show you that I am sad?

Continue by having students identify the remaining faces from Supplement 7.1. For each feeling, act out the body clues, have students describe what your body looks like, and write down their responses. Examples of body clues include the following:

- *Happy*—smile, open arms, stand up straight, walk with head high, laugh

- *Sad*—frown, put head down, pull arms close to body, shuffle feet, cry

- *Angry*—turn red in the face, puff up lips, bare teeth, make threatening eye contact, clench fists, cross arms, take up space (e.g., hold arms away from body), walk quickly, shake

- *Scared*—open eyes wide, drop head, walk backwards slowly, tremble

- *Disgusted*—stick tongue out, scrunch up eyes and nose, turn head away

- *Surprised*—open eyes wide, open mouth, step back, put hands on face

Model each feeling again. Have the students guess which feeling you are modeling. Practice with students until they can correctly identify five feelings and tell the clues that helped them to know.

Note: You may need to spend more time on this if the class does not display mastery of interpreting the clues. Consider using student volunteers who can demonstrate mastery to model the feelings.

Charades Activity

Break the students into large groups, small groups, or pairs, and give each group a set of the pictures of the six basic feelings from Supplement 7.1. Have the children act out the feelings for one another. Encourage students to refer to the overhead transparency or chart paper for ideas on how to act out each feeling.

Sample Script

Now that we know some clues to look for, we can try to figure out how someone else is feeling. Let's practice.

Once students have completed the activity, explain the concept that different people might have different feelings in the same situation. Be sure to point out that understanding how other people are feeling will help us to get along better.

Read a Book from the Literature List

Read a book from the following list of examples or choose your own book to share with students.

- *Arthur's Eyes* by Marc Brown

- *Harriet, You'll Drive Me Wild* by Mem Fox

- *Frog in the Middle* by Susanna Gretz
- *Chrysanthemum* by Kevin Henkes
- *Julius: The Baby of the World* by Kevin Henkes
- *The Rat and the Tiger* by Keiko Kasza
- *The True Story of the 3 Little Pigs* by A. Wolf, as told to Jon Scieszka

Be sure to point out all of the actions or ways in which the characters behave when they are acting on their feelings. Also note when different characters have different feelings in the same situation. Use the following questions to guide your discussion:

- What was one of the feelings the character had?
- Do you think it was a good or not good feeling?
- What did the character look like when he or she was feeling that way?
- What did the character do when he or she was feeling that way?
- What clues did the character use to help him or her understand how other people were feeling?
- Were there any other times during this story when two people had different feelings in the same situation?

Real-World Examples

Give students some examples of different people having different feelings in the same situation.

Sample Script

We are learning that the same experience will sometimes make different people have different feelings. For example, one time when a field trip was changed to a later day, Henry felt happy because he remembered that his mom would now be able to come, but Henry's friend was sad because he really wanted to go on the field trip. We need to make sure we look for clues that tell us how we can get along better. Henry knew that his friend was sad, so he was able to try to make his friend feel better.

Additional examples of people having different feelings in the same situation follow:

- *Climbing the rope in gym class*—students could be scared, happy, or excited
- *Moving to a new house*—students could be happy, sad, angry, excited, or scared

Closure

Gather your students together, and review the lesson objectives.

Sample Script

Today, we learned about ways we can tell how other people are feeling. We can be detectives and search for clues on others' faces and bodies. We also learned how different people may have different feelings in the same situation. Recognizing how others are feeling will help us to be good friends and problem solvers. Be sure to practice your detective skills every day.

Applying What We Learned

Anticipate

Prior to social situations (e.g., partner/group activities, field trips, recess, bus time), remind students to be detectives and use visual clues to try to understand how other people feel.

Remind

If you notice a student is not using clues to understand how other people are feeling, remind him or her to do so. This reminder may be particularly useful in situations requiring problem solving (e.g., arguing over a toy, name-calling, telling on one another).

Acknowledge

If you notice your students using their detective skills and recognizing how other people are feeling, give them praise. Remember to be specific and name the particular skill you observed. For example, if you notice a student comforting another, you might say, "Mikey, I noticed that you used the clues that John was showing to understand how he is feeling. You are a great detective and friend!"

Basic Feelings

Happy

Sad

Afraid

Angry

Surprised

Disgusted

Strong Start—Grades K–2: A Social and Emotional Learning Curriculum
by Kenneth W. Merrell, Danielle M. Parisi, and Sara A. Whitcomb © 2007 University of Oregon. All rights reserved.

STRONG START
LESSON 7

Strong Start Bulletin

Dear Family,

This week, our **Strong Start** lesson focused on **how to tell what others are feeling.** We talked about being detectives and searching for clues on others' faces and bodies. We also learned how different people might have different feelings in the same situation. Recognizing how others are feeling will help us to be **good friends** and **problem solvers.** We had fun playing charades and guessing what feelings our classmates were modeling. Before we played, we brainstormed a list similar to the one in the chart below.

Feeling	Body clues	Feeling	Body clues
Happy	Smile, open arms, stand up straight, walk with head high, laugh	*Surprised*	Open eyes wide, open mouth, step back, put hands on face
Sad	Frown, put head down, pull arms close to body, shuffle feet, cry	*Scared*	Open eyes wide, drop head, walk backward slowly, tremble
Angry	Turn red in the face, puff up lips, bare teeth, make threatening eye contact, clench fists, cross arms, take up space (e.g., hold arms away from body), walk quickly, shake	*Disgusted*	Stick tongue out, scrunch up eyes and nose, turn head away

To better understand other people's feelings, we read

_____.

Following are great examples of relevant stories that you may want to read at home:

- *Chrysanthemum* by Kevin Henkes
- *Julius: The Baby of the World* by Kevin Henkes
- *Harriet, You'll Drive Me Wild* by Mem Fox
- *The True Story of the 3 Little Pigs* by A. Wolf, as told to Jon Scieszka

At home, help your child to
1. Be a detective.
2. Look at the body clues of others.
3. Remember that others may experience different feelings during the same situation.

Thanks for all that you do in helping your child to understand the feelings of others. Your support makes a difference in how your child uses the information presented in these lessons!

LESSON 8

Being a Good Friend

TEACHER NOTES

Purpose

- To teach students basic communication and friendship-making skills

Objectives

- Students will discriminate between a nice voice and a not nice voice.
- Students will practice listening skills.
- Students will learn the importance of eye contact and body language when relating with others.
- Students will learn how to initiate and maintain friendships.

MATERIALS NEEDED

- ❑ Henry (stuffed animal mascot)
- ❑ Blank overhead transparency or chart paper
- ❑ Book from the literature list (or one of your choice)
- ❑ Supplement 8.1 (in-class handout)
- ❑ Drawing paper
- ❑ Crayons
- ❑ *Strong Start* Bulletin

Review

To activate prior knowledge, review and discuss previous topics and main ideas. Obtain 3–5 adequate ideas from the previous lesson. Make sure to provide feedback.

Sample Script

During our last meeting, we learned about understanding other people's feelings. Raise your hand if you can tell me an important idea we learned from this lesson.

Introduction

Communicate the lesson's purpose and objectives clearly.

Sample Script

Today, we will be learning about how to be a good friend. We will learn how to use our words, eyes, ears, and bodies to help us make friends. We will also talk about how to work together with friends.

Read a Book from the Literature List

Read a book from the following list of examples or choose your own book to share with students.

- *We Are Best Friends* by Aliki
- *Do You Want to Be My Friend* by Eric Carle
- *Meet the Barkers: Morgan and Moffat Go to School* by Tomie dePaola
- *Friends* by Helme Heine
- *My Best Friend* by Pat Hutchins
- *Frog and Toad Together* by Arnold Lobel
- *George and Martha* by James Marshall
- *George and Martha One Fine Day* by James Marshall
- *The Best Friends Book* by Todd Parr
- *The Rainbow Fish* by Marcus Pfister
- *The Giving Tree* by Shel Silverstein

Be sure to point out all of the actions or ways in which the characters behave as good friends. Use the following questions to guide your discussion:

- Which people were friends in the story?
- How did they talk to each other?
- How did they become friends?
- What were some of the things they did together?

8 minutes — Talking and Listening

- Communicate the necessary body clues for talking nicely, and give examples and nonexamples of a friendly voice.

Sample Script

Today, we're going to learn about how friends should talk and listen to each other. When we talk to others, we should smile and use a nice voice. A nice voice is soft and gentle and not loud like yelling.

- Model an example and a nonexample of a nice voice.
- Have children turn to their neighbors and practice their nice voices.
- Communicate the necessary body clues for listening, and give examples and nonexamples of being a good listener.

Sample Script

When friends talk to each other, they use a nice voice. Friends are also good listeners. When we listen, we use our eyes, ears, and bodies. We look at the person who is talking, we keep calm bodies, and we hear what the person is saying.

- Model an example and a nonexample of being a good listener.
- Have children turn to their neighbors and practice their listening skills.

10 minutes — Approaching Others

Explain how to begin a friendship or an activity with friends. *Note:* It is important to remember that there are cultural differences in social interaction. In some cultures, eye contact may not be an appropriate way to communicate. Please use other more appropriate examples as you see fit.

Sample Script

When we're friends, we listen to each other and use nice voices. Part of being a good friend is noticing others as they come up to you and showing them that you care. When you move close to another and smile and say hi, you're taking notice. When you ask someone to play, you show that you care and want to be a friend. Sometimes it can be hard to know how to join in with others or ask someone to play. Let's make a list of different things we can do or say to show others that we want to be friends.

On a blank overhead transparency or chart paper, make a list of ways to show others that you want to be friends.

5 minutes

Sharing and Working Together

Explain the importance of maintaining friendships through sharing and working together. Elicit from the students some examples of sharing and working together.

Sample Script

It is important to always treat our friends in a nice way so that we can stay friends. We should make sure to listen to our friends and use a nice voice. It is also important to share and to work together. Sometimes two people will want to use the same thing or play with the same toy. Friends work together, use nice talk, and listen to each other to figure out a way to both be happy. One time, Henry and I both wanted the purple marker. Instead of fighting about it, we decided that Henry would use it first. Then, I would get my turn. Can any of you share a time when you worked together or shared with your friends?

5 minutes

Make a Class Book

As a closure activity, have the students each make a page for a class book. Use Supplement 8.1, and ask students to dictate or write examples of what a good friend does. Then, have them draw a picture. If time permits and students are willing, have a few children share their drawings with the class.

1 minute

Closure

Gather your students together, and review the lesson objectives.

Sample Script

Today, we learned how to be a good friend. We can use our words, eyes, ears, and bodies to help us make friends. It is also important for us to treat our friends nicely and work together so that we can stay friends.

Applying What We Learned

Anticipate

Encourage your students to look and listen to one another and to use nice voices. Prompt them prior to social times (e.g., recess, lunch, free play, partner activities).

Remind

If you notice a student who is not using his or her friendship skills, remind him or her to listen, to use a nice voice, to share, and to work together. It might be necessary at first for you to role-play what these skills look like.

Acknowledge

If you see your students using their friendship skills, be sure to recognize their efforts (e.g., "I like how you asked Mary to play. You used a nice voice and had a smile on your face!").

STRONG KIDS™ What Does a Good Friend Do?

A good friend

_____

_____

_____

_____

Strong Start—Grades K–2: A Social and Emotional Learning Curriculum
by Kenneth W. Merrell, Danielle M. Parisi, and Sara A. Whitcomb © 2007 University of Oregon. All rights reserved.

Strong Start Bulletin

Dear Family,

This week, our **Strong Start** lesson focused on how to be a **good friend.** We discussed how friends should talk with a **nice voice** and actively listen to each other by maintaining eye contact, keeping a calm body, and hearing what others have to say. Part of being a good friend also includes noticing others as they approach and showing them that we care. Finally, we talked about how important it is to **share** and **work together** with our friends. The lesson was complete when children compiled a book of words and pictures depicting good friends.

To better understand how to be a good friend, we read

_____.

Following are great examples of relevant stories that you may want to read at home:
- *Frog and Toad Together* by Arnold Lobel
- *The Giving Tree* by Shel Silverstein
- *George and Martha* by James Marshall

At home, help your child to
- Use a nice voice
- Use eyes, ears, and bodies to show good listening
- Take notice of others by saying hi or inviting them to play
- Take turns and share

Making and keeping friends can be hard work. Thanks for supporting your child as he or she learns these important skills. Your guidance and acknowledgement will help your child to be a good friend to others.

Strong Start—Grades K–2: A Social and Emotional Learning Curriculum
by Kenneth W. Merrell, Danielle M. Parisi, and Sara A. Whitcomb © 2007 University of Oregon. All rights reserved.

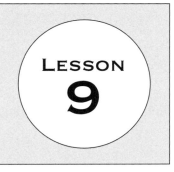

Solving
People Problems

**TEACHER
NOTES**

⭐ Purpose

- To teach students to solve problems with others

⭐ Objectives

- Students will describe problems that might occur between friends.
- Students will review Ways that Help in dealing with anger.
- Students will review the ABCs of Positive Thinking.
- Students will practice problem-solving strategies.

MATERIALS NEEDED

- ❏ Henry (stuffed animal mascot)
- ❏ Blank overhead transparency or chart paper
- ❏ Supplement 9.1 (overhead transparency)
- ❏ Supplement 9.2 (overhead transparency)
- ❏ Book from the literature list (or one of your choice)
- ❏ *Strong Start* Bulletin

2 minutes

Review

To activate prior knowledge, review and discuss previous topics and main ideas. Make sure to provide feedback and refer to the use of nice voices, good listening, and eye contact.

Sample Script

During our last meeting, we discussed how to be a friend. Raise your hand if you can tell me one way that you might be a friend.

2 minutes

Introduction

Communicate the lesson's purpose and objectives clearly.

Sample Script

Today, we will talk about solving problems with others. Everyone has problems sometimes. Problems often happen when we don't agree or when we want to do something that our friends don't. Problems often make us feel mad or sad, and these are not good feelings. Today, we will think about how we can make ourselves feel happy when we are mad or sad and how we can solve problems when they happen.

10 minutes

Read a Book from the Literature List

Read a book from the following list of examples or choose your own book to share with students.

- *Move Over, Twerp* by Martha Alexander
- *I Can't Wait* by Elizabeth Crary
- *I'm Frustrated* by Elizabeth Crary
- *Bet You Can't* by Penny Dale
- *The Knight and the Dragon* by Tomie dePaola
- *Chester's Way* by Kevin Henkes
- *Peter's Chair* by Ezra Jack Keats
- *When Pigasso Met Mootisse* by Nina Laden

Be sure to point out all of the actions or ways in which the characters behave when they are acting on their feelings. Use the following questions to guide your discussion:

- What was one of the feelings the character had?
- Do you think it was a good or not good feeling?

- What was the problem?
- What did the character do when he or she was faced with a problem?
- How did the character solve his or her problem?

Define and Brainstorm Types of People Problems

Explain the idea of disagreement, or *people problems*, and use Henry to provide an example.

Sample Script

We have a problem when we disagree or we want to do something our friends don't. Problems often make us feel sad or mad, and these are not good feelings.

For example, one time Henry was excited for a playdate at his friend's house because his friend has really cool Legos. When Henry arrived, his friend wanted to paint pictures instead of build with Legos. Henry had a problem, and he did not feel good. Raise your hand if you have ever had a problem.

- Have students share problems they have encountered. Possible examples include arguing over toys, not taking turns, cutting in line, and not working together on a group assignment.
- Engage in a Think/Pair/Share activity. Have students think about other times when they had problems. Then, have them turn to their neighbors and share their ideas.
- Ensure respectful sharing by reminding students not to use names and to remember to use nice words.
- Reconvene and add any examples to a blank overhead transparency or chart paper. Save your list for the Booster Lesson (see Appendix B).

Review Ways that Help and Positive Thinking

Review the concept of Ways that Help for handling anger using the Stop, Count, In, Out strategy on Supplement 9.1 and Positive Thinking using Supplement 9.2.

Sample Script

As we begin to think about how we feel when we have problems, it is important that we review Ways that Help us feel better when we are angry.

The Stop, Count, In, Out Strategy

STOP	When you feel a spark, **stop** what you are doing.
COUNT	**Count** to 10.
IN	Take a deep breath **in.**
OUT	Breathe **out.**

Sample Script

It is also important to review the ABCs of Positive Thinking. Positive Thinking will help us to feel better when we have a problem. Remember, when we use Positive Thinking, we have the feeling that everything is going to be okay. It also helps us to feel better if we are experiencing not good feelings. Positive Thinking is like jogging or playing because the more we do it, the healthier we are. We are strong on the inside just like we are on the outside. When we don't use Positive Thinking, we might get stuck feeling sad or mad.

Review the ABCs of Positive Thinking as a helpful tool to remember how to achieve positive thinking.

The ABCs of Positive Thinking

A	A problem	Whenever there's a problem . . .
B	Bad feelings	that gives you a not good feeling . . .
C	Comfort yourself	comfort yourself by thinking about it in a way that makes you feel better.

Comforting Yourself and Solving People Problems

10 minutes

Introduce strategies for solving problems.

- Stop, Count, In, Out

- Comfort yourself.

- Be a friend.

- Brainstorm a solution.

Sample Script

Today, we are going to think more about what to do when we are feeling mad or sad about a problem. When a problem sparks a not good feeling, we need to Stop, Count, In, Out. After taking a deep breath, we need to continue to comfort ourselves by remembering how to be a friend. When we use nice voices, listen, and look at our friends, it will be easier for us to tell them what is wrong and brainstorm ideas for solving our problems. Finally, when we brainstorm ideas, we share ideas for fixing the problem so that we both feel better.

There are many different ways for friends to solve their problems. When Henry and his friend wanted to do two different things, they came up with many ideas for solving the problem. They thought about picking a whole new activity, painting first and then playing with Legos, playing with Legos first and then painting, asking an adult for help, or deciding to play together on another day. They decided to paint pictures for a while and then switch to playing with Legos so that they both got to do what they wanted. When you brainstorm with your friends, remember there are many ways to solve the problem.

Use the following examples to deepen students' understanding of problem solving.

Problem	What Henry does after Stop, Count, In, Out	Is he problem-solving or not problem-solving?
Henry wants a turn on the swings, but they are all being used.	Henry looks at his friend on the swing and says, "Could I have a turn in a few minutes?"	He is problem-solving.
Henry wants a turn on the swings, but they are all being used.	Henry yells loudly, "It's my turn!" He runs away to tell a teacher.	He is not problem-solving.
Henry wants to be his friend's partner in a math activity, but his friend has another partner.	Henry's friend said, "Could we all work together?" Henry said, "Sure!"	He is problem-solving.
Henry wants to be his friend's partner in a math activity, but his friend has another partner.	Henry said, "I'll never be your partner again. You are not my friend anymore."	He is not problem-solving.
Henry wants to play with Legos, but his friend wants to paint.	Henry and his friend decide to paint for a while and then play Legos.	He is problem-solving.
Henry wants to play with Legos, but his friend wants to paint.	Henry does not listen to his friend's ideas and says, "I'm not going to play with you anymore."	He is not problem-solving.

Role-Play Activity

For older students, have them break into small groups or pairs and choose a problem from the list of problems brainstormed earlier. Ask students to role-play the situation, using the problem-solving strategies presented earlier.

For younger students, choose children to come up and help you to role-play problem-solving strategies based on the problem situations listed previously.

 Closure

Gather your students together, and review the lesson objectives.

Sample Script

Today, we learned about problem solving with others. Everyone has problems sometimes, and these problems often make us have not good feelings. We can use the Stop, Count, In, Out strategy and the ABCs of Positive Thinking to solve problems with others.

Applying What We Learned

Anticipate

Encourage your students to be problem solvers when they disagree with one another. Remind them to use the Stop, Count, In, Out strategy and the ABCs of Positive Thinking when a problem arises. Be sure to prompt them prior to events during which problems might arise (e.g., a difficult board game, a game with a lot of rules, a group project).

Remind

If you notice a student who is not problem-solving, remind him or her to use the strategies learned in class. You might have to break the problem-solving process into manageable parts. For example, first encourage the student to engage in the Stop, Count, In, Out strategy, and then prompt him or her to use the ABCs of Positive Thinking in order to help solve the problem.

Acknowledge

If you see your students problem-solving, be sure to give specific praise (e.g., "I really liked that you stopped and took a breath and then decided to take turns with that game. Great problem solving!").

The Stop, Count, In, Out Strategy

STOP	STOP	When you feel a spark, **stop** what you are doing.
COUNT	1 2 3 4 6 5 9 7 8 10	**Count** to 10.
IN		Take a deep breath **in.**
OUT		Breathe **out.**

Strong Start—Grades K–2: A Social and Emotional Learning Curriculum
by Kenneth W. Merrell, Danielle M. Parisi, and Sara A. Whitcomb © 2007 University of Oregon. All rights reserved.

The ABCs of Positive Thinking

A	A problem	Whenever there's a problem . . .
B	Bad feelings	that gives you a not good feeling . . .
C	Comfort yourself	comfort yourself by thinking about it in a way that makes you feel better.

Strong Start Bulletin

Dear Family,

This week, our **Strong Start** lesson focused on how to **solve problems** with others. We brainstormed a list of potential problems we might have with our peers. Then, we talked about the actions we might take when problems arise. We learned that we could use the **Stop, Count, In, Out breathing strategy** when we get angry, and after taking a deep breath, we could comfort ourselves by remembering how to be a friend. When we use nice voices, listen, and look at friends, it will be easier to work together and share ideas for fixing the problem so that we all feel better. We practiced our **problem-solving skills** by role-playing with classmates. The following table reflects an example of problem-solving behavior.

Problem	What Henry does after Stop, Count, In, Out	Is he problem-solving or not problem-solving?
Henry wants to play with Legos, but his friend wants to paint.	Henry and his friend decide to paint for a while and then play Legos.	He is problem-solving.
Henry wants to play with Legos, but his friend wants to paint.	Henry does not listen to his friend's ideas and says, "I'm not going to play with you anymore."	He is not problem-solving.

To better understand how to solve people problems, we read

_____.

Following are great examples of relevant stories that you may want to read at home:
- _Chester's Way_ by Kevin Henkes
- _I'm Frustrated_ by Elizabeth Crary
- _I Can't Wait_ by Elizabeth Crary

When problems arise at home, help your child to
- Stop and take a deep breath
- Be a friend by looking and listening to others
- Work with others to brainstorm a solution

If you see your child problem-solving, be sure to congratulate his or her efforts (e.g., "I really liked that you stopped and took a breath and then decided to take turns with that game. Great problem solving!"). Thanks again for your support!

LESSON 10

Finishing UP!

TEACHER NOTES

_____

_____

_____

_____

_____

_____

_____

_____

_____

_____

_____

_____

_____

_____

_____

_____

_____

_____

_____

_____

_____

_____

_____

⭐ Purpose

- To review the major concepts and skills in the _Strong Start_ curriculum

⭐ Objectives

- Students will review the purpose of the _Strong Start_ curriculum.

- Students will name feelings and describe okay and not okay ways of expressing feelings.

- Students will review the ABCs of Positive Thinking and the Stop, Count, In, Out strategy.

MATERIALS NEEDED

- ❏ Henry (stuffed animal mascot)
- ❏ Supplement 10.1 (overhead transparency)
- ❏ Supplement 10.2 (overhead transparency)
- ❏ Supplement 10.3 (overhead transparency)
- ❏ Supplement 10.4 (overhead transparency)
- ❏ Books from the literature list
- ❏ _Strong Start_ Bulletin

Preparation

The Finishing UP! lesson consists of a review of the major concepts presented in this curriculum. It may be helpful to review previous lessons prior to presenting this lesson.

Introduction

Communicate the lesson's purpose and objectives clearly. Explain to students that they will complete the final lesson of the *Strong Start* curriculum. Tell them that topics they have been covering for the past few weeks will be reviewed. Point out that they have learned many skills during this unit that are vital to their social and emotional health, and they will have opportunities to use these skills throughout their lives.

Sample Script

Today, we are going to complete a special class called Strong Start. In this class, we learned with a special friend. His name is Henry. In this class, Henry helped us understand our feelings and other people's feelings. He also helped us learn about being a good friend. He is a special part of our class. Even though this is our last lesson, Henry will continue to be with us. Every time we met over the last several weeks, we did special exercises. We didn't run outside or lift big, heavy weights. During the Feelings Exercise Group, we worked on growing strong on the inside instead of on the outside. Everyone needs to be healthy—on the inside and on the outside. This class helped us to be healthy on the inside and in the way we work and play with other people.

Use Supplement 10.1 to review the topics covered in *Strong Start*.

Sample Script

Show me your hand if you can tell me some of the important things we learned in this class.

Point to the picture cues on Supplement 10.1 to review the following lesson topics:

- Understanding our feelings
- Understanding other people's feelings
- Feeling angry
- Feeling happy
- Feeling worried
- Being a friend
- Solving people problems

Use this lesson as an opportunity to discuss any terms or concepts that may be relevant to your class at this time, to revisit any of the ideas that needed expansion during the term, or to simplify and refresh ideas.

Review of Topics

Understanding Your Feelings 1 and 2

- Display Supplement 10.2 of the six basic feelings.
- Identify feelings as good and not good.
- Identify okay and not okay ways of showing feelings.

When You're Angry

- Display Supplement 10.3, which shows the Stop, Count, In, Out strategy.
- Identify how our bodies feel when we are angry.
- Identify synonyms for *anger*.
- Identify situations when we might feel angry.
- Review Ways that Help and Ways that Hurt.

When You're Happy

- Display Supplement 10.4, which explains the ABCs of Positive Thinking.
- Identify how our bodies feel when we are happy.
- Identify synonyms for *happy*.
- Review the ABCs of Positive Thinking.

When You're Worried

- Identify how our bodies feel when we are worried.
- Identify synonyms for the word *worry*.
- Review how the ABCs of Positive Thinking and the Stop, Count, In, Out strategy can help us when we are worried.
- Review how to keep a calm body.

Understanding Other People's Feelings

- Display Supplement 10.2 of the six basic feelings.
- Identify physical cues to understand how someone else is feeling.
- Review how people may have different feelings in the same situation.

Being a Good Friend

- Identify nice voices and not nice voices.
- Review listening skills: eye contact and body language.
- Review how to initiate friendship.

Solving People Problems

- Review the Stop, Count, In, Out strategy.
- Review ways to comfort yourself.

- Review how to be a friend.
- Review how to brainstorm a solution.

10 minutes

Read a Book from the Literature List

Read a book from the following list of examples or choose your own book to share with students.

- *Feelings* by Aliki
- *The Way I Feel* by Janan Cain
- *Today I Feel Silly & Other Moods That Make My Day* by Jamie Lee Curtis
- *Feelings* by Joanne Brisson Murphy
- *The Feelings Book* by Todd Parr
- *My Many Colored Days* by Dr. Seuss

1 minute

Closure

Gather your students together, and review key points.

Sample Script

Today, we reviewed many things we have learned in Strong Start. We learned about our feelings and other people's feelings. We learned how to be a good friend and how to solve problems with others. Henry has been our very good friend and he has taught us so much. Now that we have completed our lessons, we need to continue to work hard to remember all that Henry has shared with us. He will continue to be a part of our classroom community and remind us of all that we have learned.

Congratulations! You have completed Strong Start and have learned how to be strong on the inside and in the way that you work and play with other people.

About Strong Start

We will learn about our feelings.

feeling *angry*   feeling *happy*   feeling *worried*

We will learn about other people's feelings.

We will learn about being a friend.

We will learn about solving problems.

And we will learn how to relax and feel calm.

Basic Feelings

Happy

Sad

Afraid

Angry

Surprised

Disgusted

Strong Start—Grades K–2: A Social and Emotional Learning Curriculum
by Kenneth W. Merrell, Danielle M. Parisi, and Sara A. Whitcomb © 2007 University of Oregon. All rights reserved.

STRONG START
LESSON 10

The Stop, Count, In, Out Strategy

STOP		When you feel a spark, **stop** what you are doing.
COUNT		**Count** to 10.
IN		Take a deep breath **in.**
OUT		Breathe **out.**

The ABCs of Positive Thinking

A	A problem	Whenever there's a problem . . .
B	Bad feelings	that gives you a not good feeling . . .
C	Comfort yourself	comfort yourself by thinking about it in a way that makes you feel better.

Strong Start—Grades K–2: A Social and Emotional Learning Curriculum
by Kenneth W. Merrell, Danielle M. Parisi, and Sara A. Whitcomb © 2007 University of Oregon. All rights reserved.

Strong Start Bulletin

Dear Family,

Today, your child participated in the last lesson of **Strong Start,** a curriculum designed to boost the social and emotional development of young children. In this class, we learned with a special stuffed bear, **Henry.** Henry helped us understand our feelings and other people's feelings. He also helped us learn about being a good friend. He is a special part of our class. Even though this was our last lesson, Henry will continue to be with us in class and serve as a reminder of all that we have learned. During our lessons over the last several weeks, we engaged in activities and discussions that will encourage your child to work on being **healthy** on the inside as well as the outside.

Strong Start helped your child

Learn about our feelings

Learn about other people's feelings

Learn about being a friend

Learn about solving problems

And learn how to relax and feel calm

Although the lessons of **Strong Start** have been completed, please continue to encourage your child to use the skills and strategies presented in class and in the bulletins sent home. Together, we can continue to support your child's social and emotional health. Thank you!

Appendices

APPENDIX A

Strong Start
Booster Lesson 1

TEACHER NOTES

⭐ **Purpose**

- To review *Strong Start* Lessons 1–6

⭐ **Objectives**

- Students will review the purpose of the *Strong Start* curriculum.
- Students will name feelings and describe okay and not okay ways of expressing feelings.
- Students will review the ABCs of Positive Thinking and the Stop, Count, In, Out strategy.

MATERIALS NEEDED

- ❏ Henry (stuffed animal mascot)
- ❏ Supplement 1.1 (overhead transparency)
- ❏ Supplement 2.1 (overhead transparency, in-class handout)
- ❏ Supplement 4.2 (overhead transparency)
- ❏ Supplement 5.2 (overhead transparency)
- ❏ An envelope for each student
- ❏ Enough Feelings Bingo Cards (Supplements A.1–A.5) for each student
- ❏ Bingo markers
- ❏ Paper plates, brads, scissors, and crayons
- ❏ Book from the literature list in Appendix C (or one of your choice)

Preparation

The first booster lesson consists of a review of the major concepts presented in Lessons 1–6 of this curriculum. It may be helpful to flip back through these lessons prior to presenting this lesson. This might also be an appropriate time to focus on content that students have not yet mastered. Be sure to choose a book from the literature list (Appendix C) that addresses the needs of your class.

Introduction

Communicate the lesson's purpose and objectives clearly. Explain to your students that topics from the *Strong Start* curriculum will be reviewed. Tell them that it is always important to review the many skills previously introduced because they are vital to social and emotional health, and students will have opportunities to use these skills throughout their lives. Use Supplement 1.1 (from Lesson 1).

Sample Script

Today, we are going to take time to remember a special class called Strong Start. In this class, we learned with a special friend. Henry has been with us since we began Strong Start, and he has helped us to understand our feelings and other people's feelings. He has also helped us to learn about being a good friend. He is a special part of our class. Each week, when we participated in Strong Start lessons, we completed special exercises. We didn't run outside or lift big, heavy weights. We worked on growing strong on the inside during the Feelings Exercise Group. Everyone needs to be healthy—on the inside and on the outside. This class helped us to learn how to be healthy on the inside for our whole lives.

Review of Topics

Explain that a large part of *Strong Start* had to do with naming feelings and handling our feelings. Use the following script as a guide for your discussion.

Sample Script

The lessons that we learned a long time ago included giving names to our feelings. It is important to know how to name our feelings because it helps us to tell others how we are feeling on the inside. When we can tell others how we are feeling, it may seem easier to be good friends and to solve problems.

Use the following ideas and activities to further your discussion.

1. Understanding your feelings

    •   Display and review Supplement 2.1 (from Lesson 2) of the six basic feelings.

    •   Remind students that it is okay to have any feeling and that many people will have different feelings in the same situation. This is also an appropriate time to discuss that some people might be feeling more than one feeling at once (e.g., I was surprised and happy when I arrived at my surprise birthday party).

- Engage in an activity that allows students to label feelings and determine which are good and not good feelings. Encourage students to give synonyms for various feelings and to identify how their bodies feel when they are experiencing an emotion. Examples of activities frequently used include:

  Paper Plate Faces—Have students decorate paper plates that look like themselves. Give students brads, and have them fasten smiles, frowns, and so forth to the mouth portion. Ask students to practice using the paper plate to show different feelings.

  Feelings Envelope—Have students cut the six basic feelings from Supplement 2.1 and place them in an envelope. Have them pull out the feeling they are experiencing.

  Feelings Bingo—Use the Bingo Cards (Supplements A.1–A.5) to play a game of bingo. Cut out feelings faces, and place them in a hat. Put small pieces of paper marked A, B, C, D, and E in another hat. Randomly select a letter and randomly select a face from the hats (e.g., "Put a marker down if you have a happy face in Column A.").

2. Okay and not okay ways to handle feelings

   - Remind students that there are okay and not okay ways of showing feelings.

3. Angry

   - Display Supplement 4.2 (from Lesson 4), The Stop, Count, In, Out strategy.

   - Identify situations when we might feel angry.

   - Use the following examples to remind children of Ways that Help and Ways that Hurt in handling anger.

Spark	What Henry does	Is it a Way that Helps or a Way that Hurts?	How can Henry use a Way that Helps?
Henry's best friend decided to play a board game with someone else during indoor recess.	Henry takes a deep breath and counts to 10.	It's a Way that Helps.	
Henry's group did not get called to line up first for lunch.	Henry yells at the others at his table and blames them for not getting to line up first.	It's not a Way that Helps.	Henry takes a breath and waits for the teacher to call his table to line up.

4. Happy

   - Display Supplement 5.2 (from Lesson 5), The ABCs of Positive Thinking

   - Use the following examples to help students review the ABCs of Positive Thinking.

Problem	What Henry does	Is it Positive Thinking or Not Positive Thinking?	How can Henry use Positive Thinking?
Henry's best friend decided to play a board game with someone else during indoor recess.	Henry thinks, "I hate my friend. He never wants to play with me anymore."	It's Not Positive Thinking.	Henry thinks, "I really wanted to play with my best friend, but I have lots of other friends I can play with. Maybe I will play with my best friend tomorrow."
Henry's group did not get called to line up first for lunch.	Henry thinks, "That's okay. Maybe next time we'll get to line up first."	It's Positive Thinking.	

5. Worry

- Review how the ABCs of Positive Thinking and the Stop, Count, In, Out strategy can help us when we are worried.

- Review how to keep a calm body.

- Use the following examples to review the ABCs of Positive Thinking. Expand on any examples that seem particularly relevant to your class.

Problem	What Henry does	Is he Letting Go or Not Letting Go?	How can Henry Let Go?
Henry wonders if the substitute teacher will know the daily schedule in his classroom.	Henry takes a deep breath, counts to 10, and realizes that he and his friends can help the substitute if his teacher didn't leave a schedule.	He is Letting Go.	
Henry wonders if he will know any of the other kids on his first day of baseball practice.	Henry keeps thinking about how scary baseball will be without any friends. His stomach begins to hurt.	He is Not Letting Go.	Henry calms his body and realizes that he will probably make new friends at baseball practice.

Read a Book from the Literature List

Choose a book from the literature list (Appendix C) that includes concepts relevant to your class at this time. Use the book as a forum for further discussion. Consider how characters in the story are feeling, how they handle their feelings, or how they recognize the feelings of others.

Closure

Gather your students together, and review key points.

Sample Script

Today, we reviewed much of what we learned in Strong Start. We reviewed how to label our feelings, and we discussed okay and not okay ways to handle our feelings. Henry has helped us to remember these important skills, and he will continue to do so. Next time we meet, we will talk more about being a good friend and solving problems with others.

Strong Start Feelings Bingo

	A	B	C	D	E
1					
2					
3			Free ★ Space		
4					
5					

Strong Start Feelings Bingo

	A	B	C	D	E
1					
2					
3			Free ⭐ Space		
4					
5					

121

Strong Start Feelings Bingo

	A	B	C	D	E
1					
2					
3			Free Star Space		
4					
5					

Strong Start Feelings Bingo

	A	B	C	D	E
1					
2					
3			Free ⭐ Space		
4					
5					

Strong Start—Grades K–2: A Social and Emotional Learning Curriculum
by Kenneth W. Merrell, Danielle M. Parisi, and Sara A. Whitcomb © 2007 University of Oregon. All rights reserved.

Strong Start Feelings Bingo

	A	B	C	D	E
1					
2					
3			Free ★ Space		
4					
5					

Strong Start—Grades K–2: A Social and Emotional Learning Curriculum
by Kenneth W. Merrell, Danielle M. Parisi, and Sara A. Whitcomb © 2007 University of Oregon. All rights reserved.

STRONG START
APPENDIX A

APPENDIX B

TEACHER NOTES

Strong Start Booster Lesson 2

⭐ Purpose

- To review the *Strong Start* Lessons 7–9

⭐ Objectives

- Students will review how to use physical cues to understand how someone else is feeling.
- Students will review the concept that different people have different feelings in the same situation.
- Students will review how good friends use eyes, ears, and bodies to show caring.
- Students will review problem-solving strategies.

MATERIALS NEEDED

- ❑ Henry (stuffed animal mascot)
- ❑ Supplement 7.1 (overhead transparency)
- ❑ Supplement 9.1 (overhead transparency)
- ❑ Supplement 9.2 (overhead transparency)
- ❑ Class Book developed during Lesson 8 (Being a Good Friend)
- ❑ Book from the literature list in Appendix C (or one of your choice)

Preparation

The second booster lesson consists of a review of the major concepts presented in Lessons 7–9 of this curriculum. It may be helpful to flip back through these lessons prior to presenting this lesson. This might also be an appropriate time to focus on content that students have not yet mastered. Be sure to choose a book from the literature list that addresses the needs of your class.

10 minutes

Introduction

Communicate the lesson's purpose and objectives clearly. Explain to your students that topics from the *Strong Start* curriculum will be reviewed. Remind your students that it is always important to review the many skills previously introduced because they are vital to social and emotional health, and students will have opportunities to use these skills throughout their lives.

To activate prior knowledge, review and discuss topics and main ideas from the previous booster lesson. Make sure to refer to naming feelings and identifying those that are good and not good. Have students give examples of okay and not okay ways of showing feelings. Use Supplement 7.1 (from Lesson 7).

Sample Script

During our last meeting, we discussed how to name our feelings. We talked about what our bodies look like when we are experiencing a feeling and what we do to handle our feelings. Raise your hand if you can tell me an important idea we learned during that lesson.

Today, we are going to continue to remember a special class called Strong Start. Henry will be with us and will help us to remember how to understand other people's feelings and how to be a good friend.

25 minutes

Review of Topics

Explain that a large part of *Strong Start* had to do with looking at the faces and bodies of others to understand how they are feeling. Another important part of *Strong Start* included thinking about how we use our bodies to show that we are good friends and problem solvers.

Sample Script

The lessons that we learned a long time ago helped us to be detectives and search for clues to help us figure out how other people are feeling. We learned to pay attention to the faces and bodies of the people around us. Being detectives makes it easier for us to make friends and solve problems.

Use the following ideas and activities to further your discussion.

1. Understanding other people's feelings

    *   Display and review Supplement 7.1 (from Lesson 7) of the six basic feelings.

    *   Remind students that it is okay to have any feeling and that many people will have different feelings in the same situation.

Situation	How Henry looks and feels	How Henry's friend looks and feels
During gym class, the teacher tells the class that they are going to learn a new game.	Henry smiles and jumps up and down. He is happy because he loves new games.	Darren's eyes are wide, and he does not smile or frown. His fists are clenched. He is nervous/scared about learning a new game.
Fish sticks are served with hot lunch in the cafeteria.	Henry turns his head away and scrunches up his nose. He is disgusted.	Sonya opens her eyes wide and scratches her head. She is surprised because she thought today's hot lunch included pizza.

- Use the above examples to help children better understand how different children may have different feelings in the same situation.

2. Being a good friend

- Remind students that good friends use nice voices and use eyes, ears, and calm bodies when listening to others.

- Review how good friends take notice and care. Consider engaging in one of the following review activities.

Class Book—If your class compiled a class book during Lesson 8 (Supplement 8.1), pull out the book, and read it aloud to the class. Consider adding new ideas based on what children have learned over time.

Friendship List—If your class compiled a list of ways to show how to be a friend during Lesson 8, review the list, and add any new ideas.

3. Solving people problems

- Review strategies for solving problems. Remind students to use a Way that Helps in handling anger and the ABCs of Positive Thinking (Supplement 9.2 from Lesson 9).

Stop, Count, In, Out strategy (Supplement 9.1 from Lesson 9)

Comfort yourself.

Be a friend.

Brainstorm a solution.

Emphasize that solving problems involves helping all parties to feel better.

- Engage in a Think/Pair/Share activity. Have students think about times when they have had problems (e.g., arguing over toys, not taking turns, working together). Encourage students to consider whether or not they effectively problem-solved the situation. Have them turn to their neighbors and share ideas.

- Ensure respectful sharing by reminding students not to use names and to remember to use nice words.

- Reconvene and discuss examples of problem solving that were shared.

10 minutes

Read a Book from the Literature List

 Choose a book from the literature list (Appendix C) that includes concepts relevant to your class at this time. Use the book as a forum for further discussion. Consider how characters in the story are feeling, how they handle their feelings, or how they recognize the feelings of others.

1–3 minutes

Closure

Gather your students together, and review key points.

 ### Sample Script

Today, we reviewed much of what we learned in Strong Start. We reviewed how to be detectives and look for body clues so that we know how others are feeling. We remembered how to be good friends and problem solvers. Henry has helped us to remember these important skills. He has been our very good friend and has taught us so much. Now that we have completed our review lessons, we need to continue to work hard to remember all that Henry has shared with us. He will continue to be a part of our classroom community and remind us of all that we have learned.

APPENDIX C

Recommended *Strong Start* Literature List

Lesson 1: The Feelings Exercise Group

- *Feelings* by Aliki
- *The Way I Feel* by Janan Cain
- *Feelings* by Joanne Brisson Murphy
- *The Feelings Book* by Todd Parr
- *My Many Colored Days* by Dr. Seuss

Lesson 2: Understanding Your Feelings 1

- *Feelings* by Aliki
- *Everybody Has Feelings or Todos Tenemos Sentimientos* by Charles E. Avery
- *How Are You Peeling? Foods with Moods* by Saxton Freymann and Joost Elffers
- *On Monday When it Rained* by Cherryl Kachenmeister
- *Feelings* by Joanne Brisson Murphy
- *The Feelings Book* by Todd Parr
- *Lots of Feelings* by Shelley Rotner

Lesson 3: Understanding Your Feelings 2

- *The Chocolate-Covered-Cookie Tantrum* by Deborah Blumenthal
- *Today I Feel Silly & Other Moods That Make My Day* by Jamie Lee Curtis
- *The Grumpy Morning* by Pamela Duncan Edwards
- *Chrysanthemum* by Kevin Henkes
- *Julius: The Baby of the World* by Kevin Henkes
- *Bye, Bye!* by Nancy Kaufmann
- *The Kissing Hand* by Audrey Penn
- *Sometimes I Like to Cry* by Elizabeth and Henry Stanton

Lesson 4: When You're Angry

- *The Cranky Day, and Other Thomas the Tank Engine Stories* by W. Awdry
- *When Sophie Gets Angry—Really Really Angry* by Molly Bang
- *The Chocolate-Covered-Cookie Tantrum* by Deborah Blumenthal
- *Feeling Angry* by Althea Braithwaite
- *Mean Soup* by Betsy Everitt
- *If You're Angry and You Know It* by Cecily Kaiser
- *Andrew's Angry Words* by Dorothea Lachner
- *I Was So Mad* by Norma Simon
- *When I Feel Angry* by Cornelia Maude Spelman
- *Sometimes I'm Bombaloo* by Rachel Vail
- *Alexander and the Terrible, Horrible, No Good, Very Bad Day* by Judith Viorst

Lesson 5: When You're Happy

- *Super Completely and Totally the Messiest* by Judith Viorst
- *I Like Me!* by Nancy Carlson
- *The Secret Remedy Book: A Book of Comfort and Love* by Karin Cates
- *Fun is a Feeling* by Chara M. Curtis
- *Today I Feel Silly & Other Moods That Make My Day* by Jamie Lee Curtis
- *A Bad, Bad Day* by Kristen Hall

Lesson 6: When You're Worried

- *Arthur's Baby* by Marc Brown
- *Will I Have a Friend* by Miriam Cohen
- *I'm Scared* by Elizabeth Crary
- *Mommy, Don't Go* by Elizabeth Crary
- *Even if I Did Something Awful* by Barbara Shook Hazen
- *Wemberly Worried* by Kevin Henkes
- *The Underbed* by Cathryn Clinton Hoellwarth
- *The Boy Under the Bed* by Preston McClear
- *The Kissing Hand* by Audrey Penn
- *The Good-Bye Book* by Judith Viorst

::studysync®

Reading & Writing Companion

GRADE 7 UNITS

In Pursuit • The Powers that Be
Justice Served • Getting Along

studysync.com

Send all inquiries to:
BookheadEd Learning, LLC
610 Daniel Young Drive
Sonoma, CA 95476

7 8 9 LMN 21 20 19 18 B

❖❖studysync®

STUDENT GUIDE

GETTING STARTED

Welcome to the StudySync Reading and Writing Companion! In this booklet, you will find a collection of readings based on the theme of the unit you are studying. As you work through the readings, you will be asked to answer questions and perform a variety of tasks designed to help you closely analyze and understand each text selection. Read on for an explanation of

1 INTRODUCTION

An Introduction to each text provides historical context for your reading as well as information about the author. You will also learn about the genre of the excerpt and the year in which it was written.

2 FIRST READ

During your first reading of each excerpt, you should just try to get a general idea of the content and message of the reading. Don't worry if there are parts you don't understand or words that are unfamiliar to you. You'll have an opportunity later to dive deeper into the text.

Many times, while working through the Think Questions after your first read, you will be asked to **annotate** or **make annotations** about what you are reading. This means that you should use the "Notes" column to make comments or jot down any questions you may have about the text. You may also want to note any unfamiliar vocabulary words here.

3 THINK QUESTIONS

These questions will ask you to start thinking critically about the text, asking specific questions about its purpose, and making connections to your prior knowledge and reading experiences. To answer these questions, you should go back to the text and draw upon specific evidence that you find there to support your responses. You will also begin to explore some of the more challenging vocabulary words used in the excerpt.

4 CLOSE READ & FOCUS QUESTIONS

After you have completed the First Read, you will then be asked to go back and read the excerpt more closely and critically. Before you begin your Close Read, you should read through the Focus Questions to get an idea of the concepts you will want to focus on during your second reading. You should work through the Focus Questions by making annotations, highlighting important concepts, and writing notes or questions in the "Notes" column. Depending on instructions from your teacher, you may need to respond online or use a separate piece of paper to start expanding on your thoughts and ideas.

5 WRITING PROMPT

Your study of each excerpt or selection will end with a writing assignment. To complete this assignment, you should use your notes, annotations, and answers to both the Think and Focus Questions. Be sure to read the prompt carefully and address each part of it in your writing assignment.

6 EXTENDED WRITING PROJECT

After you have read and worked through all of the unit text selections, you will move on to a writing project. This project will walk you through steps to plan, draft, revise, edit, and finally publish an essay or other piece of writing about one or more of the texts you have studied in the unit. Student models and graphic organizers will provide guidance and help you organize your thoughts as you plan and write your essay. Throughout the project, you will also study and work on specific writing skills to help you develop different portions of your writing.

studysync®

Reading & Writing Companion

What drives us to undertake a mission?

In Pursuit

UNIT 1   What drives us to undertake a mission?

In Pursuit

TEXTS

TEXTS

EXTENDED WRITING PROJECT

473

Text Fulfillment
through
StudySync

Copyright © BookheadEd Learning, LLC

BARRIO BOY

NON-FICTION
Ernesto Galarza
1971

INTRODUCTION

Ernesto Galarza was a Mexican-American union leader and writer who spent most of his life fighting for the rights of farm workers. In *Barrio Boy*, Galarza tells the story of how he immigrated to California and successfully navigated the public school system. The excerpt is about Galarza's first experience in an American school.

"...there was a sign on the door in both Spanish and English: 'Principal.'"

FIRST READ

From Part Four: Life in the Lower Part of Town

1   The two of us walked south on Fifth Street one morning to the corner of Q Street and turned right. Half of the block was occupied by the Lincoln School. It was a three-story wooden building, with two wings that gave it the shape of a double-T connected by a central hall. It was a new building, painted yellow, with a shingled roof that was not like the red tile of the school in Mazatlán. I noticed other differences, none of them very reassuring.

2   We walked up the wide staircase hand in hand and through the door, which closed by itself. A mechanical contraption screwed to the top shut it behind us quietly.

3   Up to this point the adventure of enrolling me in the school had been carefully rehearsed. Mrs. Dodson had told us how to find it and we had circled it several times on our walks. Friends in the *barrio* explained that the director was called a principal, and that it was a lady and not a man. They assured us that there was always a person at the school who could speak Spanish.

4   Exactly as we had been told, there was a sign on the door in both Spanish and English: "Principal." We crossed the hall and entered the office of Miss Nettie Hopley.

5   Miss Hopley was at a roll-top desk to one side, sitting in a swivel chair that moved on wheels. There was a sofa against the opposite wall, flanked by two windows and a door that opened on a small balcony. Chairs were set around a table and framed pictures hung on the walls of a man with long white hair and another with a sad face and a black beard.

6   The principal half turned in the swivel chair to look at us over the pinch glasses crossed on the ridge of her nose. To do this she had to duck her head slightly as if she were about to step through a low doorway.

Please note that excerpts and passages in the StudySync® library and this workbook are intended as touchstones to generate interest in an author's work. The excerpts and passages do not substitute for the reading of entire texts, and StudySync® strongly recommends that students seek out and purchase the whole literary or informational work in order to experience it as the author intended. Links to online resellers are available in our digital library. In addition, complete works may be ordered through an authorized reseller by filling out and returning to StudySync® the order form enclosed in this workbook.

Reading & Writing Companion   **5**

menace
formidable
obnoxious
idiocies

7   What Miss Hopley said to us we did not know but we saw in her eyes a warm welcome and when she took off her glasses and straightened up she smiled wholeheartedly, like Mrs. Dodson. We were, of course, saying nothing, only catching the friendliness of her voice and the sparkle in her eyes while she said words we did not understand. She signaled us to the table. Almost tiptoeing across the office, I **maneuvered** myself to keep my mother between me and the gringo lady. In a matter of seconds I had to decide whether she was a possible friend or a **menace**. We sat down.

8   Then Miss Hopley did a **formidable** thing. She stood up. Had she been standing when we entered she would have seemed tall. But rising from her chair she soared. And what she carried up and up with her was a buxom superstructure, firm shoulders, a straight sharp nose, full cheeks slightly molded by a curved line along the nostrils, thin lips that moved like steel springs, and a high forehead topped by hair gathered in a bun. Miss Hopley was not a giant in body but when she **mobilized** it to a standing position she seemed a match for giants. I decided I liked her.

9   She strode to a door in the far corner of the office, opened it and called a name. A boy of about ten years appeared in the doorway. He sat down at one end of the table. He was brown like us, a plump kid with shiny black hair combed straight back, neat, cool, and faintly obnoxious.

10 Miss Hopley joined us with a large book and some papers in her hand. She, too, sat down and the questions and answers began by way of our **interpreter**. My name was Ernesto. My mother's name was Henriqueta. My birth certificate was in San Blas. Here was my last report card from the Escuela Municipal Numero 3 para Varones of Mazatlán, and so forth. Miss Hopley put things down in the book and my mother signed a card.

11 As long as the questions continued, Doña Henriqueta could stay and I was secure. Now that they were over, Miss Hopley saw her to the door, dismissed our interpreter and without further ado took me by the hand and strode down the hall to Miss Ryan's first grade.

12 Miss Ryan took me to a seat at the front of the room, into which I shrank—the better to survey her. She was, to skinny, somewhat runty me, of a withering height when she patrolled the class. And when I least expected it, there she was, crouching by my desk, her blond radiant face level with mine, her voice patiently maneuvering me over the awful **idiocies** of the English language.

13 During the next few weeks Miss Ryan overcame my fears of tall, energetic teachers as she bent over my desk to help me with a word in the pre-primer. Step by step, she loosened me and my classmates from the safe **anchorage** of the desks for recitations at the blackboard and consultations at her desk.

Frequently she burst into happy announcements to the whole class. "Ito can read a sentence," and small Japanese Ito, squint-eyed and shy, slowly read aloud while the class listened in wonder: "Come, Skipper, come. Come and run." The Korean, Portuguese, Italian, and Polish first graders had similar moments of glory, no less shining than mine the day I conquered "butterfly," which I had been persistently pronouncing in standard Spanish as boo-ter-flee. "Children," Miss Ryan called for attention. "Ernesto has learned how to pronounce *butterfly!*" And I proved it with a perfect imitation of Miss Ryan. From that celebrated success, I was soon able to match Ito's progress as a sentence reader with "Come, butterfly, come fly with me."

14 Like Ito and several other first graders who did not know English, I received private lessons from Miss Ryan in the closet, a narrow hall off the classroom with a door at each end. Next to one of these doors Miss Ryan placed a large chair for herself and a small one for me. Keeping an eye on the class through the open door she read with me about sheep in the meadow and a frightened chicken going to see the king, coaching me out of my phonetic ruts in words like pasture, *bow-wow-wow, hay,* and *pretty,* which to my Mexican ear and eye had so many unnecessary sounds and letters. She made me watch her lips and then close my eyes as she repeated words I found hard to read. When we came to know each other better, I tried interrupting to tell Miss Ryan how we said it in Spanish. It didn't work. She only said "oh" and went on with *pasture, bow-wow-wow,* and *pretty.* It was as if in that closet we were both discovering together the secrets of the English language and grieving together over the tragedies of Bo-Peep. The main reason I was graduated with honors from the first grade was that I had fallen in love with Miss Ryan. Her radiant, no-nonsense character made us either afraid not to love her or love her so we would not be afraid, I am not sure which. It was not only that we sensed she was with it, but also that she was with us.

15 Like the first grade, the rest of the Lincoln School was a sampling of the lower part of town where many races made their home. My pals in the second grade were Kazushi, whose parents spoke only Japanese; Matti, a skinny Italian boy; and Manuel, a fat Portuguese who would never get into a fight but wrestled you to the ground and just sat on you. Our assortment of nationalities included Koreans, Yugoslavs, Poles, Irish, and home-grown Americans.

16 Miss Hopley and her teachers never let us forget why we were at Lincoln: for those who were alien, to become good Americans; for those who were so born, to accept the rest of us. Off the school grounds we traded the same insults we heard from our elders. On the playground we were sure to be marched up to the principal's office for calling someone a wop, a chink, a dago, or a greaser. The school was not so much a melting pot as a griddle where Miss Hopley and her helpers warmed knowledge into us and roasted racial hatreds out of us.

17   At Lincoln, making us into Americans did not mean scrubbing away what made us originally foreign. The teachers called us as our parents did, or as close as they could pronounce our names in Spanish or Japanese. No one was ever scolded or punished for speaking in his native tongue on the playground. Matti told the class about his mother's down quilt, which she had made in Italy with the fine feathers of a thousand geese. Encarnación acted out how boys learned to fish in the Philippines. I astounded the third grade with the story of my travels on a stagecoach, which nobody else in the class had seen except in the museum at Sutter's Fort. After a visit to the Crocker Art Gallery and its collection of heroic paintings of the golden age of California, someone showed a silk scroll with a Chinese painting. Miss Hopley herself had a way of expressing wonder over these matters before a class, her eyes wide open until they popped slightly. It was easy for me to feel that becoming a proud American, as she said we should, did not mean feeling ashamed of being a Mexican.

From BARRIO BOY by Ernesto Galarza. Copyright © 1971 by Ernesto Galarza. Used by permission of University of Notre Dame Press.

 ## THINK QUESTIONS

1. What is the most important idea in the first paragraph? Cite specific evidence from the selection or make inferences drawn from the text to support your answer.

2. How do Miss Hopley's actions in paragraphs 7 and 8 help Ernesto decide whether the principal is a possible "friend or a menace"? What does he decide about her? Cite specific evidence from the text to support your answer.

3. How does the author's word choice in paragraph 12 that begins, "Miss Ryan took me to a seat at the front of the room," help readers understand how Ernesto was feeling on his first day in Miss Ryan's class? Cite three examples from the text to support your response.

4. Which context clues helped you determine the meaning of the word **formidable** as it is used in paragraph 8 of Barrio Boy? Write your definition of "formidable" and indicate the clues that helped you figure out the meaning of the word.

5. Which context clues in the passage helped you figure out the meaning of **mobilized**, in paragraph 8? Write your definition of the word "mobilized." Tell how you figured out the meaning of the word. Then use a print or an online dictionary to confirm the definition.

CLOSE READ

Reread the excerpt from *Barrio Boy*. As you reread, complete the Focus Questions below. Then use your answers and annotations from the questions to help you complete the Writing Prompt.

FOCUS QUESTIONS

1. As you reread the excerpt from *Barrio Boy*, remember that like most authors, Galarza never explicitly states the central ideas. Instead, it is up to the reader to infer the central ideas by drawing inferences from what is stated directly in the text. Reread paragraph 17. What details in the paragraph support the opening sentence: "At Lincoln, making us into Americans did not mean scrubbing away what made us originally foreign"? Make annotations about how this sentence might state a central idea.

2. An author's word choice can impact a reader's understanding of a passage. How effective is the author's choice of the word "soared" to describe Miss Hopley in paragraph 8? Make annotations noting what the word connotes about the principal. How does the author's deliberate use of this word and other words in the paragraph help readers to see Miss Hopley through the eyes of a small boy?

3. In paragraph 16, Galarza recollects that the "school was not so much a melting pot as a griddle where Miss Hopley and her helpers warmed knowledge into us and roasted racial hatreds out of us." Highlight this powerful metaphor in the text. What idea about the school does it connote? Then make annotations noting the evidence in the paragraph that supports the comparison being made in the metaphor.

4. Reread the first and last paragraph of the excerpt. How has Ernesto changed from the beginning of the selection to the end? Make annotations jotting down words and phrases that describe him early on and then later in the excerpt. Then note two central ideas that are developed over the course of the text.

5. In paragraph 12, Ernesto credits Miss Ryan with "maneuvering . . . [him] over the awful idiocies of the English language." Find and highlight textual evidence in paragraphs 13 and 14 to demonstrate how Miss Ryan accomplishes that mission. Then write a sentence summarizing the process. Include a strong central idea in your summary sentence.

WRITING PROMPT

What is the excerpt from *Barrio Boy* all about? How does Ernesto change from the beginning of the excerpt to the end? What do the details in the text have in common? Use your understanding of central (or main) ideas to determine two central ideas that are developed over the course of the text. Then use these central ideas and the details that support them to write an objective summary of the text in your own words. Use transitions to clarify relationships among your ideas. Support your writing with textual evidence and precise language that fully explains your conclusions. Establish a formal style and be sure not to include your feelings, opinions, or judgments. Provide a conclusion that logically follows the information you have presented.

Please note that excerpts and passages in the StudySync® library and this workbook are intended as touchstones to generate interest in an author's work. The excerpts and passages do not substitute for the reading of entire texts, and StudySync® strongly recommends that students seek out and purchase the whole literary or informational work in order to experience it as the author intended. Links to online resellers are available in our digital library. In addition, complete works may be ordered through an authorized reseller by filling out and returning to StudySync® the order form enclosed in this workbook.

Reading & Writing Companion

9

THE OTHER SIDE OF THE SKY

NON-FICTION

Farah Ahmedi and
Tanim Ansary
2006

INTRODUCTION

Farah Ahmedi's memoir *The Other Side of the Sky* is a testament to the power of the human spirit. Missing a leg after stepping on a land mine when she was seven, and with her father and brothers dead from a rocket attack, Ahmedi and her mother decide to flee their home in Kabul in search of a better life. This excerpt from "Escape from Afghanistan" describes their efforts to make it across the border and into Pakistan.

"There was nothing here, no town, no hotel, no buildings, just the desert."

 FIRST READ

NOTES

From: Escape from Afghanistan

1   The gate to Pakistan was closed, and I could see that the Pakistani border guards were letting no one through. People were pushing and shoving and jostling up against that gate, and the guards were driving them back. As we got closer, the crowd thickened, and I could hear the roar and clamor at the gate. The Afghans were yelling something, and the Pakistanis were yelling back. My mother was clutching her side and gasping for breath, trying to keep up. I felt desperate to get through, because the sun was setting, and if we got stuck here, what were we going to do? Where would we stay? There was nothing here, no town, no hotel, no buildings, just the desert.

2   Yet we had no real chance of getting through. Big strong men were running up to the gate in vain. The guards had clubs, and they had carbines, too, which they turned around and used as weapons. Again and again, the crowd surged toward the gate and the guards drove them back with their sticks and clubs, swinging and beating until the crowd receded. And after that, for the next few minutes, on our side of the border, people milled about and muttered and stoked their own impatience and worked up their rage, until gradually the crowd gathered strength and surged against that gate again, only to be swept back.

3   We never even got close to the front. We got caught up in the thinning rear end of crowd, and even so, we were part of each wave, pulled forward, driven back. It was hard for me to keep my footing, and my mother was clutching my arm now, just hanging on, just trying to stay close to me, because the worst thing would have been if we had gotten separated. Finally, I saw that it was no use. We were only risking injury. We drifted back, out of the crowd. In the thickening dusk we could hear the dull roar of people still trying to get past the border guards, but we receded into the desert, farther and farther back from the border gate.

4   Night was falling, and we were stranded out there in the open.

. . .

5   On that second day, however, I learned that it was all a question of money. Someone told me about this, and then I watched closely and saw that it was true. Throughout the day, while some of the guards confronted the crowds, a few others lounged over to the side. People approached them quietly. Money changed hands, and the guards then let those people quietly through a small door to the side.

6   Hundreds could have flowed through the main gate had it been opened, but only one or two could get through the side door at a time. The fact that the guards were taking bribes did us no good whatsoever. We did not have the money to pay them. What little we had we would need to get from Peshawar to Quetta. And so the second day passed.

7   At the end of that day we found ourselves camping near a friendly family. We struck up a conversation with them. The woman told us that her husband, Ghulam Ali, had gone to look for another way across the border. He was checking out a goat path that supposedly went over the mountains several miles northeast of the border station. If one could get to Pakistan safely by that route, he would come back for his family. "You can go with us," the woman said.

8   Later that night her husband showed up. "It works," he said. "Smugglers use that path, and they bribe the guards to leave it unguarded. Of course, we don't want to run into any smugglers, either, but if we go late at night, we should be fine."

9   His wife then told him our story, and Ghulam Ali took pity on us. "Yes, of course you can come with us," he said. "But you have had two hard days. You will need some rest before you attempt this mountain crossing. Spend tonight here and sleep well, knowing that you will have nothing to do tomorrow except lounge around, rest, and catch your breath. Tomorrow, do not throw yourself against those border guards again. Let your only work be the gathering of your strength. Then tomorrow night we will all go over the mountain together, with God's grace. I will show you the way. If God wills it, we will follow that smugglers' path to safety. You and your mother are in my care now."

10 So we spent the whole next day there. It was terribly warm and we had no water, but we walked a little way and found a mosque that refugees like us had built over the years, so that people waiting to get across the border would have a place to say their prayers. We got some water to drink at the

mosque, and we said *namaz* there too. Somehow we obtained a little bit of bread as well. I can't remember how that turned up, but there it was, and we ate it. We sustained our strength. After sunset we lay down just as if were going to spend another night. In fact, I did fall asleep for a while. Long after dark—or early the next morning, to be exact, before the sun came up—that man shook us awake. "It's time," he said.

11   We got up and performed our **ablutions** quickly in the darkness, with just sand because that's allowed when you have no access to water. We said our prayers. Then Ghulam Ali began to march into the darkness with his family, and we trudged along silently behind them. After several miles the path began to climb, and my mother began to wheeze. Her asthma was pretty bad at this point, poor thing. No doubt, her anxiety made it worse, but in such circumstances how could she rid herself of anxiety? It was no use knowing that her difficulty was rooted in anxiety, just as it was no use knowing that we could have moved more quickly if we had possessed wings. Life is what it is. The path over that mountain was not actually very long, only a couple of miles. Steep as it was, we could have gotten over in little more than an hour if not for my mother. Because of her, we had to pause every few minutes, so our journey took many hours.

12   I myself hardly felt the exertion. I was walking quite well that day, quite athletically. I had that good **prosthetic** leg from Germany. The foot was a little worn by then, but not enough to slow me down. Thinking back, I'm puzzled, actually. How did I scale that mountain so easily? How did I climb down the other side? These days I find it hard to clamber up two or three flights of stairs, even. I don't know what made me so **supple** and strong that day, but I felt no hardship, no anxiety or fear, just concentration and intensity. Perhaps my mother's problems distracted me from my own. That might account for it. Perhaps desperation gave me energy and made me forget the **rigor** of the climb. Well, whatever the reason, I scrambled up like a goat. The family we were following had a girl only a bit younger than me, and she was moving slowly. Her family used my example to chide her. They kept saying, "Look at that girl. She's missing a leg, and yet she's going faster than you. Why can't you keep up? Hurry now!"

13   That Ghulam Ali was certainly a good man, so patient with us and so **compassionate**. He had never seen us before, and yet when he met us, he said, "I will help you." That's the thing about life. You never know when and where you will encounter a spot of human decency. I have felt alone in this world at times; I have known long periods of being no one. But then, without warning, a person like Ghulam Ali just turns up and says, "I see you. I am on your side." Strangers have been kind to me when it mattered most. That sustains a person's hope and faith.

Excerpted from *The Other Side of the Sky* by Farah Ahmedi, published by Simon & Schuster.

 THINK QUESTIONS

1. Why were Ahmedi and her mother near the gate to the Pakistani border? Why couldn't they get any nearer to the gate? Why was Ahmedi desperate to get through the border crossing to Pakistan? Cite specific evidence from paragraphs 1 and 2 of the text to support your answer.

2. What did Ahmedi learn on the second day about why a few people were being allowed to enter Pakistan? Why didn't this knowledge help her and her mother? What happened on the night of the second day to give Ahmedi hope? Cite specific evidence from paragraphs 5–9 to support your response.

3. What physical challenges did Ahmedi and her mother face as they crossed the mountain? Why was Ahmedi puzzled by her own physical abilities during the mountain crossing? What does she suppose is the reason for her ability to scale the mountain so easily? Support your answers with specific evidence from paragraphs 11 and 12 of the text.

4. How does sentence 8 in paragraph 12—"These days I find it hard to clamber up two or three flights of stairs, even"—help you understand the meaning of the word **supple** in the next sentence? "I don't know what made me so supple and strong that day, but I felt no hardship, no anxiety or fear, just concentration and intensity." Cite specific evidence from the text to support your answer.

5. Use the context clues provided in the last paragraph to determine the meaning of the word **compassionate**. Write your definition of "compassionate" and indicate the context clues that helped you infer the meaning of the word. Check a print or an online dictionary to confirm your definition.

compassionate means
a kind and nice person

CLOSE READ

Reread the excerpt from *The Other Side of the Sky*. As you reread, complete the Focus Questions below. Then use your answers and annotations from the questions to help you complete the Writing Prompt.

FOCUS QUESTIONS

1. The Afghans surge toward the gate, are driven back, and then mill about, stoke their impatience and rage, and surge forward again. How might this recurring action have unintentionally helped the people who were slipping money to the guards? Highlight the evidence in the text that supports your inference. Then annotate your answer.

2. What did Ghulam Ali instruct Ahmedi and her mother to do in paragraph 9? What can you infer about the next day's journey from his advice? Highlight Ghulam Ali's instructions and annotate your answer. *they must rest*

3. In paragraph 10, what can you infer about the meaning of the word *namaz* from the context clues in the paragraph? Highlight the specific clues in the text that helped you infer the meaning of the word, and annotate your answer. *IT means prayer*

4. In paragraph 12, Ahmedi writes, "These days I find it hard to clamber up two or three flights of stairs, even." What can you infer from this statement? How does this inference help you understand why Ahmedi was puzzled that she could scale the mountain so easily? Annotate how these thoughts contribute to the development of a central idea within the passage. *Bc she has a prosthetic leg she thought it would be harder*

5. As you reread the selection, think about what the text says explicitly and what you can infer. In the first paragraph, what factors drive Ahmedi to accomplish her mission of getting across the border into Pakistan? Highlight specific textual evidence to support your ideas, and annotate inferences that you can draw from this textual evidence.

WRITING PROMPT

This excerpt from *The Other Side of the Sky* assumes a certain level of understanding about the geography, history, current events, and way of life of the Afghan people, including Islamic religious practices, that readers may not have. What examples of unfamiliar vocabulary, geography, history or current events, and the Islamic way of life might have presented problems for you (or other readers) and hindered a full understanding of the text? What explicitly stated details helped you draw inferences from the text so that you could better understand it? Write a brief informative/explanatory essay to explain how you figured things out in the text. Cite specific evidence and vocabulary from the text to support your writing. Use transitions to clarify relationships among your ideas, and conclude with a statement that supports the information and central ideas in your essay.

Please note that excerpts and passages in the StudySync® library and this workbook are intended as touchstones to generate interest in an author's work. The excerpts and passages do not substitute for the reading of entire texts, and StudySync® strongly recommends that students seek out and purchase the whole literary or informational work in order to experience it as the author intended. Links to online resellers are available in our digital library. In addition, complete works may be ordered through an authorized reseller by filling out and returning to StudySync® the order form enclosed in this workbook.

Reading & Writing Companion   **15**

THE SONG OF WANDERING AENGUS

POETRY
William Butler Yeats
1899

INTRODUCTION

n Irish mythology, Aengus is the god of love and youth. He falls in love with a maiden in a dream, finds her, and the two turn into swans. In Yeats's poem, Aengus is mortal, on a quest to find the "glimmering girl" whom he met by chance and who has vanished. His wandering, a life-long search for the object of his desires, represents the human inclination and yearning for love, knowledge, and

"It had become a glimmering girl..."

FIRST READ

1 I went out to the hazel wood,
2 Because a fire was in my head,
3 And cut and peeled a hazel wand,
4 And hooked a berry to a thread;
5 And when white moths were on the wing,
6 And moth-like stars were **flickering** out,
7 I dropped the berry in a stream
8 And caught a little silver trout.

9 When I had laid it on the floor
10 I went to blow the fire a-flame,
11 But something **rustled** on the floor,
12 And someone called me by my name:
13 It had become a **glimmering** girl
14 With apple blossom in her hair
15 Who called me by my name and ran
16 And faded through the brightening air.

17 Though I am old with **wandering**
18 Through hollow lands and hilly lands,
19 I will find out where she has gone,
20 And kiss her lips and take her hands;
21 And walk among long **dappled** grass,
22 And **pluck** till time and times are done,
23 The silver apples of the moon,
24 The golden apples of the sun.

THINK QUESTIONS

1. Where did the "glimmering girl" come from? Cite specific evidence from the text to support your response.

2. How do you know that a lot of time has passed between the events in the first two stanzas and the events in the last stanza? Cite specific textual evidence.

3. Cite specific examples of repetition in the last stanza. How do the repeated words and phrases help readers understand the speaker's commitment to searching for the object of his desire?

4. Use context to determine the meaning of the word **flickering** as it is used in line 6 of "The Song of Wandering Aengus." Write your definition of "flickering" and cite specific context clues to explain how you determined its meaning.

5. Compare and contrast the meaning of **wandering** as it is used as an adjective in the title of the poem and as a noun in the first line of the third stanza. Cite specific evidence from the text. Then, look up the word in a print or online dictionary to confirm its meaning.

CLOSE READ

Reread the poem "The Song of Wandering Aengus." As you reread, complete the Focus Questions below. Then use your answers and annotations from the questions to help you complete the Writing Prompt.

FOCUS QUESTIONS

1. As you reread "The Song of Wandering Aengus," highlight the metaphor in the first stanza that explains why the speaker went fishing. How does the metaphor indicate how the speaker is feeling? How does it suggest what he is hoping might happen? Make annotations citing textual evidence to explain your analysis.

2. Which simile in the first stanza indicates the time of day when the speaker goes fishing? Highlight the simile and make annotations citing textual evidence to explain your response.

3. Which terms in the second stanza are derived from the image of light? Analyze and highlight the image of "fire a-flame" in the second line, and explain its impact on the second stanza. Make annotations supporting your response with specific evidence from the text.

4. Think about the allusion (or reference) in the poem to the mythical Aengus. How might his search for the girl in his dream be similar to the speaker's search for his "dream girl" in the poem? How does this allusion to the mythical Aengus, the Celtic god of love, youth, and beauty, suggest the poem's theme? Make annotations providing textual support for your answer.

5. Highlight specific evidence in the last stanza that suggests what motivates the speaker to undertake a lifelong mission to find the "glimmering girl." Do you think he will ever stop looking for her? Think of your own theme statement for the poem, based on the idea of undertaking a mission to accomplish a goal. Make annotations providing textual support for your theme statement.

WRITING PROMPT

Think about the speaker's mission in "The Song of Wandering Aengus." How determined is he to complete his mission of finding his "dream girl"? This question can help you identify another theme in the poem. What theme is it? Write your response in the form of a clear statement of theme. Then support that theme with specific evidence from the text. Organize and explain how figurative language, allusion, and other poetic elements in the poem support the theme you have identified. Use transitions to show the relationships among these ideas, and conclude with a statement that supports your information.

THE HOBBIT

FICTION

J.R.R. Tolkien
1937

INTRODUCTION

studysync tv

Thirteen dwarves and the great wizard, Gandalf, have come to the home of a hobbit named Bilbo Baggins. The dwarves are embarking on a journey to reclaim their Mountain and their treasure, taken from them by Smaug, a bloodthirsty dragon. For reasons unknown to the hobbit, the dwarves have recruited him as the fourteenth member of their expedition. But when Thorin, the dwarves' leader, notes that they "may never return," Bilbo collapses in a shrieking panic attack. Which side of Bilbo's family will carry more weight—the comfort-loving Bagginses or the adventurous Tooks? And will an ancient map of the Mountain yield any secrets?

"There is a lot more in him than you guess..."

 FIRST READ

From Chapter 1: An Unexpected Party

1   "Excitable little fellow," said Gandalf, as they sat down again. "Gets funny queer fits, but he is one of the best, one of the best—as fierce as a dragon in a pinch."

2   If you have ever seen a dragon in a pinch, you will realize that this was only poetical exaggeration applied to any hobbit, even to Old Took's great-granduncle Bullroarer, who was so huge (for a hobbit) that he could ride a horse. He charged the **ranks** of the goblins of Mount Gram in the Battle of the Green Fields, and knocked their king Golfimbul's head clean off with a wooden club. It sailed a hundred yards through the air and went down a rabbit hole, and in this way the battle was won and the game of Golf invented at the same moment.

3   In the meanwhile, however, Bullroarer's gentler descendant was reviving in the drawing-room. After a while and a drink he crept nervously to the door of the parlour. This is what he heard, Gloin speaking: "Humph!" (or some snort more or less like that). "Will he do, do you think? It is all very well for Gandalf to talk about this hobbit being fierce, but one shriek like that in a moment of excitement would be enough to wake the dragon and all his relatives, and kill the lot of us. I think it sounded more like fright than excitement! In fact, if it had not been for the sign on the door, I should have been sure we had come to the wrong house. As soon as I clapped eyes on the little fellow bobbing and puffing on the mat, I had my doubts. He looks more like a grocer than a burglar!"

4   Then Mr. Baggins turned the handle and went in. The Took side had won. He suddenly felt he would go without bed and breakfast to be thought fierce. As for little fellow bobbing on the mat it almost made him really fierce. Many a time afterwards the Baggins part regretted what he did now, and he said to himself: "Bilbo, you were a fool; you walked right in and put your foot in it."

NOTES

5 "Pardon me," he said, "if I have overheard words that you were saying. I don't pretend to understand what you are talking about, or your reference to burglars, but I think I am right in believing" (this is what he called being on his dignity) "that you think I am no good. I will show you. I have no signs on my door—it was painted a week ago—, and I am quite sure you have come to the wrong house. As soon as I saw your funny faces on the door-step, I had my doubts. But treat it as the right one. Tell me what you want done, and I will try it, if I have to walk from here to the East of East and fight the wild Were-worms in the Last Desert. I had a great-great-great-granduncle once, Bullroarer Took, and—"

6 "Yes, yes, but that was long ago," said Gloin. "I was talking about you. And I assure you there is a mark on this door—the usual one in the trade, or used to be. Burglar wants a good job, plenty of Excitement and reasonable Reward, that's how it is usually read. You can say Expert Treasure-hunter instead of Burglar if you like. Some of them do. It's all the same to us. Gandalf told us that there was a man of the sort in these parts looking for a Job at once, and that he had arranged for a meeting here this Wednesday tea-time."

7 "Of course there is a mark," said Gandalf. "I put it there myself. For very good reasons. You asked me to find the fourteenth man for your expedition, and I chose Mr. Baggins. Just let any one say I chose the wrong man or the wrong house, and you can stop at thirteen and have all the bad luck you like, or go back to digging coal."

8 He scowled so angrily at Gloin that the dwarf huddled back in his chair; and when Bilbo tried to open his mouth to ask a question, he turned and frowned at him and stuck out his bushy eyebrows, till Bilbo shut his mouth tight with a snap.

9 "That's right," said Gandalf. "Let's have no more argument. I have chosen Mr. Baggins and that ought to be enough for all of you. If I say he is a Burglar, a Burglar he is, or will be when the time comes. There is a lot more in him than you guess, and a deal more than he has any idea of himself. You may (possibly) all live to thank me yet.

. . .

10 "Also," went on Gandalf, "I forgot to mention that with the map went a key, a small and curious key. Here it is!" he said, and handed to Thorin a key with a long barrel and **intricate** wards, made of silver. "Keep it safe!"

11 "Indeed I will," said Thorin, and he fastened it upon a fine chain that hung about his neck and under his jacket. "Now things begin to look more hopeful. This news alters them much for the better. So far we have had no clear idea

NOTES

what to do. We thought of going East, as quiet and careful as we could, as far as the Long Lake. After that the trouble would begin—"

12 "A long time before that, if I know anything about the roads East," interrupted Gandalf.

13 "We might go from there up along the River Running," went on Thorin taking no notice, "and so to the ruins of Dale—the old town in the valley there, under the shadow of the Mountain. But we none of us liked the idea of the Front Gate. The river runs right out of it through the great cliff at the South of the Mountain, and out of it comes the dragon too—far too often, unless he has changed."

14 "That would be no good," said the wizard, "not without a mighty Warrior, even a Hero. I tried to find one; but warriors are busy fighting one another in distant lands, and in this neighbourhood heroes are scarce, or simply not to be found. Swords in these parts are mostly blunt, and axes are used for trees, and shields as cradles or dish-covers; and dragons are comfortably far-off (and therefore legendary). That is why I settled on burglary—especially when I remembered the existence of a Side-door. And here is our little Bilbo Baggins, the burglar, the chosen and selected burglar. So now let's get on and make some plans."

15 "Very well then," said Thorin, "supposing the burglar-expert gives us some ideas or suggestions." He turned with mock-politeness to Bilbo.

16 "First I should like to know a bit more about things," said he, feeling all confused and a bit shaky inside, but so far still Tookishly determined to go on with things. "I mean about the gold and the dragon, and all that, and how it got there, and who it belongs to, and so on and further."

17 "Bless me!" said Thorin, "haven't you got a map? and didn't you hear our song? and haven't we been talking about all this for hours?"

18 "All the same, I should like it all plain and clear," said he **obstinately,** putting on his business manner (usually reserved for people who tried to borrow money off him), and doing his best to appear wise and **prudent** and professional and live up to Gandalf's recommendation. "Also I should like to know about risks, out-of-pocket expenses, time required and **remuneration,** and so forth"—by which he meant: "What am I going to get out of it? and am I going to come back alive?"

• • •

19 After all the others had ordered their breakfasts without so much as a please (which annoyed Bilbo very much), they all got up. The hobbit had to find room

Please note that excerpts and passages in the StudySync® library and this workbook are intended as touchstones to generate interest in an author's work. The excerpts and passages do not substitute for the reading of entire texts, and StudySync® strongly recommends that students seek out and purchase the whole literary or informational work in order to experience it as the author intended. Links to online resellers are available in our digital library. In addition, complete works may be ordered through an authorized reseller by filling out and returning to StudySync® the order form enclosed in this workbook.

Reading & Writing Companion   23

for them all, and filled all his spare-rooms and made beds on chairs and sofas, before he got them all stowed and went to his own little bed very tired and not altogether happy.

Excerpted from The Hobbit by J. R. R. Tolkien, published by Houghton Mifflin Harcourt.

 THINK QUESTIONS

1. Why does Gandalf think that Bilbo is right for the job of burglar? Cite specific evidence from paragraphs 1 and 9 to support your answer.

2. What are the two sides of Bilbo's personality? Cite specific evidence from the text, especially in paragraphs 4, 5, and 18 to support your answer.

3. Why does Gandalf think it is important to include Bilbo as the fourteenth member of the expedition? What can you infer from the evidence in paragraph 7 about embarking on an expedition with 13 members? Cite textual evidence.

4. Use context to determine the meaning of the word **prudent** as it is used in paragraph 18 of *The Hobbit*. Write your definition of "prudent" and explain your reasoning based on context clues.

5. Find the word **remuneration** in paragraph 18 of the excerpt. Write your definition of the word, and list the context clues that helped you determine its meaning. Check your definition in a print or digital dictionary to confirm the meaning you inferred.

CLOSE READ

Reread the excerpt from *The Hobbit*. As you reread, complete the Focus Questions below. Then use your answers and annotations from the questions to help you complete the Writing Prompt.

FOCUS QUESTIONS

1. Reread paragraphs 1–4. How is one side of Bilbo's personality beginning to take over? Cite specific textual evidence from these paragraphs to support the idea that "[t]he Took side had won." Highlight the words, phrases, and sentences that support the idea that Bilbo is becoming strong and fierce. Make annotations recording your response.

2. What action sparks Gandalf's dialogue and behavior in paragraphs 7–9? What do Gandalf's words and actions reveal about his character? Why is it likely that Gandalf will influence the events of the plot? Make annotations recording evidence from the text to support your inferences and analysis.

3. Reread paragraphs 1–3. What is the setting of the story? Highlight words and phrases that indicate the time and the place. Make annotations describing the setting and answering these questions: How might the setting influence the characters in the text? How might it shape the events of the plot? Cite specific textual evidence to support your answers.

4. Reread paragraph 18 in the excerpt. Use your understanding of the strategies for analyzing a character to highlight adjectives and adverbs that describe Bilbo. Make annotations listing adjectives and adverbs and indicating in parentheses the part of speech of each word. Look in a print or digital dictionary to confirm the part of speech.

5. Reread paragraph 5. What can you infer about Bilbo's character from his dialogue? What drives him to undertake the mission? Highlight words and phrases that suggest he is determined to do what he must to join the expedition. Then draw an inference about how Bilbo will influence the events of the plot. Make annotations recording your answer.

WRITING PROMPT

Story elements—setting, character, and plot—interact. Therefore, characters in a story may influence the action of the plot, or the plot may influence the actions of the characters. How might the story element of character influence the events of the plot (or the conflict of the plot) in *The Hobbit*? For example, how might the two sides of Bilbo's personality—one excitable, nervous, and cautious, the other strong and fierce—impact the plot? Answer the question with a clear thesis statement. Draw inferences from the text, and support your writing with specific textual evidence. Organize your ideas, and use transitions to clarify and connect them. Write a strong conclusion that summarizes your ideas and "wraps up" your essay.

Please note that excerpts and passages in the StudySync® library and this workbook are intended as touchstones to generate interest in an author's work. The excerpts and passages do not substitute for the reading of entire texts, and StudySync® strongly recommends that students seek out and purchase the whole literary or informational work in order to experience it as the author intended. Links to online resellers are available in our digital library. In addition, complete works may be ordered through an authorized reseller by filling out and returning to StudySync® the order form enclosed in this workbook.

Reading & Writing Companion   25

CALL OF THE KLONDIKE

A TRUE GOLD RUSH ADVENTURE

NON-FICTION

David Meissner and
Kim Richardson
2013

INTRODUCTION

Call of the Klondike tells the story of Stanley Pearce and Marshall Bond, two men who organized one of the earliest expeditions of the Klondike Gold Rush. Authored in part by Pearce's great-great-nephew, the prospectors' account of hardship and adventure is told through primary source documents, including telegrams, letters, diary entries, and newspaper articles.

"Both groups of miners had found their gold in the same place..."

FIRST READ

NOTES

From: Gold Fever Strikes

1   Stanley Pearce and Marshall Bond were in Seattle, Washington, when it happened. On July 17, 1897, sixty-eight rugged miners stepped off the S.S. *Portland* steamship and made their way through the excited crowd. They were carrying large sacks filled with the most precious metal in the world—gold.

2   Stanley Pearce described the scene this way: "Thousands of people in the public square watched the weather-beaten and hardy adventurers stagger into the express office with sacks of gold, gold in blankets, in oil cans, and even in moccasins."

3   Together, these miners brought back an astounding four thousand pounds of gold. It was worth nearly one million dollars, which, by today's standards, would be many times that amount. Three days earlier, miners on another ship, the S.S. *Excelsior,* had arrived in San Francisco with large quantities of gold as well. Both groups of miners had found their gold in the same place: the Klondike region of northern Canada. Soon these discoveries would make headlines around the world.

4   In a matter of hours, many Seattle residents began planning their own trips to the goldfields. At a time when many Americans were either out of work or earning low wages, the prospect of striking it rich proved irresistible. Firemen, doctors, lawyers, ministers—and even the mayor of Seattle—quit their jobs and joined the rush.

5   "By the afternoon," Pearce wrote, "every man who could raise the necessary funds for a year's **grub stake** was rushing to the grocers, hardware merchants and clothiers to get together the necessary outfit to start by the next boat for the promised land, where the dreams of all should be realized."

. . .

NOTES

Staking a Claim

6 When **prospectors** found a promising spot, they staked a claim by placing posts at each corner, one with their name and date on it. The prospector then had three days to go to town and file a legal claim. Because the claims were usually measured by **crude** means, disagreements over exact boundaries were common.

7 The first claim in a new location was called the "discovery claim." **Subsequent** claims were legally referred to by their relationship to this claim, along with the name of the creek—5 Above Eldorado, or 6 Below Bonanza, for example.

—Museum at the Klondike Gold Rush National Historical Park, Seattle

. . .

Game of Claim Selling

8 We have received vague rumors about the expected rush here in the spring and we all wonder whether there will be such an enormous crowd as reported. What under the sun they will do is more than any of us can tell. Everything in the country is staked and there certainly won't be employment for all hands, as there is not enough for those here already.

9 Men are busily engaged on schemes to fleece the unsuspecting Cheecakos out of their **tenderfoot** money, and I am afraid many of them will work.

10 Perhaps the name Cheecako is not understood by some in Denver, but it is the Saguache name for greenhorn, or newcomer. We "old-timers" are called "sour doughs," as it is supposed to be part of our education to know how to make sour dough bread.

Typical Klondike Stampede

11 A story of the recent stampede to Swede creek is typical of Dawson life. I was awakened at 1 o'clock in the morning by my partner, Bond, who in a mysterious voice told me to "hurry up, dress and come." "Come where," said I. "Don't say a word but come," said he. "How far?" No answer. "Take any grub?" No answer. So I gave it up and came. Slipping a change of socks and moccasins into my knapsack, together with some hard tack, and belting on my hand ax we started in pitch darkness. We reached Tammany dance hall, where there was an unusual bustle and excitement. I was still half asleep and uncertain whether it was a dream or not. Finally we started up the river. There were about 50 in the party, including four or five dance hall girls. It was inky dark and the river trail has been freshly blown over with snow. We have to go up the river and cross it three times. Soon there was trouble. Men and women were off the

NOTES

trail and up to their necks in snow. Finally some one produced a candle and I volunteered to lead the procession, having had experience carrying a candle underground, I therefore had the **novel** experience of leading a stampede six miles up the Yukon by candle light. Our party of four was one of the first to arrive. We staked by candle light and started home, arriving at Dawson about 9 a.m., having made about 30 miles since 2 o'clock in the morning. Since our staking on Swede creek, in which I got claim number 20, they have staked as high as No. 750 or about 30 miles above my claim, but I haven't yet found out why we went or what caused that stampede.

12 Other stampedes are on very much the same order. This, however, is the only midnight stampede on record. Quite a number regretted going to Swede creek on that trip. At least six men had their feet frozen, and two men died in the hospital from pneumonia. They were careless and did not take proper care of themselves. . .

Stanley H. Pearce

Excerpted from Call of the Klondike by David Meissner and Kim Richardson, published by Calkins Creek.

THINK QUESTIONS

1. What did Stanley Pearce and Marshall Bond witness on July 17, 1897? How did Pearce describe the scene? Cite textual evidence to support your answer.

2. What process did prospectors use to stake a claim? Cite specific details from the text.

3. Who describes the stampede to Swede Creek? What role did this person play in the stampede? Why was this stampede unique? Cite textual evidence to support your answer.

4. Use context clues to determine the meaning of **grub stake** as it is used in paragraph 5 of *Call of the Klondike*. Write the definition of the word. Then provide evidence from the paragraph to support your definition of the term, and state whether the word is being used correctly in the excerpt. Consult a print or an online dictionary to find the pronunciation of the word and to verify its part of speech and definition. Examine how the use of "grub stake" has changed over time. Does it have the same meaning now that it had during the time of the Klondike Gold Rush? If not, how might it be used today?

5. Use context clues to determine the meaning of the word **tenderfoot** as it is used in paragraph 9 of *Call of the Klondike*. Write your definition of "tenderfoot." Cite the context clues you used from the text to determine the meaning of the word. Consult a print or an online dictionary to verify its part of speech, definition, and usage. When was the term first used?

CLOSE READ

Reread the excerpt from *Call of the Klondike*. As you reread, complete the Focus Questions below. Then use your answers and annotations from the questions to help you complete the Writing Prompt.

FOCUS QUESTIONS

1. Headings as well as subheads (or subheadings) that appear between paragraphs are one kind of text feature that authors of informational text sometimes use to guide readers through a chapter or a series of chapters. Headings organize the text into smaller sections that help readers locate specific information. Identify the three subheads the authors use in this selection. How do the subheads provide clues to the text structure used throughout the text?

2. Many examples of informational text include features such as sidebars. This is information related to the topic that does not easily fit into the main narrative. It is often set off by bullets or enclosed in a box, separating it from the main text. Which section of text in *Call of the Klondike* serves as a sidebar? How were you able to identify this sidebar? Why is this information separated from the text? What is its purpose?

3. How does the information in the sidebar contribute to the text as a whole, and what does it add to the development of the information in the text? Identify evidence in the text to support your answer.

4. What textual evidence indicates the organizational pattern the authors use to present information under the heading "Typical Klondike Stampede"? Cite text evidence to support your answer.

5. Though there was a lot of gold to be found in the Klondike at the time, striking it rich was not a guarantee. Reread paragraphs 1–5. What drove people to join the gold rush? Highlight textual evidence and make annotations to explain your answer.

WRITING PROMPT

How do the text structure, text features, and added sidebar help you to understand the causes and motivation behind "gold fever" and the process involved in staking a claim? In a clear topic sentence, use these informational text elements (text structure, text features, and sidebar) to make inferences about life in the Klondike, using Pearce's recollection of the stampede to Swede Creek. Organize and support your writing with evidence from the text, using precise language and specific vocabulary choices from the selection.

THE KING OF MAZY MAY

FICTION
Jack London
1899

INTRODUCTION

After gold was discovered in 1896, Jack London was one of the many prospectors who flocked to the Klondike, a remote wilderness area of northwestern Canada, in hopes of striking it rich. Although London never found gold, he came back with a wealth of ideas for his budding career as a writer. Many of London's most popular works, including the short story "The King of Mazy May," were inspired by his experiences during the Klondike Gold Rush.

"He did not dare to think what would happen if they caught him..."

 FIRST READ

1 Walt Masters is not a very large boy, but there is manliness in his make-up, and he himself, although he does not know a great deal that most boys know, knows much that other boys do not know. He has never seen a train of cars or an elevator in his life, and for that matter, he has never once looked upon a corn-field, a plow, a cow, or even a chicken. He has never had a pair of shoes on his feet, or gone to a picnic or a party, or talked to a girl. But he has seen the sun at midnight, watched the ice-jams on one of the mightiest of rivers, and played beneath the northern lights, the one white child in thousands of square miles of frozen wilderness.

2 Walt has walked all the fourteen years of his life in sun-tanned, moose-hide moccasins, and he can go to the Indian camps and "talk big" with the men, and trade calico and beads with them for their precious furs. He can make bread without baking-powder, yeast or hops, shoot a moose at three hundred yards, and drive the wild wolf-dogs fifty miles a day on the packed trail.

3 Last of all, he has a good heart, and is not afraid of the darkness and loneliness, of man or beast or thing. His father is a good man, strong and brave, and Walt is growing up like him.

4 Walt was born a thousand miles or so down the Yukon, in a trading-post below the Ramparts. After his mother died, his father and he came on up the river, step by step, from camp to camp, till now they are settled down on the Mazy May Creek in the Klondike country. Last year they and several others had spent much toil and time on the Mazy May, and endured great hardships; the creek, in turn, was just beginning to show up its richness and to reward them for their heavy labor. But with the news of their discoveries, strange men began to come and go through the short days and long nights, and many unjust things they did to the men who had worked so long upon the creek.

NOTES

5   Si Hartman had gone away on a moose-hunt, to return and find new stakes driven and his claim jumped. George Lukens and his brother had lost their claims in a like manner, having delayed too long on the way to Dawson to record them. In short, it was an old story, and quite a number of the earnest, industrious prospectors had suffered similar losses.

6   But Walt Masters's father had recorded his claim at the start, so Walt had nothing to fear, now that his father had gone on a short trip up the White River prospecting for quartz. Walt was well able to stay by himself in the cabin, cook his three meals a day, and look after things. Not only did he look after his father's claim, but he had agreed to keep an eye on the adjoining one of Loren Hall, who had started for Dawson to record it.

7   Loren Hall was an old man, and he had no dogs, so he had to travel very slowly. After he had been gone some time, word came up the river that he had broken through the ice at Rosebud Creek, and frozen his feet so badly that he would not be able to travel for a couple of weeks. Then Walt Masters received the news that old Loren was nearly all right again, and about to move on afoot for Dawson, as fast as a weakened man could.

8   Walt was worried, however; the claim was liable to be jumped at any moment because of this delay, and a fresh stampede had started in on the Mazy May. He did not like the looks of the newcomers, and one day, when five of them came by with crack dog-teams and the lightest of camping outfits, he could see that they were prepared to make speed, and resolved to keep an eye on them. So he locked up the cabin and followed them, being at the same time careful to remain hidden.

9   He had not watched them long before he was sure that they were professional stampeders, bent on jumping all the claims in sight. Walt crept along the snow at the rim of the creek and saw them change many stakes, destroy old ones, and set up new ones.

10   In the afternoon, with Walt always trailing on their heels, they came back down on the creek, unharnessed their dogs, and went into camp within two claims of his cabin. When he saw them make preparations to cook, he hurried home to get something to eat himself, and then hurried back. He crept so close that he could hear them talking quite plainly, and by pushing the underbrush aside he could catch occasional glimpses of them. They had finished eating and were smoking around the fire.

11   "The creek is all right, boys," a large, black-bearded man, evidently the leader, said, "and I think the best thing we can do is to pull out to-night. The dogs can follow the trail; besides, it's going to be moonlight. What say you?"

12 "But it's going to be beastly cold," objected one of the party. "It's forty below zero now."

13 "An' sure, can't ye keep warm by jumpin' on the sleds an' runnin' after the dogs?" cried an Irishman.

14 "An' who wouldn't? The creek as rich as a United States mint! Faith, it's an ilegant chanst to be getting' a run fer yer money! An' if ye don't run, it's mebbe you'll not get the money at all, at all."

15 "That's it," said the leader. "If we can get to Dawson and record, we're rich men; and there is no telling who's been sneaking along in our tracks, watching us, and perhaps now off to give the alarm. The thing for us to do is to rest the dogs a bit, and then hit the trail as hard as we can. What do you say?"

16 Evidently the men had agreed with their leader, for Walt Masters could hear nothing but the rattle of the tin dishes which were being washed. Peering out cautiously, he could see the leader studying a piece of paper. Walt knew what it was at a glance—a list of all the unrecorded claims on Mazy May. Any man could get these lists by applying to the gold commissioner at Dawson.

17 "Thirty-two," the leader said, lifting his face to the men. "Thirty-two isn't recorded, and this is thirty-three. Come on; let's take a look at it. I saw somebody working on it when we came up this morning."

18 Three of the men went with him, leaving one to remain in camp. Walt crept carefully after them till they came to Loren Hall's shaft. One of the men went down and built a fire on the bottom to thaw out the frozen gravel, while the others built another fire on the dump and melted water in a couple of gold-pans. This they poured into a piece of canvas stretched between two logs, used by Loren Hall in which to wash his gold.

19 In a short time a couple of buckets of dirt were sent up by the man in the shaft, and Walt could see the others grouped anxiously about their leader as he proceeded to wash it. When this was finished, they stared at the broad streak of black sand and yellow gold-grains on the bottom of the pan, and one of them called excitedly for the man who had remained in camp to come. Loren Hall had struck it rich, and his claim was not yet recorded. It was plain that they were going to jump it.

20 Walt lay in the snow, thinking rapidly. He was only a boy, but in the face of the threatened injustice against old lame Loren Hall he felt that he must do something. He waited and watched, with his mind made up, till he saw the men began to square up new stakes. Then he crawled away till out of hearing, and broke into a run for the camp of the stampeders. Walt's father had taken their own dogs with him prospecting, and the boy knew how impossible it was for him to undertake the seventy miles to Dawson without the aid of dogs.

21   Gaining the camp, he picked out, with an experienced eye, the easiest running sled and started to harness up the stampeders' dogs. There were three teams of six each, and from there he chose ten of the best. Realizing how necessary it was to have a good head-dog, he strove to discover a leader amongst them; but he had little time in which to do it, for he could hear the voices of the returning men. By the time the team was in shape and everything ready, the claim-jumpers came into sight in an open place not more than a hundred yards from the trail, which ran down the bed of the creek. They cried out to him, but he gave no heed, grabbing up one of their fur sleeping-robes which lay loosely in the snow, and leaping upon the sled.

22   "Mush! Hi! Mush on!" he cried to the animals, snapping the keen-lashed whip among them.

23   The dogs sprang against the yoke-straps, and the sled jerked under way so suddenly as to almost throw him off. Then it curved into the creek, poising perilously on one runner. He was almost breathless with suspense, when it finally righted with a bound and sprang ahead again. The creek bank was high and he could not see, although he could hear the cries of the men and knew they were running to cut him off. He did not dare to think what would happen if they caught him; he only clung to the sled, his heart beating wildly, and watched the snow-rim of the bank above him.

24   Suddenly, over this snow-rim came the flying body of the Irishman, who had leaped straight for the sled in a desperate attempt to capture it; but he was an instant too late. Striking on the very rear of it, he was thrown from his feet, backward, into the snow. Yet, with the quickness of a cat, he had clutched the end of the sled with one hand, turned over, and was dragging behind on his breast, swearing at the boy and threatening all kinds of terrible things if he did not stop the dogs; but Walt cracked him sharply across the knuckles with the butt of the dog-whip till he let go.

25   It was eight miles from Walt's claim to the Yukon—eight very crooked miles, for the creek wound back and forth like a snake, "tying knots in itself," as George Lukens said. And because it was so crooked, the dogs could not get up their best speed, while the sled ground heavily on its side against the curves, now to the right, now to the left.

26   Travellers who had come up and down the Mazy May on foot, with packs on their backs, had declined to go around all the bends, and instead had made short cuts across the narrow necks of creek bottom. Two of his **pursuers** had gone back to harness the remaining dogs, but the others took advantage of these short cuts, running on foot, and before he knew it they had almost overtaken him.

27   "Halt!" they cried after him. "Stop, or we'll shoot!"

NOTES

28 But Walt only yelled the harder at the dogs, and dashed round the bend with a couple of revolver bullets singing after him. At the next bend they had drawn up closer still, and the bullets struck uncomfortably near to him; but at this point the Mazy May straightened out and ran for half a mile as the crow flies. Here the dogs stretched out in their long wolf-swing, and the stampeders, quickly winded, slowed down and waited for their own sled to come up.

29 Looking over his shoulder, Walt reasoned that they had not given up the chase for good, and that they would soon be after him again. So he wrapped the fur robe about him to shut out the stinging air, and lay flat on the empty sled, encouraging the dogs, as he well knew how.

30 At last, twisting abruptly between two river islands, he came upon the might Yukon sweeping grandly to the north. He could not see from bank to bank, and in the quick-falling twilight it loomed a great white sea of frozen stillness. There was not a sound, save the breathing of the dogs, and the churn of the steel-shod sled.

31 No snow had fallen for several weeks, and the traffic had packed the main-river trail till it was hard and glassy as glare ice. Over this the sled flew along, and the dogs kept the trail fairly well, although Walt quickly discovered that he had made a mistake in choosing the leader. As they were driven in single file, without reins, he had to guide them by his voice, and it was evident that the head-dog had never learned the meaning of "gee" and "haw." He hugged the inside of the curves too closely, often forcing his comrades behind him into the soft snow, while several times he thus **capsized** the sled.

32 There was no wind, but the speed at which he travelled created a bitter blast, and with the thermometer down to forty below, this bit through fur and flesh to the very bones. Aware that if he remained constantly upon the sled he would freeze to death, and knowing the practice of Arctic travellers, Walt shortened up one of the lashing-thongs, and whenever he felt chilled, seized hold of it, jumped off, and ran behind till warmth was restored. Then he would climb on and rest till the process had to be repeated.

33 Looking back he could see the sled of his pursuers, drawn by eight dogs, rising and falling over the ice **hummocks** like a boat in a seaway. The Irishman and the black-bearded leader were with it, taking turns in running and riding.

34 Night fell, and in the blackness of the first hour or so, Walt toiled desperately with his dogs. On account of the poor lead-dog, they were constantly **floundering** off the beaten track into the soft snow, and the sled was as often riding on its side or top as it was in the proper way. This work and strain tried his strength sorely. Had he not been in such haste he could have avoided much of it, but he feared the stampeders would creep up in the darkness and

NOTES

overtake him. However, he could hear them occasionally yelling to their dogs, and knew from the sounds that they were coming up very slowly.

35 When the moon rose he was off Sixty Mile, and Dawson was only fifty miles away. He was almost exhausted, and breathed a sigh of relief as he climbed on the sled again. Looking back, he saw his enemies had crawled up within four hundred yards. At this space they remained, a black speck of motion on the white river-beast. Strive as they would, they could not shorten this distance, and strive as he would he could not increase it.

36 He had now discovered the proper lead-dog, and he knew he could easily run away from them if he could only change the bad leader for the good one. But this was impossible, for a moment's delay, at the speed they were running, would bring the men behind upon him.

37 When he got off the mouth of Rosebud Creek, just as he was topping a rise, the ping of a bullet on the ice beside him, and the report of a gun, told him that they were this time shooting at him with a rifle. And from then on, as he cleared the summit of each ice-jam, he stretched flat on the leaping sled till the rifle-shot from the rear warned him that he was safe till the next ice-jam.

38 Now it is very hard to lie on a moving sled, jumping and plunging and yawing like a boat before the wind, and to shoot through the deceiving moonlight at an object four hundred yards away on another moving sled performing equally wild antics. So it is not to be wondered at that the black-bearded leader did not hit him.

39 After several hours of this, during which, perhaps, a score of bullets had struck about him, their ammunition began to give out and their fire slackened. They took greater care, and only whipped a shot at him at the most favorable opportunities. He was also beginning to leave them behind, the distance slowly increasing to six hundred yards.

40 Lifting clear on the crest of a great jam off Indian River, Walt Masters met his first accident. A bullet sang past his ears, and struck the bad lead-dog.

41 The poor brute plunged in a heap, with the rest of the team on top of him.

42 Like a flash, Walt was by the leader. Cutting the **traces** with his hunting knife, he dragged the dying animal to one side and straightened out the team.

43 He glanced back. The other sled was coming up like an express-train. With half the dogs still over their traces, he cried, "Mush on!" and leaped upon the sled just as the pursuing team dashed abreast of him.

Please note that excerpts and passages in the StudySync® library and this workbook are intended as touchstones to generate interest in an author's work. The excerpts and passages do not substitute for the reading of entire texts, and StudySync® strongly recommends that students seek out and purchase the whole literary or informational work in order to experience it as the author intended. Links to online resellers are available in our digital library. In addition, complete works may be ordered through an authorized reseller by filling out and returning to StudySync® the order form enclosed in this workbook.

NOTES

44 The Irishman was just preparing to spring for him,—they were so sure they had him that they did not shoot,—when Walt turned fiercely upon them with his whip.

45 He struck at their faces, and men must save their faces with their hands. So there was not shooting just then. Before they could recover from the hot rain of blows, Walt reached out from his sled, catching their wheel-dog by the fore legs in midspring, and throwing him heavily. This brought the whole team into a snarl, capsizing the sled and tangling his enemies up beautifully.

46 Away Walt flew, the runners of his sled fairly screaming as they bounded over the frozen surface. And what had seemed an accident, proved to be a blessing in disguise. The proper lead-dog was now to the fore, and he stretched low to the trail and whined with joy as he jerked his comrades along.

47 By the time he reached Ainslie's Creek, seventeen miles from Dawson, Walt had left his pursuers, a tiny speck, far behind. At Monte Cristo Island, he could no longer see them. And at Swede Creek, just as daylight was silvering the pines, he ran plump into the camp of old Loren Hall.

48 Almost as quick as it takes to tell it, Loren had his sleeping-furs rolled up, and had joined Walt on the sled. They permitted the dogs to travel more slowly, as there was no sign of the chase in the rear, and just as they pulled up at the gold commissioner's office in Dawson, Walt, who had kept his eyes open to the last, fell asleep.

49 And because of what Walt Masters did on this night, the men of the Yukon have become very proud of him, and always speak of him now as the King of Mazy May.

THINK QUESTIONS

1. How is Walt different from most boys? Cite specific textual evidence to support your answer.

2. How do Walt's efforts to help Loren Hall lead to conflict in the story? Find specific evidence in the text to support your answer.

3. Why do the men of the Yukon call Walt "the King of Mazy May"? Refer to specific details in the text to support your answer.

4. Use context clues to determine the meaning of the word **capsized** as it is used in paragraph 31 of the text. Write your definition of "capsized" and cite the context clues that helped you figure out the meaning of the word.

5. Find the sentence in paragraph 33 that contains the word **hummocks**. Use context clues to determine the meaning of the word. Then use a print or an online dictionary to confirm the meaning as it is used in *The King of Mazy May*. Revise your definition as needed.

CLOSE READ

Reread the short story "The King of Mazy May." As you reread, complete the Focus Questions below. Then use your answers and annotations from the questions to help you complete the Writing Prompt.

FOCUS QUESTIONS

1. Reread this sentence in paragraph 9 of *Call of the Klondike*: "Men are busily engaged on schemes to fleece the unsuspecting Cheecakos out of their tenderfoot money, and I am afraid many of them will work." How does Jack London use these historical facts in paragraph 4 of "The King of Mazy May"? How does he change them? Highlight textual evidence and make annotations to explain your response.

2. In paragraph 8 of "The King of Mazy May," what inference can you make about the newcomers based on specific details in the text? Highlight textual evidence and make annotations to explain your choice.

3. In paragraphs 25 and 26 in "The King of Mazy May," how does the setting affect the plot? Highlight textual evidence and make annotations to support your ideas.

4. Compare and contrast the dangerous conditions posed by the cold as they are described in *Call of the Klondike* and "The King of Mazy May." Based on the historical account in *Call of the Klondike,* how accurately does the short story portray the effects of the frozen terrain on the people living there? Highlight textual evidence and make annotations to explain your choices.

5. In "The King of Mazy May," what motivates Walt to go to extreme lengths to protect Loren Hall's claim? What inferences can you make about Walt's character from his decision to undertake the mission to help Loren Hall? Highlight textual evidence that supports your inferences, and make annotations to cite some of Walt's character traits that affect the setting, characters, plot, and theme of the story.

WRITING PROMPT

Jack London was famous for portraying history accurately in his short stories. What inferences can you make about the Klondike Gold Rush from reading "The King of Mazy May"? What textual evidence in *Call of the Klondike*, a historical account of the Klondike Gold Rush, supports or refutes the idea that London portrayed history accurately in his short story? Begin your response to the prompt with a clear statement that explains your topic. Organize and support your writing with specific evidence, using precise language and selection vocabulary from the factual *Call of the Klondike* and from London's fictional story "The King of Mazy May." Conclude with a statement that supports your main ideas.

Please note that excerpts and passages in the StudySync® library and this workbook are intended as touchstones to generate interest in an author's work. The excerpts and passages do not substitute for the reading of entire texts, and StudySync® strongly recommends that students seek out and purchase the whole literary or informational work in order to experience it as the author intended. Links to online resellers are available in our digital library. In addition, complete works may be ordered through an authorized reseller by filling out and returning to StudySync® the order form enclosed in this workbook.

Reading & Writing Companion   **39**

THE CREMATION OF SAM MCGEE

POETRY
Robert W. Service
1907

INTRODUCTION

Originally published in 1907 in the poetry collection *Songs of a Sourdough*, "The Cremation of Sam McGee" was the most popular of Robert Service's many poems. This entertaining and colorful piece paints a vibrant picture of the characters and setting of the Klondike Gold Rush in Canada and Alaska at the end of the 19th Century. Service was an eyewitness to the end of this dynamic period of North American history, as the last great sweep of gold fever played out

"The trail was bad, and I felt half mad, but I swore I would not give in..."

FIRST READ

1 *There are strange things done in the midnight sun*
2 *By the men who moil for gold;*
3 *The Arctic trails have their secret tales*
4 *That would make your blood run cold;*
5 *The Northern Lights have seen queer sights,*
6 *But the queerest they ever did see*
7 *Was that night on the marge of Lake Lebarge*
8 *I cremated Sam McGee.*

9 Now Sam McGee was from Tennessee, where the cotton blooms and blows.
10 Why he left his home in the South to roam 'round the Pole, God only knows.
11 He was always cold, but the land of gold seemed to hold him like a spell;
12 Though he'd often say in his homely way that "he'd sooner live in hell."

13 On a Christmas Day we were mushing our way over the Dawson trail.
14 Talk of your cold! through the parka's fold it stabbed like a driven nail.
15 If our eyes we'd close, then the lashes froze till sometimes we couldn't see;
16 It wasn't much fun, but the only one to whimper was Sam McGee.

17 And that very night, as we lay packed tight in our robes beneath the snow,
18 And the dogs were fed, and the stars o'erhead were dancing heel and toe,
19 He turned to me, and "Cap," says he, "I'll cash in this trip, I guess;
20 And if I do, I'm asking that you won't refuse my last request."

21 Well, he seemed so low that I couldn't say no; then he says with a sort of moan:
22 "It's the cursed cold, and it's got right hold till I'm chilled clean through to the bone.
23 Yet 'taint being dead—it's my awful dread of the icy grave that pains;
24 So I want you to swear that, foul or fair, you'll cremate my last remains."

NOTES

25   A pal's last need is a thing to **heed**, so I swore I would not fail;
26   And we started on at the streak of dawn; but God! he looked **ghastly** pale.
27   He crouched on the sleigh, and he raved all day of his home in Tennessee;
28   And before nightfall a corpse was all that was left of Sam McGee.

29   There wasn't a breath in that land of death, and I hurried, horror-driven,
30   With a corpse half hid that I couldn't get rid, because of a promise given;
31   It was lashed to the sleigh, and it seemed to say: "You may tax your brawn and brains,
32   But you promised true, and it's up to you to cremate those last remains."

33   Now a promise made is a debt unpaid, and the trail has its own stern code.
34   In the days to come, though my lips were dumb, in my heart how I cursed that load.
35   In the long, long night, by the lone firelight, while the huskies, round in a ring,
36   Howled out their woes to the homeless snows—O God! how I **loathed** the thing.

37   And every day that quiet clay seemed to heavy and heavier grow;
38   And on I went, though the dogs were spent and the grub was getting low;
39   The trail was bad, and I felt half mad, but I swore I would not give in;
40   And I'd often sing to the hateful thing, and it hearkened with a grin.

41   Till I came to the marge of Lake Lebarge, and a derelict there lay;
42   It was jammed in the ice, but I saw in a trice it was called the "Alice May."
43   And I looked at it, and I thought a bit, and I looked at my frozen chum;
44   Then "Here," said I, with a sudden cry, "is my cre-ma-tor-eum."

45   Some planks I tore from the cabin floor, and I lit the boiler fire;
46   Some coal I found that was lying around, and I heaped the fuel higher;
47   The flames just soared and the furnace roared—such a blaze you seldom see;
48   Then I burrowed a hole in the glowing coal, and I stuffed in Sam McGee.

49   Then I made a hike, for I didn't like to hear him sizzle so;
50   And the heavens **scowled,** and the huskies howled, and the wind began to blow.
51   It was icy cold, but the hot sweat rolled down my cheeks, and I don't know why;
52   And the greasy smoke in an inky cloak went streaking down the sky.

53   I do not know how long in the snow I wrestled with **grisly** fear;
54   But the stars came out and they danced about ere again I ventured near;
55   I was sick with dread, but I bravely said: "I'll just take a peep inside.
56   I guess he's cooked, and it's time I looked;" . . . then the door I opened wide.

NOTES

57 And there sat Sam, looking cool and calm, in the heart of the furnace roar;

58 And he wore a smile you could see a mile, and he said: "Please close that door.

59 It's fine in here, but I greatly fear you'll let in the cold and storm—

60 Since I left Plumtree, down in Tennessee, it's the first time I've been warm."

61 *There are strange things done in the midnight sun*

62 *By the men who moil for gold;*

63 *The Arctic trails have their secret tales*

64 *That would make your blood run cold;*

65 *The Northern Lights have seen queer sights,*

66 *But the queerest they ever did see*

67 *Was that night on the marge of Lake Lebarge*

68 *I cremated Sam McGee.*

THINK QUESTIONS

1. Which details in the poem provide evidence that it is set during the Klondike Gold Rush in Canada and Alaska? Cite at least three specific examples from the text.

2. What is Sam McGee most afraid of? What does he ask his friend Cap to do because of this fear? Cite specific details and figurative language from the poem to support your answer.

3. This poem has a surprise ending. Use textual evidence to describe the unexpected event at the end of the poem. How does this unexpected twist add to the humor in the poem?

4. The word **cremate** appears in different forms in the poem: "cremation," "cremate," "cremated," and "crematorium." What does it mean to cremate someone? Use context clues in the poem to determine the meaning of the word. Write your definition of "cremate" and tell how you figured out the meaning. Cite specific evidence from the text.

5. Use a print or digital dictionary to determine the meaning of the word **grisly** as it is used in line 53 of stanza 13. Then find synonyms of the word in a print or digital thesaurus. Write your definition and synonyms and tell where you found them.

Please note that excerpts and passages in the StudySync® library and this workbook are intended as touchstones to generate interest in an author's work. The excerpts and passages do not substitute for the reading of entire texts, and StudySync® strongly recommends that students seek out and purchase the whole literary or informational work in order to experience it as the author intended. Links to online resellers are available in our digital library. In addition, complete works may be ordered through an authorized reseller by filling out and returning to StudySync® the order form enclosed in this workbook.

Reading & Writing Companion   **43**

CLOSE READ

Reread the poem "I Cremated Sam McGee." As you reread, complete the Focus Questions below. Then use your answers and annotations from the questions to help you complete the Writing Prompt.

FOCUS QUESTIONS

1. Highlight the rhyme within lines and at the ends of lines in stanza 3, beginning with "On a Christmas Day." Then imagine that the poet had written this 4-line stanza without using rhyme. Would this simple verse be more or less effective without rhyme? How might it sound like a story? Support your opinion with specific evidence from the text.

2. Highlight two examples of personification in stanza 12. What does the personification help you to visualize? Cite specific evidence from the text.

3. Stanza 14 includes a poetic element that is often found in tall tales—hyperbole. Hyperbole is a poetic device that uses exaggeration to express emotion or surprise, make a point, or create

humor. Highlight the hyperbole in the stanza. How does it help create humor in the poem? Cite specific evidence from the text.

4. Summarize the poetic structure used in "The Cremation of Sam McGee." Include the form of the poem in your written summary, the use of stanzas, rhyme scheme (pattern of end rhymes), refrain (or repeated stanza), and an inference about why the ballad form was likely used. Highlight specific evidence from the text and make annotations to record notes for your objective summary of the poem's structure.

5. What can the reader infer is the speaker's motivation for undertaking the mission of fulfilling Sam McGee's last wish? Highlight textual evidence to support your answer.

WRITING PROMPT

"The Cremation of Sam McGee" is a study in contrasts. It includes language and imagery that point to the grim nature of death, and yet it also makes readers laugh about this serious subject. How does the poem use poetic structure and form, as well as poetic elements like rhyme, figurative language and imagery, and tone, to produce this contrast? Begin with a statement that clearly explains your topic. Organize and support your writing with specific evidence from the text. Pay careful attention to your word choice, and use precise language and vocabulary from the selection.

NEW DIRECTIONS

NON-FICTION
Maya Angelou
1993

INTRODUCTION

"New Directions" is Maya Angelou's biographical essay about her grandmother, Annie Johnson. When Annie's marriage ends in 1903, she realizes that she must work in order to support her two small boys. As an African-American woman, her choices are limited, yet Annie "cuts a new path" for herself through hard work and resourcefulness. In sharing her grandmother's story, Angelou teaches readers a lesson about the importance of making deliberate choices.

"I decided to step off the road and cut me a new path."

FIRST READ

1 In 1903 the late Mrs. Annie Johnson of Arkansas found herself with two toddling sons, very little money, a slight ability to read and add simple numbers. To this picture add a disastrous marriage and the burdensome fact that Mrs. Johnson was a Negro.

2 When she told her husband, Mr. William Johnson, of her dissatisfaction with their marriage, he **conceded** that he too found it to be less than he expected, and had been secretly hoping to leave and study religion. He added that he thought God was calling him not only to preach but to do so in Enid, Oklahoma. He did not tell her that he knew a minister in Enid with whom he could study and who had a friendly, unmarried daughter. They parted amicably, Annie keeping the one-room house and William taking most of the cash to carry himself to Oklahoma.

3 Annie, over six feet tall, big-boned, decided that she would not go to work as a **domestic** and leave her "precious babes" to anyone else's care. There was no possibility of being hired at the town's cotton gin or lumber mill, but maybe there was a way to make the two factories work for her. In her words, "I looked up the road I was going and back the way I come, and since I wasn't satisfied, I decided to step off the road and cut me a new path." She told herself that she wasn't a fancy cook but that she could "mix groceries well enough to scare hungry away and from starving a man."

4 She made her plans **meticulously** and in secret. One early evening to see if she was ready, she placed stones in two five-gallon pails and carried them three miles to the cotton gin. She rested a little, and then, discarding some rocks, she walked in the darkness to the saw mill five miles farther along the dirt road. On her way back to her little house and her babies, she dumped the remaining rocks along the path.

NOTES

5   That same night she worked into the early hours boiling chicken and frying ham. She made dough and filled the rolled-out pastry with meat. At last she went to sleep.

6   The next morning she left her house carrying the meat pies, lard, an iron brazier, and coals for a fire. Just before lunch she appeared in an empty lot behind the cotton gin. As the dinner noon bell rang, she dropped the savors into boiling fat and the aroma rose and floated over to the workers who spilled out of the gin, covered with white lint, looking like specters.

7   Most workers had brought their lunches of pinto beans and biscuits or crackers, onions and cans of sardines, but they were tempted by the hot meat pies which Annie ladled out of the fat. She wrapped them in newspapers, which soaked up the grease, and offered them for sale at a nickel each. Although business was slow, those first days Annie was determined. She balanced her appearances between the two hours of activity.

8   So, on Monday if she offered hot fresh pies at the cotton gin and sold the remaining cooled-down pies at the lumber mill for three cents, then on Tuesday she went first to the lumber mill presenting fresh, just-cooked pies as the lumbermen covered in sawdust emerged from the mill.

9   For the next few years, on balmy spring days, blistering summer noon, and cold, wet, and wintry middays, Annie never disappointed her customers, who could count on seeing the tall, brown-skin woman bent over her brazier, carefully turning the meat pies. When she felt certain that the workers had become dependent on her, she built a stall between the two hives of industry and let the men run to her for their lunchtime provisions.

10 She had indeed stepped from the road which seemed to have been chosen for her and cut herself a brand-new path. In years that stall became a store where customers could buy cheese, meal, syrup, cookies, candy, writing tablets, pickles, canned goods, fresh fruit, soft drinks, coal oil, and leather soles for worn-out shoes.

11 Each of us has the right and the responsibility to **assess** the roads which lie ahead, and those over which we have traveled, and if the future road looms **ominous** or unpromising, and the roads back uninviting, then we need to gather our resolve and, carrying only the necessary baggage, step off that road into another direction. If the new choice is also unpalatable, without embarrassment, we must be ready to change that as well.

THINK QUESTIONS

1. Why did Annie Johnson need to find a way to make money? What information in the text tells you this? Cite specific textual evidence to support your answer.

2. What did Annie decide to do to make money? How do you know? Cite specific evidence from the text to support your answer.

3. What was the final outcome of Annie's decision to sell food to the workers in order to support her family? What clues helped you infer this? Cite specific textual evidence to support your inference.

4. What is the denotation, or dictionary definition, of the word **conceded** as it is used in paragraph 2?

What is its connotation in the text? Use context to describe the word's connotation in "New Directions." Cite specific evidence from the text to support your answer.

5. What is the definition of **meticulously** as it is used in paragraph 4? By remembering that the suffix *-ly* means "in a certain way," use that information, along with context clues provided in the passage, to determine the meaning of "meticulously." Write your definition of the word and tell how you figured out its meaning. Cite specific evidence from the text to support your answer.

CLOSE READ

Reread the essay "New Directions." As you reread, complete the Focus Questions below. Then use your answers and annotations from the questions to help you complete the Writing Prompt.

FOCUS QUESTIONS

1. As you reread the text of "New Directions," look for interactions among the individuals, events, and ideas to get a deeper understanding of the text. For example, in what ways did Annie's dissatisfaction with her marriage change her life? Highlight evidence in the text and make annotations to support your choices.

2. Connotation helps an author convey meaning. Why does Maya Angelou choose to use the word "meticulously" in paragraph 4, rather than "carefully"? Look in a dictionary for the exact meaning of "meticulous." What is the impact of this specific word choice on the meaning of the text? What does the word connote about Annie's personality? Highlight specific textual evidence and make annotations to support your response.

3. An author may use the same metaphor comparing two unlike things throughout a text. This is called an extended metaphor. In "New Directions," the metaphor of life as a road is an extended metaphor. After Annie herself is quoted in paragraph 3 as comparing her life to a road, where else does the metaphor appear in the text? How does the author use this extended metaphor to convey a central idea? Highlight textual evidence and make annotations to support your response.

4. Connotation adds depth to a text and makes reading a richer experience. Use your understanding of denotation and connotation to explain why Maya Angelou used the term "big-boned" rather than just "large" to describe Annie, and "savors" rather than just "food" to describe the pies she made. Highlight specific evidence in the text and make annotations to support your choices.

5. If you think about how ideas and events affect individuals, you might be able to explain why people act the way they do. Make an inference about what drove Annie to walk with pails of rocks to the factories. How did this action confirm her mission to find a "new direction" in life? Highlight evidence in the text and make annotations to explain your response.

WRITING PROMPT

Why does Maya Angelou use the extended metaphor that compares life to a road? What does the metaphor mean in the text? What is its purpose? Begin with a clear statement of explanation. How does this extended metaphor develop the central idea of this biographical excerpt? Organize and support your writing with specific evidence from the text. Use precise language and vocabulary from the selection. Provide a strong conclusion that supports your main ideas.

TRAVELS WITH CHARLEY

NON-FICTION
John Steinbeck
1962

INTRODUCTION

n 1960, author John Steinbeck set out on a long road trip with his poodle, Charley, in order to reacquaint himself with the land and people he wrote about. In this excerpt from his Pulitzer Prize winning book about the experience, he shares

"For how can one know color in perpetual green?"

FIRST READ

NOTES

1   I soon discovered that if a wayfaring stranger wishes to eavesdrop on a local population, the places for him to slip in and hold his peace are bars and churches. But some New England towns don't have bars, and church is only on Sunday. A good **alternative** is the roadside restaurant where men gather for breakfast before going to work or going hunting. To find these places inhabited one must get up very early. And there is a drawback even to this. Early-rising men not only do not talk much to strangers, they barely talk to one another. Breakfast conversation is limited to a series of laconic grunts. The natural New England taciturnity reaches its glorious perfection at breakfast.

2   I fed Charley, gave him a limited **promenade**, and hit the road. An icy mist covered the hills and froze on my windshield. I am not normally a breakfast eater, but here I had to be or I wouldn't see anybody unless I stopped for gas. At the first lighted roadside restaurant I pulled in and took my seat at a counter. The customers were folded over their coffee cups like ferns. A normal conversation is as follows:

3   WAITRESS: "Same?"

4   CUSTOMER: "Yep."

5   WAITRESS: "Cold enough for you?"

6   CUSTOMER: "Yep."

7   WAITRESS: "Refill?"

8   CUSTOMER: "Yep."

9   This is a really talkative customer. Some reduce it to "Burp" and others do not answer at all. An early morning waitress in New England leads a lonely life,

but I soon learned that if I tried to **inject** life and gaiety into her job with a blithe remark she dropped her eyes and answered "Yep" or "Umph." Still, I did feel that there was some kind of communication, but I can't say what it was.

10   The best of learning came on the morning radio, which I learned to love. Every town of a few thousand people has its station, and it takes the place of the old local newspaper. Bargains and trades are announced, social doings, prices of commodities, messages. The records played are the same all over the country. If "Teen-Age Angel" is top of the list in Maine, it is top of the list in Montana. In the course of a day you may hear "Teen-Age Angel" thirty or forty times. But in addition to local news and **chronicles,** some foreign advertising creeps in. As I went farther and farther north and it got colder I was aware of more and more advertising for Florida real estate and, with the approach of the long and bitter winter, I could see why Florida is a golden word. As I went along I found that more and more people lusted toward Florida and that thousands had moved there and more thousands wanted to and would. The advertising, with a side look at Federal Communications, made few claims except for the fact that the land they were selling was in Florida. Some of them went out on a limb and promised that it was above tide level. But that didn't matter; the very name Florida carried the message of warmth and ease and comfort. It was irresistible.

11   I've lived in good climate, and it bores the hell out of me. I like weather rather than climate. In Cuernavaca, Mexico, where I once lived, and where the climate is as near to perfect as is conceivable, I have found that when people leave there they usually go to Alaska. I'd like to see how long an Aroostook County man can stand Florida.

12   The trouble is that with his savings moved and invested there, he can't very well go back. His dice are rolled and can't be picked up again. But I do wonder if a down-Easter, sitting on a nylon-and-aluminum chair out on a changelessly green lawn slapping mosquitoes in the evening of a Florida October—I do wonder if the stab of memory doesn't strike him high in the stomach just below the ribs where it hurts. And in the humid ever-summer I dare his picturing mind not to go back to the shout of color, to the clean rasp of frosty air, to the smell of pine wood burning and the caressing warmth of kitchens. For how can one know color in perpetual green, and what good is warmth without cold to give it sweetness?

13   I drove as slowly as custom and the impatient law permitted. That's the only way to see anything. Every few miles the states provided places of rest off the roads, sheltered places sometimes near dark streams. There were painted oil drums for garbage, and picnic tables, and sometimes fireplaces or barbecue pits. At **intervals** I drove Rocinante off the road and let Charley out to smell over the register of previous guests. Then I would heat my coffee

Reading & Writing Companion

and sit comfortably on my back step and contemplate wood and water and the quick-rising mountains with crowns of conifers and the fir trees high up, dusted with snow. Long ago at Easter I had a looking-egg. Peering in a little porthole at the end, I saw a lovely little farm, a kind of dream farm, and on the farmhouse chimney a stork sitting on a nest. I regarded this as a fairy-tale farm as surely imagined as gnomes sitting under toadstools. And then in Denmark I saw that farm or its brother, and it was true, just as it had been in the looking-egg. And in Salinas, California, where I grew up, although we had some frost the climate was cool and foggy. When we saw colored pictures of a Vermont autumn forest it was another fairy thing and we frankly didn't believe it. In school we memorized "Snowbound" and little poems about Old Jack Frost and his paintbrush, but the only thing Jack Frost did for us was put a thin skin of ice on the watering trough, and that rarely. To find not only that this bedlam of color was true but that the pictures were pale and inaccurate translations, was to me startling. I can't even imagine the forest colors when I am not seeing them. I wondered whether constant association could cause inattention, and asked a native New Hampshire woman about it. She said the autumn never failed to amaze her; to elate. "It is a glory," she said, "and can't be remembered, so that it always comes as a surprise."

Excerpted from *Travels with Charley* by John Steinbeck, published by the Penguin Group.

THINK QUESTIONS

1. About how long ago do you think this selection was written? Highlight textual evidence and make annotations to identify details that reveal the time period.

2. Why does listening to the radio give the author a better idea of what people are thinking than visiting local roadside restaurants? Cite textual evidence to support your answer.

3. What does Steinbeck love about the weather in New England? Refer to evidence in the text to support your answer.

4. Use context to determine the meaning of the word **alternative** as it is used in the first paragraph of *Travels with Charley*. Write your definition of "alternative" and tell how you figured out its meaning.

5. By remembering that the Latin prefix *inter-* means "between," use the context clues provided in the passage to determine the meaning of **intervals,** in paragraph 13. Write your definition and tell how you determined the meaning of the word.

Please note that excerpts and passages in the StudySync® library and this workbook are intended as touchstones to generate interest in an author's work. The excerpts and passages do not substitute for the reading of entire texts, and StudySync® strongly recommends that students seek out and purchase the whole literary or informational work in order to experience it as the author intended. Links to online resellers are available in our digital library. In addition, complete works may be ordered through an authorized reseller by filling out and returning to StudySync® the order form enclosed in this workbook.

Reading & Writing Companion   **53**

CLOSE READ

Reread the excerpt from *Travels With Charley*. As you reread, complete the Focus Questions below. Then use your answers and annotations from the questions to help you complete the Writing Prompt.

FOCUS QUESTIONS

1. In *Travels with Charley*, John Steinbeck is driven to undertake a mission. During his mission—a cross-country road trip—readers come to understand that the interactions between an event, individuals, and the idea that springs from these interactions all influence one another. What did Steinbeck's interactions with New Englanders reveal about them, and what conclusions did the author reach as a result? Highlight textual evidence to support your answer.

2. What conclusions was Steinbeck able to draw about small-town life by listening to local morning radio shows? Annotate to explain how these details help develop the ideas and advance the events in the selection.

3. An author of informational text will sometimes use figurative language to persuade readers to share a point of view, or to enhance an argument. In the second half of the excerpt, Steinbeck includes descriptive details that help bring his perceptions and opinions to life. Annotate examples in the text where Steinbeck uses figurative language to underscore how he feels about Florida.

4. Why does Steinbeck describe the looking-egg he used to have? What central idea in the text does it help you understand? Look for textual evidence that supports your answer.

5. In the last paragraph, Steinbeck has a conversation with a New Hampshire woman about the colors of the forest in autumn. What does he learn from this conversation? How might it reaffirm his earlier idea that a New Englander might have regrets about moving to Florida? Support your statements with textual evidence.

WRITING PROMPT

What insights, or new ideas, has John Steinbeck gained from his decision to travel with his dog, Charley, through New England? Does he seem to be succeeding in his mission to "reacquaint himself with the land and the people he wrote about"? How are the people influencing his ideas about New England and his experiences there? Begin your writing with a clear sentence explaining your topic. Organize and support your ideas in a well-written paragraph that cites specific evidence from the text. Use precise language and vocabulary from the selection. Complete your writing with a concluding statement that summarizes your central ideas.

APOLLO 13: MISSION HIGHLIGHTS

NON-FICTION
NASA Kennedy Space Center
1970

INTRODUCTION

Their mission was to be an exploration of a lunar highland, following after the successful landings of *Apollo 11 and 12*. However, *Apollo 13* would prove unlucky. Nearing the moon, both oxygen tanks in the command module (CM) failed, shutting down power and forcing the crew to abandon the mission and focus on getting home safely—while crammed into the smaller lunar module (LM).

"Houston, we've had a problem here."

 FIRST READ

 NOTES

Mission Highlights

1 The first two days the crew ran into a couple of minor surprises, but generally *Apollo 13* was looking like the smoothest flight of the program. At 46 hours 43 minutes Joe Kerwin, the CapCom on duty, said, "The spacecraft is in real good shape as far as we are concerned. We're bored to tears down here." It was the last time anyone would mention boredom for a long time.

2 At 55 hours 46 minutes, as the crew finished a 49-minute TV broadcast showing how comfortably they lived and worked in weightlessness, Lovell stated: "This is the crew of *Apollo 13* wishing everybody there a nice evening, and we're just about ready to close out our inspection of *Aquarius (the LM)* and get back for a pleasant evening in *Odyssey (the CM)*. Good night."

3 Nine minutes later, Oxygen tank No. 2 blew up, causing No. 1 tank also to fail. *The Apollo 13* command module's normal supply of electricity, light, and water was lost, and they were about 200,000 miles from Earth.

4 The message came in the form of a sharp bang and vibration. Jack Swigert saw a warning light that accompanied the bang, and said, "Houston, we've had a problem here." Lovell came on and told the ground that it was a main B bus undervolt. The time was 2108 hours on April 13.

5 Next, the warning lights indicated the loss of two of *Apollo 13's* three fuel cells, which were the spacecraft's prime source of electricity. With warning lights blinking on, one oxygen tank appeared to be completely empty, and there were indications that the oxygen in the second tank was rapidly being **depleted.**

6 Thirteen minutes after the explosion, Lovell happened to look out of the left-hand window, and saw the final evidence pointing toward **potential**

catastrophe. "We are venting something out into the- into space," he reported to Houston. Jack Lousma, the CapCom replied, "Roger, we copy you venting." Lovell said, "It's a gas of some sort." It was oxygen gas escaping at a high rate from the second, and last, oxygen tank.

7   The first thing the crew did, even before discovering the oxygen leak, was to try to close the hatch between the CM and the LM. They reacted spontaneously, like submarine crews, closing the hatches to limit the amount of flooding. First Jack and then Lovell tried to lock the reluctant hatch, but the stubborn lid wouldn't stay shut. Exasperated, and realizing that there wasn't a cabin leak, they strapped the hatch to the CM couch.

8   The pressure in the No. 1 oxygen tank continued to drift downward; passing 300 psi, now heading toward 200 psi. Months later, after the accident investigation was complete, it was determined that, when the No. 2 tank blew up, it either ruptured a line on the No. 1 tank, or caused one of the valves to leak. When the pressure reached 200 psi, the crew and ground controllers knew that they would lose all oxygen, which meant that the last fuel cell would also die.

9   At 1 hour and 29 seconds after the bang, Jack Lousma, then CapCom, said after instructions from Flight Director Glynn Lunney: "It is slowly going to zero, and we are starting to think about the LM lifeboat." Swigert replied, "That's what we have been thinking about too."

10   Ground controllers in Houston faced a **formidable** task. Completely new procedures had to be written and tested in the simulator before being passed up to the crew. The navigation problem had to be solved; essentially how, when, and in what altitude to burn the LM descent engine to provide a quick return home.

11   With only 15 minutes of power left in the CM, CapCom told the crew to make their way into the LM. Fred and Jim Lovell quickly floated through the tunnel, leaving Jack to perform the last chores in the Command Module. The first concern was to determine if there were enough consumables to get home? The LM was built for only a 45-hour lifetime, and it needed to be stretched to 90. Oxygen wasn't a problem. The full LM descent tank alone would **suffice**, and in addition, there were two ascent-engine oxygen tanks, and two backpacks whose oxygen supply would never be used on the lunar surface. Two emergency bottles on top of those packs had six or seven pounds each in them. (At LM jettison, just before reentry, 28.5 pounds of oxygen remained, more than half of what was available after the explosion).

12   Power was also a concern. There were 2181 ampere hours in the LM batteries, Ground controllers carefully worked out a procedure where the CM batteries were charged with LM power. All non-critical systems were turned off and

NOTES

energy consumption was reduced to a fifth of normal, which resulted in having 20 percent of our LM electrical power left when Aquarius was jettisoned. There was one electrical close call during the mission. One of the CM batteries vented with such force that it momentarily dropped off the line. Had the battery failed, there would be insufficient power to return the ship to Earth.

13   Water was the main consumable concern. It was estimated that the crew would run out of water about five hours before Earth reentry, which was calculated at around 151 hours. However, data from *Apollo 11* (which had not sent its LM ascent stage crashing into the moon as in subsequent missions) showed that its mechanisms could survive seven or eight hours in space without water cooling. The crew conserved water. They cut down to six ounces each per day, a fifth of normal intake, and used fruit juices; they ate hot dogs and other wet-pack foods when they ate at all. The crew became dehydrated throughout the flight and set a record that stood up throughout *Apollo:* Lovell lost fourteen pounds, and the crew lost a total of 31.5 pounds, nearly 50 percent more than any other crew. Those stringent measures resulted in the crew finishing with 28.2 pounds of water, about 9 percent of the total.

14   Removal of Carbon Dioxide was also a concern. There were enough lithium hydroxide canisters, which remove carbon dioxide from the spacecraft, but the square canisters from the Command Module were not compatible with the round openings in the Lunar Module environmental system. There were four cartridge from the LM, and four from the backpacks, counting backups. However, the LM was designed to support two men for two days and was being asked to care for three men nearly four days. After a day and a half in the LM a warning light showed that the carbon dioxide had built up to a dangerous level. Mission Control **devised** a way to attach the CM canisters to the LM system by using plastic bags, cardboard, and tape- all materials carried on board.

15   One of the big questions was, "How to get back safely to Earth." The LM navigation system wasn't designed to help us in this situation. Before the explosion, at 30 hours and 40 minutes, Apollo 13 had made the normal midcourse correction, which would take it out of a free-return-to-Earth trajectory and put it on a lunar landing course. Now the task was to get back on a free-return course. The ground computed a 35-second burn and fired it 5 hours after the explosion. As they approached the moon, another burn was computed; this time a long 5-minute burn to speed up the return home. It took place 2 hours after rounding the far side of the moon.

. . .

16 The trip was marked by discomfort beyond the lack of food and water. Sleep was almost impossible because of the cold. When the electrical systems were turned off, the spacecraft lost an important source of heat. The temperature dropped to 38 F and condensation formed on all the walls.

17 A most remarkable achievement of Mission Control was quickly developing procedures for powering up the CM after its long cold sleep. Flight controllers wrote the documents for this innovation in three days, instead of the usual three months. The Command Module was cold and clammy at the start of power up. The walls, ceiling, floor, wire harnesses, and panels were all covered with droplets of water. It was suspected conditions were the same behind the panels. The chances of short circuits caused apprehension, but thanks to the safeguards built into the command module after the disastrous *Apollo 1* fire in January 1967, no arcing took place. The droplets furnished one sensation as we decelerated in the atmosphere: it rained inside the CM.

18 Four hours before landing, the crew shed the service module; Mission Control had insisted on retaining it until then because everyone feared what the cold of space might do to the unsheltered CM heat shield. Photos of the Service Module showed one whole panel missing, and wreckage hanging out, it was a sorry mess as it drifted away. Three hours later the crew left the Lunar Module Aquarius and then splashed down gently in the Pacific Ocean near Samoa.

THINK QUESTIONS

1. What words, phrases, or clues in the first two paragraphs help readers determine the subject (or content) area of the text? Cite specific textual evidence to support your answer.

2. What is the impact of technical language on the tone of the text? Cite specific evidence from the text to support your answer.

3. How effective is the use of technical language in the text? Cite specific textual evidence to support your answer.

4. Use context clues to determine the meaning of the word **formidable** as it is used in paragraph 10 of the text. Write your definition of "formidable" and identify the context clues you used to figure out the meaning of the word.

5. Use context clues to determine the meaning of **devised** in paragraph 14. Write your definition of "devised" and identify the context clues you used in the text to determine its meaning. Confirm your definition by looking up "devise" in the dictionary. Revise your definition as needed.

Please note that excerpts and passages in the StudySync® library and this workbook are intended as touchstones to generate interest in an author's work. The excerpts and passages do not substitute for the reading of entire texts, and StudySync® strongly recommends that students seek out and purchase the whole literary or informational work in order to experience it as the author intended. Links to online resellers are available in our digital library. In addition, complete works may be ordered through an authorized reseller by filling out and returning to StudySync® the order form enclosed in this workbook.

Reading & Writing Companion   **59**

CLOSE READ

Reread the excerpt from *Apollo 13: Mission Highlights*. As you reread, complete the Focus Questions below. Then use your answers and annotations from the questions to help you complete the Writing Prompt.

FOCUS QUESTIONS

1. As you reread the first three paragraphs, highlight the names of the two spacecraft in which the astronauts are working and living. Highlight, too, how the text helps readers understand the differences between the two spacecraft. What context clues in paragraph 3, including any Greek or Latin prefixes, suffixes, or roots of words, help readers understand the technical information and technical language in paragraph 2? Highlight specific textual evidence, and make annotations to explain your responses.

2. In paragraph 4, Lovell tells Houston that the problem is with a "main B bus undervolt." What clues in paragraph 3 help you infer what the "main B bus undervolt" supplies? Highlight textual evidence in paragraph 5, and make annotations citing the other technical problems that the spacecraft is experiencing.

3. Why was the removal of carbon dioxide from the LM a problem in paragraph 14? How did Mission Control solve the problem? Highlight specific technical language, including any Greek or Latin prefixes, suffixes, or roots of words, that helped you understand the technical information and technical language in the paragraph. Make annotations to help support your response.

4. In paragraph 17, the text states, "A most remarkable achievement of Mission Control was quickly developing procedures for powering up the CM after its long cold sleep." What did flight controllers do to solve the problem? Highlight specific technical language and evidence in the text, and make annotations explaining your response.

5. *Apollo's 13's* original mission was to explore a lunar highland, but after the explosion and failure of the spacecraft's oxygen tanks, the astronauts and mission control had a new goal in mind. What was this goal? Was it accomplished? Highlight specific evidence in paragraphs 15 and 18, and make annotations to explain your answers.

WRITING PROMPT

The *Apollo 13* mission has been called a "successful failure." Explain why in an informative/explanatory essay. Begin with a clear thesis statement. Organize your information and supporting details, citing specific textual evidence from "*Apollo 13:* Mission Highlights." Use technical language in your essay. Be sure to explain the meaning of scientific and technical terms, either by providing explicit evidence in the text or by using context clues to help readers draw inferences about the meaning of the terms. Clarify the connections among your ideas with transitions, and use a formal style suited to audience and purpose. Summarize your main ideas with a strong concluding statement.

RIKKI-TIKKI-TAVI

FICTION
Rudyard Kipling
1894

INTRODUCTION

studysync tv

" R ikki-Tikki-Tavi" is one of the most famous tales from *The Jungle Book*, a collection of short stories published in 1894 by English author Rudyard Kipling. The stories in *The Jungle Book* feature animal characters with anthropomorphic traits and are intended to be read as fables, each illustrating a moral lesson. In this story, Rikki-Tikki-Tavi is a courageous young mongoose adopted as a pet by a British family living in 19th-century colonial India.

"Rikki-tikki licked his lips. 'This is a splendid hunting-ground.'"

 FIRST READ

1 This is the story of the great war that Rikki-tikki-tavi fought single-handed, through the bath-rooms of the big bungalow in Segowlee cantonment. Darzee, the Tailorbird, helped him, and Chuchundra, the musk-rat, who never comes out into the middle of the floor, but always creeps round by the wall, gave him advice, but Rikki-tikki did the real fighting.

2 He was a mongoose, rather like a little cat in his fur and his tail, but quite like a weasel in his head and his habits. His eyes and the end of his **restless** nose were pink. He could scratch himself anywhere he pleased with any leg, front or back, that he chose to use. He could fluff up his tail till it looked like a bottle brush, and his war cry as he **scuttled** through the long grass was: "Rikk-tikk-tikki-tikki-tchk!"

3 One day, a high summer flood washed him out of the burrow where he lived with his father and mother, and carried him, kicking and clucking, down a roadside ditch. He found a little wisp of grass floating there, and clung to it till he lost his senses. When he revived, he was lying in the hot sun on the middle of a garden path, very draggled indeed, and a small boy was saying, "Here's a dead mongoose. Let's have a funeral."

4 "No," said his mother, "let's take him in and dry him. Perhaps he isn't really dead."

5 They took him into the house, and a big man picked him up between his finger and thumb and said he was not dead but half choked. So they wrapped him in cotton wool, and warmed him over a little fire, and he opened his eyes and sneezed.

6 "Now," said the big man (he was an Englishman who had just moved into the bungalow), "don't frighten him, and we'll see what he'll do."

7   It is the hardest thing in the world to frighten a mongoose, because he is eaten up from nose to tail with curiosity. The motto of all the mongoose family is "Run and find out," and Rikki-tikki was a true mongoose. He looked at the cotton wool, decided that it was not good to eat, ran all round the table, sat up and put his fur in order, scratched himself, and jumped on the small boy's shoulder.

8   "Don't be frightened, Teddy," said his father. "That's his way of making friends."

9   "Ouch! He's tickling under my chin," said Teddy.

10 Rikki-tikki looked down between the boy's collar and neck, snuffed at his ear, and climbed down to the floor, where he sat rubbing his nose.

11 "Good gracious," said Teddy's mother, "and that's a wild creature! I suppose he's so tame because we've been kind to him."

12 "All mongooses are like that," said her husband. "If Teddy doesn't pick him up by the tail, or try to put him in a cage, he'll run in and out of the house all day long. Let's give him something to eat."

13 They gave him a little piece of raw meat. Rikki-tikki liked it immensely, and when it was finished he went out into the veranda and sat in the sunshine and fluffed up his fur to make it dry to the roots. Then he felt better.

14   "There are more things to find out about in this house," he said to himself, "than all my family could find out in all their lives. I shall certainly stay and find out."

15 He spent all that day roaming over the house. He nearly drowned himself in the bath-tubs, put his nose into the ink on a writing table, and burned it on the end of the big man's cigar, for he climbed up in the big man's lap to see how writing was done. At nightfall he ran into Teddy's nursery to watch how kerosene lamps were lighted, and when Teddy went to bed Rikki-tikki climbed up too. But he was a restless companion, because he had to get up and attend to every noise all through the night, and find out what made it. Teddy's mother and father came in, the last thing, to look at their boy, and Rikki-tikki was awake on the pillow. "I don't like that," said Teddy's mother. "He may bite the child." "He'll do no such thing," said the father. "Teddy's safer with that little beast than if he had a bloodhound to watch him. If a snake came into the nursery now—"

16 But Teddy's mother wouldn't think of anything so awful.

17 Early in the morning Rikki-tikki came to early breakfast in the veranda riding on Teddy's shoulder, and they gave him banana and some boiled egg. He sat

NOTES

on all their laps one after the other, because every well-brought-up mongoose always hopes to be a house mongoose some day and have rooms to run about in; and Rikki-tikki's mother (she used to live in the general's house at Segowlee) had carefully told Rikki what to do if ever he came across white men.

18 Then Rikki-tikki went out into the garden to see what was to be seen. It was a large garden, only half cultivated, with bushes, as big as summer-houses, of Marshal Niel roses, lime and orange trees, clumps of bamboos, and thickets of high grass. Rikki-tikki licked his lips. "This is a splendid hunting-ground," he said, and his tail grew bottle-brushy at the thought of it, and he scuttled up and down the garden, snuffing here and there till he heard very sorrowful voices in a thorn-bush.

19 It was Darzee, the Tailorbird, and his wife. They had made a beautiful nest by pulling two big leaves together and stitching them up the edges with fibers, and had filled the hollow with cotton and downy fluff. The nest swayed to and fro, as they sat on the rim and cried.

20 "What is the matter?" asked Rikki-tikki.

21 "We are very miserable," said Darzee. "One of our babies fell out of the nest yesterday and Nag ate him."

22 "H'm!" said Rikki-tikki, "that is very sad—but I am a stranger here. Who is Nag?"

23 Darzee and his wife only cowered down in the nest without answering, for from the thick grass at the foot of the bush there came a low hiss—a horrid cold sound that made Rikki-tikki jump back two clear feet. Then inch by inch out of the grass rose up the head and spread hood of Nag, the big black cobra, and he was five feet long from tongue to tail. When he had lifted one-third of himself clear of the ground, he stayed balancing to and fro exactly as a dandelion tuft balances in the wind, and he looked at Rikki-tikki with the wicked snake's eyes that never change their expression, whatever the snake may be thinking of.

24 "Who is Nag?" said he. "I am Nag. The great God Brahm put his mark upon all our people, when the first cobra spread his hood to keep the sun off Brahm as he slept. Look, and be afraid!"

25 He spread out his hood more than ever, and Rikki-tikki saw the spectacle-mark on the back of it that looks exactly like the eye part of a hook-and-eye fastening. He was afraid for the minute, but it is impossible for a mongoose to stay frightened for any length of time, and though Rikki-tikki had never met a live cobra before, his mother had fed him on dead ones, and he knew that all a

Copyright © BookheadEd Learning, LLC

grown mongoose's business in life was to fight and eat snakes. Nag knew that too and, at the bottom of his cold heart, he was afraid.

26   "Well," said Rikki-tikki, and his tail began to fluff up again, "marks or no marks, do you think it is right for you to eat fledglings out of a nest?"

27   Nag was thinking to himself, and watching the least little movement in the grass behind Rikki-tikki. He knew that mongooses in the garden meant death sooner or later for him and his family, but he wanted to get Rikki-tikki off his guard. So he dropped his head a little, and put it on one side.

28   "Let us talk," he said. "You eat eggs. Why should not I eat birds?"

29   "Behind you! Look behind you!" sang Darzee.

30   Rikki-tikki knew better than to waste time in staring. He jumped up in the air as high as he could go, and just under him whizzed by the head of Nagaina, Nag's wicked wife. She had crept up behind him as he was talking, to make an end of him. He heard her savage hiss as the stroke missed. He came down almost across her back, and if he had been an old mongoose he would have known that then was the time to break her back with one bite; but he was afraid of the terrible lashing return stroke of the cobra. He bit, indeed, but did not bite long enough, and he jumped clear of the whisking tail, leaving Nagaina torn and angry.

31   "Wicked, wicked Darzee!" said Nag, lashing up as high as he could reach toward the nest in the thorn-bush. But Darzee had built it out of reach of snakes, and it only swayed to and fro.

32   Rikki-tikki felt his eyes growing red and hot (when a mongoose's eyes grow red, he is angry), and he sat back on his tail and hind legs like a little kangaroo, and looked all round him, and chattered with rage. But Nag and Nagaina had disappeared into the grass. When a snake misses its stroke, it never says anything or gives any sign of what it means to do next. Rikki-tikki did not care to follow them, for he did not feel sure that he could manage two snakes at once. So he trotted off to the gravel path near the house, and sat down to think. It was a serious matter for him.

33   If you read the old books of natural history, you will find they say that when the mongoose fights the snake and happens to get bitten, he runs off and eats some herb that cures him. That is not true. The victory is only a matter of quickness of eye and quickness of foot—snake's blow against mongoose's jump—and as no eye can follow the motion of a snake's head when it strikes, this makes things much more wonderful than any magic herb. Rikki-tikki knew he was a young mongoose, and it made him all the more pleased to think that he had managed to escape a blow from behind. It gave him confidence in

NOTES

himself, and when Teddy came running down the path, Rikki-tikki was ready to be petted.

34   But just as Teddy was stooping, something wriggled a little in the dust, and a tiny voice said: "Be careful. I am Death!" It was Karait, the dusty brown snakeling that lies for choice on the dusty earth; and his bite is as dangerous as the cobra's. But he is so small that nobody thinks of him, and so he does the more harm to people.

35   Rikki-tikki's eyes grew red again, and he danced up to Karait with the peculiar rocking, swaying motion that he had inherited from his family. It looks very funny, but it is so perfectly balanced a gait that you can fly off from it at any angle you please, and in dealing with snakes this is an advantage. If Rikki-tikki had only known, he was doing a much more dangerous thing than fighting Nag, for Karait is so small, and can turn so quickly, that unless Rikki bit him close to the back of the head, he would get the return stroke in his eye or his lip. But Rikki did not know. His eyes were all red, and he rocked back and forth, looking for a good place to hold. Karait struck out. Rikki jumped sideways and tried to run in, but the wicked little dusty gray head lashed within a fraction of his shoulder, and he had to jump over the body, and the head followed his heels close.

36   Teddy shouted to the house: "Oh, look here! Our mongoose is killing a snake." And Rikki-tikki heard a scream from Teddy's mother. His father ran out with a stick, but by the time he came up, Karait had lunged out once too far, and Rikki-tikki had sprung, jumped on the snake's back, dropped his head far between his forelegs, bitten as high up the back as he could get hold, and rolled away. That bite paralyzed Karait, and Rikki-tikki was just going to eat him up from the tail, after the custom of his family at dinner, when he remembered that a full meal makes a slow mongoose, and if he wanted all his strength and quickness ready, he must keep himself thin.

37   He went away for a dust bath under the castor-oil bushes, while Teddy's father beat the dead Karait. "What is the use of that?" thought Rikki-tikki. "I have settled it all;" and then Teddy's mother picked him up from the dust and hugged him, crying that he had saved Teddy from death, and Teddy's father said that he was a **providence,** and Teddy looked on with big scared eyes. Rikki-tikki was rather amused at all the fuss, which, of course, he did not understand. Teddy's mother might just as well have petted Teddy for playing in the dust. Rikki was thoroughly enjoying himself.

38   That night at dinner, walking to and fro among the wine-glasses on the table, he might have stuffed himself three times over with nice things. But he remembered Nag and Nagaina, and though it was very pleasant to be patted and petted by Teddy's mother, and to sit on Teddy's shoulder, his eyes would

get red from time to time, and he would go off into his long war cry of "Rikk-tikk-tikki-tikki-tchk!"

39   Teddy carried him off to bed, and insisted on Rikki-tikki sleeping under his chin. Rikki-tikki was too well bred to bite or scratch, but as soon as Teddy was asleep he went off for his nightly walk round the house, and in the dark he ran up against Chuchundra, the musk-rat, creeping around by the wall. Chuchundra is a broken-hearted little beast. He whimpers and cheeps all the night, trying to make up his mind to run into the middle of the room. But he never gets there.

40   "Don't kill me," said Chuchundra, almost weeping. "Rikki-tikki, don't kill me!"

41   "Do you think a snake-killer kills muskrats?" said Rikki-tikki scornfully.

42   "Those who kill snakes get killed by snakes," said Chuchundra, more sorrowfully than ever. "And how am I to be sure that Nag won't mistake me for you some dark night?"

43   "There's not the least danger," said Rikki-tikki. "But Nag is in the garden, and I know you don't go there."

44   "My cousin Chua, the rat, told me--" said Chuchundra, and then he stopped.

45   "Told you what?"

46   "H'sh! Nag is everywhere, Rikki-tikki. You should have talked to Chua in the garden."

47   "I didn't—so you must tell me. Quick, Chuchundra, or I'll bite you!"

48   Chuchundra sat down and cried till the tears rolled off his whiskers. "I am a very poor man," he sobbed. "I never had spirit enough to run out into the middle of the room. H'sh! I mustn't tell you anything. Can't you hear, Rikki-tikki?"

49   Rikki-tikki listened. The house was as still as still, but he thought he could just catch the faintest scratch-scratch in the world--a noise as faint as that of a wasp walking on a window-pane--the dry scratch of a snake's scales on brick-work.

50   "That's Nag or Nagaina," he said to himself, "and he is crawling into the bath-room sluice. You're right, Chuchundra; I should have talked to Chua."

51   He stole off to Teddy's bath-room, but there was nothing there, and then to Teddy's mother's bathroom. At the bottom of the smooth plaster wall there was a brick pulled out to make a sluice for the bath water, and as Rikki-tikki

stole in by the masonry curb where the bath is put, he heard Nag and Nagaina whispering together outside in the moonlight.

52 "When the house is emptied of people," said Nagaina to her husband, "he will have to go away, and then the garden will be our own again. Go in quietly, and remember that the big man who killed Karait is the first one to bite. Then come out and tell me, and we will hunt for Rikki-tikki together."

53 "But are you sure that there is anything to be gained by killing the people?" said Nag.

54 "Everything. When there were no people in the bungalow, did we have any mongoose in the garden? So long as the bungalow is empty, we are king and queen of the garden; and remember that as soon as our eggs in the melon bed hatch (as they may tomorrow), our children will need room and quiet."

55 "I had not thought of that," said Nag. "I will go, but there is no need that we should hunt for Rikki-tikki afterward. I will kill the big man and his wife, and the child if I can, and come away quietly. Then the bungalow will be empty, and Rikki-tikki will go."

56 Rikki-tikki tingled all over with rage and hatred at this, and then Nag's head came through the sluice, and his five feet of cold body followed it. Angry as he was, Rikki-tikki was very frightened as he saw the size of the big cobra. Nag coiled himself up, raised his head, and looked into the bathroom in the dark, and Rikki could see his eyes glitter.

57 "Now, if I kill him here, Nagaina will know; and if I fight him on the open floor, the odds are in his favor. What am I to do?" said Rikki-tikki-tavi.

58 Nag waved to and fro, and then Rikki-tikki heard him drinking from the biggest water-jar that was used to fill the bath. "That is good," said the snake. "Now, when Karait was killed, the big man had a stick. He may have that stick still, but when he comes in to bathe in the morning he will not have a stick. I shall wait here till he comes. Nagaina—do you hear me?—I shall wait here in the cool till daytime."

59 There was no answer from outside, so Rikki-tikki knew Nagaina had gone away. Nag coiled himself down, coil by coil, round the bulge at the bottom of the water jar, and Rikki-tikki stayed still as death. After an hour he began to move, muscle by muscle, toward the jar. Nag was asleep, and Rikki-tikki looked at his big back, wondering which would be the best place for a good hold. "If I don't break his back at the first jump," said Rikki, "he can still fight. And if he fights—O Rikki!" He looked at the thickness of the neck below the hood, but that was too much for him; and a bite near the tail would only make Nag savage.

60 "It must be the head"' he said at last; "the head above the hood. And, when I am once there, I must not let go."

61 Then he jumped. The head was lying a little clear of the water jar, under the curve of it; and, as his teeth met, Rikki braced his back against the bulge of the red earthenware to hold down the head. This gave him just one second's purchase, and he made the most of it. Then he was battered to and fro as a rat is shaken by a dog—to and fro on the floor, up and down, and around in great circles, but his eyes were red and he held on as the body cart-whipped over the floor, upsetting the tin dipper and the soap dish and the flesh brush, and banged against the tin side of the bath. As he held he closed his jaws tighter and tighter, for he made sure he would be banged to death, and, for the honor of his family, he preferred to be found with his teeth locked. He was dizzy, aching, and felt shaken to pieces when something went off like a thunderclap just behind him. A hot wind knocked him senseless and red fire singed his fur. The big man had been wakened by the noise, and had fired both barrels of a shotgun into Nag just behind the hood.

62 Rikki-tikki held on with his eyes shut, for now he was quite sure he was dead. But the head did not move, and the big man picked him up and said, "It's the mongoose again, Alice. The little chap has saved our lives now."

63 Then Teddy's mother came in with a very white face, and saw what was left of Nag, and Rikki-tikki dragged himself to Teddy's bedroom and spent half the rest of the night shaking himself tenderly to find out whether he really was broken into forty pieces, as he fancied.

64 When morning came he was very stiff, but well pleased with his doings. "Now I have Nagaina to settle with, and she will be worse than five Nags, and there's no knowing when the eggs she spoke of will hatch. Goodness! I must go and see Darzee," he said.

65 Without waiting for breakfast, Rikki-tikki ran to the thornbush where Darzee was singing a song of triumph at the top of his voice. The news of Nag's death was all over the garden, for the sweeper had thrown the body on the rubbish-heap.

66 "Oh, you stupid tuft of feathers!" said Rikki-tikki angrily. "Is this the time to sing?"

67 "Nag is dead—is dead—is dead!" sang Darzee. "The **valiant** Rikki-tikki caught him by the head and held fast. The big man brought the bang-stick, and Nag fell in two pieces! He will never eat my babies again."

68 "All that's true enough. But where's Nagaina?" said Rikki-tikki, looking carefully round him.

69   "Nagaina came to the bathroom sluice and called for Nag," Darzee went on, "and Nag came out on the end of a stick—the sweeper picked him up on the end of a stick and threw him upon the rubbish heap. Let us sing about the great, the red-eyed Rikki-tikki!" And Darzee filled his throat and sang.

70   "If I could get up to your nest, I'd roll your babies out!" said Rikki-tikki. "You don't know when to do the right thing at the right time. You're safe enough in your nest there, but it's war for me down here. Stop singing a minute, Darzee."

71   "For the great, the beautiful Rikki-tikki's sake I will stop," said Darzee. "What is it, O Killer of the terrible Nag?"

72   "Where is Nagaina, for the third time?"

73   "On the rubbish heap by the stables, mourning for Nag. Great is Rikki-tikki with the white teeth."

74   "Bother my white teeth! Have you ever heard where she keeps her eggs?"

75   "In the melon bed, on the end nearest the wall, where the sun strikes nearly all day. She hid them there weeks ago."

76   "And you never thought it worth while to tell me? The end nearest the wall, you said?"

77   "Rikki-tikki, you are not going to eat her eggs?"

78   "Not eat exactly; no. Darzee, if you have a grain of sense you will fly off to the stables and pretend that your wing is broken, and let Nagaina chase you away to this bush. I must get to the melon-bed, and if I went there now she'd see me."

79   Darzee was a feather-brained little fellow who could never hold more than one idea at a time in his head. And just because he knew that Nagaina's children were born in eggs like his own, he didn't think at first that it was fair to kill them. But his wife was a sensible bird, and she knew that cobra's eggs meant young cobras later on. So she flew off from the nest, and left Darzee to keep the babies warm, and continue his song about the death of Nag. Darzee was very like a man in some ways.

80   She fluttered in front of Nagaina by the rubbish heap and cried out, "Oh, my wing is broken! The boy in the house threw a stone at me and broke it." Then she fluttered more desperately than ever.

81　Nagaina lifted up her head and hissed, "You warned Rikki-tikki when I would have killed him. Indeed and truly, you've chosen a bad place to be lame in." And she moved toward Darzee's wife, slipping along over the dust.

82　"The boy broke it with a stone!" shrieked Darzee's wife.

83　"Well! It may be some **consolation** to you when you're dead to know that I shall settle accounts with the boy. My husband lies on the rubbish heap this morning, but before night the boy in the house will lie very still. What is the use of running away? I am sure to catch you. Little fool, look at me!"

84　Darzee's wife knew better than to do that, for a bird who looks at a snake's eyes gets so frightened that she cannot move. Darzee's wife fluttered on, piping sorrowfully, and never leaving the ground, and Nagaina quickened her pace.

85　Rikki-tikki heard them going up the path from the stables, and he raced for the end of the melon patch near the wall. There, in the warm litter above the melons, very cunningly hidden, he found twenty-five eggs, about the size of a bantam's eggs, but with whitish skin instead of shell.

86　"I was not a day too soon," he said, for he could see the baby cobras curled up inside the skin, and he knew that the minute they were hatched they could each kill a man or a mongoose. He bit off the tops of the eggs as fast as he could, taking care to crush the young cobras, and turned over the litter from time to time to see whether he had missed any. At last there were only three eggs left, and Rikki-tikki began to chuckle to himself, when he heard Darzee's wife screaming:

87　"Rikki-tikki, I led Nagaina toward the house, and she has gone into the veranda, and—oh, come quickly—she means killing!"

88　Rikki-tikki smashed two eggs, and tumbled backward down the melon-bed with the third egg in his mouth, and scuttled to the veranda as hard as he could put foot to the ground. Teddy and his mother and father were there at early breakfast, but Rikki-tikki saw that they were not eating anything. They sat stone-still, and their faces were white. Nagaina was coiled up on the matting by Teddy's chair, within easy striking distance of Teddy's bare leg, and she was swaying to and fro, singing a song of triumph.

89　"Son of the big man that killed Nag," she hissed, "stay still. I am not ready yet. Wait a little. Keep very still, all you three! If you move I strike, and if you do not move I strike. Oh, foolish people, who killed my Nag!"

90　Teddy's eyes were fixed on his father, and all his father could do was to whisper, "Sit still, Teddy. You mustn't move. Teddy, keep still."

NOTES

91   Then Rikki-tikki came up and cried, "Turn round, Nagaina. Turn and fight!"

92   "All in good time," said she, without moving her eyes. "I will settle my account with you presently. Look at your friends, Rikki-tikki. They are still and white. They are afraid. They dare not move, and if you come a step nearer I strike."

93   "Look at your eggs," said Rikki-tikki, "in the melon bed near the wall. Go and look, Nagaina!"

94   The big snake turned half around, and saw the egg on the veranda. "Ah-h! Give it to me," she said.

95   Rikki-tikki put his paws one on each side of the egg, and his eyes were blood-red. "What price for a snake's egg? For a young cobra? For a young king cobra? For the last—the very last of the brood? The ants are eating all the others down by the melon bed."

96   Nagaina spun clear round, forgetting everything for the sake of the one egg. Rikki-tikki saw Teddy's father shoot out a big hand, catch Teddy by the shoulder, and drag him across the little table with the tea-cups, safe and out of reach of Nagaina.

97   "Tricked! Tricked! Tricked! Rikk-tck-tck!" chuckled Rikki-tikki. "The boy is safe, and it was I—I—I that caught Nag by the hood last night in the bathroom." Then he began to jump up and down, all four feet together, his head close to the floor. "He threw me to and fro, but he could not shake me off. He was dead before the big man blew him in two. I did it! Rikki-tikki-tck-tck! Come then, Nagaina. Come and fight with me. You shall not be a widow long."

98   Nagaina saw that she had lost her chance of killing Teddy, and the egg lay between Rikki-tikki's paws. "Give me the egg, Rikki-tikki. Give me the last of my eggs, and I will go away and never come back," she said, lowering her hood.

99   "Yes, you will go away, and you will never come back. For you will go to the rubbish heap with Nag. Fight, widow! The big man has gone for his gun! Fight!"

100   Rikki-tikki was bounding all round Nagaina, keeping just out of reach of her stroke, his little eyes like hot coals. Nagaina gathered herself together and flung out at him. Rikki-tikki jumped up and backward. Again and again and again she struck, and each time her head came with a whack on the matting of the veranda and she gathered herself together like a watch spring. Then Rikki-tikki danced in a circle to get behind her, and Nagaina spun round to keep her head to his head, so that the rustle of her tail on the matting sounded like dry leaves blown along by the wind.

101 He had forgotten the egg. It still lay on the veranda, and Nagaina came nearer and nearer to it, till at last, while Rikki-tikki was drawing breath, she caught it in her mouth, turned to the veranda steps, and flew like an arrow down the path, with Rikki-tikki behind her. When the cobra runs for her life, she goes like a whip-lash flicked across a horse's neck.

102 Rikki-tikki knew that he must catch her, or all the trouble would begin again. She headed straight for the long grass by the thorn-bush, and as he was running Rikki-tikki heard Darzee still singing his foolish little song of triumph. But Darzee's wife was wiser. She flew off her nest as Nagaina came along, and flapped her wings about Nagaina's head. If Darzee had helped they might have turned her, but Nagaina only lowered her hood and went on. Still, the instant's delay brought Rikki-tikki up to her, and as she plunged into the rat-hole where she and Nag used to live, his little white teeth were clenched on her tail, and he went down with her—and very few mongooses, however wise and old they may be, care to follow a cobra into its hole. It was dark in the hole; and Rikki-tikki never knew when it might open out and give Nagaina room to turn and strike at him. He held on savagely, and stuck out his feet to act as brakes on the dark slope of the hot, moist earth.

103 Then the grass by the mouth of the hole stopped waving, and Darzee said, "It is all over with Rikki-tikki! We must sing his death song. Valiant Rikki-tikki is dead! For Nagaina will surely kill him underground."

104 So he sang a very mournful song that he made up on the spur of the minute, and just as he got to the most touching part, the grass quivered again, and Rikki-tikki, covered with dirt, dragged himself out of the hole leg by leg, licking his whiskers. Darzee stopped with a little shout. Rikki-tikki shook some of the dust out of his fur and sneezed. "It is all over," he said. "The widow will never come out again." And the red ants that live between the grass stems heard him, and began to troop down one after another to see if he had spoken the truth. Rikki-tikki curled himself up in the grass and slept where he was--slept and slept till it was late in the afternoon, for he had done a hard day's work.

105 "Now," he said, when he awoke, "I will go back to the house. Tell the Coppersmith, Darzee, and he will tell the garden that Nagaina is dead."

106 The Coppersmith is a bird who makes a noise exactly like the beating of a little hammer on a copper pot; and the reason he is always making it is because he is the town crier to every Indian garden, and tells all the news to everybody who cares to listen. As Rikki-tikki went up the path, he heard his "attention" notes like a tiny dinner gong, and then the steady "Ding-dong-tock! Nag is dead—dong! Nagaina is dead! Ding-dong-tock!" That set all the birds in the garden singing, and the frogs croaking, for Nag and Nagaina used to eat frogs as well as little birds.

107 When Rikki got to the house, Teddy and Teddy's mother (she looked very white still, for she had been fainting) and Teddy's father came out and almost cried over him; and that night he ate all that was given him till he could eat no more, and went to bed on Teddy's shoulder, where Teddy's mother saw him when she came to look late at night.

108 "He saved our lives and Teddy's life," she said to her husband. "Just think, he saved all our lives."

109 Rikki-tikki woke up with a jump, for the mongooses are light sleepers.

110 "Oh, it's you," said he. "What are you bothering for? All the cobras are dead. And if they weren't, I'm here."

111 Rikki-tikki had a right to be proud of himself. But he did not grow too proud, and he kept that garden as a mongoose should keep it, with tooth and jump and spring and bite, till never a cobra dared show its head inside the walls.

 THINK QUESTIONS

1. How did Rikki-tikki-tavi come to live with the English family? Cite specific evidence from the text to support your answer.

2. How effectively does the description of Nag in paragraph 23 evoke the image that he is a snake to be feared? Cite specific evidence from the text to support your answer.

3. What can you infer about Rikki-tikki's character by the fact that he has saved the family three times from snakes? How might his character and actions help readers infer the theme? Cite specific evidence from the text to support your inference.

4. Use context to determine the meaning of the word **valiant** as it is used in paragraph 67 of "Rikki-Tikki-Tavi." Write your definition of "valiant" and tell how you determined the meaning of the word.

5. By remembering that the Latin prefix *con-* means "with," the root *sol* means "comfort," and the suffix *-ation* means "the act of," how do the Latin prefix, root, and suffix provide clues to the meaning of **consolation?** Write your definition of "consolation" and tell how you figured out its meaning.

CLOSE READ

Reread the story "Rikki-Tikki-Tavi." As you reread, complete the Focus Questions below. Then use your answers and annotations from the questions to help you complete the Writing Prompt.

FOCUS QUESTIONS

1. As you reread "Rikki-Tikki-Tavi," highlight the words "frighten" and "frightened" as they are used in paragraphs 6–8 in the text. How does the repetition of the word indicate that fear or overcoming fear may be a clue to the main theme of the story? Make annotations outlining your ideas.

2. How does Rikki-tikki behave like a young child in paragraph 17? What might his behavior suggest about how he might change by the end of the story? Highlight words and phrases in the text that support your response. Make annotations to record your ideas.

3. Why does Darzee sing a death song when Rikki-tikki goes into Nagaina's burrow to try to kill her? What effect does the song have on the reader's expectation of what might happen to Rikki-tikki? Highlight evidence in the text to support your ideas, and make annotations to summarize your response.

4. Why is Rikki-tikki proud of himself in the last paragraph of the story? How does the last paragraph express how much he has grown up? Highlight the reasons for his proud feelings, as expressed by Teddy's mother. Make annotations listing some adjectives in a two-column chart to describe how Rikki-tikki was at the beginning of the story and how he has grown at the end. Use a print or digital dictionary to determine or clarify the precise meaning of each word and its part of speech as an adjective before you list it in the chart.

5. Why is Rikki-tikki so determined to undertake the mission of destroying Nag and Nagaina? What "big idea" or theme do his actions suggest? Highlight specific evidence from the text to support your statement of the theme. Then make annotations stating the theme in a few brief words.

WRITING PROMPT

A coming-of-age story focuses on the central idea or theme of a young person growing and changing by solving a problem, undertaking a mission, or accomplishing a goal. How could "Rikki-Tikki-Tavi" be considered a coming-of-age story? What problem does he solve, mission does he undertake, or goal does he accomplish by the end of the story? Cite specific evidence from the text to convey how his thoughts and actions change over the course of the text to demonstrate that he has grown up at the end.

Please note that excerpts and passages in the StudySync® library and this workbook are intended as touchstones to generate interest in an author's work. The excerpts and passages do not substitute for the reading of entire texts, and StudySync® strongly recommends that students seek out and purchase the whole literary or informational work in order to experience it as the author intended. Links to online resellers are available in our digital library. In addition, complete works may be ordered through an authorized reseller by filling out and returning to StudySync® the order form enclosed in this workbook.

Reading & Writing Companion 75

THE CALL OF THE WILD

FICTION
Jack London
1903

INTRODUCTION

studysync tv

Author Jack London (1876–1916) was a turn-of-the-century writer and adventurer, beginning his life on the San Francisco Bay, then travelling the world—seal hunting in the Far East, mucking for gold in the Yukon Territory, sailing the South Pacific, and more. While participating in the Klondike Gold Rush, he reportedly encountered a mythical wolf that served as the inspiration for *The Call of the Wild*, his most popular novel. The book details the adventures of Buck, a large and powerful St. Bernard mix, as he experiences both love and abuse from a succession of owners. In this excerpt, Buck, by now a sled-dog, stirs up rebellion among the team when he stands up to the aggressive alpha dog, Spitz.

"There is an ecstasy that marks the summit of life, and beyond which life cannot rise."

 ## FIRST READ

From Chapter III, The Dominant Primordial Beast

1 They made Sixty Mile, which is a fifty-mile run, on the first day; and the second day saw them booming up the Yukon well on their way to Pelly. But such splendid running was achieved not without great trouble and vexation on the part of Francois. The insidious revolt led by Buck had destroyed the **solidarity** of the team. It no longer was as one dog leaping in the traces. The encouragement Buck gave the rebels led them into all kinds of petty **misdemeanors**. No more was Spitz a leader greatly to be feared. The old awe departed, and they grew equal to challenging his authority. Pike robbed him of half a fish one night, and gulped it down under the protection of Buck. Another night Dub and Joe fought Spitz and made him forego the punishment they deserved. And even Billee, the good-natured, was less good-natured, and whined not half so **placatingly** as in former days. Buck never came near Spitz without snarling and bristling menacingly. In fact, his conduct approached that of a bully, and he was given to swaggering up and down before Spitz's very nose.

2 The breaking down of discipline likewise affected the dogs in their relations with one another. They quarrelled and bickered more than ever among themselves, till at times the camp was a howling bedlam. Dave and Sol-leks alone were unaltered, though they were made irritable by the unending squabbling. Francois swore strange barbarous oaths, and stamped the snow in futile rage, and tore his hair. His lash was always singing among the dogs, but it was of small avail. Directly his back was turned they were at it again. He backed up Spitz with his whip, while Buck backed up the remainder of the team. Francois knew he was behind all the trouble, and Buck knew he knew; but Buck was too clever ever again to be caught red-handed. He worked faithfully in the harness, for the toil had become a delight to him; yet it was a greater delight slyly to **precipitate** a fight amongst his mates and tangle the traces.

3　At the mouth of the Tahkeena, one night after supper, Dub turned up a snowshoe rabbit, blundered it, and missed. In a second the whole team was in full cry. A hundred yards away was a camp of the Northwest Police, with fifty dogs, huskies all, who joined the chase. The rabbit sped down the river, turned off into a small creek, up the frozen bed of which it held steadily. It ran lightly on the surface of the snow, while the dogs ploughed through by main strength. Buck led the pack, sixty strong, around bend after bend, but he could not gain. He lay down low to the race, whining eagerly, his splendid body flashing forward, leap by leap, in the wan white moonlight. And leap by leap, like some pale frost wraith, the snowshoe rabbit flashed on ahead.

4　All that stirring of old instincts which at stated periods drives men out from the sounding cities to forest and plain to kill things by chemically propelled leaden pellets, the blood lust, the joy to kill--all this was Buck's, only it was infinitely more intimate. He was ranging at the head of the pack, running the wild thing down, the living meat, to kill with his own teeth and wash his muzzle to the eyes in warm blood.

5　There is an **ecstasy** that marks the summit of life, and beyond which life cannot rise. And such is the paradox of living, this ecstasy comes when one is most alive, and it comes as a complete forgetfulness that one is alive. This ecstasy, this forgetfulness of living, comes to the artist, caught up and out of himself in a sheet of flame; it comes to the soldier, war-mad on a stricken field and refusing quarter; and it came to Buck, leading the pack, sounding the old wolf-cry, straining after the food that was alive and that fled swiftly before him through the moonlight. He was sounding the deeps of his nature, and of the parts of his nature that were deeper than he, going back into the womb of Time. He was mastered by the sheer surging of life, the tidal wave of being, the perfect joy of each separate muscle, joint, and sinew in that it was everything that was not death, that it was aglow and rampant, expressing itself in movement, flying exultantly under the stars and over the face of dead matter that did not move.

THINK QUESTIONS

1. Refer to several details in the first paragraph to explain how Buck "destroyed the solidarity of the team." Cite evidence that is directly stated in the text, and also make inferences to support your explanation.

2. What evidence is there in paragraph 2 that Buck took pleasure in causing trouble for Francois? Cite specific evidence from the text.

3. How did Buck react when Dub turned up a snowshoe rabbit? What inferences can you make about Buck from his behavior? Support your answer with specific evidence from the text.

4. Use context to determine the meaning of the word **misdemeanors** as it is used in the first paragraph of *The Call of the Wild*. Write your definition of "misdemeanors" and tell how you determined the meaning of the word. Then check your definition in a print or digital dictionary to confirm the word's meaning.

5. By understanding that the Latin word *placare* means "to calm down" or "appease," use the context clues provided in the first paragraph to determine the meaning of **placatingly.** Write your definition of "placatingly" and tell how you determined the meaning of the word.

Please note that excerpts and passages in the StudySync® library and this workbook are intended as touchstones to generate interest in an author's work. The excerpts and passages do not substitute for the reading of entire texts, and StudySync® strongly recommends that students seek out and purchase the whole literary or informational work in order to experience it as the author intended. Links to online resellers are available in our digital library. In addition, complete works may be ordered through an authorized reseller by filling out and returning to StudySync® the order form enclosed in this workbook.

Reading & Writing Companion

79

CLOSE READ

Reread the excerpt from *The Call of the Wild*. As you reread, complete the Focus Questions below. Then use your answers and annotations from the questions to help you complete the Writing Prompt.

FOCUS QUESTIONS

1. Listen to the audio recording of the first part of paragraph 2 (1:08–1:41). How does the actor (or speaker) use expression and intonation when he describes Francois' reaction to the the dogs' "unending squabbling"? Highlight textual evidence in paragraph 2 and annotate ideas from the audio recording to show the development of your understanding of media techniques.

2. Listen to the second part of the audio recording of paragraph 2 (1:42–2:00). How does the actor use expression and intonation to help listeners understand Francois' relationship with Buck? Highlight textual evidence in paragraph 2 and annotate ideas from the audio recording to show the development of your understanding of media techniques.

3. Listen to the audio recording of the second half of paragraph 3 (2:29–2:52). How does the actor use expression and pacing to convey Buck's pursuit of the snowshoe rabbit? Highlight textual evidence in paragraph 3 and annotate ideas from the audio recording to show the development of your understanding of media techniques.

4. Reread the last paragraph of the excerpt and then listen to the audio recording of the same paragraph. Use details from the audio version and the printed text to explain what the actor in the audio adds to the reader's understanding of the paragraph.

5. How does Buck's story help readers understand what drives individuals to undertake a mission? Highlight textual evidence and make annotations to support your response.

WRITING PROMPT

Compare and contrast the text and the audio versions of *The Call of the Wild*. Begin with a clear thesis statement that sets the direction for the rest of your writing. How are the two media alike, and how are they different? At what points does the audio version use expression, intonation, and /or pace to support or interpret the text? In what ways do these interpretations help to develop character, setting, plot, and theme? Using precise language and selection vocabulary, support your writing with evidence from the text and the audio file. Use transitions to show the relationships among your ideas. Present your information with a formal style. Summarize your main points in a conclusion that supports the ideas you have presented.

NOTES

INFORMATIVE/ EXPLANATORY WRITING

WRITING PROMPT

You have been reading nonfiction accounts of the lives and experiences of real people who have undertaken a mission to pursue their goals. You have also been reading fictional stories of adventure—and of characters who have also undertaken missions, often while facing great personal risk. Now you will think about the experiences of these people and characters as you write your own informative/explanatory essay.

Your essay should include:

- an introduction with a clear thesis statement, or central idea
- body paragraphs with relevant supporting details and a thorough analysis to support your thesis statement
- a conclusion that restates your thesis and summarizes your information

An **informative/explanatory essay** examines a specific topic and conveys relevant information about it in a logical way. Informative/explanatory writing can explain, compare, define, describe, and inform about a topic. Some examples of informative writing include: printed and online newspaper, magazine, and encyclopedia articles; how-to manuals; full-length books on history, science, or any nonfiction topic; travel essays; pamphlets and public-service announcements; and professional Web pages and blogs.

Strong informative writing introduces a central (or main) idea in the thesis statement, and develops that central idea with supporting details. The use of transition words or phrases helps to direct the flow of ideas and to make connections between supporting details. The conclusion of an informative/ explanatory essay should come from the facts and information presented earlier in the essay. Because this type of essay is informative or explanatory, the writing should be unbiased. In other words, the writer does not state his or her own opinion but presents ideas that are based in fact. A good way the

NOTES

writer can do this is by establishing a formal style of writing. One reason the writer should include citations of sources is so that readers can double-check the ideas in the supporting details.

The features of informative/explanatory writing include:

- an introduction with a clear thesis statement
- a logical organizational structure in body paragraphs, indicated by transitions, formatting, and text features
- relevant supporting details
- precise language
- the citation of sources
- a concluding statement

As you continue with this extended writing project, you'll receive more instructions and practice to help you craft each of the elements of informative/explanatory writing in your own essay.

 ## STUDENT MODEL

Before you get started on your own informative/explanatory essay, begin by reading this essay that one student wrote in response to the writing prompt. As you read this Student Model, highlight and annotate the features of informative/explanatory writing that the student included in the essay.

Worth the Risk

It is impossible to know what drives people to take risks, but people do crazy, often dangerous, things when they undertake a mission. For example, Stanley Pearce walked thirty miles through the snow to stake a mining claim. Farah Ahmedi climbed a mountain on a prosthetic leg to reach freedom. Annie Johnson started a business from nothing but an idea so that she could support her children and not have others care for them. These real people had different reasons for doing what they did. Pearce wanted to strike it rich, while Ahmedi and Johnson were determined to survive desperate circumstances; however, all three shared an ability to endure hardship to accomplish their goals.

Stanley Pearce

Call of the Klondike by David Meissner and Kim Richardson is a true account of the Klondike Gold Rush. The text is based on primary sources, including the diary

Please note that excerpts and passages in the StudySync® library and this workbook are intended as touchstones to generate interest in an author's work. The excerpts and passages do not substitute for the reading of entire texts, and StudySync® strongly recommends that students seek out and purchase the whole literary or informational work in order to experience it as the author intended. Links to online resellers are available in our digital library. In addition, complete works may be ordered through an authorized reseller by filling out and returning to StudySync® the order form enclosed in this workbook.

Reading & Writing Companion

83

of Stanley Pearce, a gold miner. The authors describe the hardships that Pearce and other miners faced to pursue their dream of striking it rich. After sixty-eight miners arrived in Seattle, Washington, in 1897, weighed down with bags of precious gold dust, gold fever erupted. According to Meissner and Richardson, Pearce wrote that "every man who could raise the necessary funds for a year's grub stake was rushing...to start by the next boat for the promised land, where the dreams of all should be realized." Pearce's diaries reveal that the Klondike was not the "promised land" after all. The climate was harsh, and the gold was not plentiful. As a consequence, many miners became "engaged on schemes to fleece the unsuspecting" newcomers out of their money. Others were so desperate that they responded to rumors of gold by stampeding. Pearce describes one stampede that cost people their lives because they were not prepared for the frigid weather. Pearce's own fate is not clear, but he grew wiser from his experiences.

Farah Ahmedi

Unlike Stanley Pearce, who voluntarily went to the Klondike in search of fortune, Farah Ahmedi and her mother found themselves in a dire situation through no fault of their own. They were Afghans living in a war-torn city, and their only hope was to escape to Pakistan. By the time Ahmedi and her mother made it to the border, Pakistan had closed its gates to refugees. Ahmedi and her mother were now stranded in the desert. The situation was desperate. But Ahmedi was determined, so she learned the secret to getting across the border. It was to bribe the guards, but Ahmedi and her mother had no money. Fortunately, Ahmedi made friends with another family. The father, Ghulam Ali, had learned about a smuggler's pass over the mountains. He agreed to take Ahmedi and her mother through the pass, even though they were strangers. The path was dark and steep. According to Ahmedi, although she wore a prosthetic leg, she "hardly felt the exertion" because of her "desperation." It gave her "energy" and made her "forget the rigor of the climb." Ahmedi learned a different lesson from that of Stanley Pearce. She discovered that even during a crisis, there were kind people like Ghulam Ali. He not only helped save Ahmedi's life, but he also gave her hope in humanity.

Annie Johnson

Like Farah Ahmedi, Annie Johnson was a woman with a family and a fierce survival instinct. As a divorced African American woman with two children, Annie Johnson found herself in need of a job. As her granddaughter Maya Angelou explained in

"New Directions," Johnson "decided to step off the road and cut me a new path." Instead of taking a job as a domestic or trying to get a job as a factory worker, Johnson devised an elaborate plan to cook meals for local mill and factory workers. Johnson's job was hard, and "business was slow," but she was determined to succeed in her mission. That meant "on balmy spring days, blistering summer noons, and cold, wet, and wintry middays," Johnson "never disappointed her customers." She planned her business carefully, and over time it grew into a successful store. Angelou credited her grandmother's drive and resolve for carrying her through hard times. She also suggested that Johnson's ability to handle only "unpalatable" choices with grace was the key to achieving her goals.

Pearce, Ahmedi, and Johnson all pursued their goals relentlessly and with good humor and grace, even when their situations became desperate. Pearce kept his common sense while others around him turned to schemes. Ahmedi managed to escape from a war-torn country. When she could not buy her way out of the situation, she found help from a compassionate man. Johnson became a successful businesswoman only after years of hard work. Each was driven to undertake a mission to become wealthy, to escape a war, to raise a family with dignity. Each had different levels of success, but all three learned from their experiences and passed the lessons along to those who came after them. We would all do well to learn from them.

 THINK QUESTIONS

1. How does the writer compare and contrast the information about the motivations and goals of the three real people in the Student Model? Why does the writer use subheads to help organize the information? Cite specific evidence from the Student Model to support your answer.

2. How well does the writer use supporting details, such as facts, examples, anecdotes, and quotations, to develop the topic of taking risks to accomplish a goal? Cite specific details from the Student Model to support your response.

3. Write two or three sentences evaluating the writer's ending, or conclusion. Use specific evidence from the last paragraph of the Student Model.

4. Think about the writing prompt. Which selections or other resources would you use to write your own informative essay about two of the selections from the unit? Which two texts would you use? What topic would you want to explore and analyze? Create a list of the texts you might use for your prompt. Next, choose two texts on your list and cite one topic from each that interests you.

5. Based on the selections you have read, listened to, or researched, how would you answer the question, *What makes stories about why people undertake a mission so interesting to readers?* Which people and missions might you analyze in the informative essay you will be developing? Write a short paragraph that explains your answer.

Please note that excerpts and passages in the StudySync® library and this workbook are intended as touchstones to generate interest in an author's work. The excerpts and passages do not substitute for the reading of entire texts, and StudySync® strongly recommends that students seek out and purchase the whole literary or informational work in order to experience it as the author intended. Links to online resellers are available in our digital library. In addition, complete works may be ordered through an authorized reseller by filling out and returning to StudySync® the order form enclosed in this workbook.

Reading & Writing Companion   85

NOTES

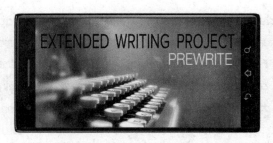

PREWRITE

WRITING PROMPT

You have been reading nonfiction accounts of the lives and experiences of real people who have undertaken a mission to pursue their goals. You have also been reading fictional stories of adventure—and of characters who have also undertaken missions, often while facing great personal risk. Now you will think about the experiences of these people and characters as you write your own informative/explanatory essay.

Your essay should include:

- an introduction with a clear thesis statement, or central idea
- body paragraphs with relevant supporting details and a thorough analysis to support your thesis statement
- a conclusion that restates your thesis and summarizes your information

You have been reading real and fictional stories about people and characters who have pursued their goals. In your extended writing project, you will explain how and why several of the people or characters from the unit texts drove themselves to undertake a mission. You will consider the steps they took to accomplish their mission to achieve their goals.

Because the topic of your informative/explanatory essay is about how and why people undertake a mission to pursue certain goals, you will want to consider the people and characters you have read about in the unit texts. Think about what their mission was and why they went after it. You might start by considering the experiences of Stanley Pearce, as described in *Call of the Klondike*. What was Pearce's goal? What drove him to pursue it? What steps did he take toward reaching his goal? How successful was Pearce? What, if anything, did he learn from undertaking his mission?

Make a list of the answers to these questions about Stanley Pearce and at least two other people or characters from other texts in the unit. As you write down your ideas, look for patterns that begin to emerge. Do the individuals' motivations or experiences have anything in common? Do you notice ideas or themes that are repeated? Looking for these patterns might help you form ideas to discuss in your own informative/explanatory essay. Use this model to help you get started with your own prewriting.

Text: *Call of the Klondike: A True Gold Rush Adventure,* by David Meissner and Kim Richardson

Person or Character: Stanley Pearce
Mission: To find gold and adventure in the Klondike
Motivation: To become rich
Steps Taken Toward Accomplishing Goal: Went to Klondike, staked a claim, endured hardship, lived through a "stampede"
Success at Accomplishing Goal: Not really; Pearce did not become wealthy because he did not find much gold.
What Person or Character Learned: Pearce became wise about how to survive in the frigid Klondike. He could have become a schemer or a thief, like many others, but he did not.

Please note that excerpts and passages in the StudySync® library and this workbook are intended as touchstones to generate interest in an author's work. The excerpts and passages do not substitute for the reading of entire texts, and StudySync® strongly recommends that students seek out and purchase the whole literary or informational work in order to experience it as the author intended. Links to online resellers are available in our digital library. In addition, complete works may be ordered through an authorized reseller by filling out and returning to StudySync® the order form enclosed in this workbook.

Reading & Writing
Companion

87

SKILL:
THESIS
STATEMENT

DEFINE

The **thesis statement** (or thesis) is the most important sentence in an informative/explanatory essay because it tells what the writer is going to say about the essay's topic. The thesis statement expresses the writer's central or main idea about that topic—the position the writer will develop in the body of the essay. The thesis statement usually appears in the essay's introductory paragraph and is often the introduction's first or last sentence. In some essays, the writer hints at the thesis indirectly in the opening paragraph because he or she wants readers to determine the central idea on their own, after reading the text. By doing so, the author shows that he or she trusts the readers to infer the main point by comprehending the details. Whether the thesis is stated directly or indirectly, all the paragraphs in the essay should support the thesis statement (or central idea) with supporting details.

IDENTIFICATION AND APPLICATION

A thesis statement:

- makes a clear statement about the writer's central (or main) idea
- lets the reader know what to expect in the body of the essay
- responds fully and completely to an essay prompt
- is stated—or hinted at indirectly—in the introduction

MODEL

The following is the introduction paragraph from the Student Model, "Worth the Risk":

It is impossible to know what drives people to take risks, but people do crazy, often dangerous, things when they undertake a mission. For example,

Copyright © BookheadEd Learning, LLC

NOTES

Stanley Pearce walked thirty miles through the snow to stake a mining claim. Farah Ahmedi climbed a mountain on a prosthetic leg to reach freedom. Annie Johnson started a business from nothing but an idea so that she could support her children and not have others care for them. These real people had different reasons for doing what they did. **Pearce wanted to strike it rich, while Ahmedi and Johnson were determined to survive desperate circumstances; however, all three shared an ability to endure hardship to accomplish their goals.**

Notice the boldfaced thesis statement. This student's thesis statement responds to the prompt. It tells readers about the topic of the essay—what Pearce, Ahmedi, and Johnson wanted, or what their goals were. It also specifically states the writer's central (or main) idea about that topic. The writer asserts that Pearce, Ahmedi, and Johnson, "shared an ability to endure hardship to accomplish their goals."

 PRACTICE

Write a thesis statement for your informative/explanatory essay that states your central idea in relation to the essay prompt. When you are finished, trade with a partner and offer each other constructive feedback. How clear is the writer's main point or idea? Is it obvious what this essay will focus on? Does it specifically address the writing prompt? Offer each other suggestions, and remember that your suggestions are most helpful when they are delivered with a positive attitude.

NOTES

Organize
INFORMATIVE
WRITING

sync skills
Writing

SKILL:
ORGANIZE
INFORMATIVE
WRITING

 ## DEFINE

The purpose of writing an informative/explanatory text is to inform readers. To do this effectively, writers need to organize and present their ideas, facts, details, and other information in a logical sequence that's easy to understand.

Experienced writers carefully choose an **organizational structure** that best suits their material. They often use an outline or another graphic organizer to determine which organizational (or text) structure will help them express their ideas effectively.

For example, scientific reports and studies often use a **cause-and-effect** text structure. This mirrors the information scientists need to relay—the experiment and the results of the experiment. Historians and writers of memoirs often use a **sequential** (or chronological) text structure, discussing events in the order in which they occurred. Other organizational structures include **problem and solution** and **compare and contrast.**

 ## IDENTIFICATION AND APPLICATION

- When selecting an organizational structure, writers must consider the purpose of their writing. They often ask themselves questions about the kind of information they are writing about. They might consider:
  - › "What is the central idea I'd like to convey?"
  - › "Would it make sense to relay events in the order they occurred?"
  - › "Is there a specific problem discussed in the texts? What solutions seem likely answers to the problem?"
  - › "Is there a natural cause and effect relationship in my information?"
  - › "Can I compare and contrast different events or individuals' responses to events?"
  - › "Am I teaching readers how to do something?"

- Writers often use word choice to create connections and transitions between ideas and to suggest the organizational structure being used:
  - › Sequential order: *first, next, then, finally, last, initially, ultimately*
  - › Cause and effect: *because, accordingly, as a result, effect, so*
  - › Compare and contrast: *like, unlike, also, both, similarly, although, while, but, however*

- Sometimes, within the overall structure, writers may find it necessary to organize individual paragraphs using other structures - a definition paragraph in a chronological structure, for instance. This should not affect the overall organization.

- Sometimes a writer may include special formatting elements in an informative/explanatory text if these are useful in clarifying organization. These elements may include headings, or phrases in bold that announce the start of a section of text. Headings are usually included only if called for in a prompt or when needed to guide a reader through a long or complex text.

 ## MODEL

The writer of the Student Model understood from her prewriting that she was mostly comparing and contrasting the life-changing experiences of three different people.

In this excerpt from the introduction in the Student Model, the writer makes the organizational structure clear by using cue (or signal) words:

> *Pearce wanted to strike it rich, **while** Ahmedi and Johnson were determined to survive desperate circumstances; however, all three shared an ability to endure hardship to accomplish their goals..*

The writer uses the words "while" and "however" to indicate contrasts. The first contrast, which uses the word "while," compares Pearce's mission with the missions of Ahmedi and Johnson. Then the writer uses "however" to indicate that even though all three individuals had a different mission, they shared something in common—an ability to endure hardship in trying to accomplish their goals.

The writer of the Student Model, "Worth the Risk," wanted to compare and contrast the missions and motivations of the three individuals. Therefore, the writer used a three-column chart to organize the ideas during the prewriting process. The writer color-coded the information to make clear which qualities or characteristics the individuals had in common. What was unique to each individual is unmarked.

STANLEY PEARCE	FARAH AHMEDI	ANNIE JOHNSON
wanted to find gold	was determined to survive	needed to support her family
was observant	had to support her family	started her own business
was able to fit in among the other miners	had to escape her homeland	had an ability to endure hardship
had an ability to endure hardship	was intelligent	was intelligent
learned from his experiences	was willing to ask for help	learned from her experiences
was intelligent	had an ability to endure hardship	made the best of a bad personal situation
discovered something unexpected about the way people act during tough times	learned from her experiences	choose her own way
	discovered something unexpected about the way people act during tough times	was an independent spirit
		was determined to survive

 PRACTICE

Use an *Organize Informative/Explanatory Writing* Three-Column Chart, such as the one you have just seen, to fill in the information you gathered in the Prewrite stage of writing your essay.

SKILL:
SUPPORTING
DETAILS

 DEFINE

In informative/explanatory writing, writers develop their thesis statement with relevant information called **supporting details**. Relevant information can be any fact, definition, concrete detail, example, or quotation that is important to the reader's understanding of the topic and closely related to the thesis, or central idea. Supporting details can be found in a variety of places, but they must develop the thesis statement in order to be considered relevant and necessary:

- Facts important to understanding the topic
- Research related to the thesis statement
- Quotations from texts or from individuals such as experts or eyewitnesses
- Conclusions of scientific findings and studies
- Definitions from reference material

Writers can choose supporting details from many sources. Encyclopedias, research papers, newspaper articles, graphs, memoirs, biographies, criticism, documentaries, and online references can all provide relevant information for source material. Though information is plentiful and the source material varied, the writer must be careful to evaluate the quality of information to determine what information is most important and most closely related to the thesis statement. If the information doesn't support the topic, or if the information doesn't strengthen the writer's point, it is not relevant.

 IDENTIFICATION AND APPLICATION

Step 1:

Review your thesis statement. To identify relevant supporting details, ask this question: What is my central or main idea about this topic? A writer might be making a statement about the value of team sports, for example:

Please note that excerpts and passages in the StudySync® library and this workbook are intended as touchstones to generate interest in an author's work. The excerpts and passages do not substitute for the reading of entire texts, and StudySync® strongly recommends that students seek out and purchase the whole literary or informational work in order to experience it as the author intended. Links to online resellers are available in our digital library. In addition, complete works may be ordered through an authorized reseller by filling out and returning to StudySync® the order form enclosed in this workbook.

Reading & Writing Companion   **93**

Copyright © BookheadEd Learning, LLC

Team sports help young players develop important skills they need in life.

Step 2:

Ask what a reader needs to know about the topic in order to understand the central idea. In order to understand a statement about how sports help players develop life skills, a reader must first know something about the specific sports and skills under discussion. He or she might write this sentence next:

Team sports, such as soccer and field hockey, provide opportunities for players to learn how to work together to meet a goal.

The writer then supplies the reason why:

Because in sports and in other areas of life, how you get to your goal is just as important as making the goal itself.

What could that possibly mean to a reader? The writer gives more information:

While reaching one's goals is highly valued in our society, we all need to remember that pursuing a goal requires hard work.

Step 3:

Look for facts, quotations, research, and the conclusions of others. They will strengthen the thesis statement. It is a building process. Build your information onto the information you gave in the sentence before. Identify supporting details. Carefully evaluate their relevance to your main idea. Ask yourself:

- Is this information necessary to the reader's understanding of the topic?
- Does this information help to prove my point?
- Does this information relate closely to my thesis statement?
- Is there stronger evidence that makes the same point?

 MODEL

The authors of *Call of the Klondike* had to determine which supporting details were most relevant to their topic—the harsh conditions experienced by miners during the Klondike Gold Rush. They included information from a reliable and valid source that would help readers understand what life was like for the miners.

Staking a Claim

When prospectors found a promising spot, they staked a claim **by placing posts at each corner,** one **with their name and date** on it. The prospector then had **three days** to go to town and **file a legal claim.** Because the claims were usually measured by crude means, **disagreements over exact boundaries were common.**

The **first claim** in a new location was called the **"discovery claim."** **Subsequent claims** were **legally referred to by their relationship** to this claim, along with the name of the creek—**5 Above Eldorado, or 6 Below Bonanza,** for example.

—**Museum at the Klondike Gold Rush National Historical Park, Seattle**

Paragraph 1 briefly explains the process of staking a claim. The authors understand that many readers would not already know how gold miners secured their land. The supporting details (set in bold) identify the steps for the official process of recording a claim. The final sentence suggests that the process was not perfect. This detail directly supports the author's topic.

Paragraph 2 explains the difference between types of claims. It includes specific examples—"5 Above Eldorado or 6 Below Bonanza"—to illustrate the naming process. In case readers wonder where the information came from, the authors identify a reliable and valid source at the end of the paragraph—a museum in Seattle, Washington, devoted to the Klondike Gold Rush.

The details included in these two paragraphs are relevant to the topic and provide readers with evidence that shows that the process of claiming land, like life in the Klondike, was imperfect and could lead to confusion and conflict.

 PRACTICE

Using sources, write a few supporting details for your informative/explanatory essay that will help develop your thesis statement. List your details on a *Supporting Details* Relevancy Graphic Organizer to determine how strong your supporting details are. Then trade your details with a partner when you are finished. Offer feedback about the details. Engage in a peer review to determine which details are most relevant and strengthen your thesis statement.

PLAN

WRITING PROMPT

You have been reading nonfiction accounts of the lives and experiences of real people who have undertaken a mission to pursue their goals. You have also been reading fictional stories of adventure—and of characters who have also undertaken missions, often while facing great personal risk. Now you will think about the experiences of these people and characters as you write your own informative/explanatory essay.

Your essay should include:

- an introduction with a clear thesis statement, or central idea
- body paragraphs with relevant supporting details and a thorough analysis to support your thesis statement
- a conclusion that restates your thesis and summarizes your information

Review the information you listed in your *Organize Informative/Explanatory Writing*

Three Column Chart listing three individuals and the details about their motivations and goals. Think about the best way to organize and present the details about the three individuals. This organized information and your thesis will help you to create a road map to use for writing your essay.

Consider the following questions as you develop the topics for your main paragraphs and their supporting details in the road map:

- What mission did each person or character undertake?
- What drove the individual to undertake the mission?
- How successful was the person or character in accomplishing the mission?

- Was the individual's goal a worthy or necessary one? Why or why not?
- What happened as a result of the process of pursuing the goal? Did each person or character change or learn anything important, even if he or she failed?
- What generalization can you make about undertaking a mission based on each individual's experience?

Use this model to get started with your road map:

Essay Road Map

Thesis statement: Pearce wanted to strike it rich, while Ahmedi and Johnson were determined to survive desperate circumstances; however, all three shared an ability to endure hardship to accomplish their goals.

Paragraph 1 Topic: Stanley Pearce

Supporting Detail #1: Like a lot of people, Pearce went to the Klondike to find gold and get rich quick, but soon figured out that the place was not "the promised land."

Supporting Detail #2: Pearce found the climate harsh and the people desperate, but instead of becoming like them, he observed the world around him and kept a diary.

Paragraph 2 Topic: Farah Ahmedi

Supporting Detail #1: Ahmedi needed to get herself and her mother out of their war-torn country, but they faced many obstacles, including a closed border and a lack of money.

Supporting Detail #2: Ahmedi made friends with another family, and together they found a way to escape; as a result, Ahmedi discovered that there were good people in the world.

Paragraph 3 Topic: Annie Johnson

Supporting Detail #1: Johnson had to take care of her family on her own, so she decided to take an unusual path—cooking meals for workers.

Supporting Detail #2: Despite many hardships, Johnson's drive and determination caused her to build a successful business that helped not only her children but also her grandchildren.

SKILL: INTRODUCTIONS

DEFINE

The **introduction** is the opening paragraph or section of a nonfiction text. In an informative/explanatory text, the introduction provides readers with important information by **introducing the topic** and **stating the thesis** that will be developed in the body of the text. A strong introduction also generates interest in the topic by engaging readers in an interesting or attentive way.

IDENTIFICATION AND APPLICATION

- In informative or explanatory writing, the introduction identifies the topic of the writing by explicitly stating what the text will be about. The writer may also use the introduction to provide some necessary background information about the topic to help the reader understand the information that is to come.

- In addition to the topic, the introduction includes the central, or main, idea that the writer will include in the text. This central (or main) idea is the **thesis statement.** A strong statement of the thesis serves as a guide for the remainder of the work. It lets the reader know what the focus of the essay is. The thesis statement should indicate the point the writer will make and the people or source materials he or she will discuss. Note, however, that a thesis is not always stated explicitly within the text. A writer might instead hint at the thesis through details and ideas in the introduction.

- It is customary to build interest in the topic by beginning the introduction with a **"hook,"** or a way to grab the reader's attention. This awakens the reader's natural curiosity and encourages him or her to read on. Hooks can ask open-ended questions, make connections to the reader or to life, or introduce a surprising fact.

MODEL

Take a look at the introduction of the text, *The Other Side of the Sky:*

> The gate to Pakistan was closed, and I could see that the Pakistani border guards were letting no one through. **People were pushing and shoving and jostling up against that gate, and the guards were driving them back. As we got closer, the crowd thickened, and I could hear the roar and clamor at the gate.** The Afghans were yelling something, and the Pakistanis were yelling back. My mother was clutching her side and gasping for breath, trying to keep up. **I felt desperate to get through, because the sun was setting, and if we got stuck here, what were we going to do?** Where would we stay? There was nothing here, no town, no hotel, no buildings, just the desert.

The writer begins with a **hook** in the form of some vivid details: People are pushing and shoving, and the crowd is roaring and clamoring at the gate. It is an effective hook because it makes readers wonder what is going on. They are likely to keep reading to find out what happens next.

The remainder of the paragraph from *The Other Side of the Sky* goes on to introduce the **topic:** the narrator's escape to Pakistan. The topic is suggested through the details of the narrator's thoughts as she stands at the gate to that country: "I felt desperate to get through, because the sun was setting, and if we got stuck here, what were we going to do?"

The **central idea,** however, is only hinted at in the introduction. The central idea of this passage focuses on the detail that the narrator is overcoming many challenges in order to escape from her war-torn homeland. However, there is no explicitly stated **thesis** here, because this is an excerpt from Farah Ahmedi's memoir, which is longer and more complex than an essay someone might write for school. The **thesis statement** for the entire book would be much longer than a sentence. The details in the introduction hint at the idea that the thesis might be about the courage and persistence it takes to survive a desperate situation.

 PRACTICE

Write an introduction for your informative essay that includes a hook, the topic, and the thesis statement. When you are finished, trade with a partner and offer each other feedback. How strong is the language of your partner's thesis statement? How clear is the topic? Were you hooked? Offer each other suggestions, and remember that suggestions are most helpful when they are constructive.

SKILL: BODY PARAGRAPHS AND TRANSITIONS

 DEFINE

Body paragraphs are the section of the essay between the introduction and the conclusion. This is where you support your thesis statement by developing your main points with evidence from the text and analysis. Typically, each body paragraph will focus on one main point or idea to avoid confusing the reader. The main point of each body paragraph must support the thesis statement.

It's important to structure your body paragraph clearly. One strategy for structuring the body paragraph for an informational essay is the following:

Topic sentence: The topic sentence is the first sentence of your body paragraph and clearly states the main point of the paragraph. It's important that your topic sentence develop the main assertion or statement you made in your thesis statement.

Evidence #1: It's important to support your topic sentence with evidence. Evidence can be relevant facts, definitions, concrete details, quotations, or other information and examples.

Analysis/Explanation #1: After presenting evidence to support your topic sentence, you will need to analyze that evidence and explain how it supports your topic sentence and, in effect, your thesis statement.

Evidence #2: Continue to develop your topic sentence with a second piece of evidence.

Analysis/Explanation #2: Analyze this second piece of evidence and explain how it supports your topic sentence and, in effect, your thesis.

Concluding sentence: After presenting your evidence you need to wrap up your main idea and transition to the next paragraph in your conclusion sentence.

NOTES

Transitions are connecting words and phrases that clarify the relationships between (or among) ideas in a text. Transitions work at three different levels: within a sentence, between paragraphs, and to indicate organizational structure.

Authors of informative/explanatory texts use transitions to help readers recognize the overall organizational structure. Transitions also help readers make connections between (or among) ideas within and across sentences and paragraphs. Also, by adding transition words or phrases to the beginning or end of a paragraph, authors guide readers smoothly through the text.

In addition, transition words and phrases help authors make connections between (or among) words within a sentence. Conjunctions such as *and, or,* and *but* and prepositions such as *with, beyond, inside,* show the relationships between (or among) words. Transitions help readers understand how words fit together to make meaning.

 ## IDENTIFICATION AND APPLICATION

- Body paragraphs are the section of the essay between the introduction and conclusion. Body paragraphs provide the evidence and analysis/explanation needed to support the thesis statement. Typically, writers develop one central idea per body paragraph.
  - › Topic sentences clearly state the central (or main) idea of the paragraph.
  - › Evidence consists of relevant facts, definitions, concrete details, quotations, or other information and examples.
  - › Analysis and explanation are needed to explain how the evidence supports the topic sentence.
  - › The concluding sentence wraps up the main point and transitions to the next body paragraph.

- Transition words or phrases are a necessary element of a successful piece of informative writing.
  - › Transition words help readers understand the organizational structure of an informative text. Here are some transition words or phrases that are frequently used in three different organizational (or text) structures:
    - › Cause-effect: *because, since, as a result, effect, so, for, since, if . . . then*
    - › Compare-contrast: *like, also, both, similarly, in the same way* to compare; *although, while, but, yet, however, whereas, on the contrary, on the other hand* to contrast
    - › Chronological (sequential, or time) order: *first, next, then, finally, last, soon, later, meanwhile, in the meantime*

Please note that excerpts and passages in the StudySync® library and this workbook are intended as touchstones to generate interest in an author's work. The excerpts and passages do not substitute for the reading of entire texts, and StudySync® strongly recommends that students seek out and purchase the whole literary or informational work in order to experience it as the author intended. Links to online resellers are available in our digital library. In addition, complete works may be ordered through an authorized reseller by filling out and returning to StudySync® the order form enclosed in this workbook.

Reading & Writing Companion **101**

> Transition words help readers understand the flow of ideas and concepts in a text. Some of the most useful transitions are words that indicate that the ideas in one paragraph are building on (or adding to) those in another. Examples include: *furthermore, therefore, in addition, moreover.*

 MODEL

The Student Model uses a body paragraph structure to develop the central ideas presented in the thesis statement. It also uses transitions to help the reader understand the relationship between (or among) ideas in the text.

Read the body paragraphs from the Student Model, "Worth the Risk." Look closely at the structure and note the transition words in bold. Think about the purpose of the information presented. Does it effectively develop the main points made in each topic sentence? How do the transition words help you understand the similarities and differences among these three individuals and their experiences?

Stanley Pearce

Call of the Klondike by David Meissner and Kim Richardson is a true account of the Klondike Gold Rush. The text is based on primary sources, including the diary of Stanley Pearce, a gold miner. The authors describe the hardships that Pearce and other miners faced to pursue their dream of striking it rich. After sixty-eight miners arrived in Seattle, Washington, in 1897, weighed down with bags of precious gold dust, gold fever erupted. According to Meissner and Richardson, Pearce wrote that "every man who could raise the necessary funds for a year's grub stake was rushing...to start by the next boat for the promised land, where the dreams of all should be realized." Pearce's diaries reveal that the Klondike was not the "promised land" after all. The climate was harsh, and the gold was not plentiful. As a consequence, many miners became "engaged on schemes to fleece the unsuspecting" newcomers out of their money. Others were so desperate that they responded to rumors of gold by stampeding. Pearce describes one stampede that cost people their lives because they were not prepared for the frigid weather. Pearce's own fate is not clear, but he grew wiser from his experiences.

Farah Ahmedi

Unlike Stanley Pearce, who voluntarily went to the Klondike in search of fortune, Farah Ahmedi and her mother found themselves in a dire situation through no fault of their own. They were Afghans living in a war-torn city, and their only hope was to escape to Pakistan. By the time Ahmedi and her mother made it to the border, Pakistan had closed its gates to refugees. Ahmedi and her mother were now stranded in the desert. The situation was desperate. But Ahmedi was determined, so she learned the secret to getting across the border. People were bribing the guards to let them into Pakistan, but she and her mother had no money. Then Ahmedi made friends with another family. The father, Ghulam Ali, learned about a smuggler's pass over the mountains. He agreed to bring Ahmedi and her mother along, even though they were strangers. The path was dark and steep. According to Ahmedi, although she wore a prosthetic leg, she "hardly felt the exertion" because of her "desperation." It gave her "energy" and made her "forget the rigor of the climb." Ahmedi learned a different lesson from that of Stanley Pearce. She discovered that even during a crisis, there were kind people like Ghulam Ali. He not only helped save Ahmedi's life but also gave her hope in humanity.

Annie Johnson

Like Farah Ahmedi, Annie Johnson was a woman with a family and a fierce survival instinct. As a divorced African American woman with two children, Annie Johnson found herself in need of a job. As her granddaughter Maya Angelou explained in "New Directions," Johnson "decided to step off the road and cut me a new path." Instead of taking a job as a domestic or trying to get a job as a factory worker, Johnson devised an elaborate plan to cook meals for local mill and factory workers. Johnson's job was hard, and "business was slow," but she was determined to succeed in her mission. That meant "on balmy spring days, blistering summer noons, and cold, wet, and wintry middays," Johnson "never disappointed her customers." She planned her business carefully, and over time it grew into a successful store. Angelou credited her grandmother's drive and resolve for carrying her through hard times. She also suggested that Johnson's ability to handle only "unpalatable" choices with grace was the key to the success of her mission.

Please note that excerpts and passages in the StudySync® library and this workbook are intended as touchstones to generate interest in an author's work. The excerpts and passages do not substitute for the reading of entire texts, and StudySync® strongly recommends that students seek out and purchase the whole literary or informational work in order to experience it as the author intended. Links to online resellers are available in our digital library. In addition, complete works may be ordered through an authorized reseller by filling out and returning to StudySync® the order form enclosed in this workbook.

Reading & Writing Companion   **103**

NOTES

Pearce, Ahmedi, and Johnson all pursued their goals relentlessly and with good humor and grace, even when their situations became desperate. Pearce kept his common sense while others around him turned to schemes. Ahmedi managed to escape from a war-torn country. When she could not buy her way out of the situation, she found help from a compassionate man. Johnson became a successful businesswoman only after years of hard work. Each was driven to undertake a mission to become wealthy, to escape a war, to raise a family with dignity. Each had different levels of success, but all three learned from their experiences and passed the lessons along to those who came after them. We would all do well to learn from them.

In previous lessons, you have learned about the thesis of the Student Model essay, which was stated clearly in the introduction: While Pearce, Ahmedi, and Johnson had different motivations, "all three shared an ability to endure hardship to accomplish their goals." Keep that thesis in mind as you consider the body paragraphs.

The first two sentences of body paragraph 1 of the Student Model provide background information about the source text *Call of the Klondike*. The third sentence states that "The authors describe the hardships that Pearce and other miners faced to pursue their dream of striking it rich." This **topic sentence** clearly establishes the central (or main) idea this body paragraph will develop. The writer will attempt to show how hard life was for miners in the Klondike despite—or because of—their efforts to become rich quickly.

This topic sentence is immediately followed by **evidence.** The writer uses details and quotations from the source text to explain how many people had high hopes of striking it rich in the Klondike, but their dreams quickly soured because the Klondike was not the "promised land." The writer explains that instead of finding riches, many miners turned to scheming or desperate stampeding. The paragraph **concludes** with an **analysis** of Pearce's character: "he not only grew wiser from his experiences, he also became a keen observer of human nature."

All three body paragraphs use **transitional words** strategically to show relationships between the main points in each body paragraph. The first sentence of the second body paragraph states "**Unlike** Stanley Pearce .... Farah Ahmedi and her mother found themselves in a dire situation through no fault of their own." The transitional word "unlike" makes it clear that the writer is highlighting an important contrast or point of difference between Pearce and Ahmedi.

The writer also uses transition words such as "but," "because," and "although" within the body paragraphs themselves to help guide readers as they transition from one sentence to the next.

 PRACTICE

Write one body paragraph for your informative essay that follows the suggested format. When you are finished, trade with a partner and offer each other feedback. How effective is the topic sentence at stating the main point of the paragraph? How strong is the evidence used to support the topic sentence? Are all quotes and paraphrased evidence cited properly? Did the analysis thoroughly support the topic sentence? Offer each other suggestions, and remember that suggestions are most helpful when they are constructive.

Please note that excerpts and passages in the StudySync® library and this workbook are intended as touchstones to generate interest in an author's work. The excerpts and passages do not substitute for the reading of entire texts, and StudySync® strongly recommends that students seek out and purchase the whole literary or informational work in order to experience it as the author intended. Links to online resellers are available in our digital library. In addition, complete works may be ordered through an authorized reseller by filling out and returning to StudySync® the order form enclosed in this workbook.

Reading & Writing Companion   **105**

SKILL:
CONCLUSIONS

DEFINE

The **conclusion** is the final paragraph or section of a nonfiction text. In an informative/explanatory text, the conclusion brings the discussion to a close. It follows directly from the introduction and body of the text by referring back to the main ideas presented there. A conclusion should reiterate the thesis statement and summarize the main ideas covered in the body of the text. Depending on the type of text, a conclusion might also include a recommendation or solution, a call to action, or an insightful statement. Many conclusions try to connect with readers by encouraging them to apply what they have learned from the text to their own lives.

IDENTIFICATION AND APPLICATION

- An effective informative conclusion reinforces the thesis statement.

- An effective informative conclusion briefly mentions or reviews the strongest supporting facts or details. This reminds readers of the most relevant information and evidence in the work.

- The conclusion leaves the reader with a final thought. In informative writing, this final thought may:

  › answer a question posed by the introduction
  › ask a question on which the reader can reflect
  › ask the reader to take action on an issue
  › present a last, compelling example
  › convey a memorable or inspiring message
  › spark curiosity and encourage readers to learn more about the topic

MODEL

In the concluding paragraph of the student model, "Worth the Risk," the writer reinforces the thesis statement, reminds the reader of relevant details, and ends with a final thought.

> *Pearce, Ahmedi, and Johnson all pursued their goals relentlessly and with good humor and grace, even when their situations became desperate. Pearce kept his common sense while others around him turned to schemes. Ahmedi managed to escape from a war-torn country. When she could not buy her way out of the situation, she found help from a compassionate man. Johnson became a successful businesswoman only after years of hard work. Each was driven to undertake a mission to become wealthy, to escape a war, to raise a family. Each had different levels of success, but all three learned from their experiences and passed the lessons along to those who came after them. We would all do well to learn from them.*

According to the thesis statement, even though Pearce, Ahmedi, and Johnson had different motivations for pursuing their mission, they shared the ability to endure hardship. The first line of the conclusion links back to that idea by reminding readers of the challenges that the three individuals faced as they pursued their mission. Relevant facts in the next few sentences highlight each individual's goal. Then the writer states that all three individuals "were driven to undertake a mission—to become wealthy, to escape a war, to raise a family. "Each had different levels of success, but all three learned from their experiences and passed the lessons along to those who came after them." These two sentences emphasize how the individuals were both different yet similar. They explicitly support the thesis of the essay. Finally, the writer concludes with a recommendation. The writer states, "We would all do well to learn from them." The writer is encouraging readers to learn from the experiences of others.

PRACTICE

Write a conclusion for your informative essay. When you are finished, trade with a partner and offer each other feedback. How effectively did the writer restate the main points of the essay in the conclusion? What final thought did the writer leave you with? Offer each other suggestions, and remember that they are most helpful when they are constructive.

Copyright © BookheadEd Learning, LLC

DRAFT

WRITING PROMPT

You have been reading nonfiction accounts of the lives and experiences of real people who have undertaken a mission to pursue their goals. You have also been reading fictional stories of adventure—and of characters who have also undertaken missions, often while facing great personal risk. Now you will think about the experiences of these people and characters as you write your own informative/explanatory essay.

Your essay should include:

- an introduction with a clear thesis statement, or central idea
- body paragraphs with relevant supporting details and a thorough analysis to support your thesis statement
- a conclusion that restates your thesis and summarizes your information

You have already made progress toward writing your own informative/explanatory text. You have thought about your purpose, audience, and topic. You've carefully examined the unit's texts and selected the people or characters about whom you want to write. Based on your analysis of textual evidence, you've identified what you want to say about their motivations for undertaking a mission. You've decided how to organize information and gathered supporting details. Now it's time to write a draft of your essay.

Use your outline and your other prewriting materials to help you as you write. Remember that informative writing begins with an introduction and presents a thesis statement. Body paragraphs develop the thesis statement with supporting ideas, details, examples, quotations, and other relevant information and explanations drawn from the texts. Transition words and phrases help the reader follow the flow of information and understand the relationship between (or among) ideas. A concluding paragraph restates or reinforces your thesis statement. An effective conclusion can also do more—it can leave a lasting impression on your readers.

When drafting, ask yourself these questions:

- How can I improve my hook to make it more appealing?
- What can I do to clarify my thesis statement?
- What textual evidence—including relevant facts, strong details, and interesting quotations in each body paragraph—supports my thesis statement?
- Would more precise language or different details about these extraordinary individuals make the text more exciting and vivid?
- How well have I communicated what these individuals experienced and achieved?
- What final thought do I want to leave with my readers?

Before you submit your draft, read it over carefully. You want to be sure that you've responded to all aspects of the prompt.

Please note that excerpts and passages in the StudySync® library and this workbook are intended as touchstones to generate interest in an author's work. The excerpts and passages do not substitute for the reading of entire texts, and StudySync® strongly recommends that students seek out and purchase the whole literary or informational work in order to experience it as the author intended. Links to online resellers are available in our digital library. In addition, complete works may be ordered through an authorized reseller by filling out and returning to StudySync® the order form enclosed in this workbook.

Reading & Writing Companion

109

NOTES

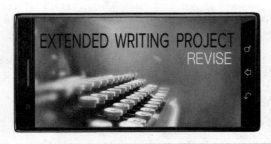

REVISE

WRITING PROMPT

You have been reading nonfiction accounts of the lives and experiences of real people who have undertaken a mission to pursue their goals. You have also been reading fictional stories of adventure—and of characters who have also undertaken missions, often while facing great personal risk. Now you will think about the experiences of these people and characters as you write your own informative/explanatory essay.

Your essay should include:

- an introduction with a clear thesis statement, or central idea
- body paragraphs with relevant supporting details and a thorough analysis to support your thesis statement
- a conclusion that restates your thesis and summarizes your information

You have written a draft of your informative/explanatory essay. You have also received input from your peers about how to improve it. Now you are going to revise your draft.

Here are some recommendations to help you revise.

- Review the suggestions made by your peers.
- Focus on maintaining a formal style. A formal style suits your purpose—giving information about a serious topic. It also fits your audience—students, teachers, and other readers interested in learning more about your topic.
  › As you revise, eliminate any slang.

> › Remove any first-person pronouns such as "I," "me," or "mine" or instances of addressing readers as "you." These are more suitable to a writing style that is informal, personal, and conversational. Check that you have used all pronouns correctly.
> › If you include your personal opinions, remove them. Your essay should be clear, direct, and unbiased.

- After you have revised elements of style, think about whether there is anything else you can do to improve your essay's information or organization.

  > › Have you clearly stated your thesis statement in your introduction? Does it make your audience and purpose clear? Does it let readers know your central idea about the topic?
  > › Do you need to add any new textual evidence to support your thesis statement or engage your readers' interest? For example, is there a detail about one individual's experiences that readers will find fascinating or with which they can identify?
  > › Did one of your subjects say anything interesting that you forgot to quote? Quotations can add life to your essay. Be sure to cite your sources.
  > › Can you substitute a more precise word for a word that is general or overused? Precise language will make your writing more interesting to read.
  > › Consider your organization. Would your essay flow better if you used specific transitions to indicate the connections between (or among) ideas in your paragraphs?

Please note that excerpts and passages in the StudySync® library and this workbook are intended as touchstones to generate interest in an author's work. The excerpts and passages do not substitute for the reading of entire texts, and StudySync® strongly recommends that students seek out and purchase the whole literary or informational work in order to experience it as the author intended. Links to online resellers are available in our digital library. In addition, complete works may be ordered through an authorized reseller by filling out and returning to StudySync® the order form enclosed in this workbook.

Reading & Writing Companion   **111**

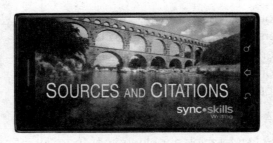

SOURCES AND CITATIONS
sync•skills
Writing

SKILL: SOURCES AND CITATIONS

DEFINE

Sources are the documents and information that an author uses to research his or her writing. Some sources are **primary sources.** A primary source is a firsthand account of thoughts or events by the individual who experienced or witnessed them. Other sources are **secondary sources.** A secondary source analyzes and interprets primary sources. **Citations** are notes that give information about the sources an author used in his or her writing. Citations are required whenever authors quote the words of other people or refer to their ideas in writing. Citations let readers know who originally came up with those words and ideas.

IDENTIFICATION AND APPLICATION

- Sources can be primary or secondary in nature. Primary sources are firsthand accounts, artifacts, or other original materials. Examples of primary sources include:
  › Letters or other correspondence
  › Photographs
  › Official documents
  › Diaries or journals
  › Autobiographies or memoirs
  › Eyewitness accounts or interviews
  › Audio recordings and radio broadcasts
  › Works of art
  › Artifacts

- Secondary sources are usually text. Secondary sources are the written interpretation and analysis of primary source materials. Some examples of secondary sources include:
  › Encyclopedia articles
  › Textbooks

> Commentary or criticism
> Histories
> Documentary films
> News analyses

- Whether sources are primary or secondary, they must be **credible** and **accurate.** Writers of informative/explanatory texts look for sources from experts in the topic about which they are writing.

  > When researching online, writers should look for URLs that contain ".gov" (government agencies), ".edu" (colleges and universities), and ".org" (museums and other nonprofit organizations).

  > Writers also use respected print and online news and information sources.

- Anytime a writer uses words from another source exactly as they are written, the words must appear in quotation marks. Quotation marks show that the words are not the writer's own words but are borrowed from another source. In the Student Model, the writer used quotation marks around words taken directly from the source, *Call of the Klondike*:

  According to Meissner and Richardson, Pearce wrote that **"every man who could raise the necessary funds for a year's grub stake was rushing...to start by the next boat for the promised land, where the dreams of all should be realized."**

- A writer includes a citation to give credit to any source, whether primary or secondary, that is quoted exactly. There are several different ways to cite a source.

  > One way to give credit is to cite the source of the quotation in the context of the sentence. This is what the writer of the Student Model does in the example above. The writer identifies the authors of the secondary source, who in turn quoted from Stanley Pearce's diary, a primary source.

  > Another way is to put the author's last name and the page number in parenthesis at the end of the sentence in which the quote appears.

  > Be sure to ask your teacher which citation style he or she prefers.

- Citations are also necessary when a writer borrows ideas from another source, even if the writer paraphrases, or puts those ideas in his or her own words. Citations credit the source, but they also help readers discover where they can learn more.

Please note that excerpts and passages in the StudySync® library and this workbook are intended as touchstones to generate interest in an author's work. The excerpts and passages do not substitute for the reading of entire texts, and StudySync® strongly recommends that students seek out and purchase the whole literary or informational work in order to experience it as the author intended. Links to online resellers are available in our digital library. In addition, complete works may be ordered through an authorized reseller by filling out and returning to StudySync® the order form enclosed in this workbook.

Reading & Writing Companion   **113**

MODEL

In this excerpt from the Student Model essay, the writer uses quotations from secondary source material. The writer identifies the source by name at the beginning of the paragraph.

> Like Farah Ahmedi, Annie Johnson was a woman with a family and a fierce survival instinct. As a divorced African American woman with two children, Annie Johnson found herself in need of a job. As her granddaughter Maya Angelou explained in "New Directions," Johnson **"decided to step off the road and cut me a new path."** Instead of taking a job as a domestic or trying to get a job as a factory worker, Johnson devised an elaborate plan to cook meals for local mill and factory workers. Johnson's job was hard, and **"business was slow,"** but she was determined to succeed in her mission. That meant **"on balmy spring days, blistering summer noons, and cold, wet, and wintry middays,"** Johnson **"never disappointed her customers."** She planned her business carefully, and over time it grew into a successful store. Angelou credited her grandmother's drive and resolve for carrying her through hard times. She also suggested that Johnson's ability to handle only "unpalatable" choices with grace was the key to the success of her mission.

Notice that each sentence begins with the writer's own words. When the writer uses portions of text from the source material, that text appears in quotation marks. The student has cited the author Maya Angelou at the beginning of the paragraph. The writer assumes that readers will understand that all the quotations in the paragraph are from Angelou.

Because the cited text is written by Angelou about her grandmother Annie Johnson, and not by Johnson herself, it is a secondary source. All references to the secondary source should be cited, to give credit to the author.

 PRACTICE

Include citations for all quoted information in your informative/explanatory essay. When you are finished, trade with a partner and offer each other feedback. How thorough was the writer in citing sources for the essay? Offer each other suggestions, and remember that they are most helpful when they are constructive. You may need to search online for each text you cite to gather its complete bibliographic information (author, date of publication, publisher, city). Jot down this information on notecards for easy reference.

EDIT, PROOFREAD, AND PUBLISH

WRITING PROMPT

You have been reading nonfiction accounts of the lives and experiences of real people who have undertaken a mission to pursue their goals. You have also been reading fictional stories of adventure—and of characters who have also undertaken missions, often while facing great personal risk. Now you will think about the experiences of these people and characters as you write your own informative/explanatory essay.

Your essay should include:

- an introduction with a clear thesis statement, or central idea
- body paragraphs with relevant supporting details and a thorough analysis to support your thesis statement
- a conclusion that restates your thesis and summarizes your information

You have revised your informative/explanatory essay and received input from your peers on that revision. Now it's time to edit and proofread your essay to produce a final version. Have you included all the valuable suggestions from your peers? Ask yourself: Have I fully developed my thesis statement with strong textual evidence? Do my transitions lead to a natural flow of ideas? Do my word choices and writing style reflect the needs of my audience and purpose? Does my conclusion fully summarize the main ideas in my essay? Have I accurately cited my sources? What more can I do to improve my essay's information and organization?

When you are satisfied with your work, move on to proofread it for errors. For example, have you used correct punctuation for quotations and citations? Have you made sure you used commas correctly to separate coordinate adjectives and to set off phrases and clauses in your compound, complex,

Please note that excerpts and passages in the StudySync® library and this workbook are intended as touchstones to generate interest in an author's work. The excerpts and passages do not substitute for the reading of entire texts, and StudySync® strongly recommends that students seek out and purchase the whole literary or informational work in order to experience it as the author intended. Links to online resellers are available in our digital library. In addition, complete works may be ordered through an authorized reseller by filling out and returning to StudySync® the order form enclosed in this workbook.

Reading & Writing Companion **115**

and compound-complex sentences? Have you used specialized vocabulary and technical terms correctly? Be sure to correct any misspelled words.

Once you have made all your corrections, you are ready to submit and publish your work. You can distribute your writing to family and friends, place it on a bulletin board, or post it on your blog. If you publish online, create links to your sources and citations. That way, readers can follow up on what they have learned from your essay and read more about your topic.

studysync®

Reading & Writing Companion

What should be the principles of a just society?

The Powers that Be

UNIT 2   What should be the principles of a just society?

The Powers that Be

TEXTS

TEXTS

EXTENDED WRITING PROJECT

473

Text Fulfillment
through
StudySync

GLADIATOR

NON-FICTION
Richard Watkins
1997

INTRODUCTION

In the Roman Empire, gladiators entertained public audiences by violently fighting other combatants and wild animals to the death. Most gladiators had little choice over their profession—they were criminals, slaves, and war prisoners condemned to the gladiatorial arena. However, there were others that willingly chose the lifestyle; some for the promise of regular meals, and some for the promise of glory. In the following excerpt from his book, *Gladiator*, Richard Watkins describes the

"As Rome's taste for slave fights grew, so did the occasions that required them."

 FIRST READ

 NOTES

Chapter II: The First Gladiators

1 The first known gladiatorial combat in Rome took place at the funeral of a nobleman named Junius Brutus in 264 B.C. His sons Marcus and Decimus revived an ancient Etruscan custom of having slaves fight at the funeral of a great leader in the belief that such a sacrifice would please the gods. During the ceremony, which took place in the Forum Boarium, or cattle market, three pairs of slaves were forced to fight to the death. This strange custom grew in popularity as more rich and powerful men presented these displays as part of the ceremonies to honor their dead.

2 In 216 B.C., twenty-two pairs of slaves fought at the funeral of a man named Marcus Lepidus. Sixty pairs fought when Publicus Licinius died in 183 B.C. These slave fighters were now known as *bustiarii,* funeral men. As Rome's taste for slave fights grew, so did the occasions that required them. If a family's reputation could be enhanced by these displays, then so could a politician's chance of election or a general's popularity. It became clear that an ambitious Roman could buy a crowd's attention, ensure his social standing, and demonstrate his power over life and death.

3 By the time of Julius Caesar, any direct association with funerals and religion was gone, and these fighters, now known as gladiators, meaning swordsmen, were a powerful force in Roman politics. Caesar's genius at entertaining the masses with extravagant gladiatorial displays equaled his skills as a general and a politician. He bought the affection of the people with magnificent banquets and spectacles that were open and free to the public. He showered his political supporters and his *legionaries* (soldiers) with gold. All this gave Caesar unlimited power and established the precedent of keeping the **populace** occupied with triumphal processions, chariot races, and gladiator shows. The bigger the event, the more impressed the people were. In 46 B.C. Caesar staged a battle between two armies, each with 500 men, 30 cavalrymen, and 20 battle elephants. He topped that with a naval battle with 1,000 sailors and 2,000 oarsman, staged on a huge artificial lake dug just for that purpose.

Reading & Writing Companion

4   These gladiatorial combats affirmed Julius Caesar's power and, to him, the cost in gold and human lives was worth it. Augustus Caesar, in 22 B.C., brought all games in Rome under his direct control, making them a state monopoly. He realized that the games were too important a political tool to be exploited by anyone else.

Chapter XI: The End of the Gladiators

5   From the first recorded gladiator fights in 264 B.C. to their final **abolition** almost seven hundred years later, countless thousands died in the arena, all victims of some of the greatest exhibitions of brutality in history. The culture that produced the gladiators also created the atmosphere that eventually led to their extinction.

6   Like all great empires, Rome reached the height of its power and then, over a long period of time, began to collapse. It became impossible to maintain the huge armies needed to protect its border from invaders, the vast number of people ruled by the empire became unmanageable, and the bureaucracy required to keep the government running became bloated and corrupt. The later emperors lacked the absolute power to demand the money and resources required to stage shows as extravagant as the ones given when Rome was at its apex.

7   Although Rome's glory faded over the centuries, Rome was still the major power of its time, and its subjects still expected to be amused by great shows. As time went on, novel acts were harder to create and exotic animals harder to obtain, and the shows became slightly less spectacular. The blood of innocent men and beasts continued to spill, however, and the crowds continued to enjoy the sight of pain and suffering.

8   It took the rise of a new faith to change the attitudes of ruler and ruled alike enough to stop gladiatorial combat. Christianity was born in the Roman Empire and found many **converts** among the poor and powerless. The pagan gods of Rome and the emperors who made themselves gods ruled the people with an attitude of total and merciless authority. These new Christians that preached peace and love often found themselves facing death in the arena when they refused to worship the emperor or his gods. The empire unknowingly aided the growth of this new faith. Every attempt to stop the spread of Christianity with the threat of **persecution** and death seemed to encourage more converts. These converts began to realize that the pain and terror inflicted in the arena was at odds with the gentle and merciful words of their new religion.

9   Christianity gained its more powerful convert in A.D. 312 when the emperor Constantine the Great adopted the faith and declared Christianity the state religion. He issued an edict abolishing gladiatorial combat in A.D. 323. This edict further stated that those condemned to the arena should serve

their sentences in the mines instead. This was a humanitarian gesture in theory only, because forced labor in the mines was nearly as deadly as combat in the arena, though far less dramatic. This ban, however, was not enforced. Constantine himself allowed several gladiator shows to be given, contradicting his own law. It is proof of the powerful attraction of the games that even a great leader like Constantine could not or would not stop them completely. Crowds still filled amphitheaters all over the empire to watch gladiators do their bloody work. Christianity needed more time to wipe out all the pagan beliefs of Rome; even some of the gladiators were Christians. It wasn't until A.D. 367 that the emperor Valentinian I stopped the condemnation of Christians to the gladiator schools. Although emperor Honorius closed the gladiator schools in A.D. 399, the games still seemed to be thriving.

10 Five years later, a tragic event finally put an end to the gladiators. In A.D. 404, a Christian monk named Telemachus jumped into an arena in Rome and tried to separate two combatants. The crowd went berserk, climbed over the walls into the arena, and tore the monk limb from limb. In response to this ugly incident, the emperor Honorius immediately and permanently banned all gladiator combats. Unlike Constantine, he enforced the law.

11 The era of the gladiator was over. Though the Roman Empire was officially a Christian state for ninety-two years before gladiators were abolished, Christianity was primarily responsible for bringing an end to gladiator combats. Violence and cruelty would continue to be all too common in history, but never again would the amphitheater fill with people gathered to watch men kill each other for sport.

Excerpts from GLADIATOR by Richard Watkins. Copyright (c) 1997 by Richard Watkins. Reprinted by permission of Houghton Mifflin Harcourt Publishing Company. All rights reserved.

THINK QUESTIONS

1. Who was responsible for the first-known combat between gladiators in Rome, and why did the custom grow? Cite specific evidence from the first paragraph of the text to support your answer.

2. In what ways did gladiatorial combat change between the time of Julius Caesar in 46 B.C. and Constantine the Great in A.D. 312? Cite textual evidence from Chapters II and XI to support your answer.

3. When did emperor Honorius ban all gladiatorial combat? Explain his reasons for banning all combat between gladiators and cite specific textual evidence from paragraph 10 to support your explanation.

4. Use context to figure out the meaning of the word **converts** as it is used in sentence 2 of paragraph 8. Write your definition of "converts" and explain how you figured out the meaning.

5. Use a print or an online dictionary to confirm the meaning of **persecution** as it is used in paragraph 8. Write the definition. Then provide evidence from the paragraph that "persecution" is being used correctly in the text.

CLOSE READ

Reread the excerpt from *Gladiator*. As you reread, complete the Focus Questions below. Then use your answers and annotations from the questions to help you complete the Writing Prompt.

FOCUS QUESTIONS

1. As you reread the excerpt from *Gladiator*, remember that the author uses sequential text structure, or time order. Highlight the dates in *Gladiator* that reveal this text structure. Annotate why each date is significant to the rise and fall of the Roman gladiator.

2. Chapter headings (number and title of chapter) organize the text into smaller sections that help readers locate specific information. As a result, chapter headings can often provide a clue to the overarching structure of a text. Highlight the two chapter headings in this selection, and explain how they indicate that the text is organized by sequential text structure, or time order. Use annotations to support your explanation.

3. In paragraph 3, how does the author use cause-and-effect text structure to explain Julius Caesar's role in the growth of the gladiator tradition? Highlight textual evidence to support your ideas and write annotations to explain your response.

4. Highlight and annotate the text evidence in paragraph 6 that shows how the author uses cause-and-effect text structure to explain how the "culture that produced the gladiators also created the atmosphere that eventually led to their extinction."

5. What text structure does the author use in paragraph 8? How does the relationship between events help readers to infer that the converts hoped their new faith would lead them to living in a more just society? Highlight your evidence in the text and make annotations to explain your analysis.

WRITING PROMPT

Why does the author use sequence (or time order) in *Gladiator* to organize his ideas? How does telling about the events in the order that they happened help you understand what brought about the beginning and end of the gladiator tradition in Rome? Introduce your ideas clearly with a thesis statement. Use transition words and text features, such as headings or a timeline, to organize and connect your writing. Support your writing with evidence from the text and develop your ideas with facts and examples. Use precise language and maintain a formal writing style. Provide a strong conclusion to support your information.

THE LOTTERY

FICTION
Shirley Jackson
1948

INTRODUCTION

When this story appeared in *The New Yorker* in 1948, the response was loud, but divided: many distressed readers wrote in to cancel their subscriptions. Others asked in which town it was modeled so they could be spectators of such an event. Called "an icon in the history of the American short story," Shirley Jackson's piece may be controversial, but once read, it engraves itself in readers' psyches forever.

"Although the villagers had forgotten the ritual...they still remembered to use stones."

FIRST READ

1   The morning of June 27th was clear and sunny, with the fresh warmth of a full-summer day; the flowers were blossoming profusely and the grass was richly green. The people of the village began to gather in the square, between the post office and the bank, around ten o'clock; in some towns there were so many people that the **lottery** took two days and had to be started on June 26th. but in this village, where there were only about three hundred people, the whole lottery took less than two hours, so it could begin at ten o'clock in the morning and still be through in time to allow the villagers to get home for noon dinner.

2   The children assembled first, of course. School was recently over for the summer, and the feeling of liberty sat uneasily on most of them; they tended to gather together quietly for a while before they broke into boisterous play, and their talk was still of the classroom and the teacher, of books and reprimands. Bobby Martin had already stuffed his pockets full of stones, and the other boys soon followed his example, selecting the smoothest and roundest stones; Bobby and Harry Jones and Dickie Delacroix—the villagers pronounced this name "Dellacroy"—eventually made a great pile of stones in one corner of the square and guarded it against the raids of the other boys. The girls stood aside, talking among themselves, looking over their shoulders at the boys, and the very small children rolled in the dust or clung to the hands of their older brothers or sisters.

3   Soon the men began to gather, surveying their own children, speaking of planting and rain, tractors and taxes. They stood together, away from the pile of stones in the corner, and their jokes were quiet and they smiled rather than laughed. The women, wearing faded house dresses and sweaters, came shortly after their menfolk. They greeted one another and exchanged bits of gossip as they went to join their husbands. Soon the women, standing by their husbands, began to call to their children, and the children came

reluctantly, having to be called four or five times. Bobby Martin ducked under his mother's grasping hand and ran, laughing, back to the pile of stones. His father spoke up sharply, and Bobby came quickly and took his place between his father and his oldest brother.

4   The lottery was conducted—as were the square dances, the teen club, the Halloween program—by Mr. Summers, who had time and energy to devote to civic activities. He was a round-faced, jovial man and he ran the coal business, and people were sorry for him because he had no children and his wife was a scold. When he arrived in the square, carrying the black wooden box, there was a murmur of conversation among the villagers, and he waved and called, "Little late today, folks." The postmaster, Mr. Graves, followed him, carrying a three- legged stool, and the stool was put in the center of the square and Mr. Summers set the black box down on it. The villagers kept their distance, leaving a space between themselves and the stool, and when Mr. Summers said, "Some of you fellows want to give me a hand?" there was a hesitation before two men, Mr. Martin and his oldest son, Baxter, came forward to hold the box steady on the stool while Mr. Summers stirred up the papers inside it.

5   The original **paraphernalia** for the lottery had been lost long ago, and the black box now resting on the stool had been put into use even before Old Man Warner, the oldest man in town, was born. Mr. Summers spoke frequently to the villagers about making a new box, but no one liked to upset even as much **tradition** as was represented by the black box. There was a story that the present box had been made with some pieces of the box that had preceded it, the one that had been constructed when the first people settled down to make a village here. Every year, after the lottery, Mr. Summers began talking again about a new box, but every year the subject was allowed to fade off without anything's being done. The black box grew shabbier each year: by now it was no longer completely black but splintered badly along one side to show the original wood color, and in some places faded or stained.

6   Mr. Martin and his oldest son, Baxter, held the black box securely on the stool until Mr. Summers had stirred the papers thoroughly with his hand. Because so much of the ritual had been forgotten or discarded, Mr. Summers had been successful in having slips of paper substituted for the chips of wood that had been used for generations. Chips of wood, Mr. Summers had argued, had been all very well when the village was tiny, but now that the population was more than three hundred and likely to keep on growing, it was necessary to use something that would fit more easily into he black box. The night before the lottery, Mr. Summers and Mr. Graves made up the slips of paper and put them in the box, and it was then taken to the safe of Mr. Summers' coal company and locked up until Mr. Summers was ready to take it to the

Please note that excerpts and passages in the StudySync® library and this workbook are intended as touchstones to generate interest in an author's work. The excerpts and passages do not substitute for the reading of entire texts, and StudySync® strongly recommends that students seek out and purchase the whole literary or informational work in order to experience it as the author intended. Links to online resellers are available in our digital library. In addition, complete works may be ordered through an authorized reseller by filling out and returning to StudySync® the order form enclosed in this workbook.

Reading & Writing Companion   **127**

square next morning. The rest of the year, the box was put way, sometimes one place, sometimes another; it had spent one year in Mr. Graves's barn and another year underfoot in the post office. and sometimes it was set on a shelf in the Martin grocery and left there.

7   There was a great deal of fussing to be done before Mr. Summers declared the lottery open. There were the lists to make up—of heads of families, heads of households in each family, members of each household in each family. There was the proper swearing-in of Mr. Summers by the postmaster, as the official of the lottery; at one time, some people remembered, there had been a recital of some sort, performed by the official of the lottery, a **perfunctory,** tuneless chant that had been rattled off duly each year; some people believed that the official of the lottery used to stand just so when he said or sang it, others believed that he was supposed to walk among the people, but years and years ago this part of the **ritual** had been allowed to lapse. There had been, also, a ritual salute, which the official of the lottery had had to use in addressing each person who came up to draw from the box, but this also had changed with time, until now it was felt necessary only for the official to speak to each person approaching. Mr. Summers was very good at all this; in his clean white shirt and blue jeans, with one hand resting carelessly on the black box, he seemed very proper and important as he talked interminably to Mr. Graves and the Martins.

8   Just as Mr. Summers finally left off talking and turned to the assembled villagers, Mrs. Hutchinson came hurriedly along the path to the square, her sweater thrown over her shoulders, and slid into place in the back of the crowd. "Clean forgot what day it was," she said to Mrs. Delacroix, who stood next to her, and they both laughed softly. "Thought my old man was out back stacking wood," Mrs. Hutchinson went on, "and then I looked out the window and the kids was gone, and then I remembered it was the twenty-seventh and came a-running." She dried her hands on her apron, and Mrs. Delacroix said, "You're in time, though. They're still talking away up there."

9   Mrs. Hutchinson craned her neck to see through the crowd and found her husband and children standing near the front. She tapped Mrs. Delacroix on the arm as a farewell and began to make her way through the crowd. The people separated good-humoredly to let her through; two or three people said, in voices just loud enough to be heard across the crowd, "Here comes your Missus, Hutchinson," and "Bill, she made it after all." Mrs. Hutchinson reached her husband, and Mr. Summers, who had been waiting, said cheerfully, "Thought we were going to have to get on without you, Tessie." Mrs. Hutchinson said, grinning, "Wouldn't have me leave m'dishes in the sink, now, would you. Joe?" and soft laughter ran through the crowd as the people stirred back into position after Mrs. Hutchinson's arrival.

10 "Well, now," Mr. Summers said soberly, "guess we better get started, get this over with, so's we can go back to work. Anybody ain't here?"

11 "Dunbar," several people said. "Dunbar, Dunbar."

12 Mr. Summers consulted his list. "Clyde Dunbar," he said. "That's right. He's broke his leg, hasn't he? Who's drawing for him?"

13 "Me, I guess," a woman said, and Mr. Summers turned to look at her. "Wife draws for her husband," Mr. Summers said. "Don't you have a grown boy to do it for you, Janey?" Although Mr. Summers and everyone else in the village knew the answer perfectly well, it was the business of the official of the lottery to ask such questions formally. Mr. Summers waited with an expression of polite interest while Mrs. Dunbar answered.

14 "Horace's not but sixteen yet," Mrs. Dunbar said regretfully. "Guess I gotta fill in for the old man this year."

15 "Right," Mr. Summers said. He made a note on the list he was holding. Then he asked, "Watson boy drawing this year?"

16 A tall boy in the crowd raised his hand. "Here," he said. "I m drawing for m'mother and me." He blinked his eyes nervously and ducked his head as several voices in the crowd said things like "Good fellow, Jack," and "Glad to see your mother's got a man to do it."

17 "Well," Mr. Summers said, "guess that's everyone. Old Man Warner make it?"

18 "Here," a voice said, and Mr. Summers nodded.

19 A sudden hush fell on the crowd as Mr. Summers cleared his throat and looked at the list. "All ready?" he called. "Now, I'll read the names—heads of families first—and the men come up and take a paper out of the box. Keep the paper folded in your hand without looking at it until everyone has had a turn. Everything clear?"

20 The people had done it so many times that they only half listened to the directions; most of them were quiet, wetting their lips, not looking around. Then Mr. Summers raised one hand high and said, "Adams." A man disengaged himself from the crowd and came forward. "Hi, Steve," Mr. Summers said, and Mr. Adams said, "Hi, Joe." They grinned at one another humorlessly and nervously. Then Mr. Adams reached into the black box and took out a folded paper. He held it firmly by one corner as he turned and went hastily back to his place in the crowd, where he stood a little apart from his family, not looking down at his hand.

21 "Allen," Mr. Summers said. "Anderson. . . . Bentham."

22 "Seems like there's no time at all between lotteries any more," Mrs. Delacroix said to Mrs. Graves in the back row. "Seems like we got through with the last one only last week."

23 "Time sure goes fast," Mrs. Graves said.

24 "Clark. . . . Delacroix."

25 "There goes my old man," Mrs. Delacroix said. She held her breath while her husband went forward.

26 "Dunbar," Mr. Summers said, and Mrs. Dunbar went steadily to the box while one of the women said, "Go on, Janey," and another said, "There she goes."

27 "We're next," Mrs. Graves said. She watched while Mr. Graves came around from the side of the box, greeted Mr. Summers gravely and selected a slip of paper from the box. By now, all through the crowd there were men holding the small folded papers in their large hands, turning them over and over nervously Mrs. Dunbar and her two sons stood together, Mrs. Dunbar holding the slip of paper.

28 "Harburt. . . . Hutchinson."

29 "Get up there, Bill," Mrs. Hutchinson said, and the people near her laughed.

30 "Jones."

31 "They do say," Mr. Adams said to Old Man Warner, who stood next to him, "that over in the north village they're talking of giving up the lottery."

32 Old Man Warner snorted, "Pack of crazy fools," he said. "Listening to the young folks, nothing's good enough for them. Next thing you know, they'll be wanting to go back to living in caves, nobody work any more, live that way for a while. Used to be a saying about 'Lottery in June, corn be heavy soon.' First thing you know, we'd all be eating stewed chickweed and acorns. There's always been a lottery," he added petulantly. "Bad enough to see young Joe Summers up there joking with everybody."

33 "Some places have already quit lotteries," Mrs. Adams said.

34 "Nothing but trouble in that," Old Man Warner said stoutly. "Pack of young fools."

35 "Martin." And Bobby Martin watched his father go forward. "Overdyke. . . . Percy."

Copyright © BookheadEd Learning, LLC

36   "I wish they'd hurry," Mrs. Dunbar said to her older son. "I wish they'd hurry."

37   "They're almost through," her son said.

38   "You get ready to run tell Dad," Mrs. Dunbar said.

39   Mr. Summers called his own name and then stepped forward precisely and selected a slip from the box. Then he called, "Warner."

40   "Seventy-seventh year I been in the lottery," Old Man Warner said as he went through the crowd. "Seventy-seventh time."

41   "Watson." The tall boy came awkwardly through the crowd. Someone said, "Don't be nervous, Jack," and Mr. Summers said, "Take your time, son."

42   "Zanini."

43   After that, there was a long pause, a breathless pause, until Mr. Summers, holding his slip of paper in the air, said, "All right, fellows." For a minute, no one moved, and then all the slips of paper were opened. Suddenly, all the women began to speak at once, saying, "Who is it?" "Who's got it?" "Is it the Dunbars?," "Is it the Watsons?" Then the voices began to say, "It's Hutchinson. It's Bill," "Bill Hutchinson's got it."

44   "Go tell your father," Mrs. Dunbar said to her older son.

45   People began to look around to see the Hutchinsons. Bill Hutchinson was standing quiet, staring down at the paper in his hand. Suddenly, Tessie Hutchinson shouted to Mr. Summers, "You didn't give him time enough to take any paper he wanted. I saw you. It wasn't fair!"

46   "Be a good sport, Tessie, " Mrs. Delacroix called, and Mrs. Graves said, "All of us took the same chance."

47   "Shut up, Tessie," Bill Hutchinson said.

48   "Well, everyone," Mr. Summers said, "that was done pretty fast, and now we've got to be hurrying a little more to get done in time." He consulted his next list. "Bill," he said, "you draw for the Hutchinson family. You got any other households in the Hutchinsons?"

49   "There's Don and Eva," Mrs. Hutchinson yelled. "Make them take their chance!"

50   "Daughters draw with their husbands' families, Tessie," Mr. Summers said gently. "You know that as well as anyone else."

51 "It wasn't fair," Tessie said.

52 "I guess not, Joe," Bill Hutchinson said regretfully. "My daughter draws with her husband's family, that's only fair. And I've got no other family except the kids."

53 "Then, as far as drawing for families is concerned, it's you," Mr. Summers said in explanation, "and as far as drawing for households is concerned, that's you, too. Right?"

54 "Right," Bill Hutchinson said.

55 "How many kids, Bill?" Mr. Summers asked formally.

56 "Three," Bill Hutchinson said. "There's Bill, Jr., and Nancy, and little Dave. And Tessie and me."

57 "All right, then," Mr. Summers said. "Harry, you got their tickets back?"

58 Mr. Graves nodded and held up the slips of paper. "Put them in the box, then," Mr. Summers directed. "Take Bill's and put it in."

59 "I think we ought to start over," Mrs. Hutchinson said, as quietly as she could. "I tell you it wasn't fair. You didn't give him time enough to choose. Everybody saw that."

60 Mr. Graves had selected the five slips and put them in the box, and he dropped all the papers but those onto the ground, where the breeze caught them and lifted them off.

61 "Listen, everybody," Mrs. Hutchinson was saying to the people around her.

62 "Ready, Bill?" Mr. Summers asked, and Bill Hutchinson, with one quick glance around at his wife and children, nodded.

63 "Remember," Mr. Summers said, "take the slips and keep them folded until each person has taken one. Harry, you help little Dave." Mr. Graves took the hand of the little boy, who came willingly with him up to the box. "Take a paper out of the box, Davy," Mr. Summers said. Davy put his hand into the box and laughed. "Take just one paper," Mr. Summers said. "Harry, you hold it for him." Mr. Graves took the child's hand and removed the folded paper from the tight fist and held it while little Dave stood next to him and looked up at him wonderingly.

64 "Nancy next," Mr. Summers said. Nancy was twelve, and her school friends breathed heavily as she went forward, switching her skirt, and took a slip daintily from the box "Bill, Jr.," Mr. Summers said, and Billy, his face red and his

feet overlarge, nearly knocked the box over as he got a paper out. "Tessie," Mr. Summers said. She hesitated for a minute, looking around defiantly, and then set her lips and went up to the box. She snatched a paper out and held it behind her.

65   "Bill," Mr. Summers said, and Bill Hutchinson reached into the box and felt around, bringing his hand out at last with the slip of paper in it.

66   The crowd was quiet. A girl whispered, "I hope it's not Nancy," and the sound of the whisper reached the edges of the crowd.

67   "It's not the way it used to be," Old Man Warner said clearly. "People ain't the way they used to be."

68   "All right," Mr. Summers said. "Open the papers. Harry, you open little Dave's."

69   Mr. Graves opened the slip of paper and there was a general sigh through the crowd as he held it up and everyone could see that it was blank. Nancy and Bill. Jr., opened theirs at the same time, and both beamed and laughed, turning around to the crowd and holding their slips of paper above their heads.

70   "Tessie," Mr. Summers said. There was a pause, and then Mr. Summers looked at Bill Hutchinson, and Bill unfolded his paper and showed it. It was blank.

71   "It's Tessie," Mr. Summers said, and his voice was hushed. "Show us her paper. Bill."

72   Bill Hutchinson went over to his wife and forced the slip of paper out of her hand. It had a black spot on it, the black spot Mr. Summers had made the night before with the heavy pencil in the coal company office. Bill Hutchinson held it up, and there was a stir in the crowd.

73   "All right, folks," Mr. Summers said. "Let's finish quickly."

74   Although the villagers had forgotten the ritual and lost the original black box, they still remembered to use stones. The pile of stones the boys had made earlier was ready; there were stones on the ground with the blowing scraps of paper that had come out of the box. Mrs. Delacroix selected a stone so large she had to pick it up with both hands and turned to Mrs. Dunbar. "Come on," she said. "Hurry up."

75   Mrs. Dunbar had small stones in both hands, and she said. gasping for breath, "I can't run at all. You'll have to go ahead and I'll catch up with you."

76   The children had stones already, and someone gave little Davy Hutchinson few pebbles.

77   Tessie Hutchinson was in the center of a cleared space by now, and she held her hands out desperately as the villagers moved in on her. "It isn't fair," she said. A stone hit her on the side of the head.

78   Old Man Warner was saying, "Come on, come on, everyone." Steve Adams was in the front of the crowd of villagers, with Mrs. Graves beside him.

79   "It isn't fair, it isn't right," Mrs. Hutchinson screamed and then they were upon her.

"The Lottery" from THE LOTTERY by Shirley Jackson. Copyright © 1948, 1949 by Shirley Jackson. Copyright renewed 1976, 1977 by Laurence Hyman, Barry Hyman, Mrs. Sarah Webster and Mrs. Joanne Schnurer. Reprinted by permission of Farrar, Straus and Giroux, LLC.

 THINK QUESTIONS

1. What specific details in the first paragraph describe the day on which the lottery takes place? Why do you think the story gives such specific details about the setting—the time and place of the story?

2. How does the lottery affect Tessie Hutchinson and her family at the end of the story? How is this a good example of how plot can influence characters? Cite specific textual evidence to support your statements.

3. What saying does Old Man Warner recite about the lottery, in paragraph 32? What does this tell you about the original reason for holding the lottery? What evidence in the text suggests that Old Man Warner thinks that giving up the lottery would have serious consequences for the townspeople? Cite specific textual evidence to support your statements.

4. Use context clues to determine the meaning of the word **tradition** as it is used in paragraph 5 of "The Lottery." Write your definition of "tradition" and explain how you figured out the meaning.

5. Knowing that the small word "lot" is contained in the word "lottery" can help you figure out the meaning of **lottery.** Use a dictionary to find several meanings for the word "lot," but jot down only those meanings that focus on the idea that something is decided by chance. Use these meanings of "lot" to help you determine the meaning of "lottery." Write your definition of "lottery" and tell how you figured out the meaning. Refer to the dictionary again to confirm or revise your definition.

CLOSE READ

Reread the short story "The Lottery." As you reread, complete the Focus Questions below. Then use your answers and annotations from the questions to help you complete the Writing Prompt.

FOCUS QUESTIONS

1. As you reread "The Lottery," remember that the actions of the characters can affect the plot. In paragraph 2, how do the actions of the village boys affect the development of the plot over the course of the text? Highlight evidence in the text and make annotations to explain your answer.

2. In paragraph 4, what can you infer from the hesitation on the part of some of the characters to help with the handling of the black box? Highlight evidence from the text and write annotations to support your inferences.

3. In paragraphs 5–7, what specific evidence from the text supports the idea that the villagers are carrying on a tradition that they no longer fully understand? Highlight textual evidence and make annotations to explain your choices.

4. In paragraph 8, what character does the author introduce who will influence both the plot and the theme? What information about the character becomes ironic as the plot develops? Highlight your evidence and make annotations to explain your thinking.

5. How do Tessie Hutchinson's actions at the end of the story help you understand how character can affect both the plot and the theme? Through the influence of setting, character, and plot, how does the theme of the story get across a message about injustice and unjust societies? Highlight your evidence and make annotations to explain your inferences.

WRITING PROMPT

Sometimes what you expect to happen doesn't happen. That is the case with "The Lottery." Explain how story elements interact in the text to lead to the surprise ending. For example, how did the warm, bright setting interact with the plot to lead you to expect that something good would happen in the story? Use precise language to demonstrate your understanding of story elements. Then provide examples of how characters influenced the plot or the plot influenced characters to turn your expectations upside down and produce the story's shocking ending. Use transitions to clarify relationships between (or among) your examples. Cite specific evidence from the text to support your response. Maintain a formal writing style and end with a strong conclusion.

Please note that excerpts and passages in the StudySync® library and this workbook are intended as touchstones to generate interest in an author's work. The excerpts and passages do not substitute for the reading of entire texts, and StudySync® strongly recommends that students seek out and purchase the whole literary or informational work in order to experience it as the author intended. Links to online resellers are available in our digital library. In addition, complete works may be ordered through an authorized reseller by filling out and returning to StudySync® the order form enclosed in this workbook.

Reading & Writing Companion   **135**

THE GIVER

FICTION

Lois Lowry
1993

INTRODUCTION

In Jonas's community, there is no hunger, disease, or poverty, but also little individual choice. All major decisions are trusted to the Committee of Elders, and at age twelve, each community member is assigned a career path by the Committee. In this excerpt, Jonas, who will soon turn twelve, expresses his

"It was a secret selection, made by the leaders of the community, the Committee of Elders..."

 FIRST READ

 NOTES

Excerpt from Chapter 2

1 Jonas shivered. He pictured his father, who must have been a shy and quiet boy, for he was a shy and quiet man, seated with his group, waiting to be called to the stage. The Ceremony of Twelve was the last of the Ceremonies. The most important.

2 "I remember how proud my parents looked—and my sister, too; even though she wanted to be out riding the bicycle publicly, she stopped fidgeting and was very still and **attentive** when my turn came.

3 "But to be honest, Jonas," his father said, "for me there was not the element of suspense that there is with your Ceremony. Because I was already fairly certain of what my Assignment was to be."

4 Jonas was surprised. There was no way, really, to know in advance. It was a secret selection, made by the leaders of the community, the Committee of **Elders,** who took the responsibility so seriously that there were never even any jokes made about assignments.

5 His mother seemed surprised, too. "How could you have known?" she asked.

6 His father smiled his gentle smile. "Well, it was clear to me—and my parents later confessed that it had been obvious to them, too—what my **aptitude** was. I had always loved the newchildren more than anything. When my friends in my age group were holding bicycle races, or building toy vehicles or bridges with their construction sets, or—"

7 "All the things I do with my friends," Jonas pointed out, and his mother nodded in agreement.

Please note that excerpts and passages in the StudySync® library and this workbook are intended as touchstones to generate interest in an author's work. The excerpts and passages do not substitute for the reading of entire texts, and StudySync® strongly recommends that students seek out and purchase the whole literary or informational work in order to experience it as the author intended. Links to online resellers are available in our digital library. In addition, complete works may be ordered through an authorized reseller by filling out and returning to StudySync® the order form enclosed in this workbook.

Reading & Writing Companion **137**

8   "I always participated, of course, because as children we must experience all of those things. And I studied hard in school, just as you do, Jonas. But again and again, during free time, I found myself drawn to the newchildren. I spent almost all of my volunteer hours helping in the Nurturing Center. Of course the Elders knew that, from their observation."

9   Jonas nodded. During the past year he had been aware of the increasing level of observation. In school, at recreation time, and during volunteer hours, he had noticed the Elders watching him and the other Elevens. He had seen them taking notes. He knew, too, that the Elders were meeting for long hours with all of the instructors that he and the other Elevens had had during their years of school.

10 "So I expected it, and I was pleased, but not at all surprised, when my Assignment was announced as **Nurturer**," Father explained.

11 "Did everyone applaud, even though they weren't surprised?" Jonas asked.

12 "Oh, of course. They were happy for me, that my Assignment was what I wanted most. I felt very fortunate." His father smiled.

13 "Were any of the Elevens disappointed, your year?" Jonas asked. Unlike his father, he had no idea what his Assignment would be. But he knew that some would disappoint him. Though he respected his father's work, Nurturer would not be his wish. And he didn't **envy** Laborers at all.

14 His father thought. "No, I don't think so. Of course the Elders are so careful in their observations and selections."

15 "I think it's probably the most important job in our community," his mother commented.

16 "My friend Yoshiko was surprised by her selection as Doctor," Father said, "but she was thrilled. And let's see, there was Andrei—I remember that when we were boys he never wanted to do physical things. He spent all the recreation time he could with his construction set, and his volunteer hours were always on building sites. The Elders knew that, of course. Andrei was given the Assignment of Engineer and he was delighted."

17 "Andrei later designed the bridge that crosses the river to the west of town," Jonas's mother said. "It wasn't there when we were children."

18 "There are very rarely disappointments, Jonas. I don't think you need to worry about that," his father reassured him. "And if there are, you know there's an appeal process." But they all laughed at that—an appeal went to a committee for study.

19 "I worry a little about Asher's Assignment," Jonas confessed. "Asher's such *fun*. But he doesn't really have any serious interests. He makes a game out of everything."

20 His father chuckled. "You know," he said, "I remember when Asher was a newchild at the Nurturing Center, before he was named. He never cried. He giggled and laughed at everything. All of us on the staff enjoyed nurturing Asher."

21 "The Elders know Asher," his mother said. "They'll find exactly the right Assignment for him. I don't think you need to worry about him. But, Jonas, let me warn you about something that may not have occurred to you. I know I didn't think about it until after my Ceremony of Twelve."

22 "What's that?"

23 "Well, it's the last of the Ceremonies, as you know. After Twelve, age isn't important. Most of us even lose track of how old we are as time passes, though the information is in the Hall of Open Records, and we could go and look it up if we wanted to. What's important is the preparation for adult life, and the training you'll receive in your Assignment."

24 "I know that," Jonas said. "Everyone knows that."

25 "But it means," his mother went on, "that you'll move into a new group. And each of your friends will. You'll no longer be spending your time with your group of Elevens. After the Ceremony of Twelve, you'll be with your Assignment group, with those in training. No more volunteer hours. No more recreation hours. So your friends will no longer be as close."

26 Jonas shook his head. "Asher and I will always be friends," he said firmly. "And there will still be school."

27 "That's true," his father agreed. "But what your mother said is true as well. There will be changes."

28 "*Good* changes, though," his mother pointed out.

Excerpted from *The Giver* by Lois Lowry, published by Houghton Mifflin Harcourt.

Please note that excerpts and passages in the StudySync® library and this workbook are intended as touchstones to generate interest in an author's work. The excerpts and passages do not substitute for the reading of entire texts, and StudySync® strongly recommends that students seek out and purchase the whole literary or informational work in order to experience it as the author intended. Links to online resellers are available in our digital library. In addition, complete works may be ordered through an authorized reseller by filling out and returning to StudySync® the order form enclosed in this workbook.

THINK QUESTIONS

1. Refer to one or more details in the text to support your understanding of why Jonas "shivered" in the opening line of the excerpt. Cite specific details that are directly stated in the text and inferences you made from clues in the first three paragraphs.

2. Why didn't Jonas's father feel an element of suspense at his Ceremony of Twelve? What is Jonas's reaction to his father's lack of suspense at his Ceremony? Cite textual evidence from paragraphs 3, 4, and 6 to support your response.

3. Use specific evidence from the text to explain why Jonas is concerned about Asher's assignment. Then explain why Jonas's mother is not worried about Asher. What can you infer about Jonas and his mother from their contrasting points of view about Asher in paragraphs 19 and 21?

4. Use context from paragraph 6 to determine the meaning of the word **aptitude** as it is used in *The Giver*. Write your definition of "aptitude" and explain how you determined the meaning of the word. Cite specific evidence from the text.

5. Use a print or digital dictionary to determine the meaning of **elders** as it is used in paragraph 4 of the excerpt. Write the definition. Then provide evidence from the paragraph to confirm that the word is being used correctly in the text.

CLOSE READ

Reread the excerpt from *The Giver*. As you reread, complete the Focus Questions below. Then use your answers and annotations from the questions to help you complete the Writing Prompt.

FOCUS QUESTIONS

1. How do the first four paragraphs of *The Giver* indicate that the narrator is using a third-person limited omniscient point of view to tell the story? Highlight evidence from the text and make annotations to support your explanation.

2. In paragraphs 8 and 9, what evidence indicates that Jonas and his father share the same point of view about the Elders' use of observation to make the Assignments? Highlight evidence from the text and make annotations to support your response.

3. What point of view does Jonas express in paragraph 13 about the different jobs that might be assigned to him? How does his point of view differ from his father's in paragraph 12? Highlight evidence from the text and make annotations to support your answer.

4. How do Jonas's mother's words to him at the end of paragraph 21 and again in paragraphs 23 and 25 express the consequences of the Ceremony? Support your answer with textual evidence and make annotations to explain your response.

5. In paragraphs 13, 18, 19, and 21, what are the basic differences between Jonas's point of view and his parents' point of view about the Ceremony of Twelve? What inference can you make about whether or not they believe they are living in a just society? Highlight evidence from the text and make annotations to support your inferences and ideas.

WRITING PROMPT

How does the point of view from which *The Giver* is told focus on Jonas's thoughts and feelings about the Ceremony of Twelve? How is Jonas's point of view revealed? How does it differ from his parents' point of view about the ceremony? How do the differences contribute to the tension in the story? State a strong topic sentence for your writing. Use transitions to clarify connections between (or among) your ideas. Organize your essay in a logical way and cite specific evidence from the text to support your writing. Maintain a formal writing style and end with a strong conclusion.

Please note that excerpts and passages in the StudySync® library and this workbook are intended as touchstones to generate interest in an author's work. The excerpts and passages do not substitute for the reading of entire texts, and StudySync® strongly recommends that students seek out and purchase the whole literary or informational work in order to experience it as the author intended. Links to online resellers are available in our digital library. In addition, complete works may be ordered through an authorized reseller by filling out and returning to StudySync® the order form enclosed in this workbook.

Reading & Writing Companion **141**

THE WISE OLD WOMAN

FICTION
Yoshiko Uchida
1965

INTRODUCTION

The *Wise Old Woman* is a traditional Japanese folktale retold by Yoshiko Uchida, a Japanese-American author who grew up in California during the Great Depression. As a child, Uchida's parents taught her to appreciate the customs and folktales of their native land, and as a result, Japanese culture is prevalent in Uchida's writing. Through her writing, Uchida expressed the hope that "all children, in whatever country they may live, have the same love of fun and a good story."

"'I have no use for old people in my village,' he said haughtily."

FIRST READ

1   Many long years ago, there lived an **arrogant** and cruel young lord who ruled over a small village in the western hills of Japan.

2   "I have no use for old people in my village," he said haughtily. "They are neither useful nor able to work for a living. I therefore **decree** that anyone over seventy-one must be **banished** from the village and left in the mountains to die."

3   "What a dreadful decree! What a cruel and unreasonable lord we have," the people of the village murmured. But the lord fearfully punished anyone who disobeyed him, and so villagers who turned seventy-one were tearfully carried into the mountains, never to return.

4   Gradually there were fewer and fewer old people in the village and soon they disappeared altogether. Then the young lord was pleased.

5   "What a fine village of young, healthy, and hard-working people I have," he bragged. "Soon it will be the finest village in all of Japan."

6   Now, there lived in this village a kind young farmer and his aged mother. They were poor, but the farmer was good to his mother, and the two of them lived happily together. However, as the years went by, the mother grew older, and before long she reached the terrible age of seventy-one.

7   "If only I could some how **deceive** the cruel lord," the farmer thought. But there were records in the village books and everyone knew that his mother had turned seventy-one.

8   Each day the son put off telling his mother that he must take her into the mountains to die, but the people of the village began to talk. The farmer knew

Please note that excerpts and passages in the StudySync® library and this workbook are intended as touchstones to generate interest in an author's work. The excerpts and passages do not substitute for the reading of entire texts, and StudySync® strongly recommends that students seek out and purchase the whole literary or informational work in order to experience it as the author intended. Links to online resellers are available in our digital library. In addition, complete works may be ordered through an authorized reseller by filling out and returning to StudySync® the order form enclosed in this workbook.

Reading & Writing Companion   **143**

that if he did not take his mother away soon, the lord would send his soldiers and throw them both into a dark dungeon to die a terrible death.

9   "Mother—" he would begin, as he tried to tell her what he must do, but he could not go on.

10 Then one day the mother herself spoke of the lord's dread decree. "Well, my son," she said, "the time has come for you to take me to the mountains. We must hurry before the lord sends his soldiers for you." And she did not seem worried at all that she must go to the mountains to die.

11 "Forgive me, dear mother, for what I must do," the farmer said sadly, and the next morning he lifted his mother to his shoulders and set off on the steep path toward the mountains. Up and up he climbed, until the trees clustered close and the path was gone. There was no longer even the sound of birds, and they heard only the soft wail of the wind in the trees. The son walked slowly, for he could not bear to think of leaving his old mother in the mountains. On and on he climbed, not wanting to stop and leave her behind. Soon, he heard his mother breaking off small twigs from the trees that they passed.

12 "Mother, what are you doing?" he asked.

13 "Do not worry, my son," she answered gently. "I am just marking the way so you will not get lost returning to the village."

14 The son stopped. "Even now you are thinking of me?" he asked, wonderingly.

15 The mother nodded. "Of course, my son," she replied. "You will always be in my thoughts. How could it be otherwise?"

16 At that, the young farmer could bear it no longer. "Mother, I cannot leave you in the mountains to die all alone," he said. "We are going home and no matter what the lord does to punish me, I will never desert you again."

17 So they waited until the sun had set and a lone star crept into the silent sky. Then, in the dark shadows of night, the farmer carried his mother down the hill and they returned quietly to their little house. The farmer dug a deep hole in the floor of his kitchen and made a small room where he could hide his mother. From that day, she spent all her time in the secret room and the farmer carried meals to her there. The rest of the time, he was careful to work in the fields and act as though he lived alone. In this way, for almost two years he kept his mother safely hidden and no one in the village knew that she was there.

18 Then one day there was a terrible **commotion** among the villagers, for Lord Higa of the town beyond the hills threatened to conquer their village and make it his own.

19 "Only one thing can spare you," Lord Higa announced. "Bring me a box containing one thousand ropes of ash and I will spare your village."

20 The cruel young lord quickly gathered together all the wise men of his village. "You are men of wisdom," he said. "Surely you can tell me how to meet Lord Higa's demands so our village can be spared."

21 But the wise men shook their heads. "It is impossible to make even one rope of ash, sire," they answered. "How can we ever make one thousand?"

22 "Fools!" the lord cried angrily. "What good is your wisdom if you cannot help me now?"

23 And he posted a notice in the village square offering a great reward of gold to any villager who could help him save their village.

24 But all the people in the village whispered, "Surely, it is an impossible thing, for ash crumbles at the touch of the finger. How could anyone ever make a rope of ash?" They shook their heads and sighed, "Alas, alas, we must be conquered by yet another cruel lord."

25 The young farmer, too, supposed that this must be, and he wondered what would happen to his mother if a new lord even more terrible than their own came to rule over them.

26 When his mother saw the troubled look on his face, she asked, "Why are you so worried, my son?"

27 So the farmer told her of the impossible demand made by Lord Higa if the village was to be spared, but his mother did not seem troubled at all. Instead she laughed softly and said, "Why, that is not such an impossible task. All one has to do is soak ordinary rope in salt water and dry it well. When it is burned, it will hold its shape and there is your rope of ash! Tell the villagers to hurry and find one thousand pieces of rope."

28 The farmer shook his head in amazement. "Mother, you are wonderfully wise," he said, and he rushed to tell the young lord what he must do.

29 "You are wiser than all the wise men of the village," the lord said when he heard the farmer's solution, and he rewarded him with many pieces of gold. The thousand ropes of ash were quickly made and the village was spared.

30 In a few days, however, there was another great commotion in the village as Lord Higa sent another threat. This time he sent a log with a small hole that curved and bent seven times through its length, and he demanded that a single piece of silk thread be threaded through the hole. "If you cannot perform this task," the lord threatened, "I shall come to conquer your village."

31 The young lord hurried once more to his wise men, but they all shook their heads in bewilderment. "A needle cannot bend its way through such curves," they moaned. "Again we are faced with an impossible demand."

32 "And again you are stupid fools!" the lord said, stamping his foot impatiently. He then posted a second notice in the village square asking the villagers for their help.

33 Once more the young farmer hurried with the problem to his mother in her secret room.

34 "Why, that is not so difficult," his mother said with a quick smile. "Put some sugar at one end of the hole. Then tie an ant to a piece of silk thread and put it in at the other end. He will weave his way in and out of the curves to get to the sugar and he will take the silk thread with him."

35 "Mother, you are remarkable!" the son cried, and he hurried off to the lord with the solution to the second problem.

36 Once more the lord **commended** the young farmer and rewarded him with many pieces of gold. "You are a brilliant man and you have saved our village again," he said gratefully.

37 But the lord's troubles were not over even then, for a few days later Lord Higa sent still another demand. "This time you will undoubtedly fail and then I shall conquer your village," he threatened. "Bring me a drum that sounds without being beaten."

38 "But that is not possible," sighed the people of the village. "How can anyone make a drum sound without beating it?"

39 This time the wise men held their heads in their hands and moaned, "It is hopeless. It is hopeless. This time Lord Higa will conquer us all."

40 The young farmer hurried home breathlessly. "Mother, Mother, we must solve another terrible problem or Lord Higa will conquer our village!" And he quickly told his mother about the impossible drum.

41 His mother, however, smiled and answered, "Why, this is the easiest of them all. Make a drum with sides of paper and put a bumblebee inside. As it tries to escape, it will buzz and beat itself against the paper and you will have a drum that sounds without being beaten."

42 The young farmer was amazed at his mother's wisdom. "You are far wiser than any of the wise men of the village," he said, and he hurried to tell the young lord how to meet Lord Higa's third demand.

43 When the lord heard the answer, he was greatly impressed. "Surely a young man like you cannot be wiser than all my wise men," he said. "Tell me honestly, who has helped you solve all these difficult problems?"

44 The young farmer could not lie. "My lord," he began slowly, "for the past two years I have broken the law of the land. I have kept my aged mother hidden beneath the floor of my house, and it is she who solved each of your problems and saved the village from Lord Higa."

45 He trembled as he spoke, for he feared the lord's displeasure and rage. Surely now the soldiers would be summoned to throw him into the dark dungeon. But when he glanced fearfully at the lord, he saw that the young ruler was not angry at all. Instead, he was silent and thoughtful, for at last he realized how much wisdom and knowledge old people possess.

46 "I have been very wrong," he said finally. "And I must ask the forgiveness of your mother and of all my people. Never again will I demand that the old people of our village be sent to the mountains to die. Rather, they will be treated with the respect and honor they deserve and share with us the wisdom of their years."

47 And so it was. From that day, the villagers were no longer forced to abandon their parents in the mountains, and the village became once more a happy, cheerful place in which to live. The terrible Lord Higa stopped sending his impossible demands and no longer threatened to conquer them, for he too was impressed.

48 "Even in such a small village there is much wisdom," he declared, "and its people should be allowed to live in peace."

49 And that is exactly what the farmer and his mother and all the people of the village did for all the years thereafter.

© 1965 by Yoshiko Uchida, THE SEA OF GOLD AND OTHER TALES FROM JAPAN. Reproduced by permission of The Bancroft Library, on behalf of the Regents of the University of California.

Please note that excerpts and passages in the StudySync® library and this workbook are intended as touchstones to generate interest in an author's work. The excerpts and passages do not substitute for the reading of entire texts, and StudySync® strongly recommends that students seek out and purchase the whole literary or informational work in order to experience it as the author intended. Links to online resellers are available in our digital library. In addition, complete works may be ordered through an authorized reseller by filling out and returning to StudySync® the order form enclosed in this workbook.

Reading & Writing Companion   **147**

THINK QUESTIONS

1. Why did the young lord issue a decree against elderly people? What did the decree say? Cite specific evidence from the second paragraph.

2. How does the "old woman" thwart Lord Higa and save the village? What inference can you make about her from her ability to solve Lord Higa's three difficult tasks? Cite evidence from the text in your response.

3. What made the young lord have a change of heart toward the elderly? How might he behave toward them in the future? Use evidence from paragraphs 41–43 to support your answer.

4. Use context clues to determine the meaning of the word **banished** as it is used in sentence 3 of paragraph 2. Write your definition of "banished" and explain how you figured out its meaning. Then check your meaning in a print or an online dictionary.

5. The word **decree** is used as a noun and a verb in paragraphs 2 and 3. Use context clues to determine the part of speech of the word in each of these paragraphs. If needed, use a dictionary to define both the noun and verb form of the word. Write your two definitions, and explain how you figured out the meaning of each use of the word.

CLOSE READ

Reread the folktale "The Wise Old Woman." As you reread, complete the Focus Questions below. Then use your answers and annotations from the questions to help you complete the Writing Prompt.

FOCUS QUESTIONS

1. As you reread "The Wise Old Woman," remember that the story is told from the third-person point of view. Although the narrator provides a few indications of what the young lord is thinking or feeling, readers really know only the thoughts of the young farmer. Highlight evidence in paragraphs 7–9 that reveals the farmer's point of view about the young lord's decree, and make annotations to support your ideas.

2. Plot events can also convey details that suggest the theme. Closely reread paragraphs 18–29 and explain how the details in these paragraphs help you begin to identify the theme (or message) of the folktale. Highlight evidence from the text and make annotations to explain your ideas.

3. Analyzing character traits can also provide readers with details that point to the theme of a story. Reread paragraphs 40–43 and highlight specific evidence that suggests what the farmer's mother is like. Make annotations noting how the character traits of the "wise old woman" might play a part in developing the central theme.

4. Which lines from paragraph 46 provide the best evidence of the central theme in this folktale? Highlight the two most important sentences and annotate how they express the theme.

5. In paragraph 7, the young farmer admits that he wishes he could "deceive the cruel lord" and save his aged mother from his terrible decree. What plan does he come up with to save her and in turn all the elderly people in the village? How does his rebellion against the decree, expressed in paragraphs 16–17, suggest his point of view about the society and its ruler? Highlight textual evidence and make annotations about your inferences to support your answer.

Please note that excerpts and passages in the StudySync® library and this workbook are intended as touchstones to generate interest in an author's work. The excerpts and passages do not substitute for the reading of entire texts, and StudySync® strongly recommends that students seek out and purchase the whole literary or informational work in order to experience it as the author intended. Links to online resellers are available in our digital library. In addition, complete works may be ordered through an authorized reseller by filling out and returning to StudySync® the order form enclosed in this workbook.

Reading & Writing Companion   **149**

WRITING PROMPT

How does the theme of "The Wise Old Woman" help you understand a larger lesson about life, human nature, or the experience of a specific people and culture? Use the details you have compiled from examining the point of view, setting, conflict, and plot, as well as the characters' thoughts, dialogue, feelings, and actions, to:

- write an objective summary of the folktale
- identify the theme
- show how the theme is developed over the course of the text

Remember to support your writing with evidence and inferences from the text. Review the vocabulary words you have learned. Be sure to check each word's etymology, or historical development, in a print or an online dictionary. Make sure that you are using the vocabulary in correct context to its meaning. Be aware of words with multiple meanings and use them appropriately.

NOTHING TO ENVY:
ORDINARY LIVES IN NORTH KOREA

NON-FICTION
Barbara Demick
2010

INTRODUCTION

In *Nothing to Envy*, Barbara Demick penetrates the shadowy dictatorship of modern North Korea, focusing on six individuals. The following excerpt features two of the main characters: Mrs. Song, a bookkeeper and loyal supporter of Kim Il-sung's regime, and her daughter Oak-hee, who is dangerously inclined to be skeptical. The episode begins with Mrs. Song and her husband Chang-bo, an independent thinker, watching television, an activity they proudly share with apartment house neighbors who cannot afford the luxury of TV.

"Spying on one's countrymen is something of a national pastime."

FIRST READ

From Chapter Three: The True Believer

1   The program that got Chang-bo in trouble was an innocuous business report about a shoe factory producing rubber boots for the rainy season. The camera panned over crisply efficient workers on an assembly line where the boots were being produced by the thousands. The narrator raved about the superb quality of the boots and reeled off the impressive production statistics.

2   "Hah. If there are so many boots, how come my children never got any?" Chang-bo laughed aloud. The words tumbled out of his mouth before he could consider the consequences.

3   Mrs. Song never figured out which neighbor blabbed. Her husband's remark was quickly reported to the head of the *inminban,* the neighborhood watchdogs, who in turn passed on the information to the Ministry for the Protection of State Security. This ominously named agency is effectively North Korea's political police. It runs an extensive network of informers. By the accounts of defectors, there is at least one informer for every fifty people—more even than East Germany's notorious Stasi, whose files were pried open after German reunification.

4   Spying on one's countrymen is something of a national pastime. There were the young **vigilantes** from the Socialist Youth League like the one who stopped Mrs. Song for not wearing a badge. They also made sure people weren't violating the dress code by wearing blue jeans or T-shirts with Roman writing—considered a capitalist indulgence—or wearing their hair too long. The party issued regular edicts saying that men shouldn't allow the hair on top of their head to grow longer than five centimeters—though an exemption was granted for balding men, who were permitted seven centimeters. If a violation was severe, the offender could be arrested by the Public Standards Police. There were also *kyuch'aldae,* mobile police units who roamed the

streets looking for offenders and had the right to barge into people's houses without notice. They would look for people who used more than their quota of electricity, a light bulb brighter than 40 watts, a hot plate, or a rice cooker. During one of the surprise inspections, one of the neighbors tried to hide their hot plate under a blanket and ended up setting their apartment on fire. The mobile police often dropped in after midnight to see if there were any overnight guests who might have come to visit without travel permits. It was a serious offense, even if it was just an out-of-town relative, and much worse if the guest happened to be a lover. But it wasn't just the police and the volunteer leagues who did the snooping. Everybody was supposed to be vigilant for subversive behavior and transgressions of the rules. Since the country was too poor and the power supply too unreliable for electronic **surveillance,** state security relied on human intelligence—snitches. The newspapers would occasionally run feature stories about heroic children who ratted out their parents. To be denounced by a neighbor for bad-mouthing the regime was nothing extraordinary.

5 Chang-bo's **interrogation** lasted three days. The agents yelled and cursed at him, although they never beat him—at least that's what he told his wife. He claimed afterward that his gift with language helped him talk his way out of the bind. He cited the truth in his defense.

6 "I wasn't insulting anybody. I was simply saying that I haven't been able to buy those boots and I'd like to have some for my family," Chang-bo protested indignantly.

7 He made a convincing case. He was a commanding figure with his potbelly and his stern expression. He looked like the epitome of a Workers' Party official. The political police in the end decided not to push the case and released him without charges.

8 When he returned home, he got a tongue-lashing from his wife that was almost harsher than the interrogation. It was the worst fight of their marriage. For Mrs. Song, it was not merely that her husband had been disrespectful of the government; for the first time in her life, she felt the stirrings of fear. Her conduct had always been so impeccable and her devotion so genuine that it never occurred to her that she might be vulnerable.

9 "Why did you say such nonsense when there were neighbors in the apartment? Didn't you realize you could have jeopardized everything we have?" she railed at him.

10 In fact, they both realized how lucky they were. If not for Chang-bo's excellent class background and his party membership, he would not have been let off so lightly. It helped, too, that Mrs. Song had at various times been head of the *inminban* in the building and commanded some respect from the state

NOTES

security officers. Chang-bo's offhand remark was precisely the kind of thing that could result in deportation to a prison camp in the mountains if the offender didn't have a solid position in the community. They had heard of a man who cracked a joke about Kim Jong-il's height and was sent away for life. Mrs. Song personally knew a woman from her factory who was taken away for something she wrote in her diary. At the time, Mrs. Song hadn't felt any pity for the woman. "The traitor probably deserved what she got," she'd said to herself. Now she felt embarrassed for having thought such a thing.

11 The incident seemed to blow over. Chastened by the experience, Chang-bo was more careful about what he said outside the family, but his thoughts were running wild. For many years, Chang-bo had been fighting off the doubts that would periodically creep into his consciousness. Now those doubts were gelling into outright disbelief. As a journalist, Chang-bo had more access to information than ordinary people. At the North Hamgyong Provincial Broadcasting Company, where he worked, he and his colleagues heard **uncensored** news reports from the foreign media. It was their job to sanitize it for domestic consumption. Anything positive that happened in capitalist countries or especially South Korea, which in 1988 hosted the Summer Olympics, was downplayed. Strikes, disasters, riots, murders—elsewhere— got plenty of coverage.

12 Chang-bo's job was to report business stories. He toured collective farms, shops, and factories with a notebook and tape recorder, interviewing the managers. Back in the newsroom, he would write his stories in fountain pen (there were no typewriters) about how well the economy was doing. He always put a positive spin on the facts, although he tried to keep them at least plausible. By the time they were edited by his superiors in Pyongyang, however, any glimmer of the truth was gone. Chang-bo knew better than anyone that the supposed triumphs of the North Korean economy were **fabrications.** He had good reason to scoff at the report about the rubber boots.

13 He had one trusted friend from the radio station who shared his increasing disdain for the regime. When the two of them got together, Chang-bo would open a bottle of Mrs. Song's *neungju* and, after a few drinks, they would let rip their true feelings.

14 "What a bunch of liars!" Chang-bo would say in an emphatic tone, taking care just the same not to speak loudly enough for the sound to carry through the thin plaster walls between the apartments.

15 "Crooks, all of them."

16 "The son is even worse than the father."

17 Oak-hee eavesdropped on her father and his friend. She nodded quietly in agreement. When her father noticed, he at first tried to shoo her away. Eventually he gave up. Swearing her to secrecy, he took her into his confidence. He told her that Kim Il-sung was not the anti-Japanese resistance fighter he claimed to be so much as a puppet of the Soviet Union. He told her that South Korea was now among the richest countries in Asia; even ordinary working people owned their own cars. Communism, he reported, was proving a failure as an economic system. China and the Soviet Union were now embracing capitalism. Father and daughter would talk for hours, always taking care to keep their voices at a whisper in case a neighbor was snooping around. And, at such times, they always made sure that Mrs. Song, the true believer, was not at home.

Excerpted from *Nothing to Envy: Ordinary Lives in North Korea* by Barbara Demick, published by Spiegel & Grau.

☁ THINK QUESTIONS

1. What caused Chang-bo to get into trouble with the Ministry for the Protection of State Security? Cite specific evidence from paragraphs 1–3 to support your response.

2. What helped Chang-bo get off so lightly when he was interrogated? Cite textual evidence from paragraphs 5, 7, and 10.

3. In paragraph 11, the author says that Chang-bo had been fighting off doubts about the North Korean government for many years but that recently "those doubts were gelling into outright disbelief." What textual evidence in paragraphs 11–17 supports this view? How did Chang-bo's job contribute to his disbelief?

4. What is the meaning of **vigilantes** as it is used in paragraph 4 of *Nothing to Envy?* Use context clues to determine the meaning of the word. Write your definition of "vigilantes" and cite the context clues you used to determine its meaning.

5. What is the meaning of **fabrications** as it is used in paragraph 12? Use context clues provided in the paragraph to determine the meaning of the word. Write your definition of "fabrications," and explain how you figured out its meaning. Then check a print or an online dictionary to confirm the meaning.

CLOSE READ

Reread the excerpt from *Nothing to Envy.* As you reread, complete the Focus Questions below. Then use your answers and annotations from the questions to help you complete the Writing Prompt.

FOCUS QUESTIONS

1. Highlight the idiom "reeled off" in the last sentence of paragraph 1, and make annotations noting the context clues that helped you determine its meaning. Then write a definition of the idiom as it is used in the text.

2. As you reread *Nothing to Envy: Ordinary Lives in North Korea,* look for interactions among ideas, individuals, and events to gain a deeper understanding of the text. For example, in paragraph 4, how did the North Korean economy affect how the government collected information about people? How did the people respond? What terrible events did these people cause? Highlight specific evidence in the text and make annotations to explain your thinking.

3. According to paragraphs 8–10, how did the events surrounding Chang-bo's experience with the state security agents begin to change his

wife's ideas about the government? Highlight specific evidence from the text and make annotations to support any inferences you make.

4. In paragraph 13, what does the idiom "let rip" mean? What context clues in paragraphs 13–14 helped you understand the meaning of this idiom as it is used in the text? How does the use of such idioms affect the meaning and tone of the text? Highlight the context clues and make annotations to explain your responses.

5. As you reread the last paragraph, determine to what degree Chang-bo shaped his daughter's ideas. How do you think his daughter feels about living in this society? Draw inferences from the text and highlight the evidence you used to make these inferences. Make annotations to explain your thinking.

WRITING PROMPT

How do ideas influence individuals or events in the text? Choose one important idea or individual, such as Chang-bo, in *Nothing to Envy: Ordinary Lives in North Korea,* and demonstrate how an idea influenced him or her, setting off a chain reaction of events. Introduce your idea with clear and precise language and with vocabulary or idioms from the selection. Use your understanding of informational text elements to determine how ideas, individuals, and events interact in the text. Provide transitions to clarify connections in your information. Use a formal style and cite specific textual evidence to support your response. Complete your writing with an effective conclusion that leaves your audience with an understanding of your topic and with an idea, fact, or question to think about.

FEED

FICTION
M.T. Anderson
2002

INTRODUCTION

M.T. Anderson's *Feed* is a young-adult science-fiction novel about a futuristic world in which technology is so intertwined with human life that a computer network feed is implanted directly into people's brains. Here, the narrator of the novel, a teenager named Titus, visits his girlfriend Violet in the hospital, where she is suffering from a malfunction of her feed.

"It's not you," I argued. "It's the feed thing. You're not like that."

 FIRST READ

From Part 4: Slumberland

1   87.3%

2   Violet's father got there half an hour after I did. I saw him running past me. I didn't wave or anything, because I didn't want to get in the way or be a pain in the butt. People, sometimes, they need to be alone. He went past me and didn't see who I was. That was okay with me. They took him into the room. I waited.

3   I clapped my hands together softly a bunch of times. I swung my arms at my sides and then clapped. I realized that they were swinging really wide. People were looking up at me. I stopped. I couldn't help a small clap, one last one.

4   He came out. He was walking real slow. He sat down.

5   I didn't know whether to talk to him. He was smoothing out the knees of his tribe-suit.

6   I went over. I said hello, and introduced myself again.

7   He said, "Oh, yes. Hello. Thank you for . . . " He was just like, nodding.

8   "Is she okay?" I asked.

9   "Yes," he said. "Yes. 'Okay.' Yes, she's 'okay.'"

10   He didn't seem much like before.

11   I was like, "What's happening?"

12 "They're fixing the **malfunction**. For the time being. The doctor's coming out." His eyes were orange with the light from his **feed** glasses.

13 The orbs went past. We waited. Two nurses were talking about the weekend. There was nothing I wanted to watch on the feed. It made me feel tired.

14 "Can you stop?" said her father to me.

15 I realized I'd like been clapping again.

16 "I hate rhythms," he said.

17 I put my hands down. I stood still, in front of him.

18 He said, "You can monitor her feed function." He sent me an address. "Go there," he said. "If things **neural** were going swimmingly with Vi, the number you detect would be about ninety-eight percent."

19 I went there. It was some kind of medical site. It said *Violet Durn, Feed Efficiency: 87.3%.* He stared at me. I stared at him. We were like, just, there. The efficiency went up to 87.4%. He turned his head. Someone was whistling two notes in the hallway.

. . .

20 87.1%

21 The next day, I was at her house. It was all weird. We didn't talk. I don't know why. We didn't open our mouths. We just sat there, silent, chatting.

22 *It's not you,* I argued. *It's the feed thing. You're not like that.*

23 *Maybe I am like that. Maybe that's what's wrong.*

24 She rubbed her hands together. *I'm sorry. Please tell Quendy I'm sorry.*

25 Her father was walking down the stairs near us. We could hear him through the wall.

26 I didn't understand, first. *What?*

27 *I lost a year. During the seizure. I can't remember anything from the year before I got the feed. When I was six. The information is just gone. There's nothing there.*

28   She was pressing her palms into her thighs as hard as she could. She watched herself real careful like it was a crafts project. She went, *Nothing. No smells. No talking. No pictures. For a whole year. All gone.*

29   I just looked at her face. There were lines on it I hadn't seen before. She looked sick, like her mouth would taste like the hospital. She saw me looking at her.

30   She was like, *Don't worry, Titus. We're still together. No matter what, we'll still be together.*

31   *Oh,* I went. *Yeah.*

32   She reached out and rubbed my hand. *I'll remember you. I'll hold on to you.*

33   *Oh,* I chatted. *Okay.*

34   She went, . . . *there's so much I need to do. . . . You can't even know. I want to go out right now and start. I want to dance. You know? That's . . . .so cliché, but that's what I see myself doing. I want to dance with like a whole lacrosse team, maybe with them holding me up on a Formica tabletop. I can't even tell you. I want to do the things that show you're alive. . . .*

35   *I want to go on rides. The flume, the teacups, the Tilt-a-Whirl? You know, a big bunch of us on the teacups, with you and me crushed together from the centrifugal force.*

36   I wasn't really wanting to think about us crushed together right then, or about us in a big group, where she might go insane again, so I just looked like, *Yeah. The teacups!*

37   And she was still saying, *I want to see things grazing through field glasses. I want to go someplace now. I want to get . . . out of here and visit some Mayan temples. I want you to take my picture next to the **sacrificial** stone. You know? I want to run down to the beach, I mean, a beach where you can go in the water. I want to have a splashing fight.*

38   I just sat there. Her father was working on something in the basement. It sounded like he had some power tools. Maybe he was drilling, or like, cutting or boring.

39   She went, *They're all sitcom openers.*

40   *What?*

41   *Everything I think of when I think of really living, living to the full—all my ideas are just the opening credits of sitcoms. See what I mean? My idea of life, it's*

what happens when they're rolling the credits. . . . What am I, without the
feed? It's all from the feed credits. My idea of real life. You know? Oh, you and
I share a snow cone at the park. Oh, funny, it's dribbling down your chin. I
wipe it off with my elbow. "Also starring Lurna Ginty as Violet." Oh, happy day!
Now we go jump in the fountain! We come out of the tunnel of love! We run
through the merry-go-round. You're checking the park with a metal detector!
I'm checking the park with a Geiger counter! We wave to the camera!

42 *Except the Mayan ruin.*

43 *What about it?*

44 *There aren't,* I like pointed out, *there aren't the sacrificial stones. In sitcoms.*

45 *No,* she said. *That's right. Chalk one up for the home team.*

46 We sat. She fixed her hair with her hand.

47 I asked her, *What did it feel like. At the party?*

48 She waited. Then, she admitted, *It felt good. Really good, just to scream*
finally. I felt like I was singing a hit single. . . .

FEED. Copyright © 2002 by M.T. Anderson. Reproduced by permission of the
publisher, Candlewick Press, Somerville, MA.

 THINK QUESTIONS

1. What has happened to Violet? Use evidence from the text that is directly stated or that you have inferred from clues to explain Violet's "illness."

2. What method are Titus and Violet using to chat in paragraph 22? Draw an inference from specific evidence in the text. Support your answer by identifying the textual evidence you used to make your inference.

3. What happened to Violet's memory when she had her seizure? Cite specific textual evidence from paragraph 22 to support your answer.

4. Remembering that the Latin prefix *mal-* means "bad," use the context clues provided in paragraph 12 of the first chapter presented to determine the meaning of **malfunction.** Write your definition of "malfunction" and explain how you determined its meaning.

5. Use context clues to determine the meaning of **feed** as it is used in paragraph 28. Write your definition of "feed" and explain how you figured out the meaning. Be sure to use a print or an online dictionary to confirm your definition.

Please note that excerpts and passages in the StudySync® library and this workbook are intended as touchstones to generate interest in an author's work. The excerpts and passages do not substitute for the reading of entire texts, and StudySync® strongly recommends that students seek out and purchase the whole literary or informational work in order to experience it as the author intended. Links to online resellers are available in our digital library. In addition, complete works may be ordered through an authorized reseller by filling out and returning to StudySync® the order form enclosed in this workbook.

Reading & Writing
Companion

161

CLOSE READ

Reread the excerpt from *Feed*. As you reread, complete the Focus Questions below. Then use your answers and annotations from the questions to help you complete the Writing Prompt.

FOCUS QUESTIONS

1. As you reread *Feed*, highlight specific textual evidence in paragraphs 22–25 that helps you make an inference about what Titus and Violet are "chatting" about. Make annotations about your inference.

2. In paragraphs 28 and 29, Violet doesn't actually say how she feels about losing her memory the year before she got her feed. Highlight specific evidence from the text that helps you draw an inference about how she feels. Make annotations to support your inference.

3. In paragraphs 30–34, Violet's and Titus's points of view about their relationship seem to differ. What inference can you draw from the text to support the idea that they don't view their relationship in the same way? Highlight several pieces of textual evidence and make annotations to support your inference.

4. In paragraphs 35 and 36, Violet expresses that she wants *"to dance with the whole lacrosse team,"* and *"go on rides."* Highlight the specific textual evidence that indicates why she wants to do these things. Make annotations explaining your inferences about her health, based on the evidence.

5. Reread paragraph 42 and highlight the specific textual evidence that allows you to infer that Violet is becoming aware of the unjust society in which she lives. Highlight textual evidence and make annotations to support your inference.

WRITING PROMPT

In a clear thesis statement, make three inferences about what has happened to Violet and how it has influenced her point of view about the society in which she lives. Organize your writing and use textual evidence, such as dialogue, description, and events, to support your inferences, or logical guesses, about what may not be directly stated by the author in the text. Use precise language and transitions to show the connections between (or among) your ideas. Consider your own experiences. What influences your point of view about society? Your answer to this question will lead you to a better understanding of what might affect Violet's point of view. Establish a formal style of writing and end with a strong conclusion to summarize your ideas.

THE HUNGER GAMES

FICTION
Suzanne Collins
2008

INTRODUCTION

Suzanne Collins's dystopian novel, *The Hunger Games*, is set in Panem—what remains of post-apocalyptic North America. In punishment for a failed uprising, the government annually requires each of the twelve districts of Panem to choose one boy and one girl to go to the Capitol, where they must participate in a televised battle to the death. At the selection ceremony, or reaping, for District 12, sixteen-year-old Katniss watches in horror as her little sister, Prim, is chosen for this year's Hunger Games—then rushes to take her place.

"'I volunteer!' I gasp. 'I volunteer as tribute!'"

 FIRST READ

From Chapter 1

1 "You look beautiful," says Prim in a hushed voice.

2 "And nothing like myself," I say. I hug her, because I know these next few hours will be terrible for her. Her first reaping. She's about as safe as you can get, since she's only entered once. I wouldn't let her take out any **tesserae.** But she's worried about me. That the unthinkable might happen.

3 I protect Prim in every way I can, but I'm powerless against the reaping. The anguish I always feel when she's in pain wells up in my chest and threatens to register on my face. I notice her blouse has pulled out of her skirt in the back again and force myself to stay calm. "Tuck your tail in, little duck," I say, smoothing the blouse back in place.

4 Prim giggles and gives me a small "Quack."

5 "Quack yourself," I say with a light laugh. The kind only Prim can draw out of me. "Come on, let's eat," I say and plant a quick kiss on the top of her head.

. . .

6 It's too bad, really, that they hold the reaping in the square — one of the few places in District 12 that can be pleasant. The square's surrounded by shops, and on public market days, especially if there's good weather, it has a holiday feel to it. But today, despite the bright banners hanging on the buildings, there's an air of grimness. The camera crews, perched like buzzards on rooftops, only add to the effect.

7 People file in silently and sign in. The reaping is a good opportunity for the Capitol to keep tabs on the population as well. Twelve- through eighteen-year-olds are herded into roped areas marked off by ages, the oldest in the

front, the young ones, like Prim, toward the back. Family members line up around the perimeter, holding tightly to one another's hands. But there are others, too, who have no one they love at stake, or who no longer care, who slip among the crowd, taking bets on the two kids whose names will be drawn. **Odds** are given on their ages, whether they're Seam or merchant, if they will break down and weep. Most refuse dealing with the racketeers but carefully, carefully. These same people tend to be informers, and who hasn't broken the law? I could be shot on a daily basis for hunting, but the appetites of those in charge protect me. Not everyone can claim the same.

· · ·

8   Just as the town clock strikes two, the mayor steps up to the podium and begins to read. It's the same story every year. He tells of the history of Panem, the country that rose up out of the ashes of a place that was once called North America. He lists the disasters, the droughts, the storms, the fires, the **encroaching** seas that swallowed up so much of the land, the brutal war for what little **sustenance** remained. The result was Panem, a shining Capitol ringed by thirteen districts, which brought peace and prosperity to its citizens. Then came the Dark Days, the uprising of the districts against the Capitol. Twelve were defeated, the thirteenth **obliterated.** The Treaty of Treason gave us the new laws to guarantee peace and, as our yearly reminder that the Dark Days must never be repeated, it gave us the Hunger Games.

9   The rules of the Hunger Games are simple. In punishment for the uprising, each of the twelve districts must provide one girl and one boy, called tributes, to participate. The twenty-four tributes will be imprisoned in a vast outdoor arena that could hold anything from a burning desert to a frozen wasteland. Over a period of several weeks, the competitors must fight to the death. The last tribute standing wins.

10   Taking the kids from our districts, forcing them to kill one another while we watch — this is the Capitol's way of reminding us how totally we are at their mercy. How little chance we would stand of surviving another rebellion.

· · ·

11   It's time for the drawing. Effie Trinket says as she always does, "Ladies first!" and crosses to the glass ball with the girls' names. She reaches in, digs her hand deep into the ball, and pulls out a slip of paper. The crowd draws in a collective breath and then you can hear a pin drop, and I'm feeling nauseous and so desperately hoping that it's not me, that it's not me, that it's not me.

12   Effie Trinket crosses back to the podium, smoothes the slip of paper, and reads out the name in a clear voice. And it's not me.

13 It's Primrose Everdeen.

From Chapter 2

14 There must have been some mistake. This can't be happening. Prim was one slip of paper in thousands! Her chances of being chosen were so remote that I'd not even bothered worrying about her. Hadn't I done everything? Taken the tesserae, refused to let her do the same? One slip. One slip in thousands. The odds had been entirely in her favor. But it hadn't mattered.

15 Somewhere far away, I can hear the crowd murmuring unhappily as they always do when a twelve-year-old gets chosen because no one thinks this is fair. And then I see her, the blood drained from her face, hands clenched in fists at her sides, walking with stiff, small steps up toward the stage, passing me, and I see the back of her blouse has become untucked and hangs out over her skirt. It's this detail, the untucked blouse forming a ducktail, that brings me back to myself.

16 "Prim!" The strangled cry comes out of my throat, and my muscles begin to move again. "Prim!" I don't need to shove through the crowd. The other kids make way immediately allowing me a straight path to the stage. I reach her just as she is about to mount the steps. With one sweep of my arm, I push her behind me.

17 "I volunteer!" I gasp. "I volunteer as tribute!"

Excerpted from *The Hunger Games* by Suzanne Collins, published by Scholastic Inc.

 THINK QUESTIONS

1. Refer to details in paragraphs 1 and 7 to make inferences about what the reaping is and why Katniss thinks Prim is safe from it.

2. What events led to the Hunger Games, and what purpose are the games meant to serve? Cite specific textual evidence from paragraph 8 to support your answer.

3. In Chapter 2, why is Katniss surprised when Prim is chosen as tribute? What does she do in response? Cite specific evidence from the text to support your response.

4. In *The Hunger Games,* people can purchase **tesserae** by agreeing to enter additional slips in the reaping. The tesserae can then be exchanged for a year's supply of grain or oil. "Tesserae" is a real word with historical roots. Use a print or an online dictionary to find which definition of tesserae most closely matches the way in which the word is used in *The Hunger Games*. Write your definition. Explain how you decided on your choice of meaning.

5. Use context clues to figure out the meaning of the word **sustenance** as it is used in paragraph 8. Write your definition of sustenance and explain how you figured out the meaning. Then use a print or an online dictionary to confirm or revise your definition.

CLOSE READ

Reread the excerpt from *The Hunger Games.* As you reread, complete the Focus Questions below. Then use your answers and annotations from the questions to help you complete the Writing Prompt.

FOCUS QUESTIONS

1. In order to compare and contrast the text with the film version of *The Hunger Games,* ask your teacher to help you access a video clip on the Web from the feature film. Then view the first 16 seconds of the video clip. Compare it to the details given in paragraph 7 of Chapter 1. Which details from the paragraph are also in the video clip? Which details aren't? Highlight the evidence in the printed text that is also in the video clip of the film, and make annotations to support your answer.

2. Reread paragraphs 11–13 in the text and view the next part of the video clip (up to 0:48). Compare and contrast how the writer builds tension in this part of the plot with the way that the filmmakers do. Highlight specific evidence from the printed text and make annotations to support your comparison.

3. The text in paragraph 14 is not evident in the film. Reread the paragraph and explain why the filmmakers likely chose not to include the narration in the paragraph as dialogue in the scene. How does the film convey Katniss's feelings about what has just happened?

4. Reread paragraph 15 and view the video clip from 0:49 to 1:23. Contrast how the plot details are presented in the printed text and film versions. Why do you think the movie conveys these events in a different way? Highlight evidence in the text and make annotations recording the differences in presentation.

5. Reread paragraphs 16 and 17 and compare the dialogue, characters, and action in the text to the corresponding shot in the video clip (1:24 to 1:34). Then access the audio version of this part of the text (6:18 to 6:44). How do the audio and film versions help you better understand the meaning of "the strangled cry comes out of my throat, and my muscles begin to move again"? How do both of these media help you empathize with Katniss and feel her pain about this unjust society? Cite textual evidence and make annotations to support your answer.

WRITING PROMPT

Consider the three versions of *The Hunger Games*—text, audio, and film—you have analyzed. Think about the similarities and differences in the way the story elements—character, setting, plot, conflict, and narration (or point of view) —are conveyed in each. Also, think about the possible theme that has begun to emerge from the part of the story you have read, heard, and seen. In a clear thesis statement, choose the medium you think would best convey the theme, and provide sound reasons for your choice. Organize and support your writing with relevant evidence from the text, audio, and film, using transitions to clarify relationships among the media. Review the vocabulary words you have learned. Be sure to check each word's etymology, or origin, in a print or digital dictionary. Make sure you are using the vocabulary correctly in context. Be aware of words with multiple meanings and use them appropriately. Use transitions to clarify how your ideas are related. Use a formal writing style and provide a strong conclusion that supports your ideas.

THE WORDS WE LIVE BY:
YOUR ANNOTATED GUIDE TO THE CONSTITUTION

NON-FICTION
Linda R. Monk
2003

INTRODUCTION

studysync tv

Providing multiple contexts for understanding and interpreting the Constitution, author Linda Monk explores the history and rationale behind the seminal text, including its 27 amendments. This excerpt begins as the constitution itself begins, with a phrase that defines the scope of the entire text, and the nature of our country as a whole, "We the People." Monk proceeds from there, line by line, phrase by phrase, to draw a closer focus on the intentions and meanings of "the words we live by."

"We the People..."

FIRST READ

From the Preamble

1   "We the People. . ."

2   The first three words of the Constitution are the most important. They clearly state that the people—not the king, not the legislature, not the courts—are the true rulers in American government. This principle is known as popular sovereignty.

3   But who are "We the People"? This question troubled the nation for centuries. As Lucy Stone, one of America's first advocates for women's rights, asked in 1853: "'We the People'? Which 'We the People'? The women were not included." Neither were white males who did not own property, American Indians, or African Americans—slave or free. Justice Thurgood Marshall, the first African American on the Supreme Court, described the limitation:

4   *For a sense of the **evolving** nature of the Constitution, we need look no further than the first three words of the document's preamble: 'We the People.' When the founding fathers used this phrase in 1787, they did not have in mind the majority of America's citizens . . . The men who gathered in Philadelphia in 1787 could not . . . have imagined, nor would they have accepted, that the document they were drafting would one day be construed by a Supreme Court to which had been appointed a woman and the descendant of an African slave.*

5   Through the **amendment** process, more and more Americans were eventually included in the Constitution's definition of "We the People." After the Civil War, the Thirteenth Amendment ended slavery, the Fourteenth Amendment gave African Americans citizenship, and the Fifteenth Amendment gave black men the vote. In 1920, the Nineteenth Amendment gave women the right to vote

nationwide, and in 1971, the Twenty-sixth Amendment extended suffrage to eighteen-year-olds.

6   ". . .of the United States, . . ."

7   Like most documents, the Constitution needed a good editor. That person was Gouverneur Morris, who served on the Constitutional Convention's Committee of Style. Morris was the Constitution's chief draftsman, while James Madison was the chief architect. Morris's task was to shape the verbiage of committees into ringing prose. He commented on his work years later: "Having rejected redundant and equivocal terms, I believed it to be as clear as our language would permit."

8   In the Constitution's Preamble, Morris's phrasing had substantive as well as stylistic consequences. The original draft of the Preamble referred to all thirteen states. But, in part because no one knew exactly which states would become the nine required to ratify the Constitution, Morris **condensed** the Preamble into the familiar words of today: "We the People of the United States."

9   Even after the Constitution's ratification, the United States was still evolving from a loose confederation of states into a cohesive national union. Only the Civil War finally achieved the latter. As historian Shelby Foote noted: "Before the war, it was said, 'The United States are.' . . . After the war, it was always 'the United States is.' . . . And that sums up what the war accomplished. It made us an 'is.'"

· · ·

10   ". . .this Constitution for the United States of America."

11   The U.S. Constitution is the oldest written constitution of a nation still being used. From the beginning, Americans and others have disagreed about its relative merits. Federalists believed that, by creating a stronger national government, the Constitution would enable the United States to survive among the competing powers of Europe and provide a surer safeguard for liberty at home. Antifederalists feared that the new Constitution would create a new form of tyranny, especially since it lacked a bill of rights. Only by promising that the new Congress would make passage of a bill of rights its top priority did the Federalists secure ratification of the Constitution.

12   To British prime minister William Gladstone, the U.S. Constitution was "the most wonderful work ever struck off at a given time by the brain and purpose of man." But according to Justice Thurgood Marshall, the U.S. Constitution was **"defective** from the start, requiring several amendments, a civil war, and momentous social transformation to attain the system of constitutional

government, and its respect for the individual freedoms and human rights, we hold as fundamental today." The Constitution was not perfect, but rather **perfectible**—through the amendment process.

13   At the Constitutional Convention, Benjamin Franklin stated that he approved of the Constitution "with all its faults" because he did not think a better one was possible at that time. The oldest delegate to the convention at eighty-one, Franklin was too weak to give speeches and instead offered his opinions through written remarks delivered by a fellow Pennsylvania delegate. Franklin reportedly signed the Constitution with tears in his eyes. But if Franklin was willing to sign a document so full of errors, according to one tart-tongued Boston critic, "no wonder he shed a tear." Perhaps Franklin's last words to the convention gave the best assessment of the prospects of the new republic. As the other delegates were signing the Constitution, Franklin remarked to those nearby that, throughout the convention, he had wondered whether the sun carved on the back of George Washington's chair was rising or setting. "Now," he said, "I have the happiness to know that it is a rising and not a setting sun."

Excerpted from *The Words We Live By: Your Annotated Guide to the Constitution* by Linda Monk, published by Hachette Books.

 THINK QUESTIONS

1.   Why are the first three words of the Constitution ("We the People") the most important words in the document? Cite specific evidence from paragraph 2 to support your answer.

2.   In paragraph 4, what reasons does Justice Thurgood Marshall give for his view that the first three words of the Preamble are evidence "of the evolving nature of the Constitution"? What specific evidence does the author provide in paragraph 5 to support Marshall's viewpoint? Cite textual evidence to support your answer.

3.   Explain why the Antifederalists were worried about ratifying the Constitution. How did the Federalists convince them to support ratification?

Cite evidence from paragraph 11 to support your response.

4.   Use context clues to determine the meaning of the word **defective** as it is used in paragraph 12. Write your definition of "defective." Explain how you figured out the meaning of the word by citing specific evidence from the text.

5.   Remembering that the Latin suffix -*ible* means "capable of," use the context clues provided in the passage to determine the meaning of **perfectible** in paragraph 12. Write your definition of "perfectible" and explain how you determined the meaning of the word.

CLOSE READ

Reread the excerpt from *The Words We Live By*. As you reread, complete the Focus Questions below. Then use your answers and annotations from the questions to help you complete the Writing Prompt.

FOCUS QUESTIONS

1. Use the following link to access the StudySync audio version of *The Words We Live By*. Listen to the audio for paragraphs 1–4, including the quotation (0:22–1:32) by Thurgood Marshall. Highlight the word the actor stresses in the first sentence of paragraph 3. Make annotations to explain why the actor might have stressed this word.

2. Highlight the text structure that Monk uses in paragraph 12. Make annotations paraphrasing what she is comparing and contrasting. With which person do you agree—Gladstone or Marshall? Cite specific evidence from the text to support your reasons.

3. Monk makes a strong case for the idea that "We the People" was not an accurate phrase to use in the Preamble to the Constitution because the document excluded many people in American society. Reread paragraphs 1–5. Highlight the groups of people in paragraph 3 who were not included in this document. Then use the following link to access the StudySync audio version of *The Words We Live By*. Listen to the audio for paragraphs 1–5 (0:00–2:05) Make annotations explaining which version—print or audio—helped you better understand what the phrase "We the People" connotes, and why it was inaccurate, given its historical context.

4. In the third sentence of paragraph 7, highlight the words "draftsman" and "architect." Use a dictionary to find the denotation of each word. Ask yourself: How was Morris the draftsman and Madison the architect of the Constitution? Distinguish among the connotations of these two words that have a similar meaning, or denotation. Make annotations recording your reasoning.

5. In the last paragraph, Monk describes the Boston critic as "tart-tongued." What is the connotation of the phrase "tart-tongued"? Which context clues helped you figure out the connotation and whether its meaning is neutral, positive, or negative in this context? Make annotations explaining how you determined the connotation of the phrase.

WRITING PROMPT

Listen to the audio version of *The Words We Live By* in StudySync.com
Compare and contrast the printed text version of the selection with the audio version, which has the same content. Focus your writing on the following questions:

- How are the two versions alike?
- How are they different?
- How does the medium affect the impact of the words?
- How does it shape the message or central idea?
- How does the delivery of the words affect the meaning of the selection and how you understand it?
- How does the medium affect how you experience or enjoy the material?

Begin with a clear thesis statement. Support your writing with specific evidence from both the text and audio versions of *The Words We Live By,* using precise language. Use transitions to show clear connections between the versions. Use a formal style, and end with a strong conclusion to support your information.

I, TOO, SING AMERICA

POETRY
Langston Hughes
1925

INTRODUCTION

Born in Joplin Missouri, (James Mercer) Langston Hughes was an influential figure during the Harlem Renaissance, where he helped pioneer a new literary art form called jazz poetry. Inspired by Carl Sandburg and Walt Whitman, Hughes wrote poems that gave voice to his own experiences and the shared experiences of other African-Americans during the era of segregation. "I, Too, Sing America" starts as a personal statement and extends to inspire future

"They'll see how beautiful I am..."

FIRST READ

 NOTES

1 I, too, sing America.

2 I am the **darker** brother.

3 They send me to eat in the kitchen

4 When **company** comes,

5 But I laugh,

6 And eat well,

7 And grow strong.

8 **Tomorrow,**

9 I'll be at the table

10 When company comes.

11 Nobody'll **dare**

12 Say to me,

13 "Eat in the kitchen,"

14 Then.

15   Besides,

16   They'll see how beautiful I am

17   And be **ashamed**—

18   I, too, am America.

"I, Too" from THE COLLECTED POEMS OF LANGSTON HUGHES by Langston Hughes, edited by Arnold Rampersad with David Roessel, Associate Editor, copyright © 1994 by the Estate of Langston Hughes. Used by permission of Alfred A. Knopf, an imprint of the Knopf Doubleday Publishing Group, a division of Random House LLC. All rights reserved.

 ## THINK QUESTIONS

1. Who is the speaker of the poem? How do you know? Refer to one or more details from the beginning of the text to support your response.

2. What is the speaker comparing in lines 2–4 and 8–10? How are these two sets of lines similar? How are they different? How does the second group of lines act as a response to the first set of lines? Cite specific textual evidence to support your answer.

3. Why will those who made him "eat in the kitchen", in line 3, "be ashamed" in the future? Cite specific evidence from the text to support your response.

4. The word **company** is a multiple-meaning word. Use context clues to determine the meaning of "company" as it is used in line 4 and repeated in line 10 in "I, Too, Sing America." Write your definition of "company" and cite the clues you used in the text to help you figure out the meaning.

5. Based on the context of the poem, what do you think the word **dare** in line 11 means? Write your definition of "dare" and confirm the meaning in a print or online dictionary.

Please note that excerpts and passages in the StudySync® library and this workbook are intended as touchstones to generate interest in an author's work. The excerpts and passages do not substitute for the reading of entire texts, and StudySync® strongly recommends that students seek out and purchase the whole literary or informational work in order to experience it as the author intended. Links to online resellers are available in our digital library. In addition, complete works may be ordered through an authorized reseller by filling out and returning to StudySync® the order form enclosed in this workbook.

Reading & Writing Companion   **177**

CLOSE READ

Reread the poem "I, Too, Sing America." As you reread, complete the Focus Questions below. Then use your answers and annotations from the questions to help you complete the Writing Prompt.

FOCUS QUESTIONS

Questions 2, and 4 ask you to use documents located on the web. Ask your teacher for URLs to find these documents.

1. In "I Hear America Singing," Walt Whitman uses the idea of "America singing" as a metaphor. One interpretation of this metaphor is that it stands for telling one's story of America and of being heard. Another interpretation is that it represents the participation of Americans in their society. Both meanings support Whitman's metaphor that all Americans, regardless of their position in society, have the freedom to "sing," to be heard, and to participate in the building of America. Highlight evidence in "I, Too, Sing America" that supports the idea that Hughes is making an allusion to Whitman's metaphor. Make annotations to support your analysis.

2. Reread the poem. Then listen to Denzel Washington's reading of "I, Too, Sing America" at. Where does the poem have a shift in focus and structure? Highlight this line in the printed text. Make annotations explaining how Denzel Washington's reading of the line alerts the reader to the shift in structure and theme in the poem.

3. Free verse often uses assonance (the repetition of vowel sounds in nearby words) and alliteration (the repetition of consonant sounds at the beginning of nearby words) to produce interesting sounds in a poem. Reread lines 15–17. Highlight the use of assonance and alliteration in some of the words. Make annotations explaining why a poem written in free verse might rely on assonance and alliteration to create a pleasing sound and rhythm in a poem.

4. Listen again to Denzel Washington's reading of "I, Too, Sing America" at. Focus on the last line of the poem (0:42–0:47). Highlight this line in the printed text and make annotations describing how the spoken presentation adds to your understanding of the theme of the poem.

5. Highlight evidence in the text that suggests that Hughes is using the metaphor of a home to explore his theme of the African American hope for racial equality in the future. Do you think that this metaphor works in the poem? How effective is his portrayal of America as an unjust society waiting for change? Make annotations explaining your response.

WRITING PROMPT

What is the central theme of "I, Too, Sing America"? In a clear thesis statement, explain how Langston Hughes uses the open form of free verse, alliteration and assonance, and figurative language, such as allusion and metaphor, to develop the theme of the poem. In what ways does hearing the poem recited affect your understanding of it and the theme? Focus your writing on these questions:

- How are the print and the audio versions alike?
- How are they different?
- How does the medium affect the impact of the words?
- How does it shape the message or theme?
- How does the delivery of the words affect the meaning of the poem and how you understand it?
- How does the medium affect how you experience or enjoy the material?

Begin with a clear thesis statement. Support your writing with specific evidence from both the text and audio versions, using precise language. Use transitions to show clear connections between the versions. Maintain a formal style, and end with a strong conclusion to support your writing.

REALITY TV AND SOCIETY

NON-FICTION
2014

INTRODUCTION

In these two articles, the writers make arguments for and against reality TV shows. One writer discusses the negative impacts of shows like *Jersey Shore* and *Here Comes Honey Boo Boo*, while the other focuses on the positive influence of shows like *American Idol* and *Supernanny*. Both writers present strong arguments and support their claims with evidence. Which of the writers' arguments do you find to be more convincing?

"...if what Americans see on reality TV is truly who we are, then we are in big trouble."

FIRST READ

NOTES

Reality TV Shows: Harmless Entertainment or Bad Influence?

Point: Stop Rewarding Bad Behavior

1 Television has been an important part of American life for nearly seven decades. But instead of improving with age, programming has **degenerated** into mindless reality TV. Even though these programs claim to picture real people in real situations, there is actually very little *real* in reality TV. There is, however, a real influence on TV viewers, and this influence is often negative, especially on young people. Many people claim that reality TV portrays an accurate and vivid picture of our society. But if what Americans see on reality TV is truly who we are, then we are in big trouble.

2 According to Nielsen, a television ratings company, in 2014 nearly 300 million Americans ages two and up live in homes with televisions. That figure represents more than 90 percent of the population who have access to hundreds of channels and the programs they show. Unfortunately, ratings show that many television viewers are choosing *Here Comes Honey Boo Boo* over political talk shows, broadcasts of national political conventions, or other programming reflecting issues that affect us all.

3 Of course, reality TV has turned many people into instant celebrities. Viewers see that people without talent or hard work can become rich and famous. All they have to do is behave badly in front of the camera. But what message does this send to young people? According to Russ Rankin, who often writes for the arts, young people are not viewing reality TV as mindless entertainment. They look up to the programs' stars and imitate them. They are easily influenced by what they see, and they see that bad behavior is rewarded. Young viewers learn that those who treat others with pettiness and contempt become rich and famous. In fact, in 2011, one of the stars of *Jersey Shore* was

paid more to address Rutgers University students than was Toni Morrison, a Nobel prize-winning author.

4   Tom Green is a comedian and actor who benefited from reality TV. Yet he is one of the most vocal voices against the genre. The difference for him, he says, is that he was not **exploited** and was in charge of his program. As the demand increased for more outrageous and negative programs, Green saw that "the audience became addicted to the cheap thrills." The quality of TV degenerated. He says, "The days of looking up to inventors, artists, and genuinely successful people are gone. Most people assume the behavior they see on TV is acceptable simply because it is on TV in the first place. Our media is shaping culture and training the audience to no longer demand quality programming. I had always presumed that the major corporations that ruled our media were far more responsible than I. Apparently, I was wrong."

5   Television producer Michael Slezak, senior editor of TVLine.com, says that he thinks reality TV shows are so prevalent because "networks love a good reality show since they're less expensive to produce. They don't require drawing in big stars."

6   It seems that no matter how often people are told that what they are watching is far from reality, they still watch. They continue to nurture false expectations that they too could become rich and famous if only they could be selected to participate in reality TV. In a recent survey, 10 percent of British teenagers were motivated by the dream of money and success. They said they would give up a good education to become a reality TV star.

7   It's not really the job of television networks to police the influences of television on culture and society. Yet networks do need to take some responsibility for what they have created with reality TV. As Tom Green says, "The networks should self-regulate by putting power back into the hands of artists and comedians." The media has done a massively good job of influencing society against smoking. They are now working on educating the public about obesity and healthy eating habits. They should be just as concerned about influencing the public about intelligent viewing and showing the best of how people should treat one another.

Counterpoint: Reality TV Can Educate and Inspire

8   Which came first: the chicken or the egg? This age-old question can easily be applied to the **controversy** surrounding reality television. Have these shows **corrupted** our society? Or do they reflect the natural changes that have occurred in the way we see our world?

9   Most people who claim that reality TV has had a negative effect on society are mainly referring to shows that focus on celebrities, such as *Keeping Up With the Kardashians*, or on contrived competitions such as *Survivor*. *Survivor* can be said to build teamwork, but the challenges the contestants face are admittedly not real. And even though the participants are not in any real danger, they are encouraged to create drama to thrill viewers.

10   Other competitive reality TV shows truly showcase talent. Programs such as *Project Runway, American Idol, America's Got Talent,* and *So You Think You Can Dance* give artists and performers the chance to appear before millions of TV viewers. As a result, the careers of many participants have been launched by way of these programs, even though these contestants did not win the competition. One dancer from Texas, for example, has danced professionally in music videos and on TV shows such as *Glee* since appearing on *So You Think You Can Dance*. These shows inspire young viewers. They see people like them succeeding. So they may think, "I can do that." In this way, reality shows encourage young people to reach for the stars.

11   Reality shows that focus on the lives of everyday people may also give people comfort. As the Greek philosopher Aristotle once said of those who attended theater performances, they did so "to be cured, relieved, restored to psychic health." Viewers can identify with people who seem just like them. They see people with problems similar to (or worse than) their own. As a result, they may realize that their own struggles are not as bad as they thought.

12   Reality TV also introduces viewers to lifestyles, cultures, and people different from themselves. The NAACP reported in 2008 that reality programs are the only segment of television that fairly represents nonwhite groups. At least the people viewers see reflect the wide **diversity** of people in our nation.

13   Some reality TV shows actually improve society. For example, shows such as *Hoarders* increase public awareness of a serious mental health problem. Other shows, such as *Supernanny,* give parents and caregivers tips on how to handle children.

14   Blaming reality TV for society's challenges is a convenient way to avoid taking a hard look at ourselves and finding solutions to our problems. Life is messy, and reality TV honestly reveals that truth. Once we realize that we are far from perfect, we can learn to accept others for who they are. Certainly, acceptance of others, with all their faults, is a big step toward creating a better society for everyone.

Please note that excerpts and passages in the StudySync® library and this workbook are intended as touchstones to generate interest in an author's work. The excerpts and passages do not substitute for the reading of entire texts, and StudySync® strongly recommends that students seek out and purchase the whole literary or informational work in order to experience it as the author intended. Links to online resellers are available in our digital library. In addition, complete works may be ordered through an authorized reseller by filling out and returning to StudySync® the order form enclosed in this workbook.

THINK QUESTIONS

1. What position does the "Point" author take in the debate over reality TV? Cite two pieces of evidence from the "Point" essay to support your answer.

2. The "Point" author uses the opinion of comedian Tom Green to support the argument. How does Green's opinion help the author explain what has caused the quality of TV to decline? Cite specific evidence from the fourth paragraph of the "Point" essay to support your answer.

3. What position does the "Counterpoint" author take in the debate over reality TV? Cite two pieces of evidence from the fifth and sixth paragraph of the "Counterpoint" essay to support your response.

4. Use context clues to determine the meaning of the word **degenerated** as it is used in the first paragraph of the Point section in "Reality TV and Society." Write your definition of "degenerated" and identify the clues that helped you figure out the meaning. Look up the word in a dictionary to confirm or revise your definition.

5. Use context clues in the sentence and in surrounding sentences to determine the meaning of the word **controversy** as it is used in the first paragraph of the Counterpoint section in "Reality TV and Society." Write your definition of "controversy." Then look up the definition in a dictionary to confirm or revise your meaning. Tell how you determined the meaning of the word, explaining how your definition supports the idea of a debate between the two authors in the text.

CLOSE READ

Reread the debate "Reality TV and Society." As you reread, complete the Focus Questions below. Then use your answers and annotations from the questions to help you complete the Writing Prompt.

FOCUS QUESTIONS

1. How does the "Point" author use the first paragraph and the "Counterpoint" author the third paragraph of their essays to establish their purpose and point of view? How does each author distinguish his or her position on reality TV from that of the other writer, even though they are writing about the same topic? Highlight relevant evidence from the text. Make annotations to compare and contrast the different points of view that the two authors express about the same topic.

2. In paragraph 4, the "Point" author quotes the comedian Tom Green. In what ways does Green support the "Point" author's argument? Highlight your textual evidence and make annotations to explain your ideas.

3. Trace and evaluate the specific claim in paragraph 5 under "Point: Stop Rewarding Bad Behavior." How does it differ from the other evidence this author has presented up to this point? Do the reasons and evidence support the author's

claim? Why or why not? Highlight textual evidence and make annotations to support your answer.

4. Reread paragraph 6 under "Point: Stop Rewarding Bad Behavior" and paragraph 3 under "Counterpoint: Reality TV Can Educate and Inspire." Which author has convinced you of his or her argument? Is reality TV good or bad for society? Evaluate the merit and reasonableness of the claim offered by the author you chose. Highlight evidence from the text and make annotations to support your response.

5. Based on the evidence in paragraph 2 under "Counterpoint: Reality TV Can Educate and Inspire," what do you think the author's point of view is on reality shows such as *Keeping Up With the Kardashians* and *Survivor*? Support your point of view with strong reasons. Highlight relevant evidence from the text and be sure that it's sufficient. Make annotations to highlight the evidence you found most convincing.

WRITING PROMPT

You have read the opposing viewpoints in the article titled "Are Reality Shows Good for Society?" With which author's point of view do you agree? Are reality shows bad or beneficial for society? Use transitions to show relationships between ideas. In your opinion, which author made the stronger argument? Which writer was more convincing? Why? How strong was the author's reasons and evidence? Support your own writing with clear reasons and relevant evidence from the text to explain why one author and not the other persuaded you to accept his or her point of view about the influence of reality TV on society. Maintain a formal writing style and end with a strong conclusion.

Please note that excerpts and passages in the StudySync® library and this workbook are intended as touchstones to generate interest in an author's work. The excerpts and passages do not substitute for the reading of entire texts, and StudySync® strongly recommends that students seek out and purchase the whole literary or informational work in order to experience it as the author intended. Links to online resellers are available in our digital library. In addition, complete works may be ordered through an authorized reseller by filling out and returning to StudySync® the order form enclosed in this workbook.

Reading & Writing Companion   **185**

NARRATIVE WRITING

WRITING PROMPT

Imagine how you would feel if the government banned your favorite TV show. You would probably find it terribly unfair if the authorities took your show off the air. In this unit, you have been reading fiction and nonfiction narratives—imagined and true stories—about characters or real people who do not live in fair, or just, societies. All these selections have something in common: like the gladiators of ancient Rome or the people of North Korea, the characters or people in these texts are the victims of unfair laws and unjust rulers. Think about the principles of an open and just society, and contrast them with the rules of a closed and unjust society. Then write a fictional narrative (or story) about a character who is seeking justice in an unjust society. Model your story on one of the texts you have read in this unit.

Your narrative should include:

- a beginning in which you set the scene
- a clear description of the characters
- a series of clearly described events
- an underlying theme (or message)
- a narrator with a specific point of view

A **narrative** is the retelling of real or imagined experiences or events. Narratives can be fiction or nonfiction. Fictional narratives are made-up stories and can take the form of novels, short stories, poems, or plays. Nonfiction narratives are true stories, often expressed in memoirs or diary entries, personal essays or letters, autobiographies or biographies, eyewitness accounts or histories. Many narratives have a narrator who tells the story as it unfolds. In nonfiction narratives, the author usually tells the story. In fictional narratives, the narrator may or may not be a character in the story. Good narrative writing uses storytelling techniques, descriptive details, and often a clear sequence of events that are told in the order in which the events happen.

The features of narrative writing include:

- setting
- characters
- plot
- theme
- point of view

As you actively participate in this Extended Writing Project, you will receive more instructions and practice to help you craft each of the elements of narrative writing.

 ## STUDENT MODEL

Before you begin to write your own fictional narrative (or story), begin by reading this story that one student wrote in response to the writing prompt. As you read this student model, highlight and annotate the features of narrative writing that the student included in her fictional narrative.

Theo's Song

Clang, clang, clang! Fifty apprentices toiled away in the infernally hot smithy. Their hammers rang out as they pounded red disks of metal into the things the Community needed—horseshoes, armor, and nails. Fifty young people, their faces taut with concentration, swung their hammers relentlessly. No one spoke because no one could hear a puny human voice over the clamor of the workshop.

Theo was a newly apprenticed blacksmith. The Authorities had only recently assigned him to the smithy. As with all the children in the Community, the day Theo had turned thirteen, the Authorities removed him from the nursery pod where he had spent his first twelve years cared for by the Nanny. The Nanny said nothing as he was taken away.

The Authorities had taken Theo to the Interview Room, where he met an older woman, known as the Decider. She considered Theo carefully. She asked him about his goals and dreams. He gladly talked about his desire to become a songwriter and how his greatest wish was to share his music with the Community.

After the interview, the woman gently squeezed Theo's delicate hand and wished him luck. Following a medical examination, the Authorities pronounced his Assignment. Theo, the slight, sensitive, and musical boy, was to become a blacksmith. He would spend the rest of his life laboring in a hot, noise-filled room where he would likely grow deaf to the music inside him.

That had been the Authorities' intention, as Neema, a fellow apprentice, told Theo later. She was two months older than he and still adjusting to her Assignment. She was surprisingly chatty after a day of swinging a hammer, and even yet had the energy to speak with the others during a meal in the crowded Community Room.

"It's their plan," she explained to Theo in a low voice because she knew that Others were listening. "The Authorities, the Decider—they choose the one task that suits you least. I wanted to be a dancer. Now I'm a blacksmith. You know who gets to dance? The people with two left feet!"

"And people who sing can't even carry a tune," Theo lamented. "I don't get it at all. Why make people so miserable? Why not let us do what we're good at?"

Neema whispered now. "Because they can control us if we're unhappy! The hammers bang all day long. All I can think about is getting a minute of quiet. And some sleep," Neema said, yawning.

That night, Theo thought about Neema's words. He, too, spent the hours of his working day trying to block out the deafening noise around him. He realized that he hadn't heard any music in his head since the day he left the Pod. As a result, even in the quiet Sleep Room, because his ears were ringing so loudly, he could not remember even one tune. It was so unfair, so unjust, so *cruel,* he thought. His chest tightened as he considered never singing again. Just before falling into a dreamless sleep, Theo made a resolution that would change his life.

The next day, Theo approached his station at the smithy with a new purpose. As he wound his fingers around the handle of his hammer, instead of closing himself off to the noise around him, he opened his ears. He paid attention to the sounds of the hammers around him. He noticed patterns of rhythms. He heard how the hammers rang out as they struck. Soon, a song began forming in the back of his mind. He coaxed it forward by changing the rhythm of his own hammering. Now he hammered as if striking a drum instead of a horseshoe. He looked around him.

The other blacksmiths had their heads down over their work. But now words were forming in Theo's mind. A moment later, he threw back his head and sang out:

"Oh, a hammer is a powerful tool! A hammer can shape the world! Yes, a hammer can change the world! You know it, too!"

His voice cracked, but he didn't care. He wanted only to release the song. He pounded his hammer in time with the words and shouted out the notes. Some blacksmiths around him joined in singing, transforming their hammering into a powerful percussion section. Soon, the room echoed with singing so loud that it nearly drowned out the hammering. When the song ended, Theo heard laughter. Someone shouted, "Great song!"

Within minutes, the Authorities collected Theo and led him back to the Interview Room where the older woman sat waiting at a table.

"What you have done is not acceptable, Theo," she told him. "The Authorities decide who may sing and who may not. Your role is to make things."

But Theo was not afraid. He said simply, "Singing makes people happy."

The woman said, "I am sorry for what must happen next, Theo." One of the Authorities entered the room and placed a black thread loosely around Theo's neck. "This thread has the power to cancel human speech. You will not be able to speak—or sing—for one month," the woman said before she dismissed him.

Theo returned to the smithy, where he silently took up his hammer. Word quickly spread of his punishment. Neema was outraged, and decided to take a stand. Within minutes, she was banging her hammer in time and singing Theo's song, and the entire smithy sang along with her. The Authorities were amazed. Never before had they faced such rebellion. They placed a silence thread on Neema and then on others, but song kept breaking out in the smithy. Eventually, the Authorities gave up on the terrible thread. They reassigned some blacksmiths to other tasks, including Theo, who was made a singer. In the end, they did something no one in the Community had ever dreamed of: They assigned all the blacksmithing tasks to apprentices who wanted to take them. Soon the rebellion stopped.

THINK QUESTIONS

1. Where and when might this story take place? What inferences can you make from specific details in the text about the setting and the way in which it affects the plot?

2. What is Theo like? Use specific details in paragraph 3 to describe him. What can you infer about his personality from his physical attributes?

3. Consider what happens to Theo and use time-order (or sequence) words to summarize the key events in the Student Model. How do these events reflect a theme, or central idea, in the story?

4. Think about the writing prompt. Which selections or other resources that you have read or used in this unit would you like to apply to writing your own narrative? What are some ideas that you might like to develop into a story? Make a list of ideas and discuss them with a partner. Support ideas with specific evidence from the texts you have read.

5. Based on what you have read, listened to, or researched, how would you answer the question, "What is it like to live in an unjust society?" Write a paragraph that focuses on a fiction or nonfiction narrative that you could write. Establish a context for action and introduce characters. Address some of the ways that people or characters develop their points of view toward injustice in the world.

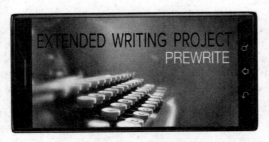

PREWRITE

WRITING PROMPT

Imagine how you would feel if the government banned your favorite TV show. You would probably find it terribly unfair if the authorities took your show off the air. In this unit, you have been reading fiction and nonfiction narratives—imagined and true stories—about characters or real people who do not live in fair, or just, societies. All these selections have something in common: like the gladiators of ancient Rome or the people of North Korea, the characters or people in these texts are the victims of unfair laws and unjust rulers. Think about the principles of an open and just society, and contrast them with the rules of a closed and unjust society. Then write a fictional narrative (or story) about a character who is seeking justice in an unjust society. Model your story on one of the texts you have read in this unit.

Your narrative should include:

- a beginning in which you set the scene
- a clear description of the characters
- a series of clearly described events
- an underlying theme (or message)
- a narrator with a specific point of view

In addition to studying the techniques authors use to tell stories, you have been reading real and imagined stories about people or characters living in unjust societies. In the extended writing project, you will use those storytelling techniques to compose your own made-up narrative, or story.

Because your story will be about life in an unjust society, you will want to think about how the characters or people you have read about have responded when they have witnessed or participated in an injustice. Think back to when you read "The Lottery": How do the people in the community feel about the lottery? Do they think it is fair or unfair? How do they change as a result of their experiences? What does the narrator think about the lottery and the characters who participate in it? What do you think about a society that has created such a practice? What would you do if you lived in the village?

Make a list of the answers to these questions about "The Lottery." Then consider how at least two other characters you have read about in this unit— for example, Prim's sister in *The Hunger Games* and Jonas in *The Giver*—feel about participating in their societies. As you write down your ideas, look for similarities and differences in the narratives. Do the characters' experiences have anything in common? Do you notice events that are repeated? What do you notice about the narrators who tell these stories? Look for patterns that will help you develop the characters, plot events, including the conflict (or problem) in your story. When you think about how the narrator views the characters and events, you will begin to develop your own point of view. Use this model to help you get started with your own prewriting:

Text: "The Lottery," by Shirley Jackson

How the Characters Feel: Before the lottery, people in the village are friendly and joking. After the lottery, people become hostile because Tessie Hutchinson says the lottery is unfair. All the other villagers disagree. One says, "All of us took the same chance."

How the Narrator Feels: The narrator doesn't seem upset by the events in the story. He or she is just telling the story as a detached or indifferent observer, which is kind of harsh.

How I Feel: I think the lottery is scary and unfair. But the people probably have lived in the village for so long that it's an important tradition for them. The lottery must have had a real purpose long ago. However, it seems really unnecessary and cruel now. Like the character Tessie, I would speak up if someone in my family got the paper with the black dot. I would try to save my family member from a terrible, painful end. If I couldn't, I would figure out a way to leave the village.

After you have completed your prewriting, consider your thoughts and ideas as you work through the following Skills lessons to help you map out your analysis.

Please note that excerpts and passages in the StudySync® library and this workbook are intended as touchstones to generate interest in an author's work. The excerpts and passages do not substitute for the reading of entire texts, and StudySync® strongly recommends that students seek out and purchase the whole literary or informational work in order to experience it as the author intended. Links to online resellers are available in our digital library. In addition, complete works may be ordered through an authorized reseller by filling out and returning to StudySync® the order form enclosed in this workbook.

Reading & Writing Companion **193**

NOTES

Organize NARRATIVE WRITING

sync•skills

SKILL: ORGANIZE NARRATIVE WRITING

 DEFINE

The purpose of writing a narrative is to entertain readers while also inviting them to think about an important theme (or message)—a larger lesson about life or human nature. To convey the theme of a story, writers need to consider how to structure the story and organize the events in a way that makes sense.

Experienced writers carefully choose a **narrative text structure** that best suits their story. Most narratives use chronological (or sequential) text structure. To put it in simpler terms, this organization of a text is also called time order. It means that an author (or narrator) tells the events in the order in which they happen in a story. By telling what happens first, second, third, and so on, an author is giving the sequence of events. Along the way, this text structure enables the author to establish the setting, the characters, and the conflict (or problem) of the plot. Telling the events in time order also allows the characters and the action of the plot to move forward, through the middle of the story, when the main character (or characters) will attempt to resolve the conflict, or solve the problem. Finally, the story ends with the resolution of the conflict.

Sometimes, instead of moving the plot forward in time and action, the plot moves the action backward in time, or even starts the action in the middle of the story. For example, if the story is character-driven, the plot might focus on the character's internal thoughts and feelings, so the writer might begin with a flashback to establish the character's issues or situation before moving into the present time. Similarly, if the story is a mystery, the writer might start the story in the middle to build suspense by making readers question why the person was murdered, for example, and "who done it." To organize their story, writers often use a sequence-of-events chart, a timeline, or a flow chart. This type of graphic organizer will help them visualize and plot the order of events.

IDENTIFICATION AND APPLICATION

- When selecting a text structure for a story, writers consider the theme and the kind of story they want to tell. They consider questions about character and plot events:
  › Should I tell the story in the order that the events happen?
  › Should I use a flashback at the beginning to create mystery and suspense?
  › Who are my characters and how will they grow or change?
  › What is the conflict (or problem) of the plot?
  › What will be the most exciting moment of my story?
  › How will my story end?

- Writers often use signal words to hint at the organizational text structure:
  › Time order: *first, next, then, finally, before, after, now, soon, at last*
  › Cause-effect: *because, so, therefore, as a result*
  › Compare-contrast: *like, also* to compare; *unlike, but* to contrast Order of importance: *mainly, most important, to begin with, first*

- Even though a story is usually told in time order, writers may organize individual paragraphs by using a second narrative text structure. For example, when a plot event leads to serious consequences for a character, the writer may use cause-and-effect text structure in a paragraph. Despite these paragraph shifts in text structure, the overall text structure for the story is still time order.

- The sequence of events in a narrative helps shape how a reader responds to what happens, and it also contributes to the overall development of the story's plot from beginning to end. You will learn more about narrative sequencing, and the elements and techniques that move the plot forward, in a later lesson.

 MODEL

The writer of the Student Model understood from her prewriting that she would be telling her story in chronological order by giving events in time order—from beginning to end. In this excerpt from the first paragraph of the model, the writer makes the organizational structure clear. The narrator is telling the events in the workshop in the order they happened. However, by using the past tense (e.g., *toiled, rang, swung, spoke*) in the description, the narrator is telling the events to the reader sometime after they happened.

Please note that excerpts and passages in the StudySync® library and this workbook are intended as touchstones to generate interest in an author's work. The excerpts and passages do not substitute for the reading of entire texts, and StudySync® strongly recommends that students seek out and purchase the whole literary or informational work in order to experience it as the author intended. Links to online resellers are available in our digital library. In addition, complete works may be ordered through an authorized reseller by filling out and returning to StudySync® the order form enclosed in this workbook.

Reading & Writing Companion **195**

Clang, clang, clang! Fifty apprentices toiled away in the infernally hot smithy. Their hammers rang out as they pounded red disks of metal into the things needed by the Community—horseshoes, armor, and nails. Fifty young people, their faces taut with concentration, swung their hammers relentlessly. No one spoke because no one could hear a puny human voice over the clamor of the workshop.

In the second paragraph, the writer provides some background about the main character, Theo. Therefore, the narrator uses flashback to go back in time to just before the beginning of the story. Notice how the writer changes from using the past tense to the past perfect verb tense ("the day Theo *had turned* thirteen, the Authorities removed him from the nursery pod") to indicate that an event happened in the past ("the day Theo *had turned* thirteen") before another event happened ("the Authorities removed him from the nursery pod"), as well as signal words and phrases—*newly,* and *his first twelve years*—to let readers in on the time shift:

> *Theo was a newly apprenticed blacksmith. The Authorities had only recently assigned him to the smithy. As with all the children in the Community, the day Theo had turned thirteen, the Authorities removed him from the nursery pod where he had spent his first twelve years cared for by the Nanny. The Nanny said nothing as he was taken away.*

After "flashing back" in paragraphs 2 and 3, to fill in Theo's personal history, the writer returns in paragraph 4 to the smithy, the setting of the story, and to where he left off in paragraph 1. The writer uses time-order words and phrases in paragraph 4—*later, still, after, even, yet*— to help readers keep up.

> *That had been the Authorities' intention, as Neema, a fellow apprentice, told Theo later. She was two months older than he and was still adjusting to her Assignment. She was surprisingly chatty after a day of swinging a hammer and even yet had the energy to speak with others during a meal in the crowded Community Room.*

In order to organize the order in which she would tell her events, the writer used an Organize Narrative Writing Timeline. She listed the events and then numbered them in the order in which she first thought that she wanted them to appear in her story.

Event #2: The blacksmiths are working in the smithy.

Event #1: Theo gets taken from the Pod and given his Assignment.

Event #3: Neema explains what the Authorities are doing.

Event #4: Theo makes a resolution.

Event #5: Theo defies the Authorities by singing in the smithy.

Event #6: Theo gets taken to the Decider and punished.

Event #8: The authorities realize they can't control the rebellion and change their ways.

Event #7: Neema and the other blacksmiths continue to rebel by singing.

 PRACTICE

By using an Organize Narrative Writing timeline, you'll be able to fill in the events for your story that you considered in the prewriting stage of your Extended Writing Project. When you are finished, exchange organizers with a partner to offer and receive feedback on the structure of events the writer has planned, and the use of transitions to make shifts in time order and setting clear for the reader.

Please note that excerpts and passages in the StudySync® library and this workbook are intended as touchstones to generate interest in an author's work. The excerpts and passages do not substitute for the reading of entire texts, and StudySync® strongly recommends that students seek out and purchase the whole literary or informational work in order to experience it as the author intended. Links to online resellers are available in our digital library. In addition, complete works may be ordered through an authorized reseller by filling out and returning to StudySync® the order form enclosed in this workbook.

Reading & Writing Companion **197**

NOTES

SKILL: DESCRIPTIVE DETAILS

 DEFINE

One way a writer develops the setting, characters, and plot in a narrative is by using description and descriptive details. In a story, the descriptive details help readers imagine the world in which the story takes place and the characters who live in it.

Descriptive details often use precise language—specific nouns and action verbs—to convey experiences or events. Many descriptive details use sensory language to appeal to one or more of the reader's five senses. Sensory words tell how something looks, sounds, feels, smells, or tastes.

Descriptive details should be relevant to the story, such as a character's actions or the setting. In a story, it is easy to include many interesting details, but not every detail is relevant. For example, what a character smells might be less relevant than how he or she feels or what he or she sees or hears during a key moment in the story. Too many details can make the reader feel overwhelmed. Plus, they can slow the pace of a story. It's a good idea to select only the most important, or relevant, details for your story. Think about what the reader really needs to know to understand or picture what is happening. Consider what your narrator actually knows and can share with the reader, especially if he or she is a character in the story. Then choose the details that will most help the readers imagine what the setting looks like, what the characters are experiencing, or how the events are happening.

 IDENTIFICATION AND APPLICATION

One way to generate descriptive details is to use a graphic organizer. It can help you ask questions about your setting, characters, and plot events to determine which details the reader might need to know. The following details in this Descriptive Details Graphic Organizer are from the Student Model, "Theo's Song":

DESCRIPTIVE DETAILS	CHARACTER: THEO	SETTING: SMITHY
Looks like	Young, slender	Full of hard-working apprentices
Sounds like	Voice cracked by thirst	Noisy, full of clanging hammers
Thinks or feels like	Rebellious against the no-singing rules	——
Smells (or tastes) like	——	Like burning metal and hot, sweaty apprentices

As the writer planned the Student Model, she asked some questions to determine which descriptive details would be the most relevant to developing the narrative:

- Will this detail help the reader understand who the character is and why he or she thinks, says, feels, or acts a certain way?
- What does this detail reveal about the narrator's point of view? How does the narrator know this detail? What does the narrator reveal about himself or herself by sharing it?
- Will this detail help the reader experience what the character is feeling?
- Does this detail use language that is interesting and will appeal to one or more of the reader's five senses?
- Will this detail add to the story and help it move forward, or will it slow down the pace of the story?

MODEL

In the following excerpt from the Student Model, the writer uses sensory language to provide relevant descriptive details about the setting. Notice how many of the details appeal to the senses. Think about how vivid, precise language and specific details add to your understanding of the story.

NOTES

Clang, clang, clang! Fifty apprentices toiled away in the infernally hot smithy. Their hammers rang out as they pounded red disks of metal into the things the Community needed—horseshoes, armor, and nails. Fifty young people, their faces taut with concentration, swung their hammers relentlessly. No one spoke because no one could hear a puny human voice over the clamor of the workshop.

The first sentence appeals to the reader's sense of hearing: "Clang, clang, clang!" is an example of onomatopoeia in that the word *clang* actually mimics the sound that the hammers are making as they hit the metal. From the first sentence, readers can tell immediately that the setting is loud and noisy. The second sentence appeals to the sense of touch, smell, or taste: The smithy is hot, and you can almost feel, smell, and taste the heat and sweat. The third sentence includes details that appeal to the sense of hearing ("hammers rang out") and sight ("they pounded red disks of metal"). The fourth sentence appeals to the sense of sight. Because the characters' faces are described as "taut" and their hammers as swinging "relentlessly," you can actually picture the action. The paragraph ends with a sensory detail that appeals to your sense of hearing and helps you imagine how loud the workshop is.

PRACTICE

Create some descriptive details for your story that appeal to the senses. Then trade your details with a partner when you are finished. Offer feedback about the details. Engage in a peer review to determine which details will help keep your story moving forward. Offer feedback on how well sensory details establish context and reveal character point of view.

PLAN

WRITING PROMPT

Imagine how you would feel if the government banned your favorite TV show. You would probably find it terribly unfair if the authorities took your show off the air. In this unit, you have been reading fiction and nonfiction narratives—imagined and true stories—about characters or real people who do not live in fair, or just, societies. All these selections have something in common: like the gladiators of ancient Rome or the people of North Korea, the characters or people in these texts are the victims of unfair laws and unjust rulers. Think about the principles of an open and just society, and contrast them with the rules of a closed and unjust society. Then write a fictional narrative (or story) about a character who is seeking justice in an unjust society. Model your story on one of the texts you have read in this unit.

Your narrative should include:

- a beginning in which you set the scene
- a clear description of the characters
- a series of clearly described events
- an underlying theme (or message)
- a narrator with a specific point of view

Review the ideas you brainstormed in the prewrite activity and then take another look at the events you listed in your Organize Narrative Writing Timeline. Think about what you have learned about audience and purpose and about developing descriptive details for a narrative. These ideas will help you create a road map to use for writing your story.

Please note that excerpts and passages in the StudySync® library and this workbook are intended as touchstones to generate interest in an author's work. The excerpts and passages do not substitute for the reading of entire texts, and StudySync® strongly recommends that students seek out and purchase the whole literary or informational work in order to experience it as the author intended. Links to online resellers are available in our digital library. In addition, complete works may be ordered through an authorized reseller by filling out and returning to StudySync® the order form enclosed in this workbook.

Reading & Writing Companion   **201**

Consider the following questions as you develop the events of your narrative in the road map and consider the audience and purpose for which you are writing:

- Who are your characters? What are they like?
- Where and when does your story take place?
- Who is telling your story? Is the narrator a character in the story? Or is he or she telling the story from outside the text? What is his or her point of view about the setting, the characters, and the plot?
- What kind of society do your characters live in?
- What problem, or injustice, do they encounter?
- How do your characters resolve the conflict (or problem) of injustice that they face?
- How do your characters grow or change as the story moves forward?
- What is the most exciting moment in your story?
- What happens to your characters at the end?
- What theme (or message) do you want your audience to take away from your story?

Use this graphic organizer to get started with your road map. It has been completed with details from the Student Model, "Theo's Song."

Copyright © Bookheaded Learning, LLC

STORY ROAD MAP

Narrator & Character(s):	Narrator: Someone outside the story Characters: Theo, Neema, the Decider, the Authorities
Setting:	Blacksmith workshop and Community Room of an unknown society
Beginning:	Theo is a thirteen-year-old-boy who wants to become a singer. He is Assigned to be a blacksmith. Theo finds the smithy to be noisy and hot.
Middle:	Neema tells Theo that the Authorities control the people by giving them jobs they are not suited for. Upset at the thought he may never sing again, Theo makes a resolution. At work the next day, he leads the other blacksmiths in song before being taken away by the Authorities. He is punished with a terrible thread that cancels his voice. Neema rebels and leads the blacksmiths when Theo cannot.
End:	The Authorities can't control the rebellion. They re-assign Theo to be among the singers. They give the blacksmith jobs to those people who want them. The society changes to become more fair, or just,

SKILL:
INTRODUCTION/
STORY
BEGINNING

 DEFINE

The beginning of a fictional narrative is the opening passage in which the writer provides the exposition, or the important details about the story's setting, narrator, characters, plot, conflict, and even the theme. A strong introduction captures the readers' attention by making them want to read on to find out what happens next.

 IDENTIFICATION AND APPLICATION

- The beginning of a narrative (or story) includes exposition. The exposition establishes the setting, the narrator's point of view, the characters, the plot, and even the theme. As in other forms of writing, writers build interest by using a "hook" to capture the reader's interest. In a narrative, a hook can be an exciting moment, a detailed description, or a surprising or thoughtful comment made by the narrator or the main character.

- The beginning of a narrative also establishes the structure of the story. Remember: A story does not have to open with the start of the action. It can begin in the middle. This strategy "grabs" the reader's attention and builds suspense by making the reader wonder what's going on. Some stories even begin at the end and work their way backward in time. These strategies use flashbacks to capture the reader's attention, but they are not necessary. Most good stories start at the beginning of the action and tell the events in time order. They use descriptive supporting details, engaging characters, and unexpected plot twists to keep readers interested.

- The beginning of a story might also offer clues about the theme. The theme is the message or "big idea" about life that the writer wants readers to understand. The theme is developed over the course of the text as the characters grow, change, and make decisions about life. Good writers drop hints at the beginning of the story so that readers can consider the "big idea" as they read.

Reading & Writing Companion

MODEL

Reread the first paragraph of Shirley Jackson's famous short story, "The Lottery":

> The morning of June 27th was clear and sunny, with the fresh warmth of a full-summer day; the flowers were blossoming profusely and the grass was richly green. The people of the village began to gather in the square, between the post office and the bank, around ten o'clock; in some towns there were so many people that the lottery took two days and had to be started on June 26th, but in this village, where there were only about three hundred people, the whole lottery took less than two hours, so it could begin at ten o'clock in the morning and still be through in time to allow the villagers to get home for noon dinner.

The author begins by establishing the setting—the time and place in which the plot of the story will unfold. The details about the weather and the village suggest a beautiful summer day in an ordinary small town, with no specific characters being introduced. These details might not "hook" the reader, but then again, what is this lottery? The lottery is mentioned twice in the opening paragraph without any explanation, as if the narrator is "hooking" the readers in the hope of "reeling them in."

As it turns out, the running of the lottery provides the action of the plot, and the outcome of the lottery provides the story's theme—that blindly following tradition is dangerous, especially when it leads to injustice.

Notice that the author has done several key things in the opening paragraph—introduced the setting, or time and place of the story, and given readers an inking of the conflict of the plot as well as the theme.

 PRACTICE

Write a beginning for your story. It should introduce your setting and main character (or characters) and the conflict (or problem) of the plot. Try to include hints that might lead to the theme, or "big idea" about life or human experience. A hint to the theme might be a simple observation that the narrator or the main character makes—or an offhand remark that will turn out to be rich in meaning.

Please note that excerpts and passages in the StudySync® library and this workbook are intended as touchstones to generate interest in an author's work. The excerpts and passages do not substitute for the reading of entire texts, and StudySync® strongly recommends that students seek out and purchase the whole literary or informational work in order to experience it as the author intended. Links to online resellers are available in our digital library. In addition, complete works may be ordered through an authorized reseller by filling out and returning to StudySync® the order form enclosed in this workbook.

Reading & Writing Companion   **205**

NOTES

SKILL:
NARRATIVE
TECHNIQUES AND
SEQUENCING

 DEFINE

When writing a story, authors use a variety of narrative techniques to develop both the plot and the characters, explore the setting, and engage the reader. These techniques include dialogue, a sequencing of events, pacing, and description. **Dialogue,** what the characters say to one another, is often used to develop characters and move the events of the plot forward. Every narrative contains a **sequence of events,** which is carefully planned and controlled by the author as the story unfolds. Writers often manipulate the **pacing** of a narrative, or the speed with which events occur, to slow down or speed up the action at certain points in a story. This can create tension and suspense. Writers use **description** to build story details and reveal information about the characters, setting, and plot.

The beginning of a story is called the **introduction** or **exposition.** This is the part of the story in which the writer provides the reader with essential information, introducing the characters, the time and place in which the action occurs, and the problem or conflict the characters must face and attempt to solve.

As the story continues, the writer includes details and events to develop the conflict and move the story forward. These events—known as the **rising action** of the story—build until the story reaches its **climax.** This is a turning point in the story, where the most exciting and intense action usually occurs. It is also the point at which the characters begin to find a solution to the problem or conflict in the plot.

The writer then focuses on details and events that make up the **falling action** of the story. This is everything that happens after the climax, leading to a **resolution.** These elements make up a story's **conclusion,** which often contains a message or final thought for the reader.

IDENTIFICATION AND APPLICATION

Copyright © BookheadEd Learning, LLC

- Most narratives are written in sequential order. However, arranging events in time order is not the only skill involved in narrative sequencing. Writers group events to shape both a reader's response to what happens and the development of the plot from beginning to end.
  - › *Exposition* refers to the essential information at the start of a story.
  - › *Rising action* refers to the sequence of events leading up to a story's turning point.
    - › The turning point is called the climax, and it's usually the most suspenseful moment in the story.
    - › During the rising action, readers may experience anticipation, curiosity, concern, or excitement.
  - › *Falling action* refers to the sequence of events following the story's turning point, or climax, and leading to the resolution of the story's conflict or problem.
    - › During the falling action, readers may look forward to finding out how the story will end.
- Pacing is a technique that writers use to control the speed with which events are revealed. Description and dialogue can help writers vary the pacing in a narrative.
- Description uses specific details, precise language, and sensory words to develop characters, setting, and events. It can be used to slow down pacing.
- Dialogue, or the exchange of words between two or more characters, can reveal character traits and important plot details. Dialogue can be used to speed up or slow down pacing. A short, snappy line of dialogue might speed up a story. A long speech might slow it down.
  - › Dialogue is set in its own paragraph and inside quotation marks. A line of dialogue might look like this: "My name is Jeannette."
  - › Dialogue is usually followed by a tag, such as *she said* or *he asked,* to indicate who is speaking.
  - › Dialogue should suit the character who speaks it. Business executives at an important meeting would speak differently from teenagers playing a game at a friend's house.

MODEL

After the writer gives exposition in the introduction, he or she develops the characters and the events of the story, including the conflict (or problem) that the main character faces. The writer uses description and dialogue to enrich the story and to vary the pacing of events. Some paragraphs are longer than

NOTES

others. Some include dialogue, and some don't. Some include more descriptive details than others or different types of sentences. By varying the pacing, writers hold readers' interest.

Reread paragraphs 4–7 of the story, which appear in the middle of the Student Model "Theo's Song." Look closely at the text structure and at how the events begin to build the rising action of the story. Notice the writer's use of dialogue, pacing and description and the transitions that help to move the action of the story forward.

> That had been the Authorities' intention, as Neema, a fellow apprentice, told Theo **later.** She was two months older than he, and **still** adjusting to her Assignment. She was surprisingly chatty **after** a day of swinging a hammer, and even yet had the energy to engage with others during a meal in the crowded Community Room.
>
> "It's their plan," she explained to Theo in a low voice **because** she knew that Others were listening. "The Authorities, the Decider—they choose the one task that suits you least. I wanted to be a dancer. **Now** I'm a blacksmith. You know who gets to dance? The people with two left feet!"
>
> "And people who sing can't carry a tune," Theo lamented. "I don't get it at all. Why make people so miserable? Why not let us do what we're good at?"
>
> Neema whispered now. "Because they can control us if we're unhappy! The hammers bang all day long. All I can think about is getting a minute of quiet. And some sleep," Neema said, yawning.
>
> **That night,** Theo thought about Neema's words. He, **too,** spent the hours of his working day trying to block out the deafening noise around him. He realized that he hadn't heard any music in his head **since** the day he left the Pod. As a result, even in the quiet Sleep Room, **because** his ears were ringing so loudly, he could not remember even one tune. It was so unfair, so unjust, so *cruel,* he thought. His chest tightened **as** he considered never singing again. Just **before** falling into a dreamless sleep, Theo made a resolution that would change his life.

Notice how the fourth paragraph of the story (the first body paragraph) focuses on one part of an event—Neema and Theo talking in the Community Room. It includes descriptive details that tell which characters are involved, where they are, and what they are doing or saying. It also includes transition words—*later, still, after*—that indicate time order and that move the action along.

The fifth paragraph of the story features dialogue. All the words are spoken by Neema. A tag "she explained to Theo. . ." tells readers who is speaking and to whom. Notice that when a character speaks, his or her words appear in a new paragraph. As you follow the rest of the conversation, notice how the dialogue sets the stage for events that will likely occur. The writer's use of dialogue also reveals certain qualities about each character. The description of Theo's day, revisited by him as he falls asleep, gives the reader a very distinct impression, both of the setting in which he has found himself, and in the clarity of his feelings toward his situation. Notice the final sentence in the last paragraph. In it, the writer has picked up the pacing of the story. We know that Theo has made a sudden resolution and that it will have a significant impact on his life. The writer unveils this in single sentence intended to move the reader forward into the action with a feeling of suspense and anticipation.

 PRACTICE

Write a paragraph that conveys a point of rising action in your narrative. Focus on one event or one character's dialogue to move your story forward. Use the narrative techniques presented in the lesson, such as description, dialogue, and pacing, to guide readers through your paragraph. Be sure to include descriptive details that will make your story vivid and interesting to your readers.

SKILL:
CONCLUSION/
STORY ENDING

 DEFINE

The **conclusion** is the final section of a narrative (or story). It is where the readers find out what happens to the characters. The plot winds down, and the main character's conflict (or problem) is resolved. The ending of a narrative is called the resolution. In some stories, the narrator or a character leaves readers with a final lesson about life or human experience. More often, however, readers have to figure out the theme on their own by drawing inferences from the end of the story.

 IDENTIFICATION AND APPLICATION

- An effective ending brings the story to a satisfying close. It resolves the conflict, ties up loose ends, and may hint at what happens to the characters when the story is over.
  › The way a problem is resolved (the resolution) should be logical and feel like a natural part of the plot, but it can still be a surprise.
  › The resolution should tell clearly how the characters resolved the conflict (or problem)—or how it was resolved for them.
  › At the end of the story, the reader should be able to think about the narrator's role–how his or her point of view affected the way the story was told.
  › The concluding statement may sum up the story and leave readers feeling as if they were thoroughly entertained and thinking "That was a great story!"
- The conclusion might also include a memorable comment from the narrator or a character that helps readers understand the theme–the larger lesson about life or human nature that the story conveyed.

MODEL

 NOTES

In the conclusion to Shirley Jackson's well-known story "The Lottery," readers find out what winning the village lottery entails. Just before the end of the story, the villagers discover that Tessie Hutchinson holds the paper with the black dot. She has "won" the lottery. But winning is losing in this story, and if readers have been paying attention to the events leading up to this point, then they noticed that Tessie doesn't want anyone in her family to be a winner. Something is not quite right here. In the end, the story takes a surprising—even shocking—turn.

"All right, folks," Mr. Summers said. "Let's finish quickly."

Although the villagers had forgotten the ritual and lost the original black box, they still remembered to use stones. The pile of stones the boys had made earlier was ready; there were stones on the ground with the blowing scraps of paper that had come out of the box. Mrs. Delacroix selected a stone so large she had to pick it up with both hands and turned to Mrs. Dunbar. "Come on," she said. "Hurry up."

Mrs. Dunbar had small stones in both hands, and she said, gasping for breath, "I can't run at all. You'll have to go ahead and I'll catch up with you."

The children had stones already, and someone gave little Davy Hutchinson a few pebbles.

Tessie Hutchinson was in the center of a cleared space by now, and she held her hands out desperately as the villagers moved in on her. "It isn't fair," she said. A stone hit her on the side of the head.

Old Man Warner was saying, "Come on, come on, everyone." Steve Adams was in the front of the crowd of villagers, with Mrs. Graves beside him.

"It isn't fair, it isn't right," Mrs. Hutchinson screamed and then they were upon her.

The narrator does not describe exactly what happens to Tessie, but readers can infer that the villagers stone her to death. It's an ugly ending to a story that starts out on a lovely June day. Readers might be horrified to discover what the lottery means. They might also be shocked when they realize that this lottery has taken place every year for generations and is a tradition in the village. The story ends with Tessie crying out, "It isn't fair, it isn't right," a refrain that suggests the danger of blindly following tradition, especially when it leads to unfairness, or injustice. The narrator is completely silent on the matter. Not a character in the text, the narrator is completely detached, just relaying the events without any emotion.

 PRACTICE

Write an ending for your story. It should let your readers know how the main character (or characters) resolved the conflict (or problem). Your ending might also hint at what happens to the character after the story is over. In your conclusion (or ending), try to include a thoughtful statement about life or human nature. Your message might be something that the narrator or a character says, or it might be an inference about the theme that the reader can draw from specific evidence in the text.

DRAFT

WRITING PROMPT

Imagine how you would feel if the government banned your favorite TV show. You would probably find it terribly unfair if the authorities took your show off the air. In this unit, you have been reading fiction and nonfiction narratives—imagined and true stories—about characters or real people who do not live in fair, or just, societies. All these selections have something in common: like the gladiators of ancient Rome or the people of North Korea, the characters or people in these texts are the victims of unfair laws and unjust rulers. Think about the principles of an open and just society, and contrast them with the rules of a closed and unjust society. Then write a fictional narrative (or story) about a character who is seeking justice in an unjust society. Model your story on one of the texts you have read in this unit.

Your narrative should include:

- a beginning in which you set the scene
- a clear description of the characters
- a series of clearly described events
- an underlying theme (or message)
- a narrator with a specific point of view

You've already made progress toward writing your own fictional narrative. You've thought about your characters, setting, plot, conflict (or problem), and theme. You've considered your audience and purpose, determined an appropriate text structure to organize your ideas and events, generated plenty of descriptive details, and utilized narrative techniques, such as description, pacing, and dialogue. Now it's time to write a draft of your story.

Please note that excerpts and passages in the StudySync® library and this workbook are intended as touchstones to generate interest in an author's work. The excerpts and passages do not substitute for the reading of entire texts, and StudySync® strongly recommends that students seek out and purchase the whole literary or informational work in order to experience it as the author intended. Links to online resellers are available in our digital library. In addition, complete works may be ordered through an authorized reseller by filling out and returning to StudySync® the order form enclosed in this workbook.

Reading & Writing Companion   **213**

NOTES

Use your timeline of events and other graphic organizers to help you as you write. Remember that a fictional narrative has an introduction, a middle, and a conclusion. The introduction (or beginning) gives exposition that establishes the setting, the narrator, the characters, and conflict (or problem) of the story. The middle section, which consists of the rising action, develops the plot by using description, pacing, and dialogue to tell about each event. Transitions connect ideas and events, help the organization (or text structure), and enable readers to follow the flow of events. The conclusion (or ending) tells how the characters resolve their problem, or how it is resolved for them. It ties up loose ends and hints at the theme of the story and its important message. An effective ending can also do more—it can leave a lasting impression on your readers.

When drafting your story, ask yourself these questions:

- How can I improve my introduction to "hook" my readers?
- Who is the narrator of my story? Is it a character from inside or outside the text? How does the narrator's point of view affect the way I tell my story?
- What descriptive details can I add to make my setting, characters, and plot more relevant to my readers?
- Have I ordered the events of the plot so that narrative techniques, such as description, pacing, and dialogue, move the characters and action forward?
- What transition words and phrases can I add to make the order of events clearer?
- Is the end of my story interesting or surprising? Is the resolution of the conflict believable?
- Will my readers understand the theme? What changes can I make to present a clearer theme (or message) to my readers?

Before you submit your draft, read it over carefully. You want to be sure that you have responded to all aspects of the prompt.

REVISE

WRITING PROMPT

Imagine how you would feel if the government banned your favorite TV show. You would probably find it terribly unfair if the authorities took your show off the air. In this unit, you have been reading fiction and nonfiction narratives—imagined and true stories—about characters or real people who do not live in fair, or just, societies. All these selections have something in common: like the gladiators of ancient Rome or the people of North Korea, the characters or people in these texts are the victims of unfair laws and unjust rulers. Think about the principles of an open and just society, and contrast them with the rules of a closed and unjust society. Then write a fictional narrative (or story) about a character who is seeking justice in an unjust society. Model your story on one of the texts you have read in this unit.

Your narrative should include:

- a beginning in which you set the scene
- a clear description of the characters
- a series of clearly described events
- an underlying theme (or message)
- a narrator with a specific point of view

You have written a draft of your narrative. You have also received input and advice from your peers about how to improve it. Now you are going to revise your draft.

Here are some recommendations to help you revise:

- Review the suggestions made by your peers.
- Focus on your body paragraphs and your use of transitions. Remember: Transitions are words or phrases that help your readers follow the flow of ideas.
  - > As you revise, look for places where you can add transition words or phrases to help make the order of events or the relationship between ideas clearer.
  - > Test the transitions you have used or want to add. Make sure they reflect the relationship that you want to convey. Review the types of transition words you can use—chronological (sequential or time order), cause-effect, compare-contrast, problem-solution, spatial, order of importance, and so on.

- After you have revised your body paragraphs for transitions, think about whether there is anything else you can do to improve your story's organizational structure.
  - > Do you need to reorder any events to make the story clearer or more interesting?
  - > Do you need to add an event or provide description so that your readers can better understand the story?
  - > Do you need to cut an unnecessary event or description to keep the story from bogging down?
  - > Could you change some description to dialogue to pick up the pace of the story?

- As you revise, be aware of how you are using language to express characters' thoughts, words, and actions, along with the events that make up the narrative.
  - > Are you varying the types of sentences you're using? Writing becomes boring when it sounds the same. Incorporating a variety of simple, compound, complex, and compound-complex sentences into your writing adds interest.
  - > Are you choosing words carefully? Remember that in writing, less is often more. Look for ideas or sentences that you can combine or delete to avoid unnecessary repetition, and make your word choice as precise as it can be.

EDIT, PROOFREAD, AND PUBLISH

Copyright © BookheadEd Learning, LLC

WRITING PROMPT

Imagine how you would feel if the government banned your favorite TV show. You would probably find it terribly unfair if the authorities took your show off the air. In this unit, you have been reading fiction and nonfiction narratives—imagined and true stories—about characters or real people who do not live in fair, or just, societies. All these selections have something in common: like the gladiators of ancient Rome or the people of North Korea, the characters or people in these texts are the victims of unfair laws and unjust rulers. Think about the principles of an open and just society, and contrast them with the rules of a closed and unjust society. Then write a fictional narrative (or story) about a character who is seeking justice in an unjust society. Model your story on one of the texts you have read in this unit.

Your narrative should include:

- a beginning in which you set the scene
- a clear description of the characters
- a series of clearly described events
- an underlying theme (or message)
- a narrator with a specific point of view

You have revised your narrative and received input from your peers on your revised writing. Now it's time to edit and proofread your story to produce a final version. Have you included all the valuable suggestions from your peers? Ask yourself: Have I fully developed my setting, characters, plot, conflict (or problem), and theme? What more can I do to improve my story's descriptive details? Did I do a good job of introducing my story? Did I use transitions well to move from event to event in my body paragraphs? Did I provide an interesting or surprising ending? Did I use a writing style and tone that matched my story elements of setting, characters, plot, and theme?

When you are satisfied with your work, proofread it for errors. Use this list to check for correct:

- capitalization
- punctuation
- spelling
- grammar
- usage

In addition, check for correct punctuation in the dialogue. Check that you placed a comma correctly after an introductory phrase or clause and that you used a comma to separate a series of coordinate adjectives, such as a *small, pleasant woman.*

Once you have made your corrections to your writing, you are ready to submit and publish your work. You can distribute your story to family and friends, attach it to a bulletin board, or post it to your blog. If you publish online, create links to the stories of injustice that inspired you. That way, readers can read more stories such as the one you wrote.

studysync®

Reading & Writing Companion

Why is it essential to defend human rights?

Justice Served

UNIT 3   Why is it essential to defend human rights?

Justice Served

TEXTS

TEXTS

EXTENDED WRITING PROJECT

473

Text Fulfillment
through
StudySync

MOTHER JONES:
FIERCE FIGHTER FOR WORKERS' RIGHTS

NON-FICTION
Judith Pinkerton Josephson
1996

INTRODUCTION

Born in 1837, Mary Harris Jones, known as Mother Jones, was an American schoolteacher and dressmaker who went on to become a prominent workers' rights activist and community organizer. This excerpt from author Judith Pinkerton Josephson's biography of the fearless crusader describes her groundbreaking demonstrations against unfair child labor practices and her historic 1903 march from Philadelphia to Sagamore Hill, New York, to protest the poor conditions endured by young workers.

"About a sixth of the strikers were children under sixteen."

 FIRST READ

NOTES

From Chapter Nine: The March of the Mill Children

1 "I love children," Mother Jones once told a reporter.

2 In countless shacks and shanties across the country, she had tied the shoes of children, wiped their noses, hugged them while they cried, scrambled to find food for them, fought for their rights. By the turn of the century, almost two million children under the age of sixteen worked in mills, factories, and mines. Images of the child workers Mother Jones had seen stayed with her—the torn, bleeding fingers of the breaker boys, the mill children living on coffee and stale bread.

3 In June 1903, Mother Jones went to Philadelphia, Pennsylvania—the heart of a vast textile industry. About one hundred thousand workers from six hundred different mills were on strike there. The strikers wanted their workweek cut from sixty to fifty-five hours, even if it meant lower wages. About a sixth of the strikers were children under sixteen.

4 Nationwide, eighty thousand children worked in the textile industry. In the South, Mother Jones had seen how dangerous their jobs were. Barefooted little girls and boys reached their tiny hands into the **treacherous** machinery to repair snapped threads or crawled underneath the machinery to oil it. At textile union headquarters, Mother Jones met more of these mill children. Their bodies were bone-thin, with hollow chests. Their shoulders were rounded from long hours spent hunched over the workbenches. Even worse, she saw "some with their hands off, some with the thumb missing, some with their fingers off at the knuckles"—victims of mill accidents.

5 Pennsylvania, like many other states, had laws that said children under thirteen could not work. But parents often lied about a child's age. Poor

families either put their children to work in the mills or starved. Mill owners looked the other way, because child labor was cheap.

6 Mother Jones asked various newspaper publishers why they didn't write about child labor in Pennsylvania. The publishers told her they couldn't, since owners of the mills also owned stock in their newspapers. "Well, I've got stock in these little children," she said, "and I'll arrange a little **publicity.**"

7 Mother Jones, now seventy-three, gathered a large group of mill children and their parents. She led them on a one-mile march from Philadelphia's Independence Square to its courthouse lawn. Mother Jones and a few children climbed up on a platform in front of a huge crowd. She held one boy's arm up high so the crowd could see his **mutilated** hand. "Philadelphia's mansions were built on the broken bones, the quivering hearts, and drooping heads of these children," she said. She lifted another child in her arms so the crowd could see how thin he was.

8 Mother Jones looked directly at the city officials standing at the open windows across the street. "Some day the workers will take possession of your city hall, and when we do, no child will be sacrificed on the altar of profit." Unmoved, the officials quickly closed their windows.

9 Local newspapers and some New York newspapers covered the event. How, Mother Jones wondered, could she draw national attention to the evils of child labor? Philadelphia's famous Liberty Bell, currently on a national tour and drawing huge crowds, gave her an idea. She and the textile union leaders would stage their own tour. They would march the mill children all the way to the president of the United States—Theodore Roosevelt. Mother Jones wanted the president to get Congress to pass a law that would take children out of the mills, mines, and factories, and put them in school.

10 When Mother Jones asked parents for permission to take their children with her, many hesitated. The march from Philadelphia to Sagamore Hill—the president's seaside mansion on Long Island near New York City—would cover 125 miles. It would be a difficult journey. But finally, the parents agreed. Many decided to come along on the march. Other striking men and women offered their help, too.

11 On July 7, 1903, nearly three hundred men, women, and children—followed by four wagons with supplies—began the long march. Newspapers carried daily reports of the march, calling the group "Mother Jones's Industrial Army," or "Mother Jones's Crusaders." The army was led by a fife-and-drum corps of three children dressed in Revolutionary War uniforms. Mother Jones wore her familiar, lace-fringed black dress. The marchers sang and carried flags, banners, and placards that read "We Want to Go to School!" "We Want Time

to Play." **"Prosperity** Is Here, Where is Ours?" "55 Hours or Nothing." "We Only Ask for Justice." "More Schools, Less Hospitals."

12 The temperature rose into the nineties. The roads were dusty, the children's shoes full of holes. Many of the young girls returned home. Some of the marchers walked only as far as the outskirts of Philadelphia. For the hundred or so marchers who remained, this trip was an adventure in spite of the heat. They bathed and swam in brooks and rivers. Each of them carried a knapsack with a knife, fork, tin cup, and plate inside. Mother Jones took a huge pot for cooking meals on the way. Mother Jones also took along costumes, makeup, and jewelry so the children could stop in towns along the route and put on plays about the struggle of textile workers. The fife-and-drum corps gave concerts and passed the hat. People listened and donated money. Farmers met the marchers with wagonloads of fruit, vegetables, and clothes. Railroad engineers stopped their trains and gave them free rides. Hotel owners served free meals.

13 On July 10th, marchers camped across the Delaware river from Trenton, New Jersey. They had traveled about forty miles in three days. At first, police told the group they couldn't enter the city. Trenton mill owners didn't want any trouble. But Mother Jones invited the police to stay for lunch. The children gathered around the cooking pot with their tin plates and cups. The policemen smiled, talked kindly to them, and then allowed them to cross the bridge into Trenton. There Mother Jones spoke to a crowd of five thousand people. That night, the policemen's wives took the children into their homes, fed them, and packed them lunches for the next day's march.

14 By now, many of the children were growing weak. More returned home. Some adults on the march grumbled that Mother Jones just wanted people to notice *her*. They complained to reporters that Mother Jones often stayed in hotels while the marchers camped in hot, soggy tents filled with whining mosquitoes. Sometimes Mother Jones did stay in hotels, because she went ahead of the marchers to arrange for lodging and food in upcoming towns and to get publicity for the march.

15 As the remaining marchers pushed on to Princeton, New Jersey, a thunderstorm struck. Mother Jones and her army camped on the grounds of former President Grover Cleveland's estate. The Clevelands were away, and the caretaker let Mother Jones use the big, cool barn for a **dormitory.**

16 Mother Jones got permission from the mayor of Princeton to speak opposite the campus of Princeton University. Her topic: higher education. She spoke to a large crowd of professors, students, and residents. Pointing to one ten-year-old boy, James Ashworth, she said, "Here's a textbook on economics." The boy's body was stooped from carrying seventy-five-pound bundles of

NOTES

yarn. "He gets three dollars a week and his sister, who is fourteen, gets six dollars. They work in a carpet factory ten hours a day while the children of the rich are getting their higher education." Her piercing glance swept over the students in the crowd.

17 Mother Jones talked about children who could not read or write because they spent ten hours a day in Pennsylvania's silk mills. Those who hired these child workers used "the hands and feet of little children so they might buy automobiles for their wives and police dogs for their daughters to talk French to." She accused the mill owners of taking "babies almost from the cradle."

18 The next night, the marchers slept on the banks of the Delaware River. In every town, Mother Jones drew on what she did best—speaking—to gather support for her cause. One reporter wrote, "Mother Jones makes other speakers sound like tin cans."

19 Battling heat, rain, and swarms of mosquitoes at night, the marchers arrived in Elizabeth. Socialist party members helped house and feed the weary adults and children. The next morning, two businessmen gave Mother Jones her first car ride. She was delighted with this new "contraption."

20 On July 15, Mother Jones wrote a letter to President Roosevelt. She told him how these poor mill children lived, appealed to him as a father, and asked him to meet with her and the children. President Roosevelt did not answer Mother Jones's letter. Instead, he assigned secret service officers to watch her. They thought she might be a threat to the president. That made her furious.

21 On July 24, after more than two weeks on the road, the marchers reached New York City. By now, just twenty marchers remained. One of them was Eddie Dunphy, a child whose job was to sit on a high stool eleven hours a day handing thread to another worker. For this he was paid three dollars a week. Mother Jones talked about Eddie and about Gussie Rangnew, a child who packed stockings in a factory. She too worked eleven hours a day for pennies.

22 At one meeting, a crowd of thirty thousand gathered. "We are quietly marching toward the president's home," she told the people. "I believe he can do something for these children, although the press declares he cannot."

23 One man wanted the children to have some fun while they were in New York City. Frank Bostick owned the wild animal show at Coney Island, an amusement park and resort. He invited the mill children to spend a day at the park. The children swam in the ocean and played along the beach.

24 When Frank Bostick's wild animal show ended that night, he let Mother Jones speak to the crowd that had attended. To add drama, she had some of the children crawl inside the empty cages. The smells of sawdust and animals

hung in the air. But instead of lions and tigers, the cages held children. The children gripped the iron bars and solemnly stared out at the crowd while Mother Jones spoke.

25 "We want President Roosevelt to hear the wail of the children who never have a chance to go to school, but work eleven and twelve hours a day in the textile mills of Pennsylvania," she said, "who weave the carpets that he and you walk upon; and the lace curtains in your windows, and the clothes of the people."

26 She continued, "In Georgia where children work day and night in the cotton mills they have just passed a bill to protect songbirds. What about the little children from whom all song is gone?" After Mother Jones finished speaking, the crowd sat in stunned silence. In the distance, a lone lion roared.

27 The grueling walk had taken almost three weeks. Mother Jones had written the president twice with no answer. On July 29, she took three young boys to Sagamore Hill, where the president was staying. But the secret service stopped them at the mansion's gates. The president would not see them.

28 The group returned to New York City. Discouraged, Mother Jones reported her failure to the newspapers. Most of the marchers decided to return home. She stayed on briefly with the three children. Once more, she wrote President Roosevelt: "The child of today is the man or woman of tomorrow....I have with me three children who have walked one hundred miles.... If you decide to see these children, I will bring them before you at any time you may set."

29 The president's secretary replied that the president felt that child labor was a problem for individual states to solve. "He is a brave guy when he wants to take a gun out and fight other grown people," said Mother Jones in disgust, "but when those children went to him, he could not see them."

30 In early August, Mother Jones finally took the last three children home. Soon after, the textile workers gave up and ended their strike. Adults and children went back to work, their working conditions unchanged.

31 Though she had not met with the president, Mother Jones had drawn the attention of the nation to the problem of child labor. She became even more of a national figure. Within a few years, Pennsylvania, New York, New Jersey, and other states did pass tougher child labor laws. The federal government finally passed a child labor law (part of the Fair Labor Standards Act) in 1938— thirty-five years after the march of the mill children.

THINK QUESTIONS

1. Refer to several details in paragraphs 2-4 to support your understanding of why Mother Jones was concerned for the safety of children working in the textile industry.

2. Use details to write two or three sentences describing how Mother Jones got the idea for the march of the mill children and what her goal was. Cite evidence from paragraph 9.

3. What happened when Mother Jones tried to meet with President Roosevelt at Sagamore Hill? Support your answer with evidence from the text.

4. By remembering that the Latin suffix *-ity* means "the state of," use context to determine the meaning of the word **publicity** as it is used in paragraph 6 of *Mother Jones: Fierce Fighter For Workers' Rights*. Write your definition of "publicity" and tell how you determined the meaning of the word.

5. Use context to determine the meaning of the word **mutilated** as it is used in paragraph 7 of *Mother Jones: Fierce Fighter For Workers' Rights*. Write your definition of "mutilated" and explain the context clues you used to figure out its meaning. Then confirm your definition in a print or digital dictionary.

CLOSE READ

Reread the excerpt from *Mother Jones: Fierce Fighter For Workers' Rights*. As you reread, complete the Focus Questions below. Then use your answers and annotations from the questions to help you complete the Writing Prompt.

FOCUS QUESTIONS

1. In an attempt to influence city officials, Mother Jones uses figurative language and negative connotations to imply that children are being abused so that mill owners can make money. Identify the figurative phrase in paragraph 8 and two words that convey a negative connotation. Then analyze how this phrase affects the meaning of the economic term "profit." Use context or a dictionary to help you analyze the words. Highlight evidence in the text and make annotations to explain your choices.

2. In paragraph 10, how did Mother Jones use her ideas to influence the actions and ideas of some of the mill children's parents? Highlight evidence in the text and make annotations to support your response.

3. In paragraph 12, how did Mother Jones use the children, as well as the events illustrating the children's plight, to influence the opinions and ideas of others? Highlight evidence in the text and annotate your reasoning.

4. What action at the wild animal show, described in paragraphs 23-26, did Mother Jones take to make the plight of the children more dramatic? Highlight textual evidence and make annotations to support your explanation.

5. What evidence in the last paragraph suggests that Mother Jones was successful in defending human rights, particularly the rights of child workers? Highlight evidence in the text and make annotations to support your answer.

WRITING PROMPT

How is Mother Jones like other individuals you have heard of who have worked hard to defend human rights? Begin with a clear thesis statement to introduce this topic. Think about the ways in which Mother Jones attempted to influence individuals, ideas, and events, especially the ideas of government officials. Organize and cite specific evidence from the text to support your response. Use transitions within your body paragraphs to show the relationships among your ideas. Choose specific vocabulary from the text and use precise language to deliver your ideas. Then, summarize these ideas in a concluding statement that leads logically from the information you have presented.

Copyright © BookheadEd Learning, LLC

SPEECH TO THE YOUNG:

SPEECH TO THE PROGRESS-TOWARD

POETRY
Gwendolyn Brooks
1932

INTRODUCTION

A highly regarded and widely admired poet, Gwendolyn Brooks was the poet laureate of Illinois and the first African American to win the Pulitzer Prize. In her poem "Speech to the Young: Speech to the Progress-Toward," the speaker gives wise advice to young people about how to live life.

"Live not for the-end-of-the-song."

FIRST READ

1 Say to them,
2 say to the down-**keepers,**
3 the sun-**slappers,**
4 the self-**soilers,**
5 the **harmony-hushers,**
6 "even if you are not ready for day
7 it cannot always be night."
8 You will be right.
9 For that is the hard home-run.

10 Live not for battles won.
11 Live not for the-end-of-the-song.
12 Live in the along.

"Speech to the Young: Speech to the Progress Forward" by Gwendolyn Brooks. Reprinted by Consent of Brooks Permissions.

Please note that excerpts and passages in the StudySync® library and this workbook are intended as touchstones to generate interest in an author's work. The excerpts and passages do not substitute for the reading of entire texts, and StudySync® strongly recommends that students seek out and purchase the whole literary or informational work in order to experience it as the author intended. Links to online resellers are available in our digital library. In addition, complete works may be ordered through an authorized reseller by filling out and returning to StudySync® the order form enclosed in this workbook.

Reading & Writing Companion   **231**

THINK QUESTIONS

1. What evidence is there in the first stanza of the poem that the speaker is giving advice? To whom is the speaker giving advice? Cite textual evidence to support your answer.

2. Who are the young supposed to address? What are they supposed to say? Cite textual evidence to support your answer.

3. How does the speaker want young people to live? Cite textual evidence to support your response.

4. Use context to determine the meaning of **slappers** as it is used in line 3. Write down the meaning. What do you think the connotation of "sun-slappers" is? Cite clues to demonstrate how you determined the meaning of the word.

5. The word **harmony** in line 5 comes from the Greek word *harmos*, which means "a fitting" or "a combining of parts into a whole." Based on the Greek root of the word, what do you think "harmony" means in the context of the poem? What do the "harmony-hushers" want to do? Cite clues to show how you figured out the meaning of the word. Then confirm your meaning of "harmony" in a print or digital dictionary.

CLOSE READ

Reread the poem "Speech to the Young: Speech to the Progress-Toward." As you reread, complete the Focus Questions below. Then use your answers and annotations from the questions to help you complete the Writing Prompt.

FOCUS QUESTIONS

1. Brooks uses the repetition of words in the first two lines of the poem to make clear that she is lumping together the people mentioned in lines 2-5. Highlight the repetition in lines 1 and 2, and make annotations explaining how this repetition unites the people.

2. Highlight the use of figurative language in lines 6-7. What do these metaphors mean? How do they support one of the themes of the poem? Make annotations explaining your response.

3. Brooks uses alliteration and figurative language in line 9. Highlight the examples of alliteration and figurative language. What is Brooks trying to say through these poetic elements? Make annotations explaining Brooks's message, or theme.

4. In the last stanza, what metaphor does Brooks use to represent the past? What metaphor does she use to represent the future? Highlight the words, and make annotations explaining how the metaphors might relate to the theme of progress toward racial equality and social justice.

5. Highlight the metaphor that Brooks uses in line 12. Make annotations explaining its meaning. How might this metaphor relate to a theme of progress in social justice?

WRITING PROMPT

How does the use of alliteration and other forms of repetition help Gwendolyn Brooks develop her themes in "Speech to the Young: Speech to the Progress-Toward"? How does the use of figurative language, such as metaphors, contribute to the development of the themes? Use your understanding of poetic elements to determine the themes that emerge in this poem. Support your writing with specific evidence from the text.

Please note that excerpts and passages in the StudySync® library and this workbook are intended as touchstones to generate interest in an author's work. The excerpts and passages do not substitute for the reading of entire texts, and StudySync® strongly recommends that students seek out and purchase the whole literary or informational work in order to experience it as the author intended. Links to online resellers are available in our digital library. In addition, complete works may be ordered through an authorized reseller by filling out and returning to StudySync® the order form enclosed in this workbook.

Reading & Writing Companion   **233**

FLESH AND BLOOD SO CHEAP:
THE TRIANGLE FIRE AND ITS LEGACY

NON-FICTION
Albert Marrin
2011

INTRODUCTION

The Triangle Shirtwaist Factory fire in 1911 was the most lethal workplace tragedy in American history until the attack on the World Trade Center on September 11, 2001. The lower Manhattan blaze killed 146 workers, most of them young, female immigrants of Jewish and Italian descent. Author Albert Marrin traces the history of the garment industry, exploring the immigrant experience of the early 1900s, including the sweatshop conditions many new arrivals to America were forced to endure. The Triangle fire prompted activists to lobby for reforms, resulting in improved safety standards and working conditions that we now take

"Seconds later, the fire leaped out of control."

 FIRST READ

Excerpt from Chapter V

Holocaust

1   We will never know for sure what started the Triangle Fire. Most likely, a cutter flicked a hot ash or tossed a live cigarette butt into a scrap bin. Whatever the cause, survivors said the first sign of trouble was smoke pouring from beneath a cutting table.

2   Cutters flung buckets of water at the smoking spot, without effect. Flames shot up, **igniting** the line of hanging paper patterns. "They began to fall on the layers of thin goods underneath them," recalled cutter Max Rothen. "Every time another piece dropped, light scraps of burning fabric began to fly around the room. They came down on the other tables and they fell on the machines. Then the line broke and the whole string of burning patterns fell down." A foreman ran for the hose on the stairway wall. Nothing! No water came. The hose had not been connected to the **standpipe.** Seconds later, the fire leaped out of control.

3   Yet help was already on the way. At exactly 4:45 p.m., someone pulled the eighth-floor fire alarm. In less than two minutes, the horse-drawn vehicles of Engine Company 72 arrived from a firehouse six blocks away. The moment they arrived, the firefighters unloaded their equipment and prepared to swing into action. As they did, the area pumping station raised water pressure in the hydrants near the Asch Building. Other units soon arrived from across the Lower East Side with more equipment.

4   Meanwhile, workers on the eighth-floor rang furiously for the two passenger elevators. Safety experts have always advised against using elevators in a fire. Heat can easily damage their machinery, leaving trapped passengers dangling in space, to burn or **suffocate.** Despite the danger, the operators

made several trips, saving scores of workers before heat bent the elevators' tracks and put them out of action.

5   Those who could not board elevators rushed the stairway door. They caused a pile up so that those in front could not open the door. Whenever someone tried to get it open, the crowd pinned her against it. "All the girls were falling on me and they squeezed me to the door," Ida Willensky recalled. "Three times I said to the girls, 'Please, girls, let me open the door. Please!' But they would not listen to me." Finally, cutter Louis Brown barged through the crowd and forced the door open.

6   Workers, shouting, crying, and gasping for air, slowly made their way downstairs. There were no lights in the stairway, so they had to grope their way in darkness. A girl fell; others fell on top of her, blocking the stairs until firefighters arrived moments later. Yet everyone who took the stairway from the eighth floor got out alive, exiting through the Washington Place doors. Those on the ninth floor were not so lucky.

• • •

7   Those who reached the ninth-floor stairway door found it locked. This was not unusual, as employers often locked doors to discourage latecomers and keep out union organizers. "My God, I am lost!" cried Margaret Schwartz as her hair caught fire. Nobody who went to that door survived, nor any who reached the windows.

8   With a wave of fire rolling across the room, workers rushed to the windows, only to meet more fire. Hot air expands. Unless it escapes, pressure will keep building, eventually blowing a hole even in a heavy iron container like a boiler. Heat and pressure blew out the eight-floor windows. Firefighters call the result "lapping in" —that is sucking flames into open windows above. That is why you see black scorch marks on the wall above the window of a burnt out room.

9   With fire advancing from behind and flames rising before them, people knew they were doomed. Whatever they did meant certain death. By remaining in the room, they chose death by fire or suffocation. Jumping ninety-five feet to the ground meant death on the sidewalk. We cannot know what passed through the minds of those who decided to jump. Yet their thinking, in those last moments of life, may have gone like this: If I jump, my family will have a body to identify and bury, but if I stay in this room, there will be nothing left.

10   A girl clung to a window frame until flames from the eighth floor lapped in, burning her face and setting fire to her hair and clothing. She let go. Just then, Frances Perkins reached the scene from her friend's town house on the north

side of Washington Square. "Here they come," onlookers shouted as Engine Company 72 reined in their horses. "Don't jump; stay there." Seconds later, Hook and Ladder Company 20 arrived.

11   Firefighters charged into the building, stretching a hose up the stairways as they went. At the sixth-floor landing, they connected it to the standpipe. Reaching the eighth floor, they crawled into the **inferno** on their bellies, under the rising smoke, with their hose. Yet nothing they did could save those at the windows. Photos of the portable towers show streams of water playing on the top three floors. (A modern high-pressure pumper can send water as high as one thousand feet.) Plenty of water got through the windows, but not those with people standing in them. A burst of water under high pressure would have hurled them backward, into the flames.

12   Hoping to catch jumpers before they hit the ground, firefighters held up life nets, sturdy ten-foot-square nets made of rope. It was useless. A person falling from the ninth floor struck with a force equal to eleven thousand pounds. Some jumpers bounced off the nets, dying when they hit the ground; others tore the nets, crashing through to the pavement. "The force was so great it took men off their feet," said Captain Howard Ruch of Engine Company 18. "Trying to hold the nets, the men turned somersaults. The men's hands were bleeding, the nets were torn and some caught fire" from burning clothing. Officers, fearing their men would be struck by falling bodies, ordered the nets removed. The **aerial** ladders failed, too, reaching only to the sixth floor. Desperate jumpers tried to grab hold of a rung on the way down, missed, and landed on the sidewalk.

. . .

13   Onlookers saw many dreadful sights, none more so than the end of a love affair. A young man appeared at a window. Gently, he helped a young woman step onto the windowsill, held her away from the building—and let go. He helped another young woman onto the windowsill. "Those of us who were looking saw her put her arms around him and kiss him," Shepherd wrote. "Then he held her out into space and dropped her. But quick as a flash he was on the windowsill himself.... He was brave enough to help the girl he loved to a quicker death, after she had given him a goodbye kiss."

. . .

14   By 5:15 p.m., exactly thirty-five minutes after flames burst from beneath a cutting table, firefighters had brought the blaze under control. An hour later, Chief Croker made his inspection. He found that the Asch Building had no damage to its structure. Its walls were in good shape; so were the floors. It had passed the test. It was fireproof.

15   The woodwork, furniture, cotton goods, and people who worked in it were not. Of the 500 Triangle employees who reported for work that day, 146 died. Of these, sixteen men were identified. The rest were women or bodies and body parts listed as "unidentified." The Triangle Fire was New York's worst workplace disaster up to that time. Only the September 11, 2001, terrorist attacks on the twin towers of the World Trade Center took more (about 2,500) lives.

Excerpted from *Flesh and Blood So Cheap: The Triangle Fire and Its Legacy* by Albert Marrin, published by Alfred A. Knopf.

 THINK QUESTIONS

1.   Refer to several details in the first two paragraphs to support your understanding of how the Triangle Fire likely started and how the fire spread on the eighth floor.

2.   Write two or three sentences describing what caused the windows to blow out on the eighth floor and how this affected the ninth floor above. Cite specific textual evidence from paragraph 8.

3.   What did firefighters attempt to do to help those who jumped from the ninth floor? Why were these efforts not successful? Support your answer with evidence from paragraph 12 of the text.

4.   Use context to determine the meaning of the word **standpipe** as it is used in paragraphs 2 and 11 of *Flesh and Blood So Cheap*. Write your definition of "standpipe" and tell how you determined the meaning of the word.

5.   By keeping in mind that the Greek root *aer* means "air" and the Latin suffix *-ial* means "having the characteristics of," use the context clues provided in paragraph 12 to determine the meaning of **aerial** ladders. Write your definition of "aerial" and tell how you got it. Then describe what an aerial ladder would be.

CLOSE READ

Reread the excerpt from *Flesh and Blood So Cheap.* As you reread, complete the Focus Questions below. Then use your answers and annotations from the questions to help you complete the Writing Prompt.

FOCUS QUESTIONS

1. Explain how the author uses a cause-and-effect text structure in paragraph 4. Highlight evidence from the text and make annotations to explain your reasoning.

2. In paragraphs 6 and 7, Marrin sets up a comparison-contrast between what happened to the workers on the eighth and ninth floors. What other text structure does he use in sentences 2-4 of paragraph 6? Highlight the transition word in sentence 2, and annotate to label the text structure.

3. What text structure does the author use in paragraph 9? How does this organizational structure contribute to the development of ideas? Highlight evidence and make annotations to explain your answer.

4. In the first three sentences of paragraph 11, the author uses a descriptive text structure at the sentence level. What evidence supports this claim? What would you say is the overall text structure of the paragraph? Highlight evidence from the text and make annotations to support your explanations.

5. Use evidence from paragraphs 2, 6, 7, 14, and 15 to support the claim that the owners of the Triangle Shirtwaist Factory did not do enough to protect workers' rights. Highlight evidence from the text and make annotations to support the claim.

WRITING PROMPT

A legacy of the Triangle Fire described in *Flesh and Blood So Cheap* was the call for laws to protect workers' rights. What evidence is there that the health and safety of workers were not adequately protected at the Triangle Shirtwaist Factory? Begin with a clear thesis statement, and use your understanding of informational text structure to write a short essay to answer the question: Why is it necessary for the government to protect the health and safety of workers? Summarize your points with a strong conclusion, and support your writing with evidence and inferences drawn from the text.

Please note that excerpts and passages in the StudySync® library and this workbook are intended as touchstones to generate interest in an author's work. The excerpts and passages do not substitute for the reading of entire texts, and StudySync® strongly recommends that students seek out and purchase the whole literary or informational work in order to experience it as the author intended. Links to online resellers are available in our digital library. In addition, complete works may be ordered through an authorized reseller by filling out and returning to StudySync® the order form enclosed in this workbook.

Reading & Writing Companion **239**

ABOUT CÉSAR

NON-FICTION
Cesar Chavez Foundation
2012

INTRODUCTION

César Chávez was a Mexican-American activist who dedicated his life to promoting non-violent approaches to labor reform. He drew on his experiences as a migrant worker to found the National Farm Workers Association with fellow activist, Dolores Huerta in 1962. Through boycotts, hunger strikes, and marches, Chávez and his supporters successfully improved the lives of farmers around the country, and his speeches about justice, community, and education still resonate with community activists and politicians today. President Barack Obama adopted Chávez's most famous motto, "Si, se puede," as his 2008 campaign slogan. This excerpt from the César Chávez Foundation describes union victories and the legacy of the famed labor leader and activist.

"The significance of César's life transcends any one cause or struggle."

 ## FIRST READ

Senator Robert F. Kennedy described Cesar Chavez as "one of the heroic figures of our time."

1 A true American hero, Cesar was a civil rights, Latino and farm labor leader; a genuinely religious and spiritual figure; a community organizer and social entrepreneur; a champion of militant nonviolent social change; and a crusader for the environment and consumer rights.

2 A first-generation American, he was born on March 31, 1927, near his family's small homestead in the North Gila River Valley outside Yuma, Arizona. At age 11, his family lost their farm during the Great Depression and became migrant farm workers. Throughout his youth and into adulthood, Cesar traveled the migrant streams throughout California laboring in the fields, orchards and vineyards, where he was exposed to the hardships and injustices of farm worker life.

3 After attending numerous schools as the family migrated, Cesar finished his formal education after the eighth grade and worked the fields full-time to help support his family. Although his formal education ended then, he later satisfied an insatiable intellectual curiosity and was self-taught on an eclectic range of subjects through reading during the rest of his life.

4 Cesar joined the U.S. Navy in 1946, in the aftermath of World War II, and served in the Western Pacific. He returned from the service in 1948 to marry Helen Fabela, whom he met while working in fields and vineyards around Delano. Together they settled in the East San Jose barrio of *Sal Si Puedes* (Get Out if You Can), and had eight children, later enjoying 31 grandchildren.

Historic Victories for Union

5 The coming years would bring much more **adversity:** Strikes and boycotts, marches and fasts, victories and defeats. But through it all, Cesar learned and taught others how commitment and sacrifice can set you free from the **constraints** imposed by depending entirely on money and material things.

6 Over four decades, Cesar saw his share of defeats, but also historic victories. Under Cesar, the UFW achieved **unprecedented** gains for farm workers, establishing it as the first successful farm workers union in American history. Among them were:

7 The first genuine collective bargaining agreements between farm workers and growers in American history.

8 The first union contracts requiring rest periods, toilets in the fields, clean drinking water, hand washing facilities, banning discrimination in employment and sexual harassment of women workers, requiring protective clothing against pesticide exposure, prohibiting pesticide spraying while workers are in the fields and outlawing DDT and other dangerous pesticides (years before the U.S. Environmental Protection Agency acted).

9 The first comprehensive union medical (and later dental and vision) benefits for farm workers and their families through a joint union-employer health and welfare fund, the Robert F. Kennedy Medical Plan, which has paid out more than $250 million in benefits.

10 The first and only functioning pension plan for retired farm workers, the Juan de la Cruz Pension Plan, with present assets of more than $100 million.

11 The first union contracts providing for profit sharing and parental leave.

12 Abolishment of the infamous short-handled hoe that crippled generations of farm workers.

13 Extending to farm workers state coverage under unemployment insurance, disability and workers' compensation, as well as federal amnesty rights for immigrants.

14 Because of Cesar and millions of Americans who supported farm workers by boycotting grapes and other products, under then-Gov. Jerry Brown California passed the landmark Agricultural Labor Relations Act of 1975, the nation's first, and still the only, law guaranteeing farm workers the right to organize, choose their own union representative and **negotiate** with their employers.

Cesar Chavez's Legacy

15 The significance of Cesar's life **transcends** any one cause or struggle. He was a unique and humble leader, as well as a great humanitarian and communicator who influenced and inspired millions of Americans from all walks of life. Cesar forged a national and extraordinarily diverse **coalition** for farm worker boycotts, which included students, middle class consumers, trade unionists, religious activists and minorities.

16 Cesar passed away peacefully in his sleep on April 23, 1993 in the small farm worker town of San Luis, Arizona, not far from where he was born 66 years earlier on the family homestead. More than 50,000 people attended his funeral services in Delano, the same community in which he had planted the seeds of social justice decades before.

17 Cesar's motto, "Sí, se puede!" ("Yes, it can be done!"), coined during his 1972 fast in Arizona, embodies the uncommon legacy he left for people around the world. Since his death, hundreds of communities across the nation have named schools, parks, streets, libraries, and other public facilities, as well as awards and scholarships in his honor. His birthday, March 31st, is an official holiday in 10 states. In 1994, President Clinton posthumously awarded Cesar the Presidential Medal of Freedom, the nation's highest civilian honor, at the White House.

18 Cesar liked to say that his job as an organizer was helping ordinary people do extraordinary things. Cesar made everyone, especially the farm workers, feel the jobs they were doing in the movement were very important. It did not matter if they were lawyers working in the courtrooms or cooks in the kitchen feeding the people involved in the strike, he showed the farm workers that they could win against great odds. He gave people the faith to believe in themselves, even if they were poor and unable to receive the best education. Cesar succeeded where so many others failed for 100 years to organize farm workers. He was able to do the impossible by challenging and overcoming the power of one of the country's richest industries in California.

19 As a common man with an uncommon vision, Cesar Chavez stood for equality, justice and dignity for all Americans. His universal principles remain as relevant and inspiring today as they were when he first began his movement.

"About Cesar". Used by permission of The Cesar Chavez Foundation, http://www. chavezfoundation.org/

THINK QUESTIONS

1. Use specific details from paragraphs 1-3 to write three or four sentences summarizing Cesar Chavez's early life before joining the U.S. Navy in 1946.

2. Refer to details from paragraph 8 to support your understanding of how the UFW, under Chavez's leadership, used union contracts to make working conditions safer for farm workers. Cite specific evidence from the text.

3. In the next-to-last paragraph, readers are told that Chavez believed "that his job as an organizer was helping ordinary people do extraordinary things." Write two or three sentences exploring how Chavez did this. Support your answer with textual evidence.

4. Use context clues to determine the meaning of the word **adversity** as it is used in paragraph 5 of "About Cesar." Write your definition of "adversity" and tell how you determined its meaning. Then check the meaning you inferred in a print or digital dictionary.

5. By remembering that the Latin prefix *trans-* means "over" or "across" and the Latin root *scandere* means "to climb," use the context clues provided in the passage to determine the meaning of **transcends** as it is used in paragraph 15 of "About Cesar." Write your definition of "transcends" and tell how you figured out its meaning.

CLOSE READ

Reread the essay "About Cesar." As you reread, complete the Focus Questions below. Then use your answers and annotations from the questions to help you complete the Writing Prompt.

FOCUS QUESTIONS

1. What can a reader infer from the details in paragraph 3 about how life as a migrant farm worker affected Chavez's formal education? What steps did Chavez take to satisfy his intellectual curiosity throughout the rest of his life? Highlight textual evidence and make annotations to explain your responses.

2. Which details in paragraphs 6 and 7 indicate that Chavez was able to have a positive influence on the lives of migrant farm workers through his actions and ideas? Highlight textual evidence and make annotations to explain your choices.

3. Which details in paragraph 14 indicate the influence that Chavez had on legislation by leading millions of American supporters of farm workers in boycotts of grapes and other products? Highlight textual evidence and make annotations to explain your choices.

4. What evidence in paragraph 17 shows that Chavez's influence extended far beyond migrant farm workers? Highlight textual evidence and make annotations to support your explanation.

5. According to paragraph 18, why was Chavez able to succeed in organizing farm workers when so many other organizers had failed? Highlight textual evidence and make annotations to explain your answer.

WRITING PROMPT

Why is "Sí, se puede!" ("Yes, it can be done!") a fitting motto for Cesar Chavez's life and for the influence he had on events, ideas, and the people around him? Why do you think Chavez thought it was important to defend human rights? In crafting your response, begin with a clear thesis statement and use your understanding of informational text elements by analyzing the interaction among people, ideas, and events in the selection. Organize and support your writing with textual evidence, and use precise language and vocabulary from the selection. Use transitions to show the relationships among your ideas, and provide a concluding statement that summarizes your key points.

ELEGY ON THE DEATH OF CÉSAR CHÁVEZ

POETRY
Rudolfo Anaya
2000

INTRODUCTION

In this poem, Rudolfo Anaya eulogizes César Chávez, who fought for the rights of migrant farm workers in America. The poem celebrates Chávez's life and

"How can the morning star die?"

 FIRST READ

NOTES

1 César is dead,
2 And we have wept for him until our eyes are dry.
3 Dry as the fields of California that
4 He loved so well and now lie **fallow.**
5 Dry as the orchards of Yakima, where dark buds
6 Hang on trees and do not blossom.
7 Dry as el Valle de Tejas where people cross
8 Their Foreheads and pray for rain.

9 This earth he loved so well is dry and mourning
10 For César has fallen, our morning star has fallen.

11 The messenger came with the sad news of his death—
12 O, kill the messenger and steal back the life
13 Of this man who was a guide across fields of toil.
14 Kill the day and stop all time, stop la muerte
15 Who has robbed us of our morning star, that
16 Luminous light that greeted workers as they
17 Gathered around the dawn campfires
18 Let the morning light of Quetzacótal and Christian saint
19 Shine again. Let the wings of the Holy Ghost unfold
20 And give back the spirit it took from us in sleep.

21 Across the land we heard las campanas doblando:
22 *Ha muerto César, Ha muerto César.*

23 How can the morning star die? We ask. How can

24 This man who moved like the light of justice die?

Please note that excerpts and passages in the StudySync® library and this workbook are intended as touchstones to generate interest in an author's work. The excerpts and passages do not substitute for the reading of entire texts, and StudySync® strongly recommends that students seek out and purchase the whole literary or informational work in order to experience it as the author intended. Links to online resellers are available in our digital library. In addition, complete works may be ordered through an authorized reseller by filling out and returning to StudySync® the order form enclosed in this workbook.

Reading & Writing Companion   **247**

25 Hijo de la Virgen de Guadalupe, hombre de la gente,
26 You starved your body so we might know your spirit.

27 The days do carry hope, and the days do carry treason.

28 O, fateful day, April 23, 1993, when our morning
29 Star did not rise and we knew that in his sleep
30 César had awakened to a greater dream.

31 And we, left lost on this dark, dry Earth,
32 Cursed the day la muerte came to claim
33 The light within his noble body.

34 He was a wind of change that swept over our land.
35 From the San Joaquin Valley north to Sacramento
36 From northwest Yakima to el Valle de Tejas
37 From el Valle de San Luis to Midwest fields of corn
38 He loved the land, he loved la gente.

39 His name was a soft breeze to cool the campesino's sweat
40 A scourge on the **oppressors** of the poor.

41 Now he lies dead, and storms still rage around us.
42 The dispossessed walk hopeless streets,
43 Campesinos gather by roadside ditches to sleep,
44 Shrouded by pesticides, unsure of tomorrow,
45 Hounded by **propositions** that keep their children
46 Uneducated in a land grown fat with greed.

47 Yes, the **arrogant** hounds of hate
48 Are loose upon this land again, and César
49 Weeps in the embrace of La Virgen de Guadalupe,
50 Still praying for his people.

51 "Rise, mi gente, rise," he prays.

52 His words echo across the land, like the righteous

53 Thunder of summer storms, like the call of a
54 Warrior preparing for the struggle. I hear his
55 Voice in the fields and orchards, in community halls,
56 In schools, churches, campesino homes and
57 Presidential palaces.
58 "Rise, mi gente, rise."
59 That was his common chant. Rise and organize,

NOTES

60 Build the House of Workers.
61 Build the House of Justice now!

62 Do not despair in violence and abuse.
63 Rise together and build a new society.
64 Build a new democracy, build equality,
65 And build a dream for all to share.

66 His voice stirs me now, and I rise from my grief.
67 I hear the words of the poet cry:
68 "Peace, peace! He is not dead, he doth not sleep—
69 He hath awakened from the dream of life."

70 I hear César calling for us to gather.

71 I hear the call to a new Huelga,
72 I hear the sound of marching feet
73 The guitarra strums of the New Movimiento
74 The old and young, rich and poor, all move
75 To build the House of Justice of César's dream!

76 The trumpet of righteousness calls us to battle!
77 And the future opens itself like the blossom
78 That is his soul, the fruit of his labor.
79 He calls for us to share in the fruit.

80 "He lives, he wakes—'tis Death is dead, not he;
81 Mourn not for Adonais."

82 Do not weep for César, for he is not dead.
83 He lives in the hearts of those who loved him,
84 Worked and marched and ate with him, and those
85 Who believed in him.

86 His disciples know he is not dead.
87 For in the dawn we see the morning star!
88 El lucero de Dios!
89 Light comes to illuminate the struggle,
90 And bless the work yet to be done.

91 Throughout Aztlán we call the young to gather;
92 Rise and put aside violence and temptations.
93 Rise and be swept up by the truth of his deeds,
94 Rise not against each other, but for each other,
95 Rise against the oppressors who take your seat
96 And labor and sell it cheap.

97   "Rise, mi gente, rise!"

98   Our César has not died!

99   He is the light of the new day.

100   He is the rain that renews **parched** fields.

101   He is the hope that builds the House of Justice.

102   He is with us! Here! Today!

103   Listen to his voice in the wind.

104   He is the spirit of Hope,

105   A movement building to sweep away oppression!

106   His spirit guides us in the struggle.

107   Let us join his spirit to ours!

108   Sing with me. Sing all over this land!

109   "Rise, mi gente, rise!

110   Rise, mi gente, rise!"

From "Elegy on the Death of Cesar Chavez". Copyright © 2000 by Rudolfo Anaya.
Published by Cinco Punto Press. By permission of Susan Bergholz Literary Services,
New York, NY and Lamy, NM. All rights reserved.

 THINK QUESTIONS

1. What language confirms that this is an elegy, a poem about someone who has died? Cite textual evidence to support your answer.

2. What terms of praise does Rudolfo Anaya apply to Chavez in the elegy? Cite evidence from the text to support your answer.

3. What chant does the poet repeat in the poem? Cite evidence to explain why the chant is important to the theme (or message) of the poem.

4. Use context clues to determine the meaning of **fallow** as it is used in line 4 of the first stanza. Write the meaning of the word. Cite clues to demonstrate how you got your answer.

5. Use context clues to determine the meaning of **oppressors** as it is used in lines 40 and 95. Write the meaning of the word. Cite clues from lines 40 and 95 and surrounding lines to indicate how you inferred the meaning of the word. Then use a print or digital dictionary to confirm or revise your definition.

CLOSE READ

Reread the poem "Elegy on the Death of Cesar Chavez." As you reread, complete the Focus Questions below. Then use your answers and annotations from the questions to help you complete the Writing Prompt.

FOCUS QUESTIONS

1. In the first stanza of the poem, the poet uses a long simile to compare the campesinos' eyes made dry from crying over César's death with other things that the eyes could not possibly be. Highlight the comparison in the stanza and explain how it creates the desired image of something dry. Make annotations to explain how the simile works.

2. Both Rudolfo Anaya and the writers at the Cesar Chavez Foundation wrote about the life and work of César Chávez. However, the two selections, although about the same person and time period, are very different. Compare and contrast the two texts. What are the similarities between "About Cesar" and "Elegy on the Death of Cesar Chavez"? What are the differences? Focus on genre, use of language, and historical accuracy. Highlight the similarities and make annotations citing how the texts differ.

3. In lines 41-46, Anaya uses personification (giving human traits to nonhuman things) to express how he feels about the propositions. Highlight three examples of personification in the stanza. Make annotations explaining them, and tell why he might have used them to get across his point about propositions.

4. What is the denotation of the word "righteousness" in line 76 of stanza 21? What is its connotation in lines 76-79? Highlight the word and make annotations explaining your response.

5. What explicit metaphors does Anaya use in the last full stanza of the elegy, lines 98-108? Highlight these metaphors, in which one thing is said to be another. Then annotate to explain how these metaphors provide supporting evidence for the poem's message (or theme)—that Chávez dedicated his life to fighting for the human rights of migrant farm workers.

WRITING PROMPT

Think about how Rudolfo Anaya uses figurative language and connotation in "Elegy on the Death of Cesar Chavez." How does his use of figurative language and connotation help him develop his message (or theme)? Begin your writing with a clear thesis statement. Then think about what you know of Chavez from having read "About Cesar," an informational text. How do both texts support the evidence that Chavez was a protector of human rights? Use textual evidence from both texts to support Anaya's message (or theme), and draw on specific vocabulary and precise language from the selection. Consider how Anaya might have altered history a bit in his poem. Organize your support and use transitions to show the relationships among your ideas. Lastly, provide a conclusion that summarizes your main points.

Please note that excerpts and passages in the StudySync® library and this workbook are intended as touchstones to generate interest in an author's work. The excerpts and passages do not substitute for the reading of entire texts, and StudySync® strongly recommends that students seek out and purchase the whole literary or informational work in order to experience it as the author intended. Links to online resellers are available in our digital library. In addition, complete works may be ordered through an authorized reseller by filling out and returning to StudySync® the order form enclosed in this workbook.

Reading & Writing Companion   **251**

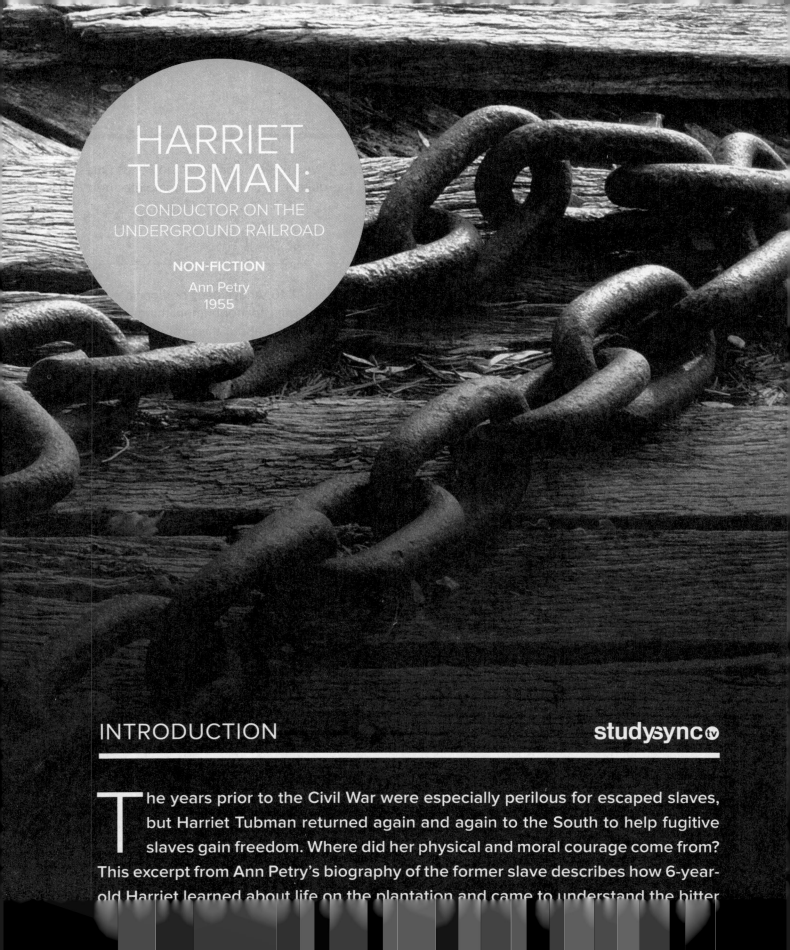

HARRIET TUBMAN:
CONDUCTOR ON THE UNDERGROUND RAILROAD

NON-FICTION
Ann Petry
1955

INTRODUCTION

The years prior to the Civil War were especially perilous for escaped slaves, but Harriet Tubman returned again and again to the South to help fugitive slaves gain freedom. Where did her physical and moral courage come from? This excerpt from Ann Petry's biography of the former slave describes how 6-year-old Harriet learned about life on the plantation and came to understand the bitter

"...the patrollers were going past, in pursuit of a runaway."

 FIRST READ

 NOTES

Excerpt from Chapter Three: Six Years Old

1 By the time Harriet Ross was six years old, she had **unconsciously** absorbed many kinds of knowledge, almost with the air she breathed. She could not, for example, have said how or at what moment she learned that she was a slave.

2 She knew that her brothers and sisters, her father and mother, and all the other people who lived in the quarter, men, women and children, were slaves.

3 She had been taught to say, "Yes, Missus," "No, Missus," to white women, "Yes, Mas'r," "No, Mas'r," to white men. Or, "Yes, sah," "No, sah."

4 At the same time, someone had taught her where to look for the North Star, the star that stayed **constant,** not rising in the east and setting in the west as the other stars appeared to do; and told her that anyone walking toward the North could use that star as a guide.

5 She knew about fear, too. Sometimes at night, or during the day, she heard the **furious** galloping of horses, not just one horse, several horses, thud of the hoofbeats along the road, jingle of harness. She saw the grown folks freeze into stillness, not moving, scarcely breathing, while they listened. She could not remember who first told her that those furious hoofbeats meant the patrollers were going past, in pursuit of a runaway. Only the slaves said patterollers, whispering the word.

6 Old Rit would say a prayer that the hoofbeats would not stop. If they did, there would be the dreadful sound of screams. Because the runaway slave had been caught, would be whipped, and finally sold to the chain gang.

7 Thus Harriet already shared the uneasiness and the fear of the grownups. But she shared their pleasures, too. She knew moments of pride when the overseer consulted Ben, her father, about the weather. Ben could tell if it was going to rain, when the first frost would come, tell whether there was going to be a long stretch of clear sunny days. Everyone on the plantation admired this skill of Ben's. Even the master, Edward Brodas.

8 The other slaves were in awe of Ben because he could **prophesy** about the weather. Harriet stood close to him when he studied the sky, licked his forefinger and held it up to determine the direction of the wind, then announced that there would be rain or frost or fair weather.

9 There was something free and wild in Harriet because of Ben. He talked about the arrival of the wild ducks, the thickness of the winter coat of muskrats and of rabbits. He was always talking about the woods, the berries that grew there, the strange haunting cries of some of the birds, the loud sound their wings made when they were disturbed and flew up suddenly. He spoke of the way the owls flew, their feathers so soft that they seemed to glide, soundless, through the air.

10 Ben knew about rivers and creeks and swampy places. He said that the salt water from the Bay reached into the rivers and streams for long distances. You could stick your finger in the river water and lick it and you could taste the salt from the Bay.

11 He had been all the way to the Chesapeake. He had seen storms there. He said the Big Buckwater River, which lay off to the southeast of the plantation, was just a little stream compared to the Choptank, and the Choptank was less than nothing compared to the Bay.

12 All through the plantation, from the Big House to the stables, to the fields, he had a reputation for absolute honesty. He had never been known to tell a lie. He was a valued worker and a trusted one.

13 Ben could tell wonderful stories, too. So could her mother, Old Rit, though Rit's were mostly from the Bible. Rit told about Moses and the children of Israel, about how the sea parted so that the children walked across on dry land, about the plague of locusts, about how some of the children were afraid on the long journey to the Promised Land, and so cried out: "It had been better for us to serve the Egyptians, than that we should die in the wilderness."

14 Old Rit taught Harriet the words of that song that the slaves were forbidden to sing, because of the man named Denmark Vesey, who had urged the other slaves to revolt by telling them about Moses and the children of Israel. Sometimes, in the quarter, Harriet heard snatches of it, sung under the breath,

almost whispered: "Go down, Moses. . . ." But she learned the words so well that she never forgot them.

15 She was aware of all these things and many other things too. She learned to separate the days of the week. Sunday was a special day. There was no work in the fields. The slaves cooked in the quarter and washed their clothes and sang and told stories.

16 There was another special day, issue day, which occurred at the end of the month. It was the day that food and clothes were issued to the slaves. One of the slaves was sent to the Big House, with a wagon, to bring back the monthly allowance of food. Each slave received eight pounds of pickled pork or its **equivalent** in fish, one bushel of Indian meal (corn meal), one pint of salt.

17 Once a year, on issue day, they received clothing. The men were given two tow-linen shirts, two pairs of trousers, one of tow-linen, the other woolen, and a woolen jacket for winter. The grownups received one pair of yarn stockings and a pair of shoes.

18 The children under eight had neither shoes, stockings, jacket nor trousers. They were issued two tow-linen shirts a year—short, one-piece garments made of a coarse material like burlap, reaching to the knees. These shirts were worn night and day. They were changed once a week. When they were worn out, the children went naked until the next allowance day.

19 Men and women received a coarse blanket apiece. The children kept warm as best they could.

Excerpted from Harriet Tubman: Conductor on the Underground Railroad *by Ann Petry, published by Amistad Press.*

Please note that excerpts and passages in the StudySync® library and this workbook are intended as touchstones to generate interest in an author's work. The excerpts and passages do not substitute for the reading of entire texts, and StudySync® strongly recommends that students seek out and purchase the whole literary or informational work in order to experience it as the author intended. Links to online resellers are available in our digital library. In addition, complete works may be ordered through an authorized reseller by filling out and returning to StudySync® the order form enclosed in this workbook.

Reading & Writing Companion   **255**

THINK QUESTIONS

1. Write two or three sentences explaining what six-year-old Harriet knew about the North Star. Support your answer with textual evidence.

2. Refer to one or more details in paragraph 5 to support your understanding of what uneasiness or fear Harriet shared with the grownups. Cite textual evidence to support your explanation.

3. Use details from paragraphs 15-18 to write two or three sentences describing which days were special to the slaves and why. Cite evidence from the text to support your explanation.

4. By remembering that the Latin prefix *un-* means "not" and the Latin suffix *-ly* means "in the manner of," use context clues to determine the meaning of the word **unconsciously** as it is used in the first paragraph of *Harriet Tubman: Conductor on the Underground Railroad*. Write your definition of "unconsciously" and tell how you determined the meaning of the word.

5. Use context to determine the meaning of the word **furious** as it is used in sentence 2 of paragraph 5 and repeated in sentence 4 of this paragraph in *Harriet Tubman: Conductor on the Underground Railroad*. Write your definition of "furious" and tell how you figured it out from the context clues. Then check the inferred meaning in the dictionary.

CLOSE READ

Reread the excerpt from *Harriet Tubman: Conductor on the Underground Railroad*. As you reread, complete the Focus Questions below. Then use your answers and annotations from the questions to help you complete the Writing Prompt.

FOCUS QUESTIONS

1. What phenomenon led Tubman to realize she was a slave? How did this affect her? Cite textual evidence to support your response.

2. What was the relationship like between Harriet and her father? How do you think this relationship influenced what she went on to do with her life? Make annotations to explain your reasoning.

3. In paragraph 12, the author states that Ben "was a valued worker and a trusted one." What textual evidence in paragraphs 7–11 supports this statement? Highlight the evidence and make annotations to explain your choices.

4. What clues in the text show you that the slaves had their own language—words and phrases that they used only with each other? Make annotations citing the textual evidence of your response. What purpose do you think this special language served?

5. Harriet's father and mother both had a strong impact on her character and her life. In what ways did they influence her similarly? Are there major differences in how they impacted her? Cite specific examples from the text in your response.

WRITING PROMPT

Harriet Tubman grew up to be a defender of human rights, despite great personal risks, as demonstrated by her work on the Underground Railroad. How and why do you think she was able to achieve what she did? What drove her to take these risks? Write a short essay in which you explore Tubman's motivations and the roots of her strength of character.

Please note that excerpts and passages in the StudySync® library and this workbook are intended as touchstones to generate interest in an author's work. The excerpts and passages do not substitute for the reading of entire texts, and StudySync® strongly recommends that students seek out and purchase the whole literary or informational work in order to experience it as the author intended. Links to online resellers are available in our digital library. In addition, complete works may be ordered through an authorized reseller by filling out and returning to StudySync® the order form enclosed in this workbook.

Reading & Writing Companion **257**

THE PEOPLE COULD FLY:
AMERICAN BLACK FOLKTALES

FICTION
Virginia Hamilton
1985

INTRODUCTION

The folktales in Virginia Hamilton's book are filled with humor, magic, and mystery. In this excerpt, discover why enslaved West Africans took off their wings and how an old man helped them to fly again.

"The young woman lifted one foot on the air. Then the other."

FIRST READ

1 They say the people could fly. Say that long ago in Africa, some of the people knew magic. And they would walk upon the air like climbin' up on a gate. And they flew like blackbirds over the fields. Black, shiny wings flappin' against the blue up there.

2 Then, many of the people were captured for Slavery. The ones that could fly **shed** their wings. They couldn't take their wings across the water on slave ships. Too crowded, don't you know.

3 The folks were full of **misery**, then. Got sick with the up and down of the sea. So they forgot about flyin' when they could no longer breathe the sweet scent of Africa.

4 Say the people who could fly kept their power, although they shed their wings. They looked the same as the other people from Africa who had been coming over, who had dark skin. Say you couldn't tell anymore one who could fly from one who couldn't.

5 One such who could was an old man, call him Toby. And standin' tall, yet afraid, was a young woman who once had wings. Call her Sarah. Now Sarah carried a babe tied to her back. She **trembled** to be so hard worked and scorned.

6 The slaves labored in the fields from sunup to sundown. The owner of the slaves callin' himself their Master. Say he was a hard lump of clay. A hard, glinty coal. A hard rock pile, wouldn't be moved. His Overseer on horseback pointed out the slaves who were slowin' down. So the one called Driver cracked his whip over the slow ones to make them move faster. That whip was a slice-open cut of pain. So they did move faster. Had to.

NOTES

7   Sarah hoed and chopped the row as the babe on her back slept.

8   Say the child grew hungry. That babe started up **bawling** too loud. Sarah couldn't stop to feed it. Couldn't stop to soothe and quiet it down. She let it cry. She didn't want to. She had no heart to **croon** to it.

9   "Keep that thing quiet," called the Overseer. He pointed his finger at the babe. The woman scrunched low. The Driver cracked his whip across the babe anyhow. The babe hollered like any hurt child, and the woman fell to the earth.

10   The old man that was there, Toby, came and helped her to her feet.

11   "I must go soon," she told him.

12   "Soon," he said.

13   Sarah couldn't stand up straight any longer. She was too weak. The sun burned her face. The babe cried and cried, "Pity me, oh, pity me," say it sounded like. Sarah was so sad and starving, she sat down in the row.

14   "Get up, you black cow," called the Overseer. He pointed his hand and the Driver's whip snarled around Sarah's legs. Her sack dress tore into rags. Her legs bled onto the earth. She couldn't get up.

15   Toby was there where there was no one to help her and the babe.

16   "Now, before it's too late," panted Sarah. "Now, Father!"

17   "Yes, Daughter, the time is come," Toby answered. "Go as you know how to go!"

18   He raised his arms, holding them out to her. *"Kum...yali, kum buba tambe,"* and more magic words, said so quickly; they sounded like whispers and sighs.

19   The young woman lifted one foot on the air. Then the other. She flew clumsily at first, with the child now held tightly in her arms. Then she felt the magic, the African mystery. Say she rose just as free as a bird. As light as a feather.

20   The Overseer rode after her, hollerin'. Sarah flew over the fences. She flew over the woods. Tall trees could not snag her. Nor could the Overseer. She flew like an eagle now, until she was gone from sight. No one dared speak about it. Couldn't believe it. But it was, because they that was there saw that it was.

Excerpted from *The People Could Fly* by Virginia Hamilton, published by Alfred A. Knopf.

THINK QUESTIONS

1. Why did the people lose their wings? Cite evidence from the first two paragraphs to explain your answer.

2. Why does Sarah need to leave the plantation? Use ideas that are directly stated in the text and ideas you have inferred from clues in the selection. Support your inferences with textual evidence.

3. Why is Sarah able to fly without wings at the end of the folktale? Refer to one or more details that are directly stated as well as inferences drawn from the text.

4. Use context to determine the meaning of the word **misery** as it is used in paragraph 3 of *The People Could Fly: American Black Folktales*. Write your definition of "misery" and tell how you determined its meaning. Check the inferred meaning in context, and then verify it in a print or an online dictionary.

5. By remembering that **shed** is a multiple-meaning word and that depending on its context, it may be a noun or a verb, use the context clues provided in paragraph 2 to determine the meaning of "shed" as it is used in this excerpt. Write your definition of "shed" and tell how you figured out its meaning. Consult a print or digital dictionary to determine the exact definition of the word and its part of speech, as used in the text.

CLOSE READ

Reread the excerpt from *The People Could Fly*. As you reread, complete the Focus Questions below. Then use your answers and annotations from the questions to help you complete the Writing Prompt.

FOCUS QUESTIONS

1. In the first paragraph of *Harriet Tubman: Conductor on the Underground Railroad,* the narrator explains that Harriet "unconsciously absorbed many kinds of knowledge, almost with the air she breathed." In paragraphs 2-4 of *The People Could Fly,* the narrator explains that the people "forgot about flyin'" when they "were captured for Slavery," yet those "who could fly kept their power." How does the idea of secret knowledge empower the slaves in both texts? Highlight textual evidence and make annotations to explain your response.

2. In paragraph 7 of *Harriet Tubman: Conductor on the Underground Railroad,* the narrator says that "Harriet already shared the uneasiness and the fear of the grownups." Based on paragraphs 5 and 6 of *Harriet Tubman* and on paragraphs 8 and 9 of *The People Could Fly,* explain how the enslaved children grew up in a culture of fear. Support your response with textual evidence and make annotations to explain your analysis.

3. In paragraph 9 of *Harriet Tubman: Conductor on the Underground Railroad,* the author describes Ben's connection to nature by referencing a number of birds—for example, ducks and owls. In *The People Could Fly,* the narrator compares the people to blackbirds in the first paragraph and compares Sarah to an eagle in the last paragraph. Explain the connotations of these "bird" references in each text. Highlight specific evidence from the text and make annotations to explain your thinking.

4. In paragraphs 16 and 17 of *The People Could Fly,* Sarah and Toby call each other "Father" and "Daughter." Discuss the connotative meaning of these two words to explain how they express the relationship between the two characters. Highlight textual evidence and make annotations to support your response.

5. Both texts focus on the enslavement and mistreatment of African slaves during one of the most tragic periods in American history. How do the two texts demonstrate the necessity of defending human rights? Highlight textual evidence and make annotations to explain your response.

WRITING PROMPT

Harriet Tubman: Conductor on the Underground Railroad and *The People Could Fly: American Black Folktales* are similar, yet different. The first is a historical account of slavery in American history. The second is a fictional portrayal of the same topic or theme. Compare and contrast the two texts. How did Virginia Hamilton use historical fact in *The People Could Fly* to suit her purposes? Introduce your topic with a clear thesis statement. Then, organize and support your writing with specific evidence and vocabulary from both texts. Use transitions to show relationships among your ideas, and provide a conclusion that summarizes your main points.

1976 DEMOCRATIC NATIONAL CONVENTION

KEYNOTE ADDRESS

NON-FICTION
Barbara Jordan
1976

INTRODUCTION

n 1966, Barbara Jordan became the first African-American woman elected to the Texas State Senate. She later became the first African-American woman to represent a southern state in Congress when she was elected to the U.S. House of Representatives in 1972. Jordan worked hard to improve the lives of people in her district, sponsored bills that increased workers' wages, and fought for women's rights. She was considered a gifted public speaker and, was selected to give the keynote speech at the 1976 Democratic National Convention in New York. Her highly acclaimed speech is excerpted here.

"We are a people in search of our future."

 FIRST READ

1   Thank you ladies and gentlemen for a very warm reception.

2   It was one hundred and forty-four years ago that members of the Democratic Party first met in convention to select a Presidential candidate. Since that time, Democrats have continued to convene once every four years and draft a party platform and nominate a Presidential candidate. And our meeting this week is a continuation of that tradition. But there is something different about tonight. There is something special about tonight. What is different? What is special?

3   I, Barbara Jordan, am a keynote speaker.

4   A lot of years passed since 1832, and during that time it would have been most unusual for any national political party to ask a Barbara Jordan to deliver a keynote address. But tonight, here I am. And I feel that notwithstanding the past that my presence here is one additional bit of evidence that the American Dream need not forever be **deferred.**

5   Now that I have this grand distinction, what in the world am I supposed to say? . . . I could list the many problems which Americans have. I could list the problems which cause people to feel cynical, angry, frustrated: problems which include lack of integrity in government; the feeling that the individual no longer counts; the reality of material and spiritual poverty; the feeling that the grand American experiment is failing or has failed. I could recite these problems, and then I could sit down and offer no solutions. But I don't choose to do that either. The citizens of America expect more. They deserve and they want more than a recital of problems.

6   We are a people in a **quandary** about the present. We are a people in search of our future. We are a people in search of a national community. We are a

people trying not only to solve the problems of the present, unemployment, inflation, but we are attempting on a larger scale to fulfill the promise of America. We are attempting to fulfill our national purpose, to create and sustain a society in which all of us are equal.

...

7   And now we must look to the future. Let us heed the voice of the people and recognize their common sense. If we do not, we not only blaspheme our political heritage, we ignore the common ties that bind all Americans. Many fear the future. Many are distrustful of their leaders, and believe that their voices are never heard. Many seek only to satisfy their private wants; to satisfy their private interests. But this is the great danger America faces—that we will cease to be one nation and become instead a collection of interest groups: city against suburb, region against region, individual against individual; each seeking to satisfy private wants. If that happens, who then will speak for America? Who then will speak for the common good?

8   This is the question which must be answered in 1976: Are we to be one people bound together by common spirit, sharing in a common **endeavor;** or will we become a divided nation? For all of its uncertainty, we cannot flee the future. We must not become the "New Puritans" and reject our society. We must address and master the future together. It can be done if we restore the belief that we share a sense of national community, that we share a common national endeavor. It can be done.

9   There is no executive order; there is no law that can require the American people to form a national community. This we must do as individuals, and if we do it as individuals, there is no President of the United States who can veto that decision.

10 As a first step, we must restore our belief in ourselves. We are a generous people, so why can't we be generous with each other? We need to take to heart the words spoken by Thomas Jefferson:

11 "Let us restore to social intercourse that harmony and that affection without which liberty and even life are but dreary things."

12 A nation is formed by the willingness of each of us to share in the responsibility for upholding the common good. A government is **invigorated** when each one of us is willing to participate in shaping the future of this nation. In this election year, we must define the "common good" and begin again to shape a common future. Let each person do his or her part. If one citizen is unwilling to participate, all of us are going to suffer. For the American idea, though it is shared by all of us, is realized in each one of us.

13 And now, what are those of us who are elected public officials supposed to do? We call ourselves "public servants" but I'll tell you this: We as public servants must set an example for the rest of the nation. It is hypocritical for the public official to admonish and exhort the people to uphold the common good if we are derelict in upholding the common good. More is required of public officials than slogans and handshakes and press releases. More is required. We must hold ourselves strictly accountable. We must provide the people with a vision of the future.

14 If we promise as public officials, we must deliver. If we as public officials propose, we must produce. If we say to the American people, "It is time for you to be sacrificial"—sacrifice. If the public official says that, we [public officials] must be the first to give. We must be. And again, if we make mistakes, we must be willing to admit them. We have to do that. What we have to do is strike a balance between the idea that government should do everything and the idea, the belief, that government ought to do nothing. Strike a balance.

15 Let there be no **illusions** about the difficulty of forming this kind of a national community. It's tough, difficult, not easy. But a spirit of harmony will survive in America only if each of us remembers that we share a common destiny; if each of us remembers, when self-interest and bitterness seem to prevail, that we share a common destiny.

16 I have confidence that we can form this kind of national community.

. . .

17 I have that confidence.

18 We cannot improve on the system of government handed down to us by the founders of the Republic. There is no way to improve upon that. But what we can do is to find new ways to implement that system and realize our destiny.

19 Now I began this speech by commenting to you on the uniqueness of a Barbara Jordan making a keynote address. Well I am going to close my speech by quoting a Republican President and I ask you that as you listen to these words of Abraham Lincoln, relate them to the concept of a national community in which every last one of us participates:

20 "As I would not be a slave, so I would not be a master. This expresses my idea of Democracy. Whatever differs from this, to the extent of the difference, is no Democracy."

21 Thank you.

THINK QUESTIONS

1. Why does Barbara Jordan say in the opening to her speech that "there is something different about tonight . . . something special"? Cite one or more details from paragraph 4 to support your response.

2. What does Jordan say are some of the problems that cause the American "people to feel cynical, angry, frustrated"? Cite specific evidence from paragraph 5.

3. What does Jordan think might happen if Americans fail to "share in a common endeavor"? Cite specific evidence from paragraph 8 to explain your response.

4. Use context to determine the meaning of the word **deferred** as it is used in paragraph 4 of Jordan's keynote address to the 1976 Democratic National Convention. Write your definition of "deferred" and tell how you determined its meaning.

5. Use the context clues in paragraph 6 to determine the meaning of the word **quandary** as it is used in this keynote address. Write your definition of "quandary" and tell how you figured out its meaning. Verify your definition in a print or digital dictionary.

Please note that excerpts and passages in the StudySync® library and this workbook are intended as touchstones to generate interest in an author's work. The excerpts and passages do not substitute for the reading of entire texts, and StudySync® strongly recommends that students seek out and purchase the whole literary or informational work in order to experience it as the author intended. Links to online resellers are available in our digital library. In addition, complete works may be ordered through an authorized reseller by filling out and returning to StudySync® the order form enclosed in this workbook.

Reading & Writing Companion **267**

CLOSE READ

Reread Barbara Jordan's speech. As you reread, complete the Focus Questions below. Then use your answers and annotations from the questions to help you complete the Writing Prompt.

FOCUS QUESTIONS

1. What does Barbara Jordan mean in paragraph 8 when she says, "We must not become the 'New Puritans' and reject our society"? What does she want the American people to do instead? Highlight textual evidence and make annotations to explain your response.

2. In paragraph 13, why does Jordan try to persuade elected public officials to "set an example" for the American people? What reasons does she give? What persuasive word does she repeat? Why? Highlight evidence in the text and make annotations to support your analysis.

3. What does Jordan mean in paragraph 15 when she says, "Let there be no illusions about the difficulty of forming this kind of a national community"? Why does she think that coming together as one nation will not be an easy task? Highlight textual evidence and make annotations to support your analysis.

4. Why do you think Jordan ends her speech with a quotation from a Republican President, Abraham Lincoln? How does the quotation support Jordan's "idea of Democracy"? Highlight textual evidence and make annotations to support your explanation.

5. In paragraph 12 of her speech, Jordan states that "[a] nation is formed by the willingness of each of us to share in the responsibility for upholding the common good." How does her view of equal participation of all citizens to uphold the "common good" illustrate that Jordan was a champion of human rights? Highlight specific evidence from the text and make annotations to support your answer.

WRITING PROMPT

How does Barbara Jordan's speech demonstrate that she believed it was essential to defend human rights? What ideas does she put forth in the speech to support this interpretation? In writing your response, use your understanding of informational text elements to analyze the interaction among individuals, ideas, and events in her speech. Begin with a clear statement to introduce your topic. Organize and support your writing with specific evidence from the text. Use precise language and selection vocabulary where possible. Develop body paragraphs and use transitions to show the relationships among your ideas. Establish a formal style that underlines the importance of your topic, and provide a conclusion that summarizes your central (or main) ideas.

THE NEW COLOSSUS

POETRY
Emma Lazarus
1883

INTRODUCTION

Emma Lazarus was a 19th century American poet best known for her work "The New Colossus," a poetic tribute to the Statue of Liberty. Originally written for a Liberty fundraiser, the poem lay forgotten for almost twenty years before revived interest led to it being engraved on a brass plaque at the base of the statue in 1903. The title of the poem refers to the Colossus of Rhodes, a towering bronze statue of the sun god Helios that was erected in the ancient Greek city of Rhodes to celebrate a military victory over Cyprus. Almost one hundred feet high, the Colossus of Rhodes was one of the tallest statues of its time and is now considered one of the Seven Wonders of the Ancient World.

"Send these, the homeless, tempest-tost to me..."

FIRST READ

1 Not like the **brazen** giant of Greek fame,
2 With conquering limbs astride from land to land;
3 Here at our sea-washed, sunset gates shall stand
4 A mighty woman with a torch, whose flame
5 Is the imprisoned lightning, and her name
6 Mother of **Exiles.** From her beacon-hand
7 Glows world-wide welcome; her mild eyes command
8 The air-bridged harbor that twin cities frame.

9 "Keep, ancient lands, your storied **pomp!**" cries she
10 With silent lips. "Give me your tired, your poor,
11 Your huddled masses yearning to breathe free,
12 The **wretched refuse** of your teeming shore.
13 Send these, the homeless, tempest-tost to me,
14 I lift my lamp beside the golden door!"

THINK QUESTIONS

1. The title of the poem refers to the Colossus of Rhodes—a giant statue of the sun god, Helios—erected in the ancient Greek city of Rhodes to celebrate the city's victory over Cyprus. How do you know from the poem that the "mighty woman with a torch" is also a statue? Cite textual evidence to support your understanding.

2. Who is the "mighty woman with a torch" not like? How is she different? Cite textual evidence to support your answer.

3. To whom is the "mighty woman with a torch" offering a "world-wide welcome"? Cite specific evidence from the poem to support your answer.

4. Use context clues and reference materials to determine two possible meanings of the word **brazen** as it is used in the first line of "The New Colossus." Write your two definitions of "brazen" and tell where you found them. Verify the part of speech and the usage for each meaning of the word.

5. Use context to determine the meaning of the word **exiles** as it is used in line 6 of "The New Colossus." Write your definition of "exiles" and tell the context clues you used to infer the meaning of the word. Then look in a print or digital dictionary to verify the meaning you inferred.

Please note that excerpts and passages in the StudySync® library and this workbook are intended as touchstones to generate interest in an author's work. The excerpts and passages do not substitute for the reading of entire texts, and StudySync® strongly recommends that students seek out and purchase the whole literary or informational work in order to experience it as the author intended. Links to online resellers are available in our digital library. In addition, complete works may be ordered through an authorized reseller by filling out and returning to StudySync® the order form enclosed in this workbook.

Reading & Writing Companion   **271**

CLOSE READ

Reread the poem "The New Colossus." As you reread, complete the Focus Questions below. Then use your answers and annotations from the questions to help you complete the Writing Prompt.

FOCUS QUESTIONS

1. In line 3 of "The New Colossus," "sea-washed, sunset gates" is a metaphor. What might this metaphor mean in the context of the poem and its theme? Highlight specific evidence from the text, and make annotations recording your explanation.

2. Highlight evidence in the last six lines that "The New Colossus" is a Petrarchan sonnet. Make annotations to explain your analysis.

3. What evidence of personification can be found in lines 9–10 of the poem? Highlight specific evidence in the text, and make annotations to explain your reasoning.

4. "Tempest" is often used in a figurative sense. Highlight its use in line 13. Given the theme (or message) of the poem, how might Lazarus be using "tempest-tost" here? Make annotations recording your ideas.

5. What evidence in the last six lines supports the idea that Emma Lazarus was concerned with human rights? Highlight textual evidence and annotate to explain your reasoning.

WRITING PROMPT

Consider the use of allusion and the structure of the poem, "The New Colossus." What does Emma Lazarus want readers to know about the United States? Begin with a clear thesis statement that addresses your topic. What insight does the message (or theme) of the poem convey about the importance of defending human rights? Use your understanding of poetic structure and figurative language, particularly the allusion to the Greek Colossus that Lazarus uses in the poem, to determine her message. Organize and support your response with specific evidence from the text, including precise language and selection vocabulary wherever possible. Use transitions to show the relationships among your ideas, and provide a conclusion that summarizes your key points.

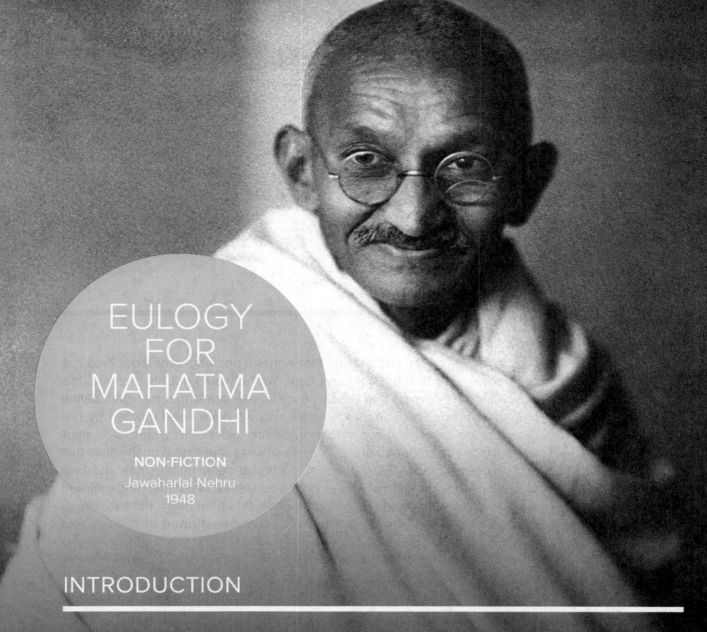

EULOGY FOR MAHATMA GANDHI

NON-FICTION
Jawaharlal Nehru
1948

INTRODUCTION

Mahatma Gandhi was born in India in 1869. At that time, India had been ruled by Great Britain for centuries. Although colonial India benefitted from mass transportation and communication systems, British rule in India was harsh. Indians endured limited rights and became economically dependent on the British colonizers. Gandhi believed that India should be free, and he worked to unite all Indians to protest British rule without using violence. Thousands of people followed Gandhi's example, and he became one of India's foremost leaders. India achieved independence in 1947, but Gandhi was assassinated the following year. Jawaharlal Nehru, a reformer who had worked side by side with Gandhi and the first prime minister after India became independent, delivered a public eulogy to memorialize his fallen friend.

"He lives in the hearts of millions and he will live for immemorial ages."

 FIRST READ

1   A glory has departed and the sun that warmed and brightened our lives has set, and we shiver in the cold and dark. Yet he would not have us feel this way. After all, that glory that we saw for all these years, that man with **divine** fire, changed us also—and such as we are, we have been molded by him during these years; and out of that divine fire many of us also took a small spark which strengthened and made us work to some extent on the lines that he fashioned. And so if we praise him, our words seem rather small, and if we praise him, to some extent we also praise ourselves. Great men and **eminent** men have monuments in bronze and marble set up for them, but this man of divine fire managed in his lifetime to become **enshrined** in millions and millions of hearts so that all of us became somewhat of the stuff that he was made of, though to an infinitely lesser degree. He spread out in this way all over India, not just in palaces, or in select places or in assemblies, but in every hamlet and hut of the lowly and those who suffer. He lives in the hearts of millions and he will live for immemorial ages.

2   What, then, can we say about him except to feel humble on this occasion? To praise him we are not worthy—to praise him whom we could not follow adequately and sufficiently. It is almost doing him an injustice just to pass him by with words when he demanded work and labor and sacrifice from us; in a large measure he made this country, during the last thirty years or more, attain to heights of sacrifice which in that particular domain have never been equaled elsewhere. He succeeded in that. Yet ultimately things happened which no doubt made him suffer tremendously, though his tender face never lost its smile and he never spoke a harsh word to anyone. Yet, he must have suffered—suffered for the failing of this generation whom he had trained, suffered because we went away from the path that he had shown us. And ultimately the hand of a child of his—for he, after all, is as much a child of his as any other Indian—the hand of a child of his struck him down.

3   Long ages afterwards history will judge of this period that we have passed through. It will judge of the successes and the failures—we are too near it to be proper judges and to understand what has happened and what has not happened. All we know is that there was a glory and that it is no more; all we know is that for the moment there is darkness, not so dark certainly, because when we look into our hearts we still find the living flame which he lighted there. And if those living flames exist, there will not be darkness in this land, and we shall be able, with our effort, remembering him and following his path, to **illumine** this land again, small as we are, but still with the fire that he instilled into us.

4   He was perhaps the greatest symbol of the India of the past, and may I say, of the India of the future, that we could have had. We stand on this **perilous** edge of the present, between that past and the future to be, and we face all manner of perils. And the greatest peril is sometimes the lack of faith which comes to us, the sense of frustration that comes to us, the sinking of the heart and of the spirit that comes to us when we see ideals go overboard, when we see the great things that we talked about somehow pass into empty words, and life taking a different course. Yet, I do believe that perhaps this period will pass soon enough.

5   He has gone, and all over India there is a feeling of having been left **desolate** and forlorn. All of us sense that feeling, and I do not know when we shall be able to get rid of it. And yet together with that feeling there is also a feeling of proud thankfulness that it has been given to us of this generation to be associated with this mighty person. In ages to come, centuries and maybe millennia after us, people will think of this generation when this man of God trod on earth, and will think of us who, however small, could also follow his path and tread the holy ground where his feet had been.

6   Let us be worthy of him.

Please note that excerpts and passages in the StudySync® library and this workbook are intended as touchstones to generate interest in an author's work. The excerpts and passages do not substitute for the reading of entire texts, and StudySync® strongly recommends that students seek out and purchase the whole literary or informational work in order to experience it as the author intended. Links to online resellers are available in our digital library. In addition, complete works may be ordered through an authorized reseller by filling out and returning to StudySync® the order form enclosed in this workbook.

Reading & Writing Companion   **275**

THINK QUESTIONS

1. Why does Nehru feel that it is difficult to praise Gandhi? Cite evidence from paragraphs 1 and 2 to support your answer.

2. According to Nehru, what things made Gandhi suffer? Support your answer with evidence from paragraph 2.

3. Nehru states that the people of India "stand on this perilous edge of the present, between that past and the future." What perils does Nehru list? Cite textual evidence from paragraph 4 to support your response.

4. By remembering that the Greek prefix *en-* means "in," use context to determine the meaning of the word **enshrined** as it is used in the first paragraph of "Eulogy for Mahatma Gandhi." Write your definition of "enshrined" and tell the context clues you used to determine the meaning of the word.

5. Use a dictionary to look up the word **illumine** to find its origin. Notice the Latin verb from which the word comes: *illuminare*, meaning "to light up." By knowing the Latin root of the word, use the context clues provided to determine the meaning of "illumine" in paragraph 3. Write your definition of "illumine" and explain how you figured out its meaning.

CLOSE READ

Reread "Eulogy for Mahatma Gandhi." As you reread, complete the Focus Questions below. Then use your answers and annotations from the questions to help you complete the Writing Prompt.

FOCUS QUESTIONS

1. When reading "Eulogy for Mahatma Gandhi," it is up to the reader to interpret Nehru's central or main ideas by making inferences from what he directly states in the text. Based on the details in the last three sentences of paragraph 1, what is the central idea that you can infer from Nehru's statements? Highlight evidence in the text and make annotations to support your explanation.

2. In paragraph 2, Nehru says, "[t]o praise him [Gandhi] we are not worthy." Find and highlight textual evidence in paragraph 2 that supports Nehru's statement. Then annotate and write a sentence summarizing the evidence.

3. Which details in paragraph 3 support Nehru's central idea that although things look dark, there is hope for the future? Highlight textual evidence and make annotations to support your choices.

4. What is the central idea of paragraph 4? Highlight the supporting details and make annotations to explain your reasoning.

5. What evidence is there in paragraphs 5 and 6 that Nehru is calling on the people of India to carry on Gandhi's fight for human rights? Highlight evidence from the text and make annotations to support your claim.

WRITING PROMPT

What are two central ideas that are developed over the course of "Eulogy for Mahatma Gandhi"? How do these two central ideas and the details that support them help to answer the Essential Question: *Why is it essential to defend human rights?* Begin with a clear thesis statement to introduce the topic. Use your understanding of the central or main idea to guide you as you identify central ideas in the selection and analyze how they relate to the Essential Question. Organize and support your writing with specific evidence from the text, including relevant selection vocabulary. Use transitions in your body paragraphs to show the relationships between (or among) your ideas. Establish a formal style to emphasize the nature of your topic, and provide a conclusion that summarizes your two central (or main) ideas.

LONG WALK TO FREEDOM

NON-FICTION
Nelson Mandela
1994

INTRODUCTION

From prisoner to president of South Africa, Nelson Mandela was one of the political stories of the twentieth century. In 1944, Mandela became a leader in the African National Congress, a political party that opposed South Africa's policy of racial segregation. In 1962, Mandela was jailed for his political activities, and after a widely publicized trial, was sentenced to life in prison. Over the years, Mandela became the world's best-known political prisoner, gaining international support for his fight against apartheid. He was released from captivity in 1990, and went on to become South Africa's first black president. The excerpt here is from Mandela's autobiography *Long Walk to Freedom*.

"Man's goodness is a flame that can be hidden but never extinguished."

 FIRST READ

From Part Eleven: Freedom

1   On the day of the inauguration, I was overwhelmed with a sense of history. In the first decade of the twentieth century, a few years after the bitter Anglo-Boer War and before my own birth, the white-skinned peoples of South Africa patched up their differences and erected a system of racial domination against dark-skinned peoples of their own land. The structure they created formed the basis of one of the harshest, most inhumane societies the world has ever known. Now, in the last decade of the twentieth century, and my own eighth decade as a man, that system had been overturned forever and replaced by one that recognized the rights and freedoms of all peoples regardless of the color of their skin.

2   That day had come about through the unimaginable sacrifices of thousands of my people, people whose suffering and courage can never be counted or repaid. I felt that day, as I have on so many other days, that I was simply the sum of all those African patriots who had gone before me. That long and noble line ended and now began again with me. I was pained that I was not able to thank them and that they were not able to see what their sacrifices had wrought.

3   The policy of **apartheid** created a deep and lasting wound in my country and my people. All of us will spend many years, if not generations, recovering from that profound hurt. But the decades of oppression and **brutality** had another, unintended effect, and that was that it produced the Oliver Tambos, the Walter Sisulus, the Chief Luthulis, the Yusuf Dadoos, the Bram Fischers, the Robert Sobukwes of our time—men of such extraordinary courage, wisdom, and generosity that their like may never be known again. Perhaps it requires such depth of **oppression** to create such heights of character. My country is rich in the minerals and gems that lie beneath its soil, but I have

NOTES

always known that its greatest wealth is its people, finer and truer than the purest diamonds.

4   It is from these comrades in the struggle that I learned the meaning of courage. Time and again, I have seen men and women risk and give their lives for an idea. I have seen men stand up to attacks and torture without breaking, showing a strength and **resiliency** that defies the imagination. I learned that courage was not the absence of fear, but the triumph over it. I felt fear myself more times than I can remember, but I hid it behind a mask of boldness. The brave man is not he who does not feel afraid, but he who conquers that fear.

5   I never lost hope that this great **transformation** would occur. Not only because of the great heroes I have already cited, but because of the courage of the ordinary men and women of my country. I always knew that deep down in every human heart, there is mercy and generosity. No one is born hating another person because of the color of his skin, or his background, or his religion. People must learn to hate, and if they can learn to hate, they can be taught to love, for love comes more naturally to the human heart than its opposite. Even in the grimmest times in prison, when my comrades and I were pushed to our limits, I would see a glimmer of humanity in one of the guards, perhaps just for a second, but it was enough to reassure me and keep me going. Man's goodness is a flame that can be hidden but never extinguished.

6   We took up the struggle with our eyes wide open, under no illusion that the path would be an easy one. As a young man, when I joined the African National Congress, I saw the price my comrades paid for their beliefs, and it was high. For myself, I have never regretted my commitment to the struggle, and I was always prepared to face the hardships that affected me personally. But my family paid a terrible price, perhaps too dear a price for my commitment.

7   In life, every man has twin obligations—obligations to his family, to his parents, to his wife and children; and he as an obligation to his people, his community, his country. In a civil and human society, each man is able to fulfill those obligations according to his own inclinations and abilities. But in a country like South Africa, it was almost impossible for a man of my birth and color to fulfill both of those obligations. In South Africa, a man of color who attempted to live as a human being was punished and isolated. In South Africa, a man who tried to fulfill his duty to his people was inevitably ripped from his family and home and was forced to live a life apart, a twilight existence of secrecy and rebellion. I did not in the beginning choose to place my people above my family, but in attempting to serve my people, I found that I was prevented from serving my obligations as a son, a brother, a father, and a husband.

8   In that way, my commitment to my people, to the millions of South Africans I would never know or meet, was at the expense of the people I knew best and loved most. It was as simple and yet as incomprehensible as the moment a small child asks her father, "Why can you not be with us?" And the father must utter the terrible words: "There are other children like you, a great many of them. . . " and then one's voice trails off.

9   I was not born with a hunger to be free. I was born free—free in every way that I could know. Free to run in the fields near my mother's hut, free to swim in the clear stream that ran through my village, free to roast mealies under the stars and ride the broad backs of slow-moving bulls. As long as I obeyed my father and abided by the customs of my tribe, I was not troubled by the laws of man or God.

10 It was only when I began to learn that my boyhood freedom was an illusion, when I discovered as a young man that my freedom had already been taken from me, that I began to hunger for it. At first, as a student, I wanted freedom only for myself, the transitory freedoms of being able to stay out at night, read what I pleased, and go where I chose. Later, as a young man in Johannesburg, I yearned for the basic and honorable freedoms of achieving my potential, of earning my keep, of marrying and having a family—the freedom not to be obstructed in a lawful life.

11 But then I slowly saw that not only was I not free, but my brothers and sisters were not free. I saw that it was not just my freedom that was curtailed, but the freedom of everyone who looked like I did. That is when I joined the African National Congress, and that is when the hunger for my own freedom became the greater hunger for the freedom of my people to live their lives with dignity and self-respect that animated my life, that transformed a frightened young man into a bold one, that drove a law-abiding attorney to become a criminal, that turned a family-loving husband into a man without a home, that forced a life-loving man to live like a monk. I am not more virtuous or self-sacrificing than the next man, but I found that I could not even enjoy the poor and limited freedoms I was allowed when I knew my people were not free. Freedom is indivisible; the chains on any one of my people were the chains on all of them, the chains on all of my people were the chains on me.

12 It was during those long and lonely years that my hunger for the freedom of my own people became a hunger for the freedom of all people, white and black. I knew as well as I knew anything that the oppressor must be liberated just as surely as the oppressed. A man who takes away another man's freedom is a prisoner of hatred, he is locked behind the bars of prejudice and narrow-mindedness. I am not truly free if I am taking away someone else's freedom, just as surely as I am not free when my freedom is taken from me. The oppressed and the oppressor alike are robbed of their humanity.

13   When I walked out of prison, that was my mission, to liberate the oppressed and the oppressor both. Some say that has now been achieved. But I know that is not the case. The truth is that we are not yet free; we have merely achieved the freedom to be free, the right not to be oppressed. We have not taken the final step of our journey, but the first step on a longer and even more difficult road. For to be free is not merely to cast off one's chains, but to live in a way that respects and enhances the freedom of others. The true test of our devotion to freedom is just beginning.

14   I walked that long road to freedom. I have tried not to falter; I have made missteps along the way. But I have discovered the secret that after climbing a great hill, one only finds that there are many more hills to climb. I have taken a moment here to rest, to steal a view of the glorious vista that surrounds me, to look back on the distance I have come. But I can rest only for a moment, for with freedom comes responsibility, and I dare not linger, for my long walk is not yet ended.

From *Long Walk to Freedom* by Nelson Mandela. Copyright © 1994, 1995 by Nelson Rolihlahla Mandela. Reprinted by permission of Little, Brown and Company.

THINK QUESTIONS

1. Use details from the first paragraph to explain the social and political changes that have taken place in South Africa since the 1990s.

2. Write two or three sentences explaining Mandela's point of view about courage and his own reaction to fear. Support your answer with evidence from paragraph 4.

3. Refer to one or more details to explain Mandela's view of a person's "twin obligations"—both from ideas that are directly stated in paragraph 7 and from ideas you have inferred from clues in the text.

4. Use context clues and word relationships to determine the meaning of the word **resiliency** as it is used in paragraph 4 of *Long Walk to Freedom*. Write your definition of "resiliency" here and tell how you determined its meaning.

5. By recalling that the Latin prefix *trans-* means "across" or "to change completely" and that the suffix *-ation* means "act or process," use the context clues provided in paragraph 5 to determine the meaning of **transformation**. Write your definition of "transformation" and tell how you figured out its meaning.

CLOSE READ

Reread the excerpt from *Long Walk to Freedom*. As you reread, complete the Focus Questions below. Then use your answers and annotations from the questions to help you complete the Writing Prompt.

FOCUS QUESTIONS

1. Based on paragraph 3, explain Mandela's point of view regarding the effects of apartheid on South Africa and its people. Highlight evidence from the text and make annotations to explain your response.

2. In paragraph 5, analyze Mandela's point of view regarding the qualities of a courageous person and a person who lacks courage. To which category does Mandela belong? To which category does the guard belong? Support your answer with textual evidence and inferences. Make annotations justifying your response.

3. Based on paragraph 10, explain Mandela's point of view regarding "transitory freedoms" and

"basic and honorable freedoms." Highlight textual evidence and make annotations to support your explanation.

4. In paragraph 13, what does Mandela want the reader to know about freedom? What action does he want people to take? Highlight your evidence and make annotations to support your explanation.

5. How might Mandela respond to the Essential Question: *Why is it essential to defend human rights?* Highlight textual evidence and make annotations to explain your ideas.

WRITING PROMPT

This excerpt from Nelson Mandela's autobiography *Long Walk to Freedom* may be more philosophical than autobiographical as he reflects on oppression and transformation in South Africa. How does Mandela influence people's views about courage and freedom through his observations about and experiences with apartheid? In what ways do Mandela's observations and experiences impact his own feelings about the importance of defending human rights? Use your understanding of author's purpose and point of view in your response. Support your writing with strong reasons and specific evidence from the text.

Please note that excerpts and passages in the StudySync® library and this workbook are intended as touchstones to generate interest in an author's work. The excerpts and passages do not substitute for the reading of entire texts, and StudySync® strongly recommends that students seek out and purchase the whole literary or informational work in order to experience it as the author intended. Links to online resellers are available in our digital library. In addition, complete works may be ordered through an authorized reseller by filling out and returning to StudySync® the order form enclosed in this workbook.

Reading & Writing Companion   283

LITERARY ANALYSIS

WRITING PROMPT

Imagine what it would be like to work long hours under dangerous conditions for little pay. Think about how your life would be different if you had to work in a factory or on a farm as a migrant farm worker, instead of going to school. The world is full of injustice, but fortunately, there are people who believe in speaking up for the powerless and defending human rights.

In this unit, you have been reading nonfiction texts about real people who stood up for the rights of others and brought about social change. From Mother Jones, a fierce fighter for child labor laws, to Cesar Chavez, who fought for the rights of ill-treated farm workers, these great people had something in common: They fought for fairness and inspired social change.

Mahatma Gandhi and Nelson Mandela also fought for change. Both Gandhi and Mandela are inspiring, but the texts that you have read about them are very different. Write a literary analysis in which you compare and contrast the text about Gandhi with the text about Mandela to determine which is more convincing in presenting and supporting the claim that this individual was a great defender of justice and human rights. Analyze the reasons and evidence presented in the text as well as the language that is used to describe the individual's words, actions, and accomplishments. Then decide which writer was more persuasive in defending his claim about the impact this person had on human rights.

Your literary analysis should include

- a comparison-contrast of two nonfiction texts you have read in this unit.

Please note that excerpts and passages in the StudySync® library and this workbook are intended as touchstones to generate interest in an author's work. The excerpts and passages do not substitute for the reading of entire texts, and StudySync® strongly recommends that students seek out and purchase the whole literary or informational work in order to experience it as the author intended. Links to online resellers are available in our digital library. In addition, complete works may be ordered through an authorized reseller by filling out and returning to StudySync® the order form enclosed in this workbook.

Reading & Writing Companion **285**

NOTES

WRITING PROMPT

- an explicitly stated claim about the topic.
- a logically organized presentation of sound reasons and textual evidence.
- a conclusion that sums up your literary analysis of which text was more persuasive and leaves your readers with an original thought about the topic.

A **literary analysis** considers the themes or central ideas of one or more pieces of literature. It may explain connections between (or among) different texts, between the writer and the text, or between literature and its effect on the reader or a larger audience.

Literary analysis can be a form of argumentative writing: The writer makes a claim about the literature and then provides relevant textual evidence—details, descriptions, examples, observations, and quotations—to support the argument and claims. After first introducing a claim, the writer develops his or her ideas in the body of the literary analysis, using transitions to show connections and create a smooth flow of ideas. Often, the author's purpose for writing a literary analysis is to convince readers that the claims the writer is making are valid.

Therefore, the features of a literary analysis may include the following:

- a comparison-contrast of two literary texts
- an introduction with a thesis statement (or claim), a central idea, and support built on sound reasons and textual evidence
- a text structure that organizes the analysis in a logical way, using clear transitions to create a smooth flow of ideas
- embedded quotations that are cited from the texts or from outside sources
- precise word choice
- a concluding statement that restates the thesis statement (or claim), and that summarizes the central idea (or ideas)

As you work on this Extended Writing Project, you will learn more about crafting each of the elements of a literary analysis.

MODEL

Before you begin writing your literary analysis, start by reading this essay that one student wrote to a prompt that is slightly different from the one you will use. Instead of writing about Nelson Mandela and Mahatma Gandhi, who will be the subjects of your writing prompt, this student compared and contrasted the unit texts about Mother Jones and Cesar Chavez to see which text was more persuasive. This Student Model will help you identify the features of a literary analysis. As you read, highlight and annotate the features of a literary analysis that the Student Model includes.

Mother Jones and Cesar Chavez: Standing Up for Workers' Rights

You have probably spent your day sitting in a classroom, learning important facts so that you can go to college or get a good job after you graduate from high school. But if you had been born one hundred years ago, you might have ended up working long and hard for meager wages in a factory. Similarly, if you had been born fifty or seventy-five years ago, you might have wound up working in the fields of California instead of getting a good education. Life was unfair for a lot of workers in the early-to-mid-twentieth century, especially for children and migrant farm workers. Two people, however, worked hard to change all that—Mary Harris "Mother" Jones and Cesar Chavez. Both championed the rights of workers and called for laws that guaranteed fair pay, shorter working hours, and better working conditions. Although Jones and Chavez lived very different lives in very different times, both defended workers' rights, Jones defending child workers, Chavez championing the rights of farm laborers. Clearly, the authors of *Mother Jones: Fierce Fighter for Workers' Rights* and *About Cesar* admire their subjects, although this literary analysis will prove the point that Chavez was the greater fighter for human rights. As the authors from the Cesar Chavez Foundation state, "Chavez not only righted many of the injustices that farm workers faced, but he also inspired "Americans from all walks of life."

The author Judith Pinkerton Josephson paints an interesting portrait of Mother Jones as she tells the reader that Jones was seventy-three years old when she decided in June of 1903 to draw attention to the problem of child labor. As Josephson says in paragraph 4, even though it was against the law to hire children younger than 13 to work in factories, "parents often lied about a child's age," and "[m]ill owners "looked the other way, because child labor was cheap." As a result, thousands of children worked long hours under terrible working conditions in mills, with often serious effects to their health. To highlight this point, Josephson notes, in paragraph 3, how Mother Jones noticed that the children's "bodies were bone-thin with hollow chests," and that many of them were maimed, "with their hands [cut] off, some with the thumb missing." The writer explains how Jones led a group of mill children and their parents to Independence Square in Philadelphia, where she called on city officials to think about the real costs of child labor—mangled limbs, lost childhoods, no education. Jones appealed to their sympathies, stating in paragraph 6: "'Philadelphia's mansions were built on the broken bones, the quivering hearts, and the drooping heads of these children.'" But the officials ignored her. Undeterred, she decided that the best way to bring national attention to the plight of child labor was to march 125 miles to President Theodore Roosevelt's summer home in New York. She and many child workers and their families walked the whole way, stopping only to rest and hold rallies. The author admits that in the end, however, Jones did not meet her goal because President Roosevelt refused to see her. As a result, she and the children returned home without having brought about any real changes to child labor laws. In the last paragraph, Josephson sums up: "Though she had not met with the president, Mother Jones had drawn the attention of the nation to the problem of child labor." However, she does not say that national laws to protect child workers came about because of Jones's efforts. In fact, all she says at the end is that the "federal government finally passed a child labor law. . . in 1938—thirty-five years after the march of the mill children." Josephson's portrait of Mother Jones shows a woman who was committed to a cause but not completely successful at promoting change. She includes criticisms, such as that she was self-centered, that people had of Jones. In the end, Josephson fails to persuade her readers that Mother Jones had a huge impact on human rights.

Unlike Josephson, the authors of *About Cesar* are deeply enthusiastic about their subject, Cesar Chavez. In the first paragraph, these authors from the Cesar Chavez Foundation quote Robert F. Kennedy by saying that he called Chavez "'one of the heroic figures of our time.'" They begin their text by introducing Chavez as a "true American hero," a "farm labor leader . . . a community organizer . . . and a crusader for the environment and consumer rights." Later, in paragraph 15, they refer to him as a "unique and humble leader, as well as a great humanitarian and communicator who influenced and inspired millions of Americans from all walks of life." In paragraph 19, they call him "a common man with an uncommon vision." They support their claims with relevant textual evidence of Chavez's achievements. In paragraph 2, they describe how as a boy, he worked in California's "fields, orchards, and vineyards, where he was exposed to the hardships and injustices of farm worker life." Most of the selection explores Chavez's accomplishments as a leader of the migrant labor movement. The authors outline the specifics of Chavez's achievements, on behalf of migrant workers, including the right to form and join unions, such as the United Farm Workers (the UFW), and create contracts that provided rest periods, safe working conditions, clean drinking water, medical care, and pensions. They also point out that he helped to outlaw dangerous pesticides and job discrimination. More importantly, Chavez did all this while bringing people together. The authors explain, in paragraph 15, that the "significance of Cesar's life transcends any one cause or struggle." They say that he helped form "a national and extraordinarily diverse coalition for farm worker boycotts, which included students, middle class consumers, trade unionists, religious activists, and minorities." In fact, they point out that Chavez made people realize that they had a stake in providing migrant workers with a decent way of life. He made people feel special, and his motto "Sí, se puede!" ("Yes, it can be done!") gave people "the faith to believe in themselves."

Both Mother Jones and Cesar Chavez were crusaders in the fight for human rights. They stood up for workers, and their leadership helped millions of people attain a better life. The two texts support the authors' claims that Jones and Chavez were committed people who tried hard to help others. However, *About Cesar* makes a stronger argument. Its authors praise Chavez and describe him as a hard worker, a great leader, and a man who knew how to reach out to others.

Similarly, Josephson admires her subject and shows how Mother Jones was committed to bringing attention to the problem of child labor. But Mother Jones did not have the same successes with workers' rights as did Chavez. In the end, she was not able to persuade lawmakers to improve working conditions for children. In fact, the connection Josephson makes between

Please note that excerpts and passages in the StudySync® library and this workbook are intended as touchstones to generate interest in an author's work. The excerpts and passages do not substitute for the reading of entire texts, and StudySync® strongly recommends that students seek out and purchase the whole literary or informational work in order to experience it as the author intended. Links to online resellers are available in our digital library. In addition, complete works may be ordered through an authorized reseller by filling out and returning to StudySync® the order form enclosed in this workbook.

Reading & Writing Companion **289**

NOTES

the 1903 march and the child labor laws enacted in 1938 is not well supported or convincing. She does not provide sufficient evidence to suggest that lawmakers thought about Mother Jones when they passed child labor laws years later. Perhaps because Mother Jones lived so long ago, her human rights efforts seem to have had less impact than those of Chavez, who died in 1993. Although Jones and Chavez both fought to secure workers' rights, Chavez's influence was stronger. Only he improved the lives of workers in his lifetime and "inspired millions of Americans from all walks of life."

THINK QUESTIONS

1. Which sentence in the first paragraph most clearly states what the entire essay will be about?

2. How does the Student Model organize its evidence in the second and third paragraphs? Cite textual evidence to support your response.

3. In the last two paragraphs, what conclusion does the writer reach about which text is more persuasive? How does the writer support this conclusion? Cite specific evidence from the Student Model to support your claim.

4. Think about the writing prompt. Which selections or other resources would you like to use to create your own literary analysis comparing and contrasting the texts that focus on the humanitarian efforts of Mahatma Gandhi and Nelson Mandela? What are some ideas you might want to develop when you compare and contrast your two texts?

5. Based on what you have read, listened to, or researched, how would you answer the question: *Why is it essential to defend human rights?* Support your answer with relevant evidence from the Student Model.

PREWRITE

WRITING PROMPT

Imagine what it would be like to work long hours under dangerous conditions for little pay. Think about how your life would be different if you had to work in a factory or on a farm as a migrant farm worker, instead of going to school. The world is full of injustice, but fortunately, there are people who believe in speaking up for the powerless and defending human rights.

In this unit, you have been reading nonfiction texts about real people who stood up for the rights of others and brought about social change. From Mother Jones, a fierce fighter for child labor laws, to Cesar Chavez, who fought for the rights of ill-treated farm workers, these great people had something in common: They fought for fairness and inspired social change.

Mahatma Gandhi and Nelson Mandela also fought for change. Both Gandhi and Mandela are inspiring, but the texts that you have read about them are very different. Write a literary analysis in which you compare and contrast the text about Gandhi with the text about Mandela to determine which is more convincing in presenting and supporting the claim that this individual was a great defender of justice and human rights. Analyze the reasons and evidence presented in the text as well as the language that is used to describe the individual's words, actions, and accomplishments. Then decide which writer was more persuasive in defending his claim about the impact this person had on human rights.

Your literary analysis should include

- a comparison-contrast of two nonfiction texts you have read in this unit.

Please note that excerpts and passages in the StudySync® library and this workbook are intended as touchstones to generate interest in an author's work. The excerpts and passages do not substitute for the reading of entire texts, and StudySync® strongly recommends that students seek out and purchase the whole literary or informational work in order to experience it as the author intended. Links to online resellers are available in our digital library. In addition, complete works may be ordered through an authorized reseller by filling out and returning to StudySync® the order form enclosed in this workbook.

Reading & Writing
Companion

291

WRITING PROMPT

- an explicitly stated claim about the topic.
- a logically organized presentation of sound reasons and textual evidence.
- a conclusion that sums up your literary analysis of which text was more persuasive and leaves your readers with an original thought about the topic.

You have been reading about humanitarians from different places in history who stood up for the rights of others. In the extended writing project, you will consider two texts about these human rights activists, Mahatma Gandhi and Nelson Mandela. In a literary analysis, you will explore how well the authors presented their claims about their two subjects. You will also trace and evaluate how relevant and sufficient their evidence was in supporting their claims.

Begin by asking yourself these questions: Who were these two people? How did they help others? What made them great? What were the consequences of their actions? How does each author persuade you that his person devoted his life to protecting the human rights of others?

Make a list of the answers to these questions as you read, looking for patterns between the texts. What are the similarities and differences between Gandhi and Mandela? Do the texts treat their subjects in a similar or different way? Do they make similar claims? Is one text more persuasive than the other? How? Identifying patterns, details, claims, and word choice can help you decide what you will want to discuss in your essay. Follow the Student Model to help you get started with the prewriting of your own literary analysis:

Texts: *Mother Jones: Fierce Fighter for Worker's Rights* and *About Cesar*

Similarities and differences between the two subjects: Both Mother Jones and Cesar Chavez stood up for workers who were not paid enough for the hard and dangerous work they performed. Mother Jones led child workers and their parents on a 125-mile march to see President Theodore Roosevelt, but he would not meet with them. Chavez organized a farm workers' union and helped secure laws that made working conditions for migrant farm workers safer and improved the quality of their lives.

Similarities and differences between the texts, the author's claims, and ideas: The writers think that their subjects were great supporters of human rights. The

NOTES

author of the text about Mother Jones recognizes that Jones was not completely successful in helping the child workers. However, the authors of the text about Cesar Chavez are in awe of their subject, praise him, and spell out his many achievements.

Which text is more persuasive, and why: The text about Chavez is more persuasive because it uses sound reasons and relevant, sufficient evidence to support its claim about Chavez's many accomplishments as a fighter for human rights.

Please note that excerpts and passages in the StudySync® library and this workbook are intended as touchstones to generate interest in an author's work. The excerpts and passages do not substitute for the reading of entire texts, and StudySync® strongly recommends that students seek out and purchase the whole literary or informational work in order to experience it as the author intended. Links to online resellers are available in our digital library. In addition, complete works may be ordered through an authorized reseller by filling out and returning to StudySync® the order form enclosed in this workbook.

Reading & Writing Companion 293

SKILL:
THESIS
STATEMENT

DEFINE

In informative writing, a thesis statement expresses a writer's central (or main) idea about a topic. In argumentative writing, a thesis statement takes the form of a claim. The claim is the writer's opinion (or point of view) about the topic. When writing a literary analysis, a writer expresses an opinion about one or more texts. The writer's claim typically appears in the introduction, or first paragraph, of the literary analysis, often as the last sentence. Support for the claim, such as details, examples, observations, and quotations from the text, appears in the body of the essay.

IDENTIFICATION AND APPLICATION

A thesis statement, or claim

- expresses an opinion about one or more texts.
- previews what will appear in the body of the literary analysis.
- addresses all aspects of the writing prompt for the literary analysis.
- appears in the introduction, or the first paragraph.

MODEL

The following is the introduction, or first paragraph, from the Student Model, "Mother Jones and Cesar Chavez: Standing Up for Workers' Rights":

> You have probably spent your day sitting in a classroom, learning important facts, so that you can go to college or get a good job after you graduate from high school. But if you had been born one hundred years ago, you might have ended up working long and hard for meager wages in a factory. Similarly, if you had been born fifty or seventy-five years ago, you might

Copyright © BookheadEd Learning, LLC

have wound up working in the fields of California instead of getting a good education. Life was unfair for a lot of workers in the early-to-mid-twentieth century, especially for children and migrant farm workers. However, two people worked hard to help change all that—Mary Harris "Mother" Jones and Cesar Chavez. Both championed the rights of workers and called for laws that guaranteed fair pay, shorter working hours, and better working conditions. Although Jones and Chavez lived very different lives in very different times, both defended workers' rights, Jones defending child workers, Chavez championing the rights of farm laborers. Clearly, the authors of *Mother Jones: Fierce Fighter for Workers' Rights* and *About Cesar* admire their subjects, although this literary analysis will prove the point that Chavez was the greater fighter for human rights. As the authors from the Cesar Chavez Foundation state, "Chavez not only righted many of the injustices that farm workers faced, but he also inspired "Americans from all walks of life."

As you reread this excerpt from the first paragraph of the Student Model, look for the thesis statement, or student's claim. The student's claim responds to the writing prompt by identifying the texts he or she has examined. It also states his or her opinion (or point of view) about which text is more persuasive and why.

 PRACTICE

Write a thesis statement for your literary analysis that states your claim as it relates to the writing prompt. When you have finished, share your thesis statement with a partner and offer each other constructive feedback.

Please note that excerpts and passages in the StudySync® library and this workbook are intended as touchstones to generate interest in an author's work. The excerpts and passages do not substitute for the reading of entire texts, and StudySync® strongly recommends that students seek out and purchase the whole literary or informational work in order to experience it as the author intended. Links to online resellers are available in our digital library. In addition, complete works may be ordered through an authorized reseller by filling out and returning to StudySync® the order form enclosed in this workbook.

Reading & Writing Companion   **295**

SKILL: ORGANIZE ARGUMENTATIVE WRITING

DEFINE

A literary analysis can be a form of argumentative writing that tries to persuade readers to accept the writer's opinion of a particular text (or texts). To write such a literary analysis, the writer must organize and present the reasons and relevant evidence—the facts, details, examples, and quotations from the text (or texts)—in a logical and convincing way. In addition, the writer must choose an organizational (or text) structure that best suits the argument.

The writer of a literary analysis can choose from a number of organizational structures in which to couch the argument, including compare and contrast, order of importance, problem and solution, cause and effect, and sequential (chronological, or time) order. Experienced writers use an outline or another graphic organizer to decide how to order and convey their ideas persuasively.

IDENTIFICATION AND APPLICATION

- When selecting an overall organizational structure for a literary analysis, a writer must consider his or her argument or specific claims about the text (or texts). Then the writer must think about the best way of presenting the supporting evidence. He or she can do this by asking these questions:
  - › To support my idea, will I compare and contrast ideas or details in the text?
  - › Is there an order of importance to my evidence? Does all my evidence support my claim equally well? Is some evidence stronger?
  - › Will I raise a question or identify a problem in my argument? Do I have supporting evidence that suggests a solution or an answer?
  - › Does my supporting evidence suggest a cause-and-effect relationship?
  - › To support my claim, does it make sense to retell the events in sequential (or chronological) order?

Copyright © BookheadEd Learning, LLC

- Writers often use specific signal (or transition) words or phrases to help readers recognize the organizational structure or pattern of their writing. Here are some examples of transitions:

  › Compare and contrast: *like, similarly, in the same way* to compare and *unlike, different from, although, while, but, however, on the other hand* to contrast

  › Order of importance: *most, most important, least, least important, mainly*

  › Problem and solution: *problem, solution, why, how*

  › Cause and effect: *because, therefore, as a result, cause, effect, so*

  › Chronological order: *first, next, then, finally, last, during that time,*

- Writers are not limited to using only one organizational pattern throughout a text. Within a specific section or paragraph, they might use a different text structure. This does not affect the overall organization, however.

 MODEL

During the prewriting stage, the writer of the Student Model understood that the assignment required him or her to compare and contrast two texts from the unit in order to determine which text was more persuasive. The writer knew that that would involve weighing the claims and evidence from both texts in order to decide which author was more persuasive in showing that the subject of the text was the greater defender of human rights. Therefore, an overall compare-and-contrast organizational structure best suited this writer's argument.

In this excerpt from the Student Model, the author uses a compare/contrast text structure:

> **Unlike Josephson,** the authors of *About Cesar* are deeply enthusiastic about their subject, Cesar Chavez. In the first paragraph, these authors from the Cesar Chavez Foundation quote Robert F. Kennedy by saying that he called Chavez "'one of the heroic figures of our time.'"

Once a writer has selected the most appropriate organizational structure, he or she can use an outline or a graphic organizer (for example, a Venn diagram, concept map, or flowchart) to begin organizing the supporting evidence that will back up his or her claim.

The writer of the Student Model used this graphic organizer during planning to organize the evidence to support this claim: The authors of *About Chavez*

NOTES

were more persuasive than the author of *Mother Jones: Fierce Fighter for Workers' Rights* in showing that their subject was the greater fighter for human rights.

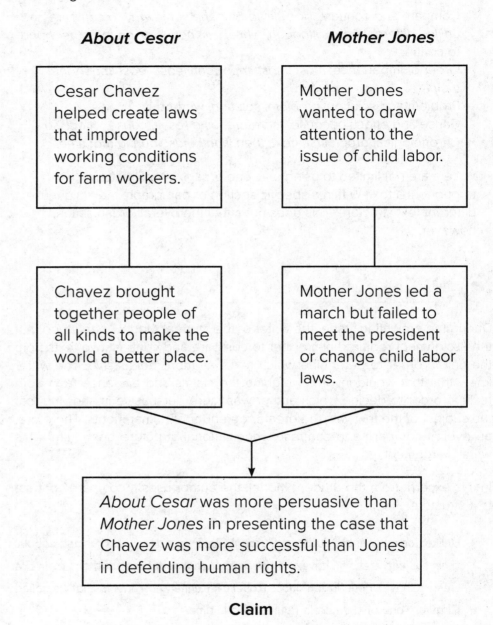

About Cesar	*Mother Jones*
Cesar Chavez helped create laws that improved working conditions for farm workers.	Mother Jones wanted to draw attention to the issue of child labor.
Chavez brought together people of all kinds to make the world a better place.	Mother Jones led a march but failed to meet the president or change child labor laws.

About Cesar was more persuasive than *Mother Jones* in presenting the case that Chavez was more successful than Jones in defending human rights.

Claim

 PRACTICE

By using an *Organize Argumentative Writing* graphic organizer like the one used with the Student Model, you'll be able to fill in the information you gathered in the Prewrite stage. Now that you've organized or structured your literary analysis, you'll soon be able to begin your own literary analysis.

Copyright © BookheadEd Learning, LLC

SKILL:
SUPPORTING
DETAILS

 DEFINE

Because a literary analysis makes a claim about one or more texts, it is a form of argumentative writing. To make his or her argument effective, the writer of a literary analysis must provide supporting details in the form of reasons and relevant textual evidence. Reasons are statements that answer the question "Why?" Writers provide reasons to support a claim and to help readers understand their analysis of the texts. Relevant evidence includes facts, definitions, quotations, observations, and examples from the text (or texts) being analyzed or from outside sources. Relevant evidence is key to the success of the writer's argument. It makes the literary analysis more persuasive, develops the ideas, and clarifies the writer's understanding and analysis of the text. Without strong reasons and relevant evidence, the writer would simply be stating his or her opinion about the texts without using support.

Because writers want to convince readers that their interpretation of a text is believable, they carefully select and present the evidence. Evidence is relevant only if it supports the claim and helps build the argument. If the evidence—a fact, detail, an example, or a quotation—does not support the claim or validate the argument, it is irrelevant and should not be used.

 IDENTIFICATION AND APPLICATION

Step 1:

Review your claim. To identify supporting details that are relevant to your claim, ask the following questions:

- What am I trying to persuade my audience (or readers) to believe?
- What kinds of supporting details—reasons and evidence—can I include that will help persuade them?

Please note that excerpts and passages in the StudySync® library and this workbook are intended as touchstones to generate interest in an author's work. The excerpts and passages do not substitute for the reading of entire texts, and StudySync® strongly recommends that students seek out and purchase the whole literary or informational work in order to experience it as the author intended. Links to online resellers are available in our digital library. In addition, complete works may be ordered through an authorized reseller by filling out and returning to StudySync® the order form enclosed in this workbook.

Reading & Writing Companion   **299**

NOTES

Step 2:

Ask what your reader needs to know about the topic in order to understand your claim. Think about the reasons you'll need to provide as evidence to convince your readers that your claim is valid.

Step 3:

Look for facts, definitions, quotations, observations, examples, and descriptions from the texts you are analyzing or from outside sources you are using as evidence. Use supporting details such as these to build on ideas you've already provided, but remember to evaluate their relevance to your argument and claims. To do this, ask yourself these questions:

- Does this detail help my reader understand the topic?
- Does this detail support my claim?
- Can I use it as evidence to help build, support, or reinforce my argument?
- Is there stronger evidence that makes the same point?

 ## MODEL

In the following excerpt from the first paragraph from *About Cesar*, the authors provide supporting details to back up their claim that Chavez was a "true American hero . . . a civil rights, Latino and farm labor leader . . . a community organizer and social entrepreneur; a champion of militant nonviolent social change; and a crusader for the environment and consumer rights."

In paragraph 15, the authors provide evidence that Chavez was an effective labor leader. They offer specific details about the union he helped organize and how it influenced migrant farm workers and others.

> The significance of Cesar's life transcends any one cause or struggle. He was a unique and humble leader, as well as a great humanitarian and communicator who influenced and inspired millions of Americans from all walks of life. **Cesar forged a national and extraordinarily diverse coalition for farm worker boycotts, which included students, middle class consumers, trade unionists, religious activists and minorities.**

Here, the authors support the claim that Chavez was a strong labor leader and community organizer. They tell how he brought together people from different professions and classes to support the cause of the farm workers. The authors list the specific kinds of people who were involved in Chavez's cause. Then, in paragraph 18, the authors employ further evidence:

> Cesar liked to say that his job as an organizer was helping ordinary people do extraordinary things. **Cesar made everyone, especially the**

farm workers, feel the jobs they were doing in the movement were very important. It did not matter if they were lawyers working in the courtrooms or cooks in the kitchen feeding the people involved in the strike, he showed the farm workers that they could win against great odds. He gave people the faith to believe in themselves, even if they were poor and unable to receive the best education.

Here, the authors give specific examples of how Chavez led people by bringing them together—by making them feel that despite the role they played in the movement, everyone was important and essential in the fight to secure human rights.

NOTES

PLAN

WRITING PROMPT

Imagine what it would be like to work long hours under dangerous conditions for little pay. Think about how your life would be different if you had to work in a factory or on a farm as a migrant farm worker, instead of going to school. The world is full of injustice, but fortunately, there are people who believe in speaking up for the powerless and defending human rights.

In this unit, you have been reading nonfiction texts about real people who stood up for the rights of others and brought about social change. From Mother Jones, a fierce fighter for child labor laws, to Cesar Chavez, who fought for the rights of ill-treated farm workers, these great people had something in common: They fought for fairness and inspired social change.

Mahatma Gandhi and Nelson Mandela also fought for change. Both Gandhi and Mandela are inspiring, but the texts that you have read about them are very different. Write a literary analysis in which you compare and contrast the text about Gandhi with the text about Mandela to determine which is more convincing in presenting and supporting the claim that this individual was a great defender of justice and human rights. Analyze the reasons and evidence presented in the text as well as the language that is used to describe the individual's words, actions, and accomplishments. Then decide which writer was more persuasive in defending his claim about the impact this person had on human rights.

Your literary analysis should include

- a comparison-contrast of two nonfiction texts you have read in this unit.

WRITING PROMPT

- an explicitly stated claim about the topic.
- a logically organized presentation of sound reasons and textual evidence.
- a conclusion that sums up your literary analysis of which text was more persuasive and leaves your readers with an original thought about the topic.

Review the information you listed in your *Organize Argumentative Writing* graphic organizer in which you cited evidence from *About Chavez* and *Mother Jones: Fierce Fighter for Workers' Rights*. This completed organizer, with its filled-in details from the two texts, along with your claim, will help you create a road map to use for writing your literary analysis.

Consider the following questions as you develop your body paragraphs and their supporting details in your road map:

- Who are the subjects of the texts? What did they accomplish?
- To what degree do the authors think their subjects are supporters of human rights? How do you know?
- What attitude does each author have toward human rights?
- How persuasive is each author in presenting his or her ideas?
- Which text did you ultimately find more persuasive?
- Why were you persuaded in favor of one person over the other?

Use this model to get started with your road map:

Literary Analysis Road Map

Claim: *About Cesar* is more persuasive than *Mother Jones: Fierce Fighter for Workers' Rights* in presenting the case that its subject was a great supporter of human rights.

Body Paragraph 1 Topic: Mother Jones wanted to draw attention to the issue of child labor.

> **Supporting Detail #1:** She led the mill children and their parents on a 125-mile march to meet President Theodore Roosevelt.

Supporting Detail #2: The president would not see Jones and the children, and they returned home without bringing about any change to child labor laws.

Body Paragraph 2 Topic: Cesar Chavez dedicated his life to helping migrant farm workers gain rights and improve their lives.

Supporting Detail #1: Under Chavez's leadership, the United Farm Workers (UFW), a labor union for farm workers in the United States, became the first successful union for farm workers in American history, offering benefits to workers.

Supporting Detail #2: Chavez brought people from all walks of life together to support the cause of the migrant farm workers.

Body Paragraph 3 Topic: The text about Cesar Chavez was more persuasive than the text about Mother Jones.

Supporting Detail #1: Mother Jones felt strongly about enacting child labor laws and improving the lives of child workers, but the author was unable to show how effective Jones's efforts were in bringing about any real change during her lifetime.

Supporting Detail #2: The authors were able to show that Cesar Chavez greatly improved the lives of farm workers, enabling them to join unions and gain workers' rights, and they provided evidence to show that many people considered Chavez to be "a great leader."

NOTES

SKILL :
INTRODUCTIONS

DEFINE

The **introduction** is the opening paragraph or section of a literary analysis. It identifies the texts and the topic to be discussed, states the writer's claim, and previews the supporting evidence that will appear in the body of the text. The introduction is also the place where most writers include a "hook" that is intended to "grab" the reader's attention and connect the reader to the text.

IDENTIFICATION AND APPLICATION

- In a literary analysis, the introduction is usually the first paragraph or section, and it is where the writer identifies the text (or texts) or topic to be analyzed. Since a literary analysis examines one or more texts in depth, the writer must let readers know what the focus of the analysis will be.

- A literary analysis is a form of argument, so the writer's specific claim is an important part of the introduction. The claim is a direct statement of the writer's opinion of the texts under discussion. By stating the claim in the introduction, the writer lets the reader know the ideas or opinion he or she will explore. Establishing a claim in the introduction also allows readers to form their own opinions, which they can then measure against the writer's opinion as they read.

- Another use of the introduction is to provide a preview of the textual evidence which readers will later assess to determine whether it is relevant and sufficient to support the writer's claim.

- The introduction enables the writer to establish an effective argument, increasing the likelihood that readers will agree with his or her claim.

- A good introduction contains a "hook" that leaves readers with a first impression about what to expect from the writer. Good hooks engage readers' interest and make them want to keep reading.

MODEL

The introductory section of Barbara Jordan's keynote address to the 1976 Democratic National Convention, which appears in this unit, contains the key elements of a good introduction. Read Jordan's introduction closely to see how she "hooks" her readers and establishes her claim.

Thank you ladies and gentlemen for a very warm reception.

It was one hundred and forty-four years ago that members of the Democratic Party first met in convention to select a Presidential candidate. Since that time, Democrats have continued to convene once every four years and draft a party platform and nominate a Presidential candidate. And our meeting this week is a continuation of that tradition. But there is something different about tonight. **There is something special about tonight. What is different? What is special?**

I, Barbara Jordan, am a keynote speaker.

A lot of years passed since 1832, and during that time it would have been most unusual for any national political party to ask a Barbara Jordan to deliver a keynote address. But tonight, here I am. And I feel that notwithstanding the past that my presence here is one additional bit of evidence that the American Dream need not forever be deferred.

Now that I have this grand distinction, what in the world am I supposed to say? . . . I could list the many problems which Americans have. I could list the problems which cause people to feel cynical, angry, frustrated: problems which include lack of integrity in government; the feeling that the individual no longer counts; the reality of material and spiritual poverty; the feeling that the grand American experiment is failing or has failed. I could recite these problems, and then I could sit down and offer no solutions. But I don't choose to do that either. The citizens of America expect more. They deserve and they want more than a recital of problems.

We are a people in a quandary about the present. We are a people in search of our future. We are a people in search of a national community. We are a people trying not only to solve the problems of the present, unemployment, inflation, but we are attempting on a larger scale to fulfill the promise of America. **We are attempting to fulfill our national purpose, to create and sustain a society in which all of us are equal.**

In her introduction, Jordan uses an effective **hook**. She engages her audience by making an observation, repeating words and phrases for emphasis, and then posing questions: "But there is something different about tonight. There is something special about tonight. What is different? What is special?" Then she makes her proclamation: " I, Barbara Jordan, am a keynote speaker." She continues: "Now that I have this grand distinction, what in the world am I supposed to say?" Jordan's answers to these questions lead to her **claim**— that her presence as the keynote speaker indicates that for African American women, the American Dream is no longer "deferred"—that the United States is beginning to "fulfill our national purpose, to create and sustain a society in which all of us are equal." Jordan's introduction also hints at the **relevant evidence** that will follow in the body of her speech. This evidence is likely to contain historical facts about the American political process, referring to the current woes of the day, such as cynicism, unemployment, and inflation, along with suggestions for ways to solve the nation's problems.

 PRACTICE

Write an introduction for your literary analysis that includes your claim and a "hook" to capture your readers' interest. When you have finished, trade your paper with a partner. Participate in a peer review of each other's introduction and hook, and offer thoughtful, constructive, and supportive feedback to your partner.

SKILL: BODY
PARAGRAPHS
AND
TRANSITIONS

 DEFINE

Body paragraphs appear between the introduction and the conclusion—between the beginning and the end—of an essay. They are also called middle paragraphs, because they appear in the middle of a text, and this middle section is the "meaty" part of any literary analysis. It is where you support your specific claims with sound reasons and relevant evidence that in turn will be sufficient enough to support your argument. In general, each body paragraph should focus on one main point, central idea, or claim so that your readers can easily follow your thinking. All the main points of the body paragraphs should collectively support the argument of your literary analysis.

It is important to structure each body paragraph clearly. One way to structure a body paragraph of a literary analysis is by including the following elements:

Topic sentence: The topic sentence is the first sentence of a body paragraph. It states the paragraph's central idea and should relate to the main point of your claim.

Evidence #1: Each middle paragraph will contain evidence from the text (or texts) you are analyzing to support the topic sentence of the body paragraph. Textual evidence can include relevant definitions, details, facts, observations, quotations, and examples.

Evidence #2: Continue to develop your claim or central idea of the body paragraph with a second piece of evidence. This evidence may come from outside research you have done on the topic or from the source texts you are comparing and contrasting.

Analysis/Explanation: After presenting your evidence, explain how it helps to support your topic sentence—and main claim—about the texts you are analyzing.

NOTES

Concluding sentence: After presenting your evidence, restate your main claim and summarize the central idea you have made in the topic sentence of each body paragraph.

Transitions are connecting words or phrases that writers use to clarify the relationships between (or among) ideas in a text. Transitions help connect words in a sentence and ideas in individual paragraphs. They also suggest the organizational structure of a text.

Connecting words such as *and, or,* and *but* help writers make connections between (or among) words in a sentence, while words and phrases such as also, *in addition,* and *likewise* show how ideas in body paragraphs relate. Adding transition words or phrases to the beginning or end of a paragraph can help a writer guide readers smoothly through a text. Transitions can also indicate the organizational structure being used by the writer to present the evidence or ideas.

 ## IDENTIFICATION AND APPLICATION

- Body paragraphs are the section of the literary analysis between the introduction and the conclusion. These paragraphs provide the main points of the literary analysis, along with the supporting evidence. Typically, writers develop one central idea or claim for each body paragraph.
    - › A topic sentence clearly states the central idea or claim of that paragraph.
    - › Evidence consists of relevant definitions, details, facts, observations, quotations, and examples.
    - › Analysis and explanation tell how the evidence supports the topic sentence.
    - › A concluding sentence summarizes the paragraph's central idea or claim.

- Certain transition words and phrases indicate the organizational structure of a text. Here are some examples of transitions used to organize text in a specific way:
    - › Cause-effect: *because, since, therefore, as a result, so, if . . . then*
    - › Compare and contrast: *likewise, also, both, similarly, in the same way* to compare, and *although, while, but, however, whereas, on the contrary* to contrast
    - › Chronological order: *first, next, then, finally, before, after, within a few years*

- Transitions also help readers understand the relationships between (or among) ideas in a text. A phrase such as *for example* can help show the relationship between a central idea or claim and its evidence. The phrase *in addition* can help link together similar ideas.

MODEL

Read the first body paragraph from the Student Model, "Mother Jones and Cesar Chavez: Standing Up for Workers' Rights." Look closely at the organizational structure and note the transition words and phrases in bold. Think about the effectiveness of the paragraph. Does it develop the main point of the claim made in the topic sentence? How do the transition words and phrases help you understand how the text is structured and how the ideas are related?

*The author Judith Pinkerton Josephson paints an interesting portrait of Mother Jones as she tells the reader that Jones was seventy-three years old when she decided in June of 1903 to draw attention to the problem of child labor. As Josephson says in paragraph 4, **even though** it was against the law to hire children younger than 13 to work in factories, "parents often lied about a child's age," and "[m]ill owners "looked the other way, **because** child labor was cheap." **As a result,** thousands of children worked long hours under terrible working conditions in mills, with often serious effects to their health. To highlight this point, Josephson notes in paragraph 3 how Mother Jones noticed that the children's "bodies were bone-thin with hollow chests," and that many children were maimed, 'with their hands [cut] off, some with the thumb missing." The writer explains how Jones led a group of mill children and their parents to Independence Square in Philadelphia, where she called on city officials to think about the real costs of child labor—mangled limbs, lost childhoods, no education. Jones appealed to their sympathies, stating in paragraph 6: "'Philadelphia's mansions were built on the broken bones, the quivering hearts, and the drooping heads of these children.'" **But** the officials ignored her. Undeterred, she decided that the best way to bring national attention to the plight of child labor was to march 125 miles to President Theodore Roosevelt's summer home in New York. She and many child workers and their families walked the whole way, stopping only to rest and hold rallies. The author admits that **in the end, however,** Jones did not meet her goal **because** President Roosevelt refused to see her. **As a result,** she and* the children returned home without having brought about any real changes to child labor laws. In the last paragraph, Josephson sums up: "**Though** she had not met with the president, Mother Jones had drawn the attention of the nation to the problem of child labor. " **However,** she does not say that national laws to protect child workers came about **because** of Jones's efforts. In fact, all she says at the end is that is that "[t]he federal government finally passed a child labor law . . . in 1938--thirty-five years after the march of the mill children." Josephson's portrait of Mother Jones shows a woman who was committed to a cause but not completely successful at promoting change. . . . **In the end,** Josephson fails to persuade her readers that Mother Jones had a huge impact on human rights.

Remember that the final sentences of the introduction of the Student Model make this claim:

Clearly, the authors of *Mother Jones: Fierce Fighter for Workers' Rights* and *About Cesar* admire their subjects, although this literary analysis will prove the point that Chavez was the greater fighter for human rights. As the authors from the Cesar Chavez Foundation state, "Chavez not only righted many of the injustices that farm workers faced, but he also inspired "Americans from all walks of life."

How does the body paragraph about Mother Jones connect to this claim? Let's take a look.

The **topic sentence** establishes that the first body paragraph will examine the text about Mother Jones. The writer follows the topic sentence with evidence in the paragraph that provides background information about Mother Jones and the issue of child labor. The writer tells about Mother Jones's role in the rally in Philadelphia's Independence Square and the march to President Roosevelt's summer home, and provides facts and quotations from the source text.

Next, the writer **explains** the significance of Mother Jones's efforts. She tells how Jones was unable to meet with President Roosevelt but still put a spotlight on the horrors of child labor. The paragraph concludes by saying that in the end, Josephson "fails to persuade her readers that Mother Jones had a huge impact on human rights." This **concluding sentence** wraps up the body paragraph. It also ties back to the claim—that the text about Chavez was more effective than the text about Mother Jones in making a case that its subject was the greater humanitarian.

Please note that excerpts and passages in the StudySync® library and this workbook are intended as touchstones to generate interest in an author's work. The excerpts and passages do not substitute for the reading of entire texts, and StudySync® strongly recommends that students seek out and purchase the whole literary or informational work in order to experience it as the author intended. Links to online resellers are available in our digital library. In addition, complete works may be ordered through an authorized reseller by filling out and returning to StudySync® the order form enclosed in this workbook.

Reading & Writing Companion   **311**

The writer uses **transition words and phrases** such as "but," "however," "even though," "because," "as a result," and "in the end" within the paragraph to show connections (contrasts, causes and effects, and chronological order) as well as the organization of the text. The transition words also guide readers from one sentence and idea to the next by creating a smooth flow of ideas.

 ## PRACTICE

Write one body paragraph for your literary analysis that follows the suggested format. When you are finished, trade with a partner and offer each other feedback. How effective is the topic sentence at stating the main point of the paragraph? How strong is the evidence used to support the topic sentence? Are all quotes and evidence cited correctly? Does the literary analysis support the topic sentence and the claim? Offer each other suggestions, and remember that feedback is most helpful when it is constructive and supportive.

DEFINE

The **conclusion** is the closing statement or section of a nonfiction text. In a literary analysis, the conclusion brings the writer's argument to a close. It follows directly from the introduction and the body paragraphs by referring to the ideas presented there. The conclusion should restate the thesis statement (or claim) made in the introduction and summarize the central ideas covered in the body paragraphs. In addition, the conclusion should focus on the writer's most convincing reasons and strongest evidence. A conclusion that emphasizes the strongest points of a literary analysis will be more likely to get readers to agree with the writer's claim. To put it simply, in a literary analysis, the conclusion wraps up the writer's argument, but it may leave the reader with an intriguing question, insight, or inspiring message.

IDENTIFICATION AND APPLICATION

- An effective conclusion of a literary analysis will restate the writer's claim about one or more texts.

- The conclusion should briefly summarize the strongest and most convincing reasons and evidence from the body paragraphs. Focusing on the strongest points makes it more likely that readers will agree with the writer's claim.

- Some conclusions offer a recommendation or some form of insight relating to the analysis. This may take any of the following forms:

  › An answer to a question first posed in the introduction
  › A question designed to elicit reflection on the part of the reader
  › A memorable or inspiring message
  › A last compelling example
  › A suggestion that readers learn more.

MODEL

In the concluding paragraph of the Student Model, "Mother Jones and Cesar Chavez: Standing Up for Workers' Rights," the writer reinforces the main claim, reminds readers of the central ideas of the literary analysis, and ends with an insightful observation. Reread the student's conclusion:

Similarly, Josephson admires her subject and shows how Mother Jones was committed to bringing attention to the problem of child labor. But Mother Jones did not have the same successes with workers' rights as did Chavez. In the end, she was not able to persuade lawmakers to improve working conditions for children. In fact, the connection Josephson makes between the 1903 march and the child labor laws enacted in 1938 is not well supported or convincing. She does not provide sufficient evidence to suggest that lawmakers thought about Mother Jones when they passed child labor laws years later. Perhaps because Mother Jones lived so long ago, her human rights efforts seem to have had less impact than those of Chavez, who died in 1993. Although Jones and Chavez both fought to secure workers' rights, Chavez's influence was stronger. Only he improved the lives of workers in his lifetime and "inspired millions of Americans from all walks of life."

Remember that the claim in the introduction of the Student Model states the writer's argument: Clearly, the authors of *Mother Jones: Fierce Fighter for Workers' Rights* and *About Cesar* admire their subjects, although this literary analysis will prove the point that Chavez was the greater fighter for human rights. As the authors from the Cesar Chavez Foundation state, "Chavez not only righted many of the injustices that farm workers faced, but he also inspired "Americans from all walks of life."

The text about Cesar Chavez makes a stronger case than the text about Mother Jones for its subject's importance as a humanitarian. The conclusion restates that claim, as well as the reasons and evidence that support it. At the end of the paragraph, the writer leaves the reader with an original thought—that perhaps Mother Jones's human rights' efforts seem less inspiring than Chavez's because she lived a long time ago. It might suggest that the writer has a bias toward events that have occurred more recently, which is something that readers should consider when reflecting on the writer's overall argument.

Copyright © BookheadEd Learning, LLC

PRACTICE

Write a conclusion for your literary analysis. Your conclusion should include a restatement of the claim on which you have already worked as well as a final thought you might wish to impart to your readers. When you have finished writing your conclusion, trade your work with a partner. Participate in a peer review of your conclusion and offer constructive feedback.

DRAFT

WRITING PROMPT

Imagine what it would be like to work long hours under dangerous conditions for little pay. Think about how your life would be different if you had to work in a factory or on a farm as a migrant farm worker, instead of going to school. The world is full of injustice, but fortunately, there are people who believe in speaking up for the powerless and defending human rights.

In this unit, you have been reading nonfiction texts about real people who stood up for the rights of others and brought about social change. From Mother Jones, a fierce fighter for child labor laws, to Cesar Chavez, who fought for the rights of ill-treated farm workers, these great people had something in common: They fought for fairness and inspired social change.

Mahatma Gandhi and Nelson Mandela also fought for change. Both Gandhi and Mandela are inspiring, but the texts that you have read about them are very different. Write a literary analysis in which you compare and contrast the text about Gandhi with the text about Mandela to determine which is more convincing in presenting and supporting the claim that this individual was a great defender of justice and human rights. Analyze the reasons and evidence presented in the text as well as the language that is used to describe the individual's words, actions, and accomplishments. Then decide which writer was more persuasive in defending his claim about the impact this person had on human rights.

Your literary analysis should include

- a comparison-contrast of two nonfiction texts you have read in this unit.

Copyright © BookheadEd Learning, LLC

NOTES

WRITING PROMPT

- an explicitly stated claim about the topic.
- a logically organized presentation of sound reasons and textual evidence.
- a conclusion that sums up your literary analysis of which text was more persuasive and leaves your readers with an original thought about the topic.

You have already begun working on your literary analysis. You have considered your purpose, audience, and topic. You have carefully examined the two unit texts you will write about. Based on your analysis of textual evidence, you have identified what you want to say how you will say it. You have decided how to organize your information, and you've gathered supporting details in the form of reasons and relevant evidence. Now it's time to write a draft of your literary analysis.

Use your road map and your other prewriting materials to help you as you write. Remember that a literary analysis begins with an introduction that states a claim (or opinion) and draws readers into the topic. Body paragraphs then develop the claim by providing supporting, relevant evidence, such as facts, details, quotations, examples, and observations. Transitions reinforce the organizational structure and help readers understand the relationships between (or among) ideas. A concluding paragraph restates your main claim and summarizes your main points, or central idea. An insight or intriguing question may be included at the end, making an interesting "takeaway" for your readers.

When drafting your literary analysis, ask yourself these questions:

- How can I "hook" my readers in the introduction?
- How well do I state my claim? Is it clear? Does it state my opinion about the two texts?
- Which textual evidence—including relevant facts, details, quotations, examples, and observations—best supports my claim? Is my evidence sufficient? Are my reasons persuasive?
- How can I improve my organization and flow of ideas by using transitions?
- How can I use a stronger topic sentence in each of my body paragraphs?

Please note that excerpts and passages in the StudySync® library and this workbook are intended as touchstones to generate interest in an author's work. The excerpts and passages do not substitute for the reading of entire texts, and StudySync® strongly recommends that students seek out and purchase the whole literary or informational work in order to experience it as the author intended. Links to online resellers are available in our digital library. In addition, complete works may be ordered through an authorized reseller by filling out and returning to StudySync® the order form enclosed in this workbook.

Reading & Writing Companion   **317**

- How can I restate my thesis statement (or claim) in the conclusion so that it is clearer and more effective?
- What final insight do I want to leave with my readers?

Be sure to read your draft carefully before you submit it. You'll want to make sure you've addressed every part of the writing prompt so that your literary analysis will be as persuasive as possible.

REVISE

WRITING PROMPT

Imagine what it would be like to work long hours under dangerous conditions for little pay. Think about how your life would be different if you had to work in a factory or on a farm as a migrant farm worker, instead of going to school. The world is full of injustice, but fortunately, there are people who believe in speaking up for the powerless and defending human rights.

In this unit, you have been reading nonfiction texts about real people who stood up for the rights of others and brought about social change. From Mother Jones, a fierce fighter for child labor laws, to Cesar Chavez, who fought for the rights of ill-treated farm workers, these great people had something in common: They fought for fairness and inspired social change.

Mahatma Gandhi and Nelson Mandela also fought for change. Both Gandhi and Mandela are inspiring, but the texts that you have read about them are very different. Write a literary analysis in which you compare and contrast the text about Gandhi with the text about Mandela to determine which is more convincing in presenting and supporting the claim that this individual was a great defender of justice and human rights. Analyze the reasons and evidence presented in the text as well as the language that is used to describe the individual's words, actions, and accomplishments. Then decide which writer was more persuasive in defending his claim about the impact this person had on human rights.

Your literary analysis should include

- a comparison-contrast of two nonfiction texts you have read in this unit.

Please note that excerpts and passages in the StudySync® library and this workbook are intended as touchstones to generate interest in an author's work. The excerpts and passages do not substitute for the reading of entire texts, and StudySync® strongly recommends that students seek out and purchase the whole literary or informational work in order to experience it as the author intended. Links to online resellers are available in our digital library. In addition, complete works may be ordered through an authorized reseller by filling out and returning to StudySync® the order form enclosed in this workbook.

Reading & Writing Companion   **319**

NOTES

WRITING PROMPT

- an explicitly stated claim about the topic.
- a logically organized presentation of sound reasons and textual evidence.
- a conclusion that sums up your literary analysis of which text was more persuasive and leaves your readers with an original thought about the topic.

You have written a draft of your literary analysis. You have also received input from your peers about how to improve it. Now you are going to revise your draft.

Here are some recommendations to help you revise the draft of your literary analysis:

- Review the suggestions made by your peers.
- Focus on maintaining a formal style. A formal style suits your purpose and audience. Your purpose for writing is to persuade your readers to agree with your opinions about two unit texts. A formal style is also appropriate for your audience: Your audience may be your teacher, your classmates, your family or friends, or other readers who might want to know more about your topic.
- As you revise your draft, eliminate any informal language, such as slang or colloquial expressions, and pay close attention to your use of voice, sentence structure and sentence variety, correct punctuation, and word choice.
  - › Remove any first-person pronouns such as *I, me,* or *mine* or instances of addressing readers as *you*, except when leaving readers with a final thought or message in the conclusion.
  - › Incorporate varying sentence structure and sentence variety, including long and short sentences, and check that you aren't beginning every sentence in the same way. Also, check that you have punctuated all simple, compound, complex, and compound-complex sentences correctly.
- Does your writing express your ideas precisely and concisely? When it comes to formal writing, less is often more. Look for wordiness and repetition in your writing. Are the exact same ideas repeated more than once? Can you substitute a more exact word for a word that is too

NOTES

general or overused? Can you replace a longer phrase with a word that means the same thing?

- After you have revised your elements of style, review your literary analysis to see whether you can make improvements to its content or organization.

  › Do you need to add any relevant textual evidence, such as quotations or examples, to fully support your claim?

  › Do you need to incorporate any academic vocabulary or persuasive language that would be appropriate for a literary analysis?

  › Is your organizational structure apparent? Would your literary analysis flow better if you added more transitions between sentences and paragraphs?

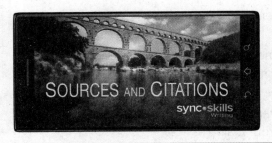

SKILL: SOURCES AND CITATIONS

 ## DEFINE

Sources are the documents and information that an author uses to research his or her writing. Some sources are primary sources, or first-hand accounts of information; others are secondary sources, which are written later and are based on primary sources. Citations give information about the sources an author used to research and write an informative/explanatory text. Citations are required whenever authors quote others' words or refer to others' ideas in their writing. Citations let readers know who originally came up with those words and ideas.

 ## IDENTIFICATION AND APPLICATION

- Sources can be either primary or secondary. Primary sources are first-hand accounts or original materials, such as the following:
  › Letters or other correspondence
  › Photographs
  › Official documents
  › Diaries or journals
  › Autobiographies or memoirs
  › Eyewitness accounts and interviews
  › Audio recordings and radio broadcasts
  › Literary texts, such as novels, poems, fables, and dramas
  › Works of art
  › Artifacts

- Secondary sources are usually texts. Secondary sources are the written interpretation and analysis of primary source materials. Some examples of secondary sources include:
  › Encyclopedia articles
  › Textbooks
  › Commentary or criticisms

> Histories
> Documentary films
> News analyses
> Biographies, obituaries, eulogies

- Whether sources are primary or secondary, they must be **credible** and **accurate**. This means the information in the sources should be reliable and up-to-date.

- When a writer of a literary analysis quotes directly from a source, he or she must copy the words exactly as they appear in the text, placing them within quotation marks. Here's an example from the student model:

  As Josephson says in paragraph 4, even though it was against the law to hire children younger than 13 to work in factories, "parents often lied about a child's age," and "[m]ill owners "looked the other way, because child labor was cheap."

- Writers of literary analyses must cite, or identify, the sources they're quoting directly. One way to do this is to name the author in the sentence. This is the method shown in the excerpt above. (The writer of the analysis also includes the paragraph number so that readers know exactly where the quoted material can be found in the text.) Another method for citing a source is to put the author's name in parentheses at the end of the sentence in which the quotation appears. Ask your teacher for the method he or she prefers.

- Writers must also provide citations when borrowing ideas from another source, even when writers are just paraphrasing, or putting the ideas into their own words. Citations serve to credit the source and to help readers find out where they can learn more.

 MODEL

In this excerpt from the Student Model, "Mother Jones and Cesar Chavez: Standing Up for Workers' Rights," the writer quotes from the text he or she is analyzing and identifies the sources of each quotation.

> *Unlike Josephson, the authors of About Cesar are deeply enthusiastic about their subject, Cesar Chavez. In the first paragraph, these authors from the Cesar Chavez Foundation quote Robert F. Kennedy by saying that he called Chavez* **"one of the heroic figures of our time."** *They begin their text by introducing Chavez as a* **"true American hero,"** *a* **"farm labor leader . . . a community organizer . . . and a crusader for the environment and consumer**

NOTES

rights." *Later, in paragraph 15, they refer to him as a* **"unique and humble leader, as well as a great humanitarian and communicator who influenced and inspired millions of Americans from all walks of life."** *Then, in paragraph 19, they call him* **"a common man with an uncommon vision."** *They support these claims with relevant textual evidence of Chavez's achievements. In paragraph 2, they describe how as a boy, he worked in California's* **"fields, orchards, and vineyards, where he was exposed to the hardships and injustices of farm worker life."**

Notice that only the portions of *About Cesar* that are taken directly from the text appear within quotation marks and that the authors of the source text (people from the Cesar Chavez Foundation) are identified in the sentence that contains the quotation. The first quote is particularly tricky because the writer of the model must cite not only the authors of *About Cesar,* but the person whom those authors are quoting—Robert F. Kennedy. Since no embedded citation is included in the remaining quotes, readers can assume that they come directly from the authors of *About Cesar*, and not from an outside source.

PRACTICE

Write in-text citations for quoted information in your literary analysis essay. When you are finished, trade with a partner and offer each other feedback. How successful was the writer in citing sources for the essay? Offer each other suggestions, and remember that they are most helpful when they are constructive and supportive.

EDIT, PROOFREAD AND PUBLISH

WRITING PROMPT

Imagine what it would be like to work long hours under dangerous conditions for little pay. Think about how your life would be different if you had to work in a factory or on a farm as a migrant farm worker, instead of going to school. The world is full of injustice, but fortunately, there are people who believe in speaking up for the powerless and defending human rights.

In this unit, you have been reading nonfiction texts about real people who stood up for the rights of others and brought about social change. From Mother Jones, a fierce fighter for child labor laws, to Cesar Chavez, who fought for the rights of ill-treated farm workers, these great people had something in common: They fought for fairness and inspired social change.

Mahatma Gandhi and Nelson Mandela also fought for change. Both Gandhi and Mandela are inspiring, but the texts that you have read about them are very different. Write a literary analysis in which you compare and contrast the text about Gandhi with the text about Mandela to determine which is more convincing in presenting and supporting the claim that this individual was a great defender of justice and human rights. Analyze the reasons and evidence presented in the text as well as the language that is used to describe the individual's words, actions, and accomplishments. Then decide which writer was more persuasive in defending his claim about the impact this person had on human rights.

Your literary analysis should include

- a comparison-contrast of two nonfiction texts you have read in this unit.

Please note that excerpts and passages in the StudySync® library and this workbook are intended as touchstones to generate interest in an author's work. The excerpts and passages do not substitute for the reading of entire texts, and StudySync® strongly recommends that students seek out and purchase the whole literary or informational work in order to experience it as the author intended. Links to online resellers are available in our digital library. In addition, complete works may be ordered through an authorized reseller by filling out and returning to StudySync® the order form enclosed in this workbook.

Reading & Writing Companion **325**

WRITING PROMPT

- an explicitly stated claim about the topic.
- a logically organized presentation of sound reasons and textual evidence.
- a conclusion that sums up your literary analysis of which text was more persuasive and leaves your readers with an original thought about the topic.

Now that you have revised your literary analysis and have received input from your peers, it's time to edit and proofread your writing to produce a final version. Ask yourself these questions: Have I fully supported my claim with strong textual evidence? Is my evidence relevant and sufficient? How well have I cited my sources? Does my literary analysis need more transitions to produce a better connection and flow of ideas? Is my organizational structure clear? How well have I used persuasive language?

Once you are satisfied with your work, proofread it for errors. For example, check that you have used correct punctuation for quotations and citations. Ask yourself if you have capitalized all proper nouns and spelled all words correctly. Have you used commas to set off coordinate adjectives? Have you used precise word choice? Could you have said the same thing using fewer words and less repetitive sentences?

Once you have made all your corrections, you are ready to submit and publish your work. You can give your writing to family and friends, display it in the classroom, or post it online. If you decide to publish it online, include links to your sources and citations. This will enable your readers to learn more from your sources on their own time.

studysync®

Reading & Writing Companion

What are the challenges of human interactions?

Getting Along

UNIT 4   What are the challenges of human interactions?

Getting Along

TEXTS

TEXTS

EXTENDED WRITING PROJECT

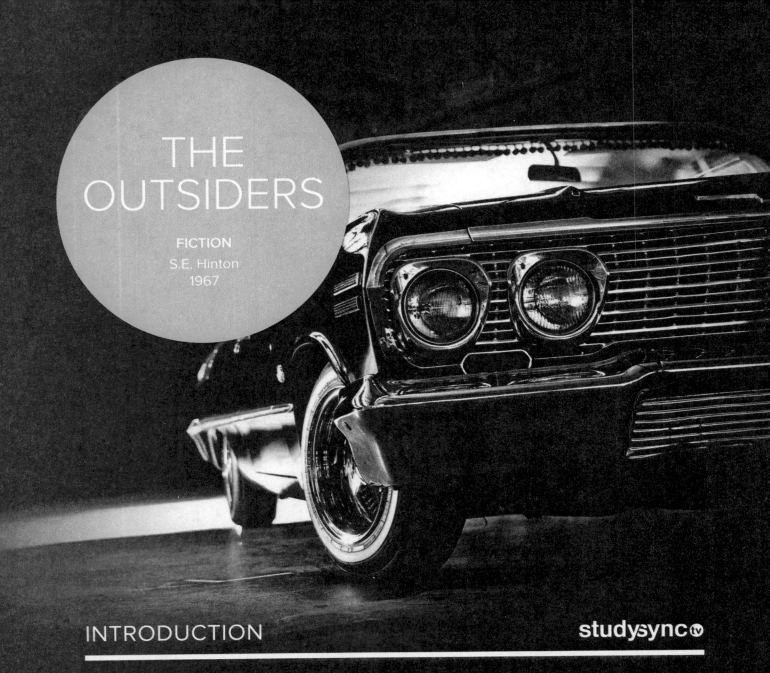

THE OUTSIDERS

FICTION
S.E. Hinton
1967

INTRODUCTION

studysync tv

Susan Eloise Hinton was only seventeen years old when her groundbreaking novel *The Outsiders* was first published. Because of the novel's explicit depiction of violence, her publisher believed that the book would do better if the author's gender remained unknown and suggested it be published under her initials. The novel explores the hearts and minds of a gang with no voice, telling the story of class conflict between the lower-class "Greasers" and the upper-class "Socs" (short for "Socials" and pronounced "Soshes") in 1960's middle America. The universal themes transcend both time and location. In the excerpt below from early in the novel, the Greasers learn that the rival Socs have viciously attacked a gang member, Johnny.

"He would carry that scar all his life."

FIRST READ

Copyright © BookheadEd Learning, LLC

Excerpt from Chapter 2

1   We were used to seeing Johnny banged up—his father clobbered him around a lot, and although it made us madder than heck, we couldn't do anything about it. But those beatings had been nothing like this. Johnny's face was cut up and bruised and swollen, and there was a wide gash from his temple to his cheekbone. He would carry that scar all his life. His white T-shirt was splattered with blood. I just stood there, trembling with sudden cold. I thought he might be dead; surely no one could be beaten like that and live. Steve closed his eyes for a second and muffled a groan as he dropped on his knees beside Soda.

2   Somehow the gang sensed what had happened. Two-Bit was suddenly there beside me, and for once his comical grin was gone and his dancing gray eyes were stormy. Darry had seen us from our porch and ran toward us, suddenly skidding to a halt. Dally was there, too, swearing under his breath, and turning away with a sick expression on his face. I wondered about it vaguely. Dally had seen people killed on the streets of New York's West Side. Why did he look sick now?

3   "Johnny?" Soda lifted him up and held him against his shoulder. He gave the limp body a slight shake. "Hey, Johnnycake."

4   Johnny didn't open his eyes, but there came a soft question. "Soda?"

5   "Yeah, it's me," Sodapop said. "Don't talk. You're gonna be okay."

6   "There was a whole bunch of them," Johnny went on, swallowing, ignoring Soda's command. "A blue Mustang full . . . I got so scared . . ." He tried to swear, but suddenly started crying, fighting to control himself, then sobbing all the more because he couldn't. I had seen Johnny take a whipping with a

Please note that excerpts and passages in the StudySync® library and this workbook are intended as touchstones to generate interest in an author's work. The excerpts and passages do not substitute for the reading of entire texts, and StudySync® strongly recommends that students seek out and purchase the whole literary or informational work in order to experience it as the author intended. Links to online resellers are available in our digital library. In addition, complete works may be ordered through an authorized reseller by filling out and returning to StudySync® the order form enclosed in this workbook.

Reading & Writing
Companion

331

two-by-four from his old man and never let out a whimper. That made it worse to see him break now. Soda just held him and pushed Johnny's hair back out of his eyes. "It's okay, Johnnycake, they're gone now. It's okay."

7 Finally, between sobs, Johnny managed to gasp out his story. He had been hunting our football to practice a few kicks when a blue Mustang had pulled up beside the lot. There were four Socs in it. They had caught him and one of them had a lot of rings on his hand—that's what had cut Johnny up so badly. It wasn't just that they had beaten him half to death—he could take that. They had scared him. They had threatened him with everything under the sun. Johnny was high-strung anyway, a nervous wreck from getting belted every time he turned around and from hearing his parents fight all the time. Living in those conditions might have turned someone else **rebellious** and bitter; it was killing Johnny. He had never been a coward. He was a good man in a **rumble.** He stuck up for the gang and kept his mouth shut good around cops. But after the night of the beating, Johnny was jumpier than ever. I didn't think he'd ever get over it. Johnny never walked by himself after that. And Johnny, who was the most **law-abiding** of us, now carried in his back pocket a six-inch switchblade. He'd use it, too, if he ever got jumped again. They had scared him that much. He would kill the next person who jumped him. Nobody was ever going to beat him like that again. Not over his dead body. . . .

8 I had nearly forgotten that Cherry was listening to me. But when I came back to reality and looked at her, I was startled to find her as white as a sheet.

9 "All Socs aren't like that," she said. "You have to believe me, Ponyboy. Not all of us are like that."

10 "Sure," I said.

11 "That's like saying all you greasers are like Dallas Winston. I'll bet he's jumped a few people."

12 I digested that. It was true. Dally had jumped people. He had told us stories about muggings in New York that had made the hair on the back of my neck stand up. But not all of us are that bad.

13 Cherry no longer looked sick, only sad. "I'll bet you think the Socs have it made. The rich kids, the West-side Socs. I'll tell you something, Ponyboy, and it may come as a surprise. We have troubles you've never heard of. You want to know something?" She looked me straight in the eye. "Things are rough all over."

14 "I believe you," I said. "We'd better get out there with the popcorn or Two-Bit'll think I ran off with his money."

• • •

15 After the movie was over it suddenly came to us that Cherry and Marcia didn't have a way to get home. Two-Bit **gallantly** offered to walk them home—the west side of town was only about twenty miles away—but they wanted to call their parents and have them come and get them. Two-Bit finally talked them into letting us drive them home in his car. I think they were still half-scared of us. They were getting over it, though, as we walked to Two-Bit's house to pick up the car. It seemed funny to me that Socs—if these girls were any example—were just like us. They liked the Beatles and thought Elvis Presley was out, and we thought the Beatles were rank and that Elvis was tuff, but that seemed the only difference to me. Of course greasy girls would have acted a lot tougher, but there was a basic sameness. I thought maybe it was money that separated us.

16 "No," Cherry said slowly when I said this. "It's not just money. Part of it is, but not all. You greasers have a different set of values. You're more emotional. We're **sophisticated**—cool to the point of not feeling anything. Nothing is real with us. You know, sometimes I'll catch myself talking to a girl-friend, and I realize I don't mean half of what I'm saying. I don't really think a beer blast on the river bottom is super-cool, but I'll rave about one to a girl-friend just to be saying something." She smiled at me. "I never told anyone that. I think you're the first person I've ever really gotten through to."

Excerpted from *The Outsiders* by S. E. Hinton, published by the Penguin Group.

THINK QUESTIONS

1. How did the Greasers react to the beatings Johnny received from his father? What evidence is there in paragraphs 1–5 that the Greasers were more deeply affected by Johnny's beating at the hands of the Socs? Why do you think this was the case? Cite specific evidence from the text to support your response.

2. How did being beaten by the Socs affect Johnny? What about the fight caused this reaction in him? Cite specific evidence from paragraph 7 to support your ideas.

3. What does Ponyboy think separates the Greasers from the Socs? How does Cherry respond to his idea? Cite specific evidence from the text to support your statements.

4. Knowing that the small word rebel is contained in the word **rebellious** in paragraph 7 of *The Outsiders* can help you figure out the meaning of *rebellious*. Use a dictionary to find several meanings for the noun *rebel*, but use only the meaning of *rebel* that will help you determine the meaning of *rebellious* in context. Write your definition of *rebellious* and tell how you figured out its meaning. Refer to the dictionary again to confirm or revise your definition.

5. Use context clues to determine the meaning of the hyphenated compound word **law-abiding** as it is used in paragraph 7 of *The Outsiders*. Write your definition of *law-abiding* and explain how you figured out the meaning of the word. What word or expression might be an antonym for *law-abiding*?

Please note that excerpts and passages in the StudySync® library and this workbook are intended as touchstones to generate interest in an author's work. The excerpts and passages do not substitute for the reading of entire texts, and StudySync® strongly recommends that students seek out and purchase the whole literary or informational work in order to experience it as the author intended. Links to online resellers are available in our digital library. In addition, complete works may be ordered through an authorized reseller by filling out and returning to StudySync® the order form enclosed in this workbook.

Reading & Writing Companion **333**

CLOSE READ

Reread the excerpt from *The Outsiders*. As you reread, complete the Focus Questions below. Then use your answers and annotations from the questions to help you complete the Writing Prompt.

FOCUS QUESTIONS

1. As you reread *The Outsiders,* highlight specific textual evidence in paragraphs 1–7 that helped you infer Ponyboy's point of view about the Socs. Make annotations to record your inferences.

2. What textual evidence in paragraphs 9–14 helps you infer that Cherry is beginning to influence Ponyboy's point of view about the Socs? Highlight the textual evidence. Make annotations to support your analysis.

3. In paragraph 15, what evidence is there that Ponyboy's point of view about the Socs is beginning to change? Highlight textual evidence and make annotations to explain your reasoning.

4. In paragraph 16, Cherry says, "You greasers have a different set of values. You're more emotional." In contrast, she says that Socs are "sophisticated— cool to the point of not feeling anything. Nothing is real with us." Highlight textual evidence collected throughout the excerpt that supports Cherry's point of view. Make annotations to explain your choices.

5. Use textual evidence and inferences drawn from *The Outsiders* to describe how this interaction between Ponyboy and Cherry demonstrates that human interactions are challenging. Highlight the specific textual evidence and make annotations to record your inferences.

WRITING PROMPT

Use textual evidence to make three inferences about how interacting with Cherry has changed Ponyboy's point of view about the Greasers and the Socs. Consider which pieces of textual evidence help you make these inferences and how your own prior knowledge supports them. Begin with a clear thesis statement. Use your understanding of textual evidence and point of view to organize and support your writing. Use transitions to show the relationships among your ideas, and provide a conclusion that summarizes your main points.

THE TEACHER WHO CHANGED MY LIFE

NON-FICTION
Nicholas Gage
1989

INTRODUCTION

Author and investigative journalist Nicholas Gage was born in Greece and came to the United States when he was 10. He is perhaps best known for two autobiographical memoirs—*Eleni*, which celebrates his mother's courage for arranging his escape from communist Greece after World War II, and a *A Place for Us*, which narrates his family's experiences as immigrants in the United States in the 1950s. The excerpt here comes from a personal essay first published in *Parade* magazine in 1989. In it, Gage describes his relationship with his junior high school English teacher, and reflects on her lasting influence in his life.

"She was the catalyst that sent me into journalism..."

 FIRST READ

1   The person who set the course of my life in the new land entered as a young war refugee—who, in fact, nearly dragged me on to the path that would bring all the blessings I've received in America—was a salty-tongued, no-nonsense schoolteacher named Marjorie Hurd. When I entered her classroom in 1953, I had been to six schools in five years, starting in the Greek village where I was born in 1939.

2   When I stepped off a ship in New York Harbor on a gray March day in 1949, I was an undersized 9-year-old in short pants who had lost his mother and was coming to live with the father he didn't know. My mother, Eleni Gatzoyiannis, had been imprisoned, tortured, and shot by Communist **guerrillas** for sending me and three of my four sisters to freedom. She died so that her children could go to their father in the United States.

3   The portly, bald, well-dressed man who met me and my sisters seemed a foreign, authoritarian figure. I secretly resented him for not getting the whole family out of Greece early enough to save my mother. Ultimately, I would grow to love him and appreciate how he dealt with becoming a single parent at the age of 56, but at first our relationship was prickly, full of hostility.

4   As Father drove us to our new home—a tenement in Worcester, Mass.—and pointed out the huge brick building that would be our first school in America, I clutched my Greek notebooks from the refugee camp, hoping that my few years of schooling would impress my teachers in this cold, crowded country. They didn't. When my father led me and my 11-year-old sister to Greendale Elementary School, the grim-faced Yankee principal put the two of us in a class for the mentally retarded. There was no facility in those days for non-English-speaking children.

Copyright © BookheadEd Learning, LLC

5 By the time I met Marjorie Hurd four years later, I had learned English, been placed in a normal, graded class, and had even been chosen for the college preparatory track in the Worcester public school system. I was 13 years old when our father moved us yet again, and I entered Chandler Junior High shortly after the beginning of the seventh grade. I found myself surrounded by richer, smarter, and better-dressed classmates who looked askance at my strange clothes and heavy accent. Shortly after I arrived, we were told to select a hobby to pursue during "club hour" on Fridays. The idea of hobbies and clubs made no sense to my immigrant ears, but I decided to follow the prettiest girl in my class—the blue-eyed daughter of the local Lutheran minister. She led me through the door marked "Newspaper Club" and into the presence of Miss Hurd, the newspaper adviser and English teacher who would become my **mentor** and my **muse**.

6 A formidable, solidly built woman with salt-and-pepper hair, a steely eye, and a flat Boston accent, Miss Hurd had no patience with layabouts. "What are all you goof-offs doing here?" she bellowed at the would-be journalists. "This is the Newspaper Club! We're going to put out a newspaper. So if there's anybody in this room who doesn't like work, I suggest you go across to the Glee Club now, because you're going to work your tails off here!"

7 I was soon under Miss Hurd's spell. She did indeed teach us to put out a newspaper, skills I honed during my next 25 years as a journalist. Soon I asked the principal to transfer me to her English class as well. There, she drilled us on grammar until I finally began to understand the logic and structure of the English language. She assigned stories for us to read and discuss; not tales of heroes, like the Greek myths I knew, but stories of underdogs—poor people, even immigrants, who seemed ordinary until a crisis drove them to do something extraordinary. She also introduced us to the literary wealth of Greece—giving me a new perspective on my war-ravaged, impoverished homeland. I began to be proud of my origins.

8 One day, after discussing how writers should write about what they know, she assigned us to compose an essay from our own experience. Fixing me with a stern look, she added, "Nick, I want you to write about what happened to your family in Greece." I had been trying to put those painful memories behind me and left the assignment until the last moment. Then, on a warm spring afternoon, I sat in my room with a yellow pad and pencil and stared out the window at the buds on the trees. I wrote that the coming of spring always reminded me of the last time I said goodbye to my mother on a green and gold day in 1948.

9 I kept writing, one line after another, telling how the Communist guerrillas occupied our village, took our home and food, how my mother started planning our escape when she learned the children were to be sent to

reeducation camps behind the Iron Curtain and how, at the last moment, she couldn't escape with us because the guerrillas sent her with a group of women to thresh wheat in a distant village. She promised she would try to get away on her own, she told me to be brave and hung a silver cross around my neck, and then she kissed me. I watched the line of women being led down into the ravine and up the other side, until they disappeared around the bend—my mother a tiny brown figure at the end who stopped for an instant to raise her hand in one last farewell.

10   I wrote about our nighttime escape down the mountain, across the minefields and into the lines of the Nationalist soldiers, who sent us to a refugee camp. It was there that we learned of our mother's execution. I felt very lucky to have come to America, I concluded, but every year, the coming of spring made me feel sad because it reminded me of the last time I saw my mother.

11   I handed in the essay, hoping never to see it again, but Miss Hurd had it published in the school paper. This **mortified** me at first, until I saw that my classmates reacted with sympathy and tact to my family's story. Without telling me, Miss Hurd also submitted the essay to a contest sponsored by the Freedoms Foundation at Valley Forge, Pa., and it won a medal. The Worcester paper wrote about the award and quoted my essay at length. My father, by then a "five-and-dime-store chef," as the paper described him, was ecstatic with pride, and the Worcester Greek community celebrated the honor to one of its own.

12   For the first time I began to understand the power of the written word. A secret ambition took root in me. One day, I vowed, I would go back to Greece, find out the details of my mother's death and write about her life, so her grandchildren would know of her courage. Perhaps I would even track down the men who killed her and write of their crimes. Fulfilling that ambition would take me 30 years.

13   Meanwhile, I followed the literary path that Miss Hurd had so forcefully set me on. After junior high, I became the editor of my school paper at Classical High School and got a part-time job at the Worcester Telegram and Gazette. Although my father could only give me $50 and encouragement toward a college education, I managed to finance four years at Boston University with scholarships and part-time jobs in journalism. During my last year of college, an article I wrote about a friend who had died in the Philippines—the first person to lose his life working for the Peace Corps—led to my winning the Hearst Award for College Journalism. And the plaque was given to me in the White House by President John F. Kennedy.

14   For a refugee who had never seen a motorized vehicle or indoor plumbing until he was 9, this was an unimaginable honor. When the Worcester paper

ran a picture of me standing next to President Kennedy, my father rushed out to buy a new suit in order to properly receive the congratulations of the Worcester Greeks. He clipped out the photograph, had it laminated in plastic and carried it in his breast pocket for the rest of his life to show everyone he met. I found the much-worn photo in his pocket on the day he died 20 years later.

15 In our isolated Greek village, my mother had bribed a cousin to teach her to read, for girls were not supposed to attend school beyond a certain age. She had always dreamed of her children receiving an education. She couldn't be there when I graduated from Boston University, but the person who came with my father and shared our joy was my former teacher, Marjorie Hurd. We celebrated not only my bachelor's degree but also the scholarships that paid my way to Columbia's Graduate School of Journalism. There, I met the woman who would eventually become my wife. At our wedding and at the baptisms of our three children, Marjorie Hurd was always there, dancing alongside the Greeks.

16 By then, she was Mrs. Rabidou, for she had married a widower when she was in her early 40s. That didn't distract her from her vocation of introducing young minds to English literature, however. She taught for a total of 41 years and continually would make a "project" of some balky student in whom she spied a spark of potential. Often these were students from the most troubled homes, yet she would alternately bully and charm each one with her own special brand of tough love until the spark caught fire. She retired in 1981 at the age of 62 but still avidly follows the lives and careers of former students while overseeing her adult stepchildren and driving her husband on camping trips to New Hampshire.

17 Miss Hurd was one of the first to call me on Dec. 10, 1987, when President Reagan, in his television address after the summit meetings with Gorbachev, told the nation that Eleni Gatzoyiannis' dying cry, "My children!" had helped inspire him to seek an arms agreement "for all the children of the world."

18 "I can't imagine a better monument for your mother," Miss Hurd said with an uncharacteristic catch in her voice.

19 Although a bad hip makes it impossible for her to join in the Greek dancing, Marjorie Hurd Rabidou is still an honored and enthusiastic guest at all family celebrations, including my 50th birthday picnic last summer, where the shish kebab was cooked on spits, clarinets and bouzoukis wailed, and costumed dancers led the guests in a serpentine line around our Colonial farmhouse, only 20 minutes from my first home in Worcester.

20 My sisters and I felt an aching void because my father was not there to lead the line, balancing a glass of wine on his head while he danced, the way he

Please note that excerpts and passages in the StudySync® library and this workbook are intended as touchstones to generate interest in an author's work. The excerpts and passages do not substitute for the reading of entire texts, and StudySync® strongly recommends that students seek out and purchase the whole literary or informational work in order to experience it as the author intended. Links to online resellers are available in our digital library. In addition, complete works may be ordered through an authorized reseller by filling out and returning to StudySync® the order form enclosed in this workbook.

NOTES

did at every celebration during his 92 years. But Miss Hurd was there, surveying the scene with quiet satisfaction. Although my parents are gone, her presence was a consolation, because I owe her so much.

21 This is truly the land of opportunity, and I would have enjoyed its bounty even if I hadn't walked into Miss Hurd's classroom in 1953. But she was the one who directed my grief and pain into writing, and if it weren't for her, I wouldn't have become an investigative reporter and foreign correspondent, recorded the story of my mother's life and death in Eleni and now my father's story in *A Place for Us,* which is also a testament to the country that took us in. She was the **catalyst** that sent me into journalism and indirectly caused all the good things that came after. But Miss Hurd would probably deny this emphatically.

22 A few years ago, I answered the telephone and heard my former teacher's voice telling me, in that won't-take-no-for-an-answer tone of hers, that she had decided I was to write and deliver the eulogy at her funeral. I agreed (she didn't leave me any choice), but that's one assignment I never want to do. I hope, Miss Hurd, that you'll accept this remembrance instead.

THINK QUESTIONS

1. Use specific details from the second paragraph to write two or three sentences summarizing why Nicholas Gage came to the United States.

2. Refer to specific details from the text to support your understanding of how Nicholas Gage first met Marjorie Hurd. What does he mean in paragraph 7 when he says, "I was soon under Miss Hurd's spell"?

3. What does Miss Hurd tell Gage to write about? In what way is the assignment a turning point in his life? Cite textual evidence from paragraphs 8–12 to support your response.

4. Use context to determine the meaning of the word **mentor** as it is used in paragraph 5 in "The Teacher Who Changed My Life." Write your definition of *mentor* and tell how you determined its meaning. Check your meaning in context and then confirm it in a print or digital dictionary.

5. Use the context clues provided in the passage to determine the meaning of the word **catalyst** as it is used in paragraph 21 in "The Teacher Who Changed My Life." Write your definition of *catalyst* and tell how you figured out the meaning of the word.

CLOSE READ

Reread the text "The Teacher Who Changed My Life." As you reread, complete the Focus Questions below. Then use your answers and annotations from the questions to help you complete the Writing Prompt.

FOCUS QUESTIONS

1. What adjectives does Gage use to describe Marjorie Hurd in paragraph 1? What details does he supply in paragraph 6 that support this view of Miss Hurd? What evidence is there in paragraph 7 that the young Gage was influenced by Hurd's personality? Highlight textual evidence and make annotations to explain your responses.

2. Which details in paragraph 7 indicate how Miss Hurd shaped the author's ideas through her teaching? Highlight textual evidence and make annotations to explain your answer.

3. What evidence is there in paragraph 7 that Miss Hurd's "Newspaper Club" helped prepare the author for a career in journalism? Highlight textual evidence and make annotations to explain your reasoning.

4. In paragraph 21, how does Gage connect events in his life to Miss Hurd's influence? Highlight textual evidence and make annotations to support your analysis.

5. When speaking about his father, the author notes that "at first our relationship was prickly, full of hostility." Cite textual evidence from paragraph 3 to explain why their interaction was challenging at first and what caused it to change. What evidence exists in paragraphs 13 and 14 to support the idea that his father's actions changed the way they interacted with each other? Highlight textual evidence and make annotations to support your reasoning.

WRITING PROMPT

In the first paragraph of Nicholas Gage's personal essay "The Teacher Who Changed My Life," his teacher Marjorie Hurd is identified as the "person who set the course of . . . [his] life," influencing his choice of a career in journalism and shaping other events in his life. Using the excerpt as a model, write a real-life story, or personal narrative, about a time when someone greatly influenced you. What was the situation? Who was involved? What was the setting? Remember that your personal narrative should be told from the first-person ("I") point of view. Write a strong introduction and include a "hook" to engage your reader. Introduce the setting. Then elaborate on your experience in your middle paragraphs. Include descriptive details. Use transitions, or time order words, such as *first, next,* and *then,* to help your readers follow the sequence of events. Include dialogue and precise or sensory language to hold your readers' attention. Try to use words with connotations that support the overall mood and tone of your story. Finally, write a conclusion that summarizes your personal narrative, and tell what you learned from the experience. What theme (or message) might you want to leave with your reader?

THE MIRACLE WORKER

DRAMA

William Gibson

1956

INTRODUCTION

"The Miracle Worker," by playwright William Gibson, was not only an award-winning Broadway play, but also an Academy Award-winning film. Based on the autobiography of Helen Keller, *The Story of My Life*, "The Miracle Worker" presents an emotional account of Keller's early life, after she lost her sight and hearing. The excerpt here comes from Act III of the play, and illustrates the unflagging efforts of teacher Annie Sullivan to break through Helen's walls of darkness and silence. In sharing the story of Helen Keller, who went on to become a world-famous author and political activist, Gibson provides a powerful portrait of two strong-willed females whose success was guided by their spirit of determination.

"...teaching her is bound to be painful, to everyone."

FIRST READ

CHARACTERS:

ANNIE SULLIVAN: young teacher trained to work with the blind and deaf; in her early twenties
HELEN KELLER: child who has been blind and deaf since infancy; now seven years old
KATE KELLER: Helen's mother; in her early thirties
CAPTAIN KELLER: Helen's father; middle-aged
JAMES KELLER: Captain Keller's grown son by a previous marriage; in his early twenties
AUNT EV: Captain Keller's sister; middle-aged
VINEY: Keller family servant

TIME: *The 1880's.*
PLACE: *In and around the Keller homestead in Tuscumbia, Alabama. . .*

1   [*Now in the family room the rear door opens, and* HELEN *steps in. She stands a moment, then sniffs in one deep grateful breath, and her hands go out vigorously to familiar things, over the door panels, and to the chairs around the table, and over the silverware on the table, until she meets* VINEY; *she pats her flank approvingly.*]

2   VINEY: Oh, we glad to have you back too, prob'ly.

3   [HELEN *hurries groping to the front door, opens and closes it, removes its key, opens and closes it again to be sure it is unlocked, gropes back to the rear door and repeats the procedure, removing its key and hugging herself gleefully.* AUNT EV *is next in by the rear door, with a relish tray; she bends to kiss* HELEN'S *cheek.* HELEN *finds* KATE *behind her, and thrusts the keys at her.*]

NOTES

4   KATE: What? Oh.

5   [*To EV*]

6   Keys.

7   [*She pockets them, lets* HELEN *feel them.*]

8   Yes, *I'll* keep the keys. I think we've had enough of locked doors, too.

9   [JAMES, *having earlier put* ANNIE'S *suitcase inside her door upstairs and taken himself out of view around the corner, now reappears and comes down the stairs as* ANNIE *and* KELLER *mount the porch steps. Following them into the family room, he pats* ANNIE'S *hair in passing, rather to her surprise.*]

10   JAMES: Evening, general.

11   [*He takes his own chair opposite.* VINEY *bears the empty water pitcher out to the porch. The remaining suggestion of garden house is gone now, and the water pump is* **unobstructed;** VINEY *pumps water into the pitcher.* KATE *surveying the table breaks the silence.*]

12   KATE: Will you say grace, Jimmie?

13   [*They bow their heads, except for* HELEN, *who palms her empty plate and then reaches to be sure her mother is there.* JAMES *considers a moment, glances across at* ANNIE, *lowers his head again, and obliges.*]

14   JAMES [*Lightly*]: And Jacob was left alone, and wrestled with an angel until the breaking of the day; and the hollow of Jacob's thigh was out of joint, as he wrestled with him; and the angel said, Let me go, for the day breaketh. And Jacob said, I will not let thee go, except thou bless me. Amen.

15   [ANNIE *has lifted her eyes suspiciously at* JAMES, *who winks expressionlessly and inclines his head to* HELEN.]

16   Oh, you angel.

17   [*The others lift their faces;* VINEY *returns with the pitcher, setting it down near* KATE, *then goes out the rear door; and* ANNIE *puts a napkin around* HELEN.]

18   AUNT EV: That's a very strange grace, James.

19   KELLER: Will you start the muffins, Ev?

20 JAMES: It's from the Good Book, isn't it?

21 AUNT EV [*Passing a plate*]: Well, of course it is. Didn't you know?

22 JAMES: Yes, I knew.

23 KELLER [*Serving*]: Ham, Miss Annie?

24 ANNIE: Please.

25 AUNT EV: Then why ask?

26 JAMES: I meant it *is* from the Good Book, and therefore a fitting grace.

27 AUNT EV: Well, I don't know about *that*.

28 KATE [*With the pitcher*]: Miss Annie?

29 ANNIE: Thank you.

30 AUNT EV: There's an awful *lot* of things in the Good Book that I wouldn't care to hear just before eating.

31 [*When* ANNIE *reaches for the pitcher,* HELEN *removes her napkin and drops it to the floor.* ANNIE *is filling* HELEN'S *glass when she notices it; she considers* HELEN'S *bland expression a moment, then bends,* **retrieves** *it, and tucks it around* HELEN'S *neck again.*]

32 JAMES: Well, fitting in the sense that Jacob's thigh was out of joint, and so is this piggie's.

33 AUNT EV: I declare, James—

34 KATE: Pickles, Aunt Ev?

35 AUNT EV: Oh, I should say so, you know my opinion of your pickles—

36 KATE: This is the end of them, I'm afraid. I didn't put up nearly enough last summer, this year I intend to—[*She interrupts herself, seeing* HELEN **deliberately** *lift off her napkin and drop it again to the floor. She bends to retrieve it, but* ANNIE *stops her arm.*]

37 KELLER [*Not noticing*]: Reverend looked in at the office today to complain his hens have stopped laying. Poor fellow, *he* was out of joint, all he could—[*He stops too, to frown down the table at* KATE, HELEN, *and* ANNIE *in turn, all suspended in mid-motion.*]

NOTES

38   JAMES [*Not noticing*]: I've always suspected those hens.

39   AUNT EV: Of what?

40   JAMES: I think they're Papist. Has he tried—[*He stops, too, following* KELLER'S *eyes.* ANNIE *now stops to pick the napkin up.*]

41   AUNT EV: James, now you're pulling my—lower extremity, the first thing you know we'll be—

42   [*She stops, too, hearing herself in the silence.* ANNIE, *with everyone now watching, for the third time puts the napkin on* HELEN. HELEN *yanks it off, and throws it down.* ANNIE *rises, lifts* HELEN'S *plate, and bears it away.* HELEN, *feeling it gone, slides down and commences to kick up under the table; the dishes jump.* ANNIE **contemplates** *this for a moment, then coming back takes* HELEN'S *wrists firmly and swings her off the chair.* HELEN *struggling gets one hand free, and catches at her mother's skirt; when* KATE *takes her by the shoulders,* HELEN *hangs quiet.*]

43   KATE: Miss Annie.

44   ANNIE: No.

45   KATE [*A pause*]: It's a very special day.

46   ANNIE [*Grimly*]: It will be, when I give in to that.

47   [*She tries to disengage* HELEN'S *hand;* KATE *lays hers on* ANNIE'S.]

48   ANNIE: Captain Keller.

49   KELLER [*Embarrassed*]: Oh, Katie, we—had a little talk, Miss Annie feels that if we **indulge** Helen in these—

50   AUNT EV: But what's the child done?

51   ANNIE: She's learned not to throw things on the floor and kick. It took us the best part of two weeks and—

52   AUNT EV: But only a napkin, it's not as if it were breakable!

53   ANNIE: And everything she's learned *is*? Mrs. Keller, I don't think we should—play tug-of-war for her, either give her to me or you keep her from kicking.

54   KATE: What do you wish to do?

NOTES

55 ANNIE: Let me take her from the table.

56 AUNT EV: Oh, let her stay, my goodness, she's only a child, she doesn't have to wear a napkin if she doesn't want to her first evening—

57 ANNIE [*Level*]: And ask outsiders not to interfere.

58 AUNT EV [*Astonished*]: Out—outsi—I'm the child's aunt!

59 KATE [*Distressed*]: Will once hurt so much, Miss Annie? I've—made all Helen's favorite foods, tonight.

60 [*A pause.*]

61 KELLER [*Gently*]: It's a homecoming party, Miss Annie.

62 [ANNIE *after a moment releases* HELEN. *But she cannot accept it, at her own chair she shakes her head and turns back, intent on* KATE.]

63 ANNIE: She's testing you. You realize?

64 JAMES [*To* ANNIE]: She's testing you.

65 KELLER: Jimmie, be quiet.

66 [JAMES *sits, tense.*]

67 Now she's home, naturally she—

68 ANNIE: And wants to see what will happen. At your hands. I said it was my main worry, is this what you promised me not half an hour ago?

69 KELLER [*Reasonably*]: But she's *not* kicking, now—

70 ANNIE: And not learning not to. Mrs. Keller, teaching her is bound to be painful, to everyone. I know it hurts to watch, but she'll live up to just what you demand of her, and no more.

71 JAMES [*Palely*]: She's testing *you*.

72 KELLER [*Testily*]: Jimmie.

73 JAMES: I have an opinion, I think I should—

74 KELLER: No one's interested in hearing your opinion.

75 ANNIE: *I'm* interested, of course she's testing me. Let me keep her to what she's learned and she'll go on learning from me. Take her out of my hands and it all comes apart.

Excerpted from *The Miracle Worker* by William Gibson, published by Scribner.

 THINK QUESTIONS

1. Who is Annie Sullivan, and why is she at the Keller homestead in Tuscumbia, Alabama? Cite evidence from information and ideas that are directly stated and from ideas you have inferred from clues in the text.

2. How would you describe Annie's emotions? Why is she feeling this way? Cite evidence from the text to support your answer.

3. What do you think Annie means when she says, "Take her out of my hands and it all comes apart"? Cite evidence from the text to support your answer.

4. Use context clues to determine the meaning of **retrieves** as it is used in the stage directions following Aunt Ev's fifth line of dialogue. Write your definition of *retrieves* and explain how you figured out its meaning. Then confirm your inferred meaning in a print or digital dictionary.

5. Use context clues to figure out the meaning of **indulge** as Captain Keller uses it in his fourth line of dialogue. Write your definition of *indulge* and explain how you figured out the meaning of the word. Find a synonym for *indulge* in a thesaurus and replace it in the sentence to see if it offers the same meaning. Then clarify the precise meaning of *indulge* in a print or digital dictionary.

CLOSE READ

Reread the excerpt from the drama "The Miracle Worker." As you reread, complete the Focus Questions below. Then use your answers and annotations from the questions to help you complete the Writing Prompt.

FOCUS QUESTIONS

1. How is the setting important to the dinner scene? What theme can you infer from this setting? Highlight evidence in the dialogue and stage directions to illustrate how the setting affects the theme. Make annotations to record specific textual evidence to support your answer.

2. Highlight a place in the dinner scene where the plot shapes the characters and their interactions with one another. Make annotations to explain your reasoning.

3. Reread the stage directions and dialogue for clues to Annie's character. How do Annie's character traits help shape the plot? Highlight specific textual evidence and make annotations to record your response.

4. Reread the stage directions and the dialogue related to James. What clues do you find about James's character and his role in the plot? Highlight specific textual evidence and make annotations to record your response.

5. The ability of people to transform their lives is one theme in the play. Identify another theme that is related to the challenges of human interactions. Highlight the textual evidence and make annotations to explain the theme.

WRITING PROMPT

How does the interaction of the elements of character, setting, and plot help develop and shape the themes in "The Miracle Worker"? Use the details you have compiled from analyzing the play to identify how

- the setting affects the characters or events of the plot.
- the plot shapes the characters and their relationship to one another.
- the characters influence the plot.
- the dramatic elements help present the theme or themes.

Begin with a clear thesis statement to introduce your topic. Remember to organize and to support your writing with specific evidence and inferences you draw from the text, using precise language and selection vocabulary. Include transitions to show the relationships among your ideas, and use a formal style of writing. Provide a conclusion that summarizes your main ideas.

THE TRAGEDY OF ROMEO AND JULIET
(ACT I, SCENE V)

DRAMA
William Shakespeare
1592

INTRODUCTION

The love story of *Romeo and Juliet* is among Shakespeare's most famous plays. The volatile family feud between the Montagues and Capulets has broken out in violence in the streets of Verona, Italy. With his two friends, Romeo, the son of Lord Montague, attends a party held by Lord Caplulet. A mask hides Romeo's identity. There, he meets and falls in love with the beautiful Juliet, a Capulet. When they first meet, their dialogue comes out as a perfect sonnet, one

"Thus from my lips, by yours, my sin is purged."

FIRST READ

ACT I, SCENE V

A hall in Capulet's house.

1 *Musicians waiting. Enter Servingmen with napkins.*

2 FIRST SERVANT: Where's Potpan, that he helps not to take away? He
3 shift a **trencher**? he scrape a trencher!

4 SECOND SERVANT: When good manners shall lie all in one or two men's
5 hands and they unwashed too, 'tis a foul thing.

6 FIRST SERVANT: Away with the joint-stools, remove the
7 court-cupboard, look to the plate. Good thou, save
8 me a piece of marchpane; and, as thou lovest me, let
9 the porter let in Susan Grindstone and Nell.
10 Antony, and Potpan!

11 SECOND SERVANT: Ay, boy, ready.

12 FIRST SERVANT: You are looked for and called for, asked for and
13 sought for, in the great chamber.

14 SECOND SERVANT: We cannot be here and there too. Cheerly, boys; be
15 brisk awhile, and the longer liver take all.

16 *[Enter CAPULET, with JULIET and others of his house, meeting the Guests and Maskers]*

17 CAPULET: Welcome, gentlemen! ladies that have their toes
18 Unplagued with corns will have a bout with you.

19   Ah ha, my mistresses! which of you all

20   Will now deny to dance? she that makes dainty,

21   She, I'll swear, hath corns; am I come near ye now?

22   Welcome, gentlemen! I have seen the day

23   That I have worn a visor and could tell

24   A whispering tale in a fair lady's ear,

25   Such as would please: 'tis gone, 'tis gone, 'tis gone:

26   You are welcome, gentlemen! come, musicians, play.

27   A hall, a hall! give room! and foot it, girls.

28   *Music plays, and they dance*

29   More light, you knaves; and turn the tables up,

30   And quench the fire, the room is grown too hot.

31   Ah, sirrah, this unlook'd-for sport comes well.

32   Nay, sit, nay, sit, good cousin Capulet;

33   For you and I are past our dancing days:

34   How long is't now since last yourself and I

35   Were in a mask?

36   SECOND CAPULET: By'r lady, thirty years.

37   CAPULET: What, man! 'tis not so much, 'tis not so much:

38   'Tis since the **nuptials** of Lucentio,

39   Come pentecost as quickly as it will,

40   Some five and twenty years; and then we mask'd.

41   SECOND CAPULET: 'Tis more, 'tis more, his son is elder, sir;

42   His son is thirty.

43   CAPULET: Will you tell me that?

44   His son was but a ward two years ago.

45   ROMEO: [*To a Servingman*] What lady is that, which doth

46   enrich the hand

47   Of yonder knight?

48   SERVANT: I know not, sir.

49   ROMEO: O, she doth teach the torches to burn bright!

50   It seems she hangs upon the cheek of night

51   Like a rich jewel in an Ethiope's ear;

52   Beauty too rich for use, for earth too dear!

53   So shows a snowy dove trooping with crows,

54   As yonder lady o'er her fellows shows.

55   The measure done, I'll watch her place of stand,

56   And, touching hers, make blessed my rude hand.

57   Did my heart love till now? forswear it, sight!

58 For I ne'er saw true beauty till this night.

59 TYBALT: This, by his voice, should be a Montague.
60 Fetch me my rapier, boy. What dares the slave
61 Come hither, cover'd with an antic face,
62 To fleer and scorn at our solemnity?
63 Now, by the stock and honour of my kin,
64 To strike him dead, I hold it not a sin.

65 CAPULET: Why, how now, kinsman! wherefore storm you so?

66 TYBALT: Uncle, this is a Montague, our foe,
67 A villain that is hither come in spite,
68 To scorn at our solemnity this night.

69 CAPULET: Young Romeo is it?

70 TYBALT: 'Tis he, that villain Romeo.

71 CAPULET: Content thee, gentle coz, let him alone;
72 He bears him like a portly gentleman;
73 And, to say truth, Verona brags of him
74 To be a virtuous and well-govern'd youth:
75 I would not for the wealth of all the town
76 Here in my house do him **disparagement:**
77 Therefore be patient, take no note of him:
78 It is my will, the which if thou respect,
79 Show a fair presence and put off these frowns,
80 And ill-beseeming semblance for a feast.

81 TYBALT: It fits, when such a villain is a guest:
82 I'll not endure him.

83 CAPULET: He shall be endured:
84 What, goodman boy! I say, he shall: go to;
85 Am I the master here, or you? go to.
86 You'll not endure him! God shall mend my soul!
87 You'll make a mutiny among my guests!
88 You will set cock-a-hoop! You'll be the man!
89 TYBALT: Why, uncle, 'tis a shame.

90 CAPULET: Go to, go to;
91 You are a saucy boy: is't so, indeed?
92 This trick may chance to scathe you, I know what:
93 You must contrary me! marry, 'tis time.
94 Well said, my hearts! You are a princox; go:

95   Be quiet, or—More light, more light! For shame!
96   I'll make you quiet. What, cheerly, my hearts!

97   TYBALT: Patience perforce with wilful choler meeting
98   Makes my flesh tremble in their different greeting.
99   I will withdraw: but this **intrusion** shall
100   Now seeming sweet convert to bitter gall.

101   *[Exit]*

102   ROMEO [*To JULIET*]: If I **profane** with my unworthiest hand
103   This holy shrine, the gentle fine is this:
104   My lips, two blushing pilgrims, ready stand
105   To smooth that rough touch with a tender kiss.

106   JULIET: Good pilgrim, you do wrong your hand too much,
107   Which mannerly devotion shows in this;
108   For saints have hands that pilgrims' hands do touch,
109   And palm to palm is holy palmers' kiss.

110   ROMEO: Have not saints lips, and holy palmers too?

111   JULIET: Ay, pilgrim, lips that they must use in prayer.

112   ROMEO: O, then, dear saint, let lips do what hands do;
113   They pray, grant thou, lest faith turn to despair.

114   JULIET: Saints do not move, though grant for prayers' sake.

115   ROMEO: Then move not, while my prayer's effect I take.
116   Thus from my lips, by yours, my sin is purged.

117   JULIET: Then have my lips the sin that they have took.

118   ROMEO: Sin from thy lips? O trespass sweetly urged!
119   Give me my sin again.

120   JULIET: You kiss by the book.

121   NURSE: Madam, your mother craves a word with you.

122   ROMEO: What is her mother?

123   NURSE: Marry, bachelor,
124   Her mother is the lady of the house,
125   And a good lady, and a wise and virtuous;
126   I nursed her daughter, that you talk'd withal;

127 I tell you, he that can lay hold of her
128 Shall have the chinks.

129 ROMEO: Is she a Capulet?
130 O dear account! my life is my foe's debt.

131 BENVOLIO: Away, begone; the sport is at the best.

132 ROMEO: Ay, so I fear; the more is my unrest.

133 CAPULET: Nay, gentlemen, prepare not to be gone;
134 We have a trifling foolish banquet towards.
135 Is it e'en so? why, then, I thank you all
136 I thank you, honest gentlemen; good night.
137 More torches here! Come on then, let's to bed.
138 Ah, sirrah, by my fay, it waxes late:
139 I'll to my rest.

140 *Exeunt all but JULIET and NURSE*

141 JULIET: Come hither, nurse. What is yond gentleman?

142 NURSE: The son and heir of old Tiberio.

143 JULIET: What's he that now is going out of door?

144 NURSE: Marry, that, I think, be young Petrucio.

145 JULIET: What's he that follows there, that would not dance?

146 NURSE: I know not.

147 JULIET: Go ask his name: if he be married,
148 My grave is like to be my wedding bed.

149 NURSE: His name is Romeo, and a Montague;
150 The only son of your great enemy.

151 JULIET: My only love sprung from my only hate!
152 Too early seen unknown, and known too late!
153 Prodigious birth of love it is to me,
154 That I must love a loathed enemy.

155 NURSE: What's this? What's this?

156 JULIET: A rhyme I learn'd even now
157 Of one I danced withal.
158 *[One calls within 'Juliet.']*

159 NURSE: Anon, anon!
160 Come, let's away; the strangers all are gone.

161 *[Exeunt.]*

 ## THINK QUESTIONS

1. Refer to two or more details from the text to support your understanding of the setting, why the people are there, and the action that is taking place. Use both direct textual evidence and inferences you can make from the speech and actions of the characters.

2. How do Capulet and Tybalt differ in their reactions to Romeo's crashing the feast as a Masker? Cite specific textual evidence, including lines from the scene's dialogue, and make inferences to support your answer.

3. What evidence is there that Romeo and Juliet experience love at first sight? Cite specific textual evidence from the scene's dialogue to support your answer.

4. By recalling that the Latin suffix *-ment* can mean "the act of," use the context clues provided in Tybalt's and Capulet's angry conversation about Romeo to determine the meaning of *disparagement*. Write your definition of *disparagement* and explain how you determined the meaning of the word.

5. Use context clues to determine the meaning of **profane** as Romeo uses it when speaking to Juliet for the first time. Write your definition of *profane* and explain how you figured out the word's meaning. Check your inferred meaning in context, or use a print or digital dictionary to verify your definition.

Please note that excerpts and passages in the StudySync® library and this workbook are intended as touchstones to generate interest in an author's work. The excerpts and passages do not substitute for the reading of entire texts, and StudySync® strongly recommends that students seek out and purchase the whole literary or informational work in order to experience it as the author intended. Links to online resellers are available in our digital library. In addition, complete works may be ordered through an authorized reseller by filling out and returning to StudySync® the order form enclosed in this workbook.

Reading & Writing Companion   **357**

CLOSE READ

Reread the excerpt from *The Tragedy of Romeo and Juliet* (Act I, Scene V). As you reread, complete the Focus Questions below. Then use your answers and annotations from the questions to help you complete the Writing Prompt.

FOCUS QUESTIONS

##

1. Highlight the last two lines in Romeo's second speech and the lines in Tybalt's first speech. How do these lines introduce the reader to the conflict of the plot? Make annotations to explain.

2. What evidence in Tybalt's last speech supports the idea that Tybalt will have a future run-in with Romeo? How does this idea contribute to your understanding of the plot structure of the play? Make annotations to explain your reasoning.

3. What metaphor does Capulet use when he questions Tybalt after Tybalt's first speech? Highlight the metaphor. Make annotations to explain its meaning.

4. In Romeo's second speech, highlight three examples of images that appeal to the sense of sight. (Note that these images may also be part of other figures of speech, such as personification or metaphor.) Make annotations to explain the pictures these images create in the mind of the reader. What do these visual images have in common? What do they reveal about the way Romeo views Juliet?

5. What challenges will Juliet face by falling in love with Romeo? Highlight the textual evidence in Juliet's next-to-last-speech that helps you understand these challenges. Use the annotation tool to show how this evidence relates to the Essential Question of the unit: *What are the challenges of human interactions?* and to the main conflict of the play.

WRITING PROMPT

Think about the rising action of Act I, Scene V in the plot structure of *The Tragedy of Romeo and Juliet*. How does this particular scene contribute to your understanding of the challenges Romeo and Juliet will likely face in their interactions with each other and with other characters? In your response, refer to Shakespeare's use of figurative language in the scene. Begin with a clear thesis statement, and support and organize your response with specific textual evidence. Use transitions to show the relationships among your ideas. Establish a formal style and use precise language and selection vocabulary. Provide an effective conclusion that summarizes your central ideas.

AMIGO BROTHERS

FICTION

Piri Thomas

1978

INTRODUCTION

Piri Thomas grew up in New York City's rough Spanish Harlem neighborhood and began writing his acclaimed autobiography *Down These Mean Streets* while serving a prison term for attempted robbery. Known for the tough reality portrayed in his works, Thomas's literary output includes memoirs, short stories, essays, and poems. In his story "Amigo Brothers," amateur boxers and best friends Antonio and Felix must fight against each other to determine which

"Each youngster had a dream of someday becoming lightweight champion of the world."

FIRST READ

NOTES

1   Antonio Cruz and Felix Varga were both seventeen years old. They were so together in friendship that they felt themselves to be brothers. They had known each other since childhood, growing up on the lower east side of Manhattan in the same tenement building on Fifth Street between Avenue A and Avenue B.

2   Antonio was fair, lean, and lanky, while Felix was dark, short, and husky. Antonio's hair was always falling over his eyes, while Felix wore his black hair in a natural Afro style.

3   Each youngster had a dream of someday becoming lightweight champion of the world. Every chance they had the boys worked out, sometimes at the Boys Club on 10th Street and Avenue A and sometimes at the pro's gym on 14th Street. Early morning sunrises would find them running along the East River Drive, wrapped in sweat shirts, short towels around their necks, and handkerchiefs Apache style around their foreheads.

4   While some youngsters were into street negatives, Antonio and Felix slept, ate, rapped, and dreamt positive. Between them, they had a collection of second to none, plus a scrapbook filled with torn tickets to every boxing match they had ever attended, and some clippings of their own. If asked a question about any given fighter, they would immediately zip out from their memory banks divisions, weights, records of fights, knock-outs, technical knock-outs, and draws or losses.

5   Each had fought many **bouts** representing their community and had won two gold-plated medals plus a silver and bronze medallion. The difference was in their style. Antonio's lean form and long reach made him the better boxer, while Felix's short and muscular frame made him the better slugger. Whenever

NOTES

they had met in the ring for sparring sessions, it had always been hot and heavy.

6 Now, after a series of elimination bouts, they had been informed that they were to meet each other in the division finals that were scheduled for the seventh of August, two weeks away—the winner to represent the Boys Club in the Golden Gloves Championship Tournament.

7 The two boys continued to run together along the East River Drive. But even when joking with each other, they both sensed a wall rising between them.

8 One morning less than a week before their bout, they met as usual for their daily work-out. They fooled around with a few jabs at the air, slapped skin, and then took off, running lightly along the dirty East River's edge.

9 Antonio glanced at Felix who kept his eyes purposely straight ahead, pausing from time to time to do some fancy leg work while throwing one-twos followed by upper cuts to an imaginary jaw. Antonio then beat the air with a **barrage** of body blows and short devastating lefts with an overhand jaw-breaking right.

10 After a mile or so, Felix puffed and said, "Let's stop a while, bro. I think we both got something to say to each other."

11 Antonio nodded. It was not natural to be acting as though nothing unusual was happening when two aceboon buddies were going to be blasting each other within a few short days.

12 They rested their elbows on the railing separating them from the river. Antonio wiped his face with his short towel. The sunrise was now creating day.

13 Felix leaned heavily on the river's railing and stared across to the shores of Brooklyn. Finally, he broke the silence.

14 "Man, I don't know how to come out with it."

15 Antonio helped. "It's about our fight, right?"

16 "Yeah, right." Felix's eyes squinted at the rising orange sun.

17 "I've been thinking about it too, *panin*. In fact, since we found out it was going to be me and you, I've been awake at night, pulling punches on you, trying not to hurt you."

18 "Same here. It ain't natural not to think about the fight. I mean, we both are *cheverote* fighters and we both want to win. But only one of us can win. There ain't no draws in the eliminations."

NOTES

19   Felix tapped Antonio gently on the shoulder. "I don't mean to sound like I'm bragging, bro. But I wanna win, fair and square."

20   Antonio nodded quietly. "Yeah. We both know that in the ring the better man wins. Friend or no friend, brother or no. . ."

21   Felix finished it for him. "Brother. Tony, let's promise something right here. Okay?"

22   "If it's fair, *hermano,* I'm for it." Antonio admired the courage of a tug boat pulling a barge five times its welterweight size.

23   "It's fair, Tony. When we get into the ring, it's gotta be like we never met. We gotta be like two heavy strangers that want the same thing and only one can have it. You understand, don'tcha?"

24   "*Si,* I know." Tony smiled. "No pulling punches. We go all the way."

25   "Yeah, that's right. Listen, Tony. Don't you think it's a good idea if we don't see each other until the day of the fight? I'm going to stay with my Aunt Lucy in the Bronx. I can use Gleason's Gym for working out. My manager says he got some sparring partners with more or less your style."

26   Tony scratched his nose **pensively**. "Yeah, it would be better for our heads." He held out his hand, palm upward. "Deal?"

27   "Deal." Felix lightly slapped open skin.

28   "Ready for some more running?" Tony asked lamely.

29   "Naw, bro. Let's cut it here. You go on. I kinda like to get things together in my head."

30   "You ain't worried, are you?" Tony asked.

31   "No way, man." Felix laughed out loud. "I got too much smarts for that. I just think it's cooler if we split right here. After the fight, we can get it together again like nothing ever happened."

32   The amigo brothers were not ashamed to hug each other tightly.

33   "Guess you're right. Watch yourself, Felix. I hear there's some pretty heavy dudes up in the Bronx. *Suavecito,* okay?"

34   "Okay. You watch yourself too, *sabe?*"

35 Tony jogged away. Felix watched his friend disappear from view, throwing rights and lefts. Both fighters had a lot of psyching up to do before the big fight.

36 The days in training passed much too slowly. Although they kept out of each other's way, they were aware of each other's progress via the ghetto grapevine.

37 The evening before the big fight, Tony made his way to the roof of his tenement. In the quiet early dark, he peered over the ledge. Six stories below the lights of the city blinked and the sounds of cars mingled with the curses and the laughter of children in the street. He tried not to think of Felix, feeling he had succeeded in psyching his mind. But only in the ring would he really know. To spare Felix hurt, he would have to knock him out, early and quick.

38 Up in the South Bronx, Felix decided to take in a movie in an effort to keep Antonio's face away from his fists. The flick was *The Champion* with Kirk Douglas, the third time Felix was seeing it.

39 The champion was getting the daylights beat out of him. He was saved only by the sound of the bell.

40 Felix became the champ and Tony the challenger.

41 The movie audience was going out of its head. The champ hunched his shoulders grunting and sniffing red blood back into his broken nose. The challenger, confident that he had the championship in the bag, threw a left. The champ countered with a dynamite right.

42 Felix's right arm felt the shock, Antonio's face, superimposed on the screen, was hit by the awesome force of the blow. Felix saw himself in the ring, blasting Antonio against the ropes. The champ had to be forcibly restrained. The challenger fell slowly to the canvas.

43 When Felix finally left the theatre, he had figured out how to psyche himself for tomorrow's fight. It was Felix the Champion vs. Antonio the Challenger.

44 He walked up some dark streets, deserted except for small pockets of wary-looking kids wearing gang colors.

45 Despite the fact that he was Puerto Rican like them, they eyed him as a stranger to their turf. Felix did a fast shuffle, bobbing and weaving, while letting loose a torrent of blows that would demolish whatever got in its way. It seemed to impress the brothers, who went about their own business.

46 Finding no takers, Felix decided to split to his aunt's. Walking the streets had not relaxed him, neither had the fight flick. All it had done was to stir him up. He let himself quietly into his Aunt Lucy's apartment and went straight to bed, falling into a fitful sleep with sounds of the gong for Round One.

47 Antonio was passing some heavy time on his rooftop. How would the fight tomorrow affect his relationship with Felix? After all, fighting was like any other profession. Friendship had nothing to do with it. A gnawing doubt crept in. He cut negative thinking real quick by doing some speedy fancy dance steps, bobbing and weaving like mercury. The night air was blurred with perpetual motions of left hooks and right crosses. Felix, his *amigo* brother, was not going to be Felix at all in the ring. Just an opponent with another face. Antonio went to sleep, hearing the opening bell for the first round. Like his friend in the South Bronx, he prayed for victory, via a quick clean knock-out in the first round.

48 Large posters plastered all over the walls of local shops announced the fight between Antonio Cruz and Felix Vargas as the main bout.

49 The fight had created great interest in the neighborhood. Antonio and Felix were well liked and respected. Each had his own loyal following.

50 Antonio's fans had unbridled faith in his boxing skills. On the other side, Felix's admirers trusted in his dynamite-packed fists.

51 Felix had returned to his apartment early in the morning of August 7th and stayed there, hoping to avoid seeing Antonio. He turned the radio on to *salsa* music sounds and then tried to read while waiting for word from his manager.

52 The fight was scheduled to take place in Tompkins Square Park. It had been decided that the gymnasium of the Boys Club was not large enough to hold all the people who were sure to attend. In Tompkins Square Park, everyone who wanted could view the fight, whether from ringside or window fire escapes or tenement rooftops.

53 The morning of the fight Tompkins Square was a beehive of activity with numerous workers setting up the ring, the seats, and the guest speakers' stand. The scheduled bouts began shortly after noon and the park had begun filling up even earlier.

54 The local junior high school across from Tompkins Square Park served as the dressing room for all the fighters. Each was given a separate classroom with desk tops, covered with mats, serving as resting tables. Antonio thought he caught a glimpse of Felix waving to him from a room at the end of the corridor. He waved back just in case it had been him.

55 The fighters changed from their street clothes into fighting gear. Antonio wore white trunks, black socks, and black shoes. Felix wore sky blue trunks, red socks, and white boxing shoes. Each had dressing gowns to match their fighting trunks with their names neatly stitched on the back.

56 The loudspeakers blared into the open windows of the school. There were speeches by dignitaries, community leaders, and great boxers of yesteryear. Some were well prepared, some improvised on the spot. They all carried the same message of great pleasure and honor at being part of such a historic event. This great day was in the tradition of champions emerging from the streets of the lower east side.

57 Interwoven with the speeches were the sounds of the other boxing events. After the sixth bout, Felix was much relieved when his trainer Charlie said, "Time change. Quick knock-out. This is it. We're on."

58 Waiting time was over. Felix was escorted from the classroom by a dozen fans in white T-shirts with the word FELIX across their fronts.

59 Antonio was escorted down a different stairwell and guided through a roped-off path.

60 As the two climbed into the ring, the crowd exploded with a roar. Antonio and Felix both bowed gracefully and then raised their arms in acknowledgment.

61 Antonio tried to be cool, but even as the roar was in its first birth, he turned slowly to meet Felix's eyes looking directly into his. Felix nodded his head and Antonio responded. And both as one, just as quickly, turned away to face his own corner.

62 Bong—bong—bong. The roar turned to stillness.

63 "Ladies and Gentlemen, *Señores y Señoras*."

64 The announcer spoke slowly, pleased at his bilingual efforts.

65 "Now the moment we have all been waiting for—the main event between two fine young Puerto Rican fighters, products of our lower east side.

66 "In this corner, weighing 134 pounds, Felix Vargas. And in this corner, weighing 133 pounds, Antonio Cruz. The winner will represent the Boys Club in the tournament of champions, the Golden Gloves. There will be no draw. May the best man win."

67 The cheering of the crowd shook the window panes of the old buildings surrounding Tompkins Square Park. At the center of the ring, the referee was giving instructions to the youngsters.

Copyright © BookheadEd Learning, LLC

Reading & Writing Companion

NOTES

68   "Keep your punches up. No low blows. No punching on the back of the head. Keep your heads up. Understand. Let's have a clean fight. Now shake hands and come out fighting."

69   Both youngsters touched gloves and nodded. They turned and danced quickly to their corners . Their head towels and dressing gowns were lifted neatly from their shoulders by their trainers' nimble fingers. Antonio crossed himself. Felix did the same.

70   BONG! BONG! ROUND ONE. Felix and Antonio turned and faced each other squarely in a fighting pose. Felix wasted no time. He came in fast, head low, half hunched toward his right shoulder, and lashed out with a straight left. He missed a right cross as Antonio slipped the punch and countered with one-two-three lefts that snapped Felix's head back, sending a mild shock coursing through him. If Felix had any small doubt about their friendship affecting their fight, it was being neatly **dispelled**.

71   Antonio danced, a joy to behold. His left hand was like a piston pumping jabs one right after another with seeming ease. Felix bobbed and weaved and never stopped boring in. He knew that at long range he was at a disadvantage. Antonio had too much reach on him. Only by coming in close could Felix hope to achieve the dreamed-of knockout.

72   Antonio knew the dynamite that was stored in his *amigo* brother's fist. He ducked a short right and missed a left hook. Felix trapped him against the ropes just long enough to pour some punishing rights and lefts to Antonio's hard midsection. Antonio slipped away from Felix, crashing two lefts to his head, which set Felix's right ear to ringing.

73   Bong! Both *amigos* froze a punch well on its way, sending up a roar of approval for good sportsmanship.

74   Felix walked briskly back to his corner. His right ear had not stopped ringing. Antonio gracefully danced his way toward his stool none the worse, except for glowing glove burns, showing angry red against the whiteness of his midribs.

75   "Watch that right, Tony." His trainer talked into his ear. "Remember Felix always goes to the body. He'll want you to drop your hands for his overhand left or right. Got it?"

76   Antonio nodded, spraying water out between his teeth. He felt better as his sore midsection was being firmly rubbed.

77   Felix's corner was also busy.

78 "You gotta get in there, fella." Felix's trainer poured water over his curly Afro locks. "Get in there or he's gonna chop you up from way back."

79 *Bong! Bong!* Round two. Felix was off his stool and rushed Antonio like a bull, sending a hard right to his head. Beads of water exploded from Antonio's long hair.

80 Antonio, hurt, sent back a blurring barrage of lefts and rights that only meant pain to Felix, who returned with a short left to the head followed by a looping right to the body. Antonio countered with his own flurry, forcing Felix to give ground. But not for long.

81 Felix bobbed and weaved, bobbed and weaved, occasionally punching his two gloves together.

82 Antonio waited for the rush that was sure to come. Felix closed in and feinted with his left shoulder and threw his right instead. Lights suddenly exploded inside Felix's head as Antonio slipped the blow and hit him with a pistonlike left, catching him flush on the point of his chin.

83 Badlam broke loose as Felix's legs momentarily buckled. He fought off a series of rights and lefts and came back with a strong right that taught Antonio respect.

84 Antonio danced in carefully. He knew Felix had the habit of playing possum when hurt, to sucker an opponent within reach of the powerful bombs he carried in each fist.

85 A right to the head slowed Antonio's pretty dancing. He answered with his own left at Felix's right eye that began puffing up within three seconds.

86 Antonio, a bit too eager, moved in too close and Felix had him entangled into a rip-roaring, punching toe-to-toe slugfest that brought the whole Tompkins Square Park screaming to its feet.

87 Rights to the body. Lefts to the head. Neither fighter was giving an inch. Suddenly a short right caught Antonio squarely on the chin. His long legs turned to jelly and his arms flailed out desperately. Felix, grunting like a bull, threw wild punches from every direction. Antonio, groggy, bobbed and weaved, evading most of the blows. Suddenly his head cleared. His left flashed out hard and straight catching Felix on the bridge of his nose.

88 Felix lashed back with a haymaker, right off the ghetto streets. At the same instant, his eye caught another left hook from Antonio. Felix swung out trying to clear the pain. Only the **frenzied** screaming of those along the ringside let him know that he had dropped Antonio. Fighting off the growing haze,

NOTES

Antonio struggled to his feet, got up, ducked, and threw a smashing right that dropped Felix flat on his back.

89 Felix got up as fast as he could in his own corner, groggy but still game. He didn't even hear the count. In a fog, he heard the roaring of the crowd, who seemed to have gone insane. His head cleared to hear the bell sound at the end of the round. He was very glad. His trainer sat his down on the stool.

90 In his corner, Antonio was doing what all fighters do when they are hurt. They sit and smile at everyone.

91 The referee signaled the ring doctor to check the fighters outs. He did so and then gave his okay. The cold water sponges brought clarity to both *amigo* brothers. They were rubbed until their circulation ran free.

92 *Bong!* Round three—the final round. Up to now it had been tic-tac-toe, pretty much even. But everyone knew there could be no draw and that this round would decide the winner.

93 This time, to Felix's surprise, it was Antonio who came out fast, charging across the ring. Felix braced himself but couldn't ward off the barrage of punches. Antonio drove Felix hard against the ropes.

94 The crowd ate it up. Thus far the two had fought with *mucho corazón*. Felix tapped his gloves and commenced his attack anew. Antonio, throwing boxer's caution to the winds, jumped in to meet him.

95 Both pounded away. Neither gave an inch and neither fell to the canvas. Felix's left eye was tightly closed. Claret red blood poured from Antonio's nose. They fought toe-to-toe.

96 The sounds of their blows were loud in contrast to the silence of a crowd gone completely mute.

97 *Bong! Bong! Bong!* The bell sounded over and over again. Felix and Antonio were past hearing. Their blows continued to pound on each other like hailstones.

98 Finally the referee and the two trainers pried Felix and Antonio apart. Cold water was poured over them to bring them back to their senses.

99 They looked around and then rushed toward each other. A cry of alarm surged through Tompkins Square Park. Was this a fight to the death instead of a boxing match?

100   The fear soon gave way to wave upon wave of cheering as the two *amigos* embraced.

101   No matter what the decision, they knew they would always be champions to each other.

102   *BONG! BONG! BONG!* "Ladies and Gentlemen. *Señores* and *Señoras*. The winner and representative to the Golden Gloves Tournament of Champions is. . ."

103   The announcer turned to point to the winner and found himself alone. Arm in arm the champions had already left the ring.

© 1978 by Piri Thomas, STORIES FROM EL BARRIO. Reproduced by permission of the Trust of Piri J. Thomas and Suzanne Dod Thomas.

 THINK QUESTIONS

1. Why does the author refer to Antonio Cruz and Feliz Varga as the "amigo brothers"? How were the boys alike? How were they different? Cite specific evidence from paragraphs 1–3 to support your answer.

2. How does the reader know that boxing was very important to Antonio and Felix? Cite specific evidence from paragraphs 3 and 4 to support your response.

3. Why was the upcoming division match a challenge for Antonio and Felix's friendship? How did the boys have the same point of view about handling the match? Cite specific evidence from paragraphs 11–25 to support your response.

4. Use context clues to determine the meaning of the word **dispelled** as it is used at the beginning of the fight scene, in paragraph 70 of "Amigo Brothers." Write your definition of *dispelled,* and explain how you figured out the meaning of the word. Then check your meaning in a print or digital dictionary.

5. Use context clues and word origin to figure out the meaning of **frenzied** as it is used during the heat of the fight, in paragraph 88 of "Amigo Brothers." Write your definition of *frenzied* and tell how you determined the meaning of the word. Consult a print or digital dictionary to find the interesting word origin (or etymology) of *frenzied* that will help you figure out its meaning. Then check the dictionary again to clarify the precise meaning of the word.

Please note that excerpts and passages in the StudySync® library and this workbook are intended as touchstones to generate interest in an author's work. The excerpts and passages do not substitute for the reading of entire texts, and StudySync® strongly recommends that students seek out and purchase the whole literary or informational work in order to experience it as the author intended. Links to online resellers are available in our digital library. In addition, complete works may be ordered through an authorized reseller by filling out and returning to StudySync® the order form enclosed in this workbook.

Reading & Writing Companion   **369**

CLOSE READ

Reread the story "Amigo Brothers." As you reread, complete the Focus Questions below. Then use your answers and annotations from the questions to help you complete the Writing Prompt.

FOCUS QUESTIONS

1. As you reread "Amigo Brothers," keep in mind that the story is told from the third-person point of view. Although readers can infer much about the boys' character traits and point of view from their dialogue, the narrator also provides important information about the boys. Highlight evidence in paragraph 4 that reveals how the narrator feels about Antonio and Felix. How does this information help you determine the theme? Make annotations to explain your ideas.

2. Dialogue can also reveal character traits and point of view, thereby helping to uncover the theme, or underlying message, of a text. What point of view do Antonio and Felix share in paragraphs 23–27? How does their shared point of view help you discover the theme? Highlight textual evidence and make annotations to explain your thinking.

3. What evidence is there in paragraphs 37–38 and 47 that Antonio and Felix are conflicted about the fight? How does this conflict relate to the theme? Highlight textual evidence and make annotations to explain your response.

4. Which lines from paragraph 54 provide strong evidence of the theme of the story? Highlight the two most important sentences and annotate how they express the theme.

5. How does the theme of the story teach a lesson about the challenges of human interactions? Highlight textual evidence and make annotations to support your answer.

WRITING PROMPT

How does the theme of "Amigo Brothers" help you understand a larger lesson about life, human nature, or human experience? Use the details and evidence you have compiled from examining the story elements of setting, character and dialogue, conflict and plot, and point of view to

- identify the theme of the story.
- analyze how the theme (or underlying message) is developed over the course of the text.

Begin with a clear thesis statement that introduces your topic. Remember to organize and support your writing with textual evidence and inferences, using precise language and selection vocabulary where possible. Include transitions to reveal the connections among your ideas, and establish a formal style of delivery. Finally, provide a conclusion that summarizes your main ideas.

THANK YOU, M'AM

FICTION
Langston Hughes
1958

INTRODUCTION

Langston Hughes was working as a busboy in Washington, D.C. when he showed some of his poems to famous poet Vachel Lindsay. Lindsay was so impressed that he read the poems that night to an audience. In time, Hughes became one of the first African Americans to make a living as a writer and lecturer, eventually moving back to New York and becoming a leader of the Harlem Renaissance. In Hughes's short story "Thank You, M'am," a teenage boy tries to snatch a woman's purse late one night and is surprised by what happens next.

"'You gonna take me to jail?' asked the boy..."

FIRST READ

Excerpt from Chapter 2: All Was Not Right

1   She was a large woman with a large purse that had everything in it but hammer and nails. It had a long strap, and she carried it slung across her shoulder. It was about eleven o'clock at night, and she was walking alone, when a boy ran up behind her and tried to snatch her purse. The strap broke with the single tug the boy gave it from behind. But the boy's weight and the weight of the purse combined caused him to lose his balance so, instead of taking off full blast as he had hoped, the boy fell on his back on the sidewalk, and his legs flew up. The large woman simply turned around and kicked him right square in his blue-jeaned sitter. Then she reached down, picked the boy up by his shirt front, and shook him until his teeth rattled.

2   After that the woman said, "Pick up my pocketbook, boy, and give it here." She still held him. But she bent down enough to permit him to stoop and pick up her purse. Then she said, "Now ain't you ashamed of yourself?"

3   Firmly gripped by his shirt front, the boy said, "Yes'm."

4   The woman said, "What did you want to do it for?"

5   The boy said, "I didn't aim to."

6   She said, "You a lie!"

7   By that time two or three people passed, stopped, turned to look, and some stood watching.

8   "If I turn you loose, will you run?" asked the woman.

9   "Yes'm," said the boy.

10 "Then I won't turn you loose," said the woman. She did not release him.

11 "I'm very sorry, lady, I'm sorry," whispered the boy.

12 "Um-hum! And your face is dirty. I got a great mind to wash your face for you. Ain't you got nobody home to tell you to wash your face?"

13 "No'm," said the boy.

14 "Then it will get washed this evening," said the large woman starting up the street, dragging the frightened boy behind her.

15 He looked as if he were fourteen or fifteen, **frail** and willow-wild, in tennis shoes and blue jeans.

16 The woman said, "You ought to be my son. I would teach you right from wrong. Least I can do right now is to wash your face. Are you hungry?"

17 "No'm," said the being dragged boy. "I just want you to turn me loose."

18 "Was I bothering *you* when I turned that corner?" asked the woman.

19 "No'm."

20 "But you put yourself in contact with *me*," said the woman. "If you think that that contact is not going to last awhile, you got another thought coming. When I get through with you, sir, you are going to remember Mrs. Luella Bates Washington Jones."

21 Sweat popped out on the boy's face and he began to struggle. Mrs. Jones stopped, jerked him around in front of her, put a half-nelson about his neck, and continued to drag him up the street. When she got to her door, she dragged the boy inside, down a hall, and into a large kitchenette furnished room at the rear of the house. She switched on the light and left the door open. The boy could hear other **roomers** laughing and talking in the large house. Some of their doors were open, too, so he knew he and the woman were not alone. The woman still had him by the neck in the middle of her room.

22 She said, "What is your name?"

23 "Roger," answered the boy.

24 "Then, Roger, you go to that sink and wash your face," said the woman, whereupon she turned him loose—at last. Roger looked at the door—looked at the woman—looked at the door—*and went to the sink.*

NOTES

25 "Let the water run until it gets warm," she said. "Here's a clean towel."

26 "You gonna take me to jail?" asked the boy, bending over the sink.

27 "Not with that face, I would not take you nowhere," said the woman. "Here I am trying to get home to cook me a bite to eat and you snatch my pocketbook! Maybe, you ain't been to your supper either, late as it be. Have you?"

28 "There's nobody home at my house," said the boy.

29 "Then we'll eat," said the woman, "I believe you're hungry—or been hungry—to try to snatch my pocketbook."

30 "I wanted a pair of blue suede shoes," said the boy.

31 "Well, you didn't have to snatch *my* pocketbook to get some suede shoes," said Mrs. Luella Bates Washington Jones. "You could of asked me."

32 "M'am?"

33 The water dripping from his face, the boy looked at her. There was a long pause. A very long pause. After he had dried his face and not knowing what else to do dried it again, the boy turned around, wondering what next. The door was open. He could make a dash for it down the hall. He could run, run, run, run, *run!*

34 The woman was sitting on the **day-bed**. After a while she said, "I were young once and I wanted things I could not get."

35 There was another long pause. The boy's mouth opened. Then he frowned, but not knowing he frowned.

36 The woman said, "Um-hum! You thought I was going to say but, didn't you? You thought I was going to say, *but I didn't snatch people's pocketbooks*. Well, I wasn't going to say that." Pause. Silence. "I have done things, too, which I would not tell you, son—neither tell God, if he didn't already know. So you set down while I fix us something to eat. You might run that comb through your hair so you will look **presentable**."

37 In another corner of the room behind a screen was a gas plate and an icebox. Mrs. Jones got up and went behind the screen. The woman did not watch the boy to see if he was going to run now, nor did she watch her purse which she left behind her on the day-bed. But the boy took care to sit on the far side of the room where he thought she could easily see him out of the corner of her eye, if she wanted to. He did not trust the woman *not* to trust him. And he did not want to be **mistrusted** now.

38   "Do you need somebody to go to the store," asked the boy, "maybe to get some milk or something?"

39   "Don't believe I do," said the woman, "unless you just want sweet milk yourself. I was going to make cocoa out of this canned milk I got here."

40   "That will be fine," said the boy.

41   She heated some lima beans and ham she had in the icebox, made the cocoa, and set the table. The woman did not ask the boy anything about where he lived, or his folks, or anything else that would embarrass him. Instead, as they ate, she told him about her job in a hotel beauty-shop that stayed open late, what the work was like, and how all kinds of women came in and out, blondes, red-heads, and Spanish. Then she cut him a half of her ten-cent cake.

42   "Eat some more, son," she said.

43   When they were finished eating she got up and said, "Now, here, take this ten dollars and buy yourself some blue suede shoes. And next time, do not make the mistake of latching onto *my* pocketbook *nor nobody else's*—because shoes come by devilish like that will burn your feet. I got to get my rest now. But I wish you would behave yourself, son, from here on in."

44   She led him down the hall to the front door and opened it. "Good-night! Behave yourself, boy!" she said, looking out into the street.

45   The boy wanted to say something else other than "Thank you, m'am" to Mrs. Luella Bates Washington Jones, but he couldn't do so as he turned at the barren stoop and looked back at the large woman in the door. He barely managed to say "Thank you" before she shut the door. And he never saw her again.

THINK QUESTIONS

1. What event brought Roger and Mrs. Luella Bates Washington Jones into contact? What was Mrs. Jones's immediate reaction to this event? Cite specific evidence from the text to support your response.

2. Rather than call the police, what does Mrs. Jones do to Roger? How does Roger initially respond? Cite specific evidence from the text to support your analysis.

3. What does Roger say when Mrs. Jones asks him why he tried to snatch her pocketbook? What does Mrs. Jones say in response? How do her words affect him? Cite specific evidence from the text to support your statements.

4. By recalling that the suffix -er means "a person who lives in," use the base word *room* and the suffix -er to determine the meaning of **roomers**. Then use context clues to confirm the meaning of the word as it is used in paragraph 21 of "Thank You, M'am." Write your definition of *roomers* and explain how you figured out the word's meaning.

5. Use the context clues provided in paragraph 37 to determine the meaning of **mistrusted**. Write your definition of *mistrusted* and verify your meaning of the word in a print or digital dictionary.

CLOSE READ

Reread the short story "Thank You, M'am." Then use your answers and annotations from the questions to help you complete the Writing Prompt.

FOCUS QUESTIONS

1. What evidence is there in paragraphs 1 and 2 that Mrs. Jones is feeling no empathy or kindness toward Roger when they first meet? Highlight the evidence in the text and make annotations to explain your choices.

2. Reread paragraphs 21–25. What emotional changes take place between Mrs. Jones and Roger over the course of these five paragraphs? Highlight the textual evidence. Make annotations to explain the significance of these changes for Mrs. Jones and Roger.

3. In paragraph 41, what does Mrs. Jones avoid asking Roger? Why do you think she does this? What does this tell you about her relationship

with him at this point in the story? Highlight textual evidence and make annotations to explain your ideas.

4. Highlight the lines in paragraph 43 that may provide evidence of the story's theme. Then make annotations to explain how the evidence may suggest the possible message, or theme.

5. How do Mrs. Jones and Roger interact with each other at the beginning of the story? How does their interaction change as the story progresses? How do these changes enable the characters to overcome the challenges of their first interaction? Highlight textual evidence and make annotations to support your response.

WRITING PROMPT

How does the setting of "Thank You, M'am" shape the plot and the characters of the story? How do the setting, characters, and plot contribute to your understanding of the theme? Begin with a clear thesis statement. Use the details you have compiled from examining the story elements of setting, plot, and characters to

- explain how the setting helps shape the characters and plot.
- identify how the characters change over the course of the text.
- identify the theme (or message) of the story.

Remember to organize and to support your writing with evidence and inferences drawn from the text. Use precise language and selection vocabulary to support your inferences. Establish and maintain a formal writing style, and include transitions to show connections among your ideas. Provide a conclusion that summarizes your key points and leaves your readers with something to think about.

Please note that excerpts and passages in the StudySync® library and this workbook are intended as touchstones to generate interest in an author's work. The excerpts and passages do not substitute for the reading of entire texts, and StudySync® strongly recommends that students seek out and purchase the whole literary or informational work in order to experience it as the author intended. Links to online resellers are available in our digital library. In addition, complete works may be ordered through an authorized reseller by filling out and returning to StudySync® the order form enclosed in this workbook.

Reading & Writing Companion   **377**

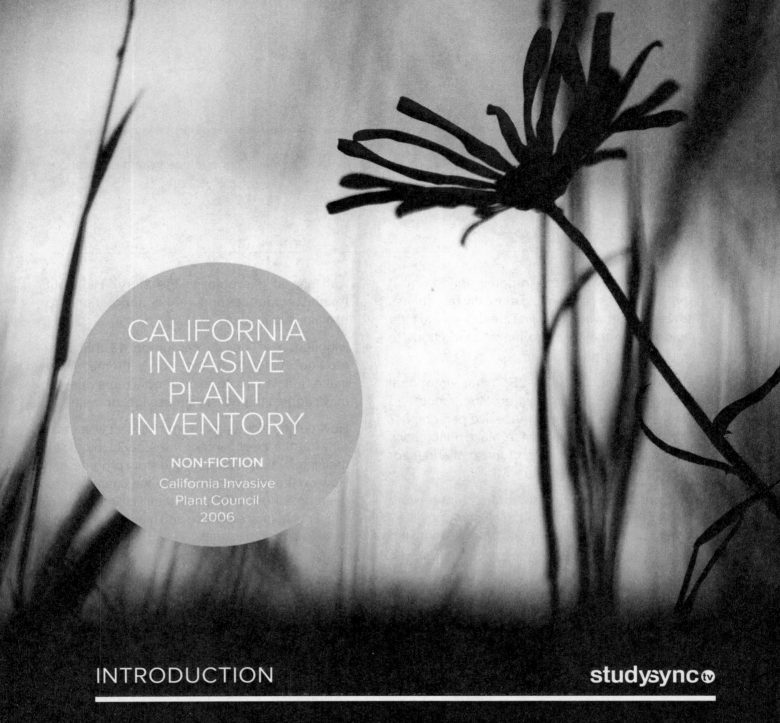

CALIFORNIA INVASIVE PLANT INVENTORY

NON-FICTION
California Invasive
Plant Council
2006

INTRODUCTION

Invasive species are plants, animals, or other organisms that are introduced to an area outside their original range, often by human activity, and cause harm in the new habitat by displacing native species and altering the environment. In California, there are more than 200 invasive plant species alone, ranging from Australia's silver wattle to Japanese eelgrass to the giant reed, a tall cane native to India that is choking waterways throughout the southwestern United States. As described here, the California Invasive Plant Council maintains a detailed inventory of invasive species to help track the threat and control the spread of intruders

"Approximately 1,800 non-native plants also grow in the wild in the state."

FIRST READ

Excerpt from Chapter 15

1   The California **Invasive** Plant **Inventory categorizes** non-native invasive plants that threaten the state's wildlands. Categorization is based on an assessment of the **ecological impacts** of each plant. The Inventory represents the best available knowledge of invasive plant experts in the state. However, it has no regulatory authority, and should be used with full understanding of the limitations described below.

2   California is home to 4,200 native plant species, and is recognized internationally as a "biodiversity hotspot." Approximately 1,800 non-native plants also grow in the wild in the state. A small number of these, approximately 200, are the ones that this Inventory considers invasive. Improved understanding of their impacts will help those working to protect California's treasured biodiversity.

The Inventory

3   The Inventory categorizes plants as High, Moderate, or Limited, reflecting the level of each species' negative ecological impact in California. Other factors, such as economic impact or difficulty of management, are not included in this assessment. It is important to note that even Limited species are invasive and should be of concern to land managers. Although the impact of each plant varies regionally, its rating represents cumulative impacts statewide. Therefore, a plant whose statewide impacts are categorized as Limited may have more severe impacts in a particular region. Conversely, a plant categorized as having a High cumulative impact across California may have very little impact in some regions.

4   The Inventory Review Committee, Cal-IPC staff, and volunteers drafted assessments for each plant based on the formal **criteria** system described below. The committee solicited information from land managers across the

NOTES

state to complement the available literature. Assessments were released for public review before the committee finalized them. The 2006 list includes 39 High species, 65 Moderate species, and 89 Limited species. Additional information, including updated observations, will be added to this website periodically, with revisions tracked and dated.

Definitions

5 The Inventory categorizes "invasive non-native plants that threaten wildlands" according to the definitions below. Plants were evaluated only if they invade California wildlands with native habitat values. The Inventory does not include plants found solely in areas of human-caused disturbance such as roadsides and cultivated agricultural fields.

6 *Wildlands* are public and private lands that support native **ecosystems,** including some working landscapes such as grazed rangeland and active timberland.

7 *Non-native plants* are species introduced to California after European contact and as a direct or indirect result of human activity.

8 *Invasive non-native plants that threaten wildlands* are plants that 1) are not native to, yet can spread into, wildland ecosystems, and that also 2) displace native species, hybridize with native species, alter biological communities, or alter ecosystem processes.

Criteria for Listing

9 The California Invasive Plant Inventory updates the 1999 "Exotic Pest Plants of Greatest Ecological Concern in California." Cal-IPC's Inventory Review Committee met regularly between 2002 and 2005 to review 238 non-native species with known or suspected impacts in California wildlands. These assessments are based on the "Criteria for Categorizing Invasive Non-Native Plants that Threaten Wildlands," developed in collaboration with the Southwestern Vegetation Management Association in Arizona and the University of Nevada Cooperative Extension so that ratings could be applied across political boundaries and adjusted for regional variation.

10 The goals of the criteria system and the Inventory are to: Provide a uniform methodology for categorizing non-native invasive plants that threaten wildlands; Provide a clear explanation of the process used to evaluate and categorize plants; Provide flexibility so the criteria can be adapted to the particular needs of different regions and states; Encourage contributions of data and documentation on evaluated species; Educate policy makers, land managers, and the public about the biology, ecological impacts, and distribution of invasive non-native plants.

NOTES

11 The criteria system generates a plant's overall rating based on an evaluation of 13 criteria, which are divided into three sections assessing Ecological Impacts, Invasive Potential, and Ecological Distribution. Evaluators assign a score of A (severe) to D (no impact) for each criterion, with U indicating unknown. The scoring scheme is arranged in a tiered format, with individual criteria contributing to section scores that in turn generate an overall rating for the plant. Detailed plant assessment forms list the rationale and applicable references used to arrive at each criterion's score. The level of documentation for each question is also rated, and translated into a numerical score for averaging. The documentation score presented in the tables is a numeric average of the documentation levels for all 13 criteria.

Inventory Categories

12 Each plant on the list received an overall rating of High, Moderate, or Limited based on evaluation using the criteria system. The meaning of these overall ratings is described below. In addition to the overall ratings, specific combinations of section scores that indicate significant potential for invading new ecosystems triggers an Alert designation so that land managers may watch for range expansions. Some plants were categorized as Evaluated But Not Listed because either we lack sufficient information to assign a rating or the available information indicates that the species does not have significant impacts at the present time.

13 High – These species have severe ecological impacts on physical processes, plant and animal communities, and vegetation structure. Their reproductive biology and other attributes are conducive to moderate to high rates of dispersal and establishment. Most are widely distributed ecologically.

14 Moderate – These species have substantial and apparent—but generally not severe—ecological impacts on physical processes, plant and animal communities, and vegetation structure. Their reproductive biology and other attributes are conducive to moderate to high rates of dispersal, though establishment is generally dependent upon ecological disturbance. Ecological amplitude and distribution may range from limited to widespread.

15 Limited – These species are invasive but their ecological impacts are minor on a statewide level or there was not enough information to justify a higher score. Their reproductive biology and other attributes result in low to moderate rates of invasiveness. Ecological amplitude and distribution are generally limited, but these species may be locally persistent and problematic.

Uses and Limitations

16 The California Invasive Plant Inventory serves as a scientific and educational report. It is designed to prioritize plants for control, to provide information to those working on habitat restoration, to show areas where research is needed, to aid those who prepare or comment on environmental planning documents, and to educate public policy makers. Plants that lack published information may be good starting points for student research projects. The Inventory cannot address, and is not intended to address, the range of geographic variation in California, nor the inherently regional nature of invasive species impacts. While we have noted where each plant is invasive, only the cumulative statewide impacts of the species have been considered in the evaluation. The impact of these plants in specific geographic regions or **habitats** within California may be greater or lesser than their statewide rating indicates. Management actions for a species should be considered on a local and site-specific basis, as the inventory does not attempt to suggest management needs for specific sites or regions. The criteria system was designed to be adapted at multiple scales, and local groups are encouraged to use the criteria for rating plants in their particular area.

Summary of the Criteria

17 The full Criteria, including explanations for scores for each question, are available at http://www.cal-ipc.org/ip/inventory/pdf/Criteria.pdf.

Section 1. Ecological Impact

18 1.1 Impact on abiotic ecosystem processes (e.g., hydrology, fire, nutrient cycling)
1.2 Impact on native plant community composition, structure, and interactions
1.3 Impact on higher trophic levels, including vertebrates and invertebrates
1.4 Impact on genetic integrity of native species (i.e., potential for hybridization)

Section 2. Invasive Potential

19 2.1 Ability to establish without anthropogenic or natural disturbance
2.2 Local rate of spread with no management
2.3 Recent trend in total area infested within state
2.4 Innate reproductive potential (based on multiple characteristics)
2.5 Potential for human-caused dispersal
2.6 Potential for natural long-distance (>1 km) dispersal
2.7 Other regions invaded worldwide that are similar to California

Section 3. Distribution

20   3.1 Ecological amplitude (ecological types invaded in California)
3.2 Ecological intensity (highest extent of infestation in any one ecological type)

Documentation Levels

21   Assessed as highest level of documentation for each criterion.

22   4 = Reviewed scientific publications
3 = Other published material (reports or other non-peer-reviewed documents)
2 = Observational (unpublished information confirmed by a professional in the field)
1 = Anecdotal (unconfirmed information)
0 = No information

 THINK QUESTIONS

1. What is the purpose of the California Invasive Plant Inventory? Cite specific evidence from the report to support your response.

2. What limitations do people need to consider when using the Inventory to plan land-management actions in their own region of the state? Cite specific evidence from paragraphs 3 and 16 to support your understanding of the issue.

3. What is the structure of the criteria system used to rate plants? How are scores assigned to the plants? Cite specific evidence from paragraph 11 in your answer.

4. Use the context clues provided in the first paragraph to determine the meaning of **invasive** as it is used in the first sentence of the text. Write your definition of *invasive* and tell how you inferred the word's meaning. Then use a print or digital dictionary to verify the meaning of the word.

5. By recalling that *eco-* is a Greek combining form meaning "environment" or "habitat," that *-logy* is also a Greek combining form meaning "science," and that *-al* is a Latin suffix meaning "of," how can you use context clues and Greek and Latin roots and affixes to figure out the meaning of **ecological**, as it is used in the first paragraph? Write your definition of *ecological* and tell how you figured out the meaning of the word. Then use a general or specialized print or digital dictionary to determine the precise meaning of this scientific term.

CLOSE READ

Reread the text "California Invasive Plant Inventory." As you reread, complete the Focus Questions below. Then use your answers and annotations from the questions to help you complete the Writing Prompt.

FOCUS QUESTIONS

1. Reread paragraph 5. What technical terms are used in the paragraph? How can the reader go about finding the definitions of these words? Highlight the terms and make annotations to explain how you can figure out what they mean.

2. Reread paragraph 9. Highlight the central idea of the paragraph. Then make annotations to record the central idea.

3. The main text structure in paragraph 12 is description. What other text structure is used in the paragraph? Highlight textual evidence and make annotations to explain your reasoning.

4. Highlight the technical term *ecological amplitude* in paragraph 15. Make annotations to record a definition based on an online search. Cite your online source.

5. What are some of the central ideas, descriptions, and technical language used in paragraphs 2, 7, and 16 of "California Invasive Plant Inventory" that help address the question "What are the challenges of human interactions with the environment?" Highlight textual evidence and make annotations to support your answer.

WRITING PROMPT

How does the information in "California Invasive Plant Inventory" support the idea that human interactions affect the environment? Use your understanding of the selection's central or main ideas, text structures, and technical language to collect evidence for your analysis. Use the details you have collected to

- identify how human interactions contribute (or have contributed) to the spread of non-native invasive plants.
- identify how human interactions can help repair the damage of invasive plants.
- identify what role the Inventory plays in understanding the processes.

Begin with a clear thesis statement that makes a claim about your understanding of the information presented. Remember to support your writing with textual evidence and inferences, using precise language and technical terms from the selection to strengthen your ideas. Use transitions to show the relationships among your ideas, and establish a formal style to deliver your information. Provide a conclusion that successfully summarizes your central ideas and leaves the reader with a final thought regarding his or her own responsibility regarding the information you have presented.

THE DANGERS OF SOCIAL MEDIA

NON-FICTION
2015

INTRODUCTION

The writers of these two articles agree that social media has become an integral part of our lives, but they disagree on who should be using it. One writer argues that it may be helpful for preteens to gain experience in the world of social media, in order that they learn how to use it appropriately as teenagers and adults. The other writer argues that social media is fraught with dangers, and could have detrimental effects on young users. Both writers present strong arguments and support their claims with sound reasoning and convincing evidence. Which argument do you feel is more persuasive?

"Once something is posted on the Internet, it remains there forever."

 FIRST READ

1 Social Media: Is it Safe for Preteens?

2 Point: Social Media Should Be Available to Preteens

3 In today's world, social media has become a tool with many uses. In addition to being a way for people to connect all over the world, websites such as Facebook and Twitter have become important ways for people to share useful information. By denying preteens access to social media, we are denying them access to a large amount of information. Currently, the Children's Online Privacy Protection Act (COPPA), created in 1998, prohibits children under the age of 13 from creating accounts on social media websites. Facebook, Twitter, Instagram, and Pinterest are off limits to kids under 13. This law is outdated and should be changed. Preteens should be allowed access to social media for a variety of reasons.

4 Because social media has become so **prevalent** in our society, it is important for adolescents to learn how to use these tools appropriately. By the time children reach the age of 11 or 12, they have already become quite aware of the **allure** of social media. Eleven is old enough for children to understand the consequences of their actions, both online and off. During the preteen years, children should begin participating in the world of social media so that they will be well prepared to interact in this world by the time they become teenagers and adults.

5 With appropriate adult supervision and guidance, preteens should have no trouble navigating the world of social media. Facebook is developing a version of the site that would allow special parental supervision for children under the age of 13. If children are aware that their parents can see everything they do, they are more likely to behave appropriately. Besides Facebook, there are already a lot of preteen-friendly social media sites that include

Copyright © BookheadEd Learning, LLC

parental controls. Many of these sites don't require much personal information in order to sign up.

6   Social media could be a good learning experience for preteens in other ways, too. Allowing preteens to use social media could be an effective way to educate them about privacy policies and Internet safety in a controlled environment. This is better than turning them loose without any guidance once they turn 13.

7   Social media can be helpful for children in a lot of ways. Interacting with others through websites such as Facebook and Twitter can be much easier for introverted kids than in-person interactions while providing the same benefits. Social media can also help create community among people who have things in common. For example, Facebook has several support groups for people who suffer from chronic illnesses such as epilepsy and diabetes. Preteens with these conditions might have trouble finding an in-person support group to join. Social media websites can provide the kind of supportive environment they need.

8   When we deny preteens access to social media, we deny them access to support groups, information, and a world of potential friends and learning experiences. It's time for COPPA to be updated to allow preteens to reap the benefits of all that social media has to offer them.

9   **Counterpoint: Social Media Is Dangerous for Preteens**

10   The world is becoming more and more fast-paced. The time that children are able to spend just being kids is shrinking all the time. Everyone knows that social media has become a huge part of our everyday lives. Facebook allows children as young as 13 to create accounts, even though there are currently no special provisions for parental supervision. The Internet is still in its infancy, and it can be a dangerous place for children. Preteens should not be allowed on social media websites.

11   The obesity epidemic in our nation is already a serious problem. Several programs have been instituted to get children exercising outdoors and away from the television set and the computer. Sanctioning social media usage for preteens would be adding just another obstacle to keeping preteens outdoors and active.

12   Facebook is working to launch a preteen-friendly, "training wheels" version of the website,. However, their main goal is to boost market share by increasing advertising **revenue**. What this means for preteens is that Facebook is more interested in advertising to them than in including them or teaching them how to use social media safely and effectively.

NOTES

13 Preteens are highly **susceptible** to marketing that is targeted at them, and they are already exposed to plenty of advertising on television, billboards, computers, and even in some schools. It is important to minimize preteens' exposure to advertising wherever possible, and social media websites are often riddled with ads.

14 Along the same lines, preteens are also susceptible to body image and self-esteem issues. The reliance on photos and the shallowness of online relationships can foster these issues, lowering the self-worth of preteens. Most social media websites make it easy to use pictures instead of words to convey information, and this **superficial** approach to friendship can make it difficult for adolescents to form deeper relationships.

15 Of course, preteens can't be expected to have the foresight necessary to keep from posting words and images that might come back to haunt them later. People are especially sensitive to criticism and embarrassment during the preteen years. Something that might seem like a good idea to post one day might be a terrible idea the next. Once something is posted on the Internet, it remains there forever. Even after you take it down, it might resurface later—even if you don't want it to! We live in a world in which politicians can be brought down by a single photo unearthed from the Internet. Allowing preteens to upload information to the Internet is too risky for their future.

16 The advent of cyberbullying shows that preteens and even teenagers are often not quite mature enough to understand how their behavior can affect others. Cyberbullying is rampant among young Facebook users. Allowing even younger people to join this social website is likely to worsen the problem.

17 Social media has become a mainstay in our society, and it doesn't look as if it is going away anytime soon. Once children turn 13, they will have their entire lives to use social media—there's no reason to rush it. When the risks are so great, why not be patient?

THINK QUESTIONS

1. What evidence is there that both the "Point" and "Counterpoint" writers believe that social media is a permanent part of American society? What different conclusion do the writers draw from this point of view? Cite specific textual evidence to support your responses.

2. What does the Children's Online Privacy Protection Act (COPPA) prohibit? What view of COPPA does the "Point" writer hold? What evidence enables you to infer that the "Counterpoint" writer would not agree with the "Point" writer's point of view? Cite specific textual evidence to support your answer.

3. What is the "Point" writer's opinion about the ability of preteens to understand the consequences of online activities? What is the "Counterpoint" writer's point of view about this? Cite specific textual evidence to support your understanding.

4. Use the context clues in the second paragraph of the "Point" text to determine the meaning of **allure.** Write your definition of *allure* and tell how you figured out the meaning of the word. Then verify the meaning you inferred by checking it in a print or digital dictionary.

5. Use the context clues in the fifth paragraph of the "Counterpoint" text to determine the meaning of **superficial.** Write your definition of *superficial* and tell how you figured out the word's meaning. Then verify your definition of the word by checking it in context.

CLOSE READ

Reread the text "The Dangers of Social Media." As you reread, complete the Focus Questions below. Then use your answers and annotations from the questions to help you complete the Writing Prompt.

FOCUS QUESTIONS

1. How do the "Point" and "Counterpoint" writers use the first paragraph of their essays to establish their purpose and point of view? What are their different points of view about preteen access to social media? Highlight relevant textual evidence. Make annotations to analyze how the "Point" writer distinguishes his or her position from the "Counterpoint" writer as they argue two different sides of the same topic.

2. Reread the fourth paragraph of the "Point" argument to trace and evaluate the writer's claim. Highlight the claim the writer makes. Then make annotations to evaluate the claim.

3. Reread the second paragraph of the "Counterpoint" argument to trace and evaluate the writer's claim. Highlight the claim the writer makes. Then make annotations to evaluate the claim.

4. Reread the second paragraph of the "Point" argument and the seventh paragraph of the "Counterpoint" argument. Highlight the claims each writer makes to determine his or her point of view. Then make annotations to discuss how the two writers distinguish their positions.

5. How do the "Point" and "Counterpoint" writers address the challenges of human interactions in terms of preteen access to social media? How does the evidence they present reflect their differing points of view? Highlight textual evidence and make annotations to support your response.

WRITING PROMPT

You have read two opposing points of view in "The Dangers of Social Media." In your opinion, which author made the stronger argument? Why was the author you chose more convincing? Support your own writing with sound reasoning and relevant evidence from the text to explain why one author and not the other persuaded you to accept his or her point of view about why preteens should (or shouldn't) have access to social media. Use transitions to show the relationships among your ideas, and establish a formal style that addresses your topic appropriately. Provide a conclusion that summarizes your key information.

MY ÁNTONIA

FICTION

Willa Cather

1918

INTRODUCTION

Willa Cather was born in Back Creek Valley, Virginia in 1873, one of seven children. When she was six, her family traveled west to live at Cather's grandfather's farm in Nebraska, alongside many European pioneers. These early days helped inspire *My Ántonia*, a rhapsodic tale of a spirited young Bohemian woman making her way on the plains. In this chapter, the book's narrator,

"...there, on one of those dry gravel beds, was the biggest snake I had ever seen."

 FIRST READ

Excerpt from Book I: The Shimerdas
Chapter VII

1   Much as I liked Ántonia, I hated a superior tone that she sometimes took with me. She was four years older than I, to be sure, and had seen more of the world; but I was a boy and she was a girl, and I resented her protecting manner. Before the autumn was over, she began to treat me more like an equal and to **defer** to me in other things than reading lessons. This change came about from an adventure we had together.

2   One day when I rode over to the Shimerdas' I found Ántonia starting off on foot for Russian Peter's house, to borrow a spade Ambrosch needed. I offered to take her on the pony, and she got up behind me. There had been another black frost the night before, and the air was clear and heady as wine. Within a week all the blooming roads had been despoiled, hundreds of miles of yellow sunflowers had been transformed into brown, rattling, burry stalks.

3   We found Russian Peter digging his potatoes. We were glad to go in and get warm by his kitchen stove and to see his squashes and Christmas melons, heaped in the storeroom for winter. As we rode away with the spade, Ántonia suggested that we stop at the prairie-dog-town and dig into one of the holes. We could find out whether they ran straight down, or were horizontal, like mole-holes; whether they had underground connections; whether the owls had nests down there, lined with feathers. We might get some puppies, or owl eggs, or snakeskins.

4   The dog-town was spread out over perhaps ten acres. The grass had been nibbled short and even, so this stretch was not shaggy and red like the surrounding country, but grey and velvety. The holes were several yards

apart, and were disposed with a good deal of regularity, almost as if the town had been laid out in streets and avenues. One always felt that an orderly and very sociable kind of life was going on there. I picketed Dude down in a draw, and we went wandering about, looking for a hole that would be easy to dig. The dogs were out, as usual, dozens of them, sitting up on their hind legs over the doors of their houses. As we approached, they barked, shook their tails at us, and scurried underground. Before the mouths of the holes were little patches of sand and gravel, scratched up, we supposed, from a long way below the surface. Here and there, in the town, we came on larger gravel patches, several yards away from any hole. If the dogs had scratched the sand up in excavating, how had they carried it so far? It was on one of these gravel beds that I met my adventure.

5 We were examining a big hole with two entrances. The burrow sloped into the ground at a gentle angle, so that we could see where the two corridors united, and the floor was dusty from use, like a little highway over which much travel went. I was walking backward, in a crouching position, when I heard Ántonia scream. She was standing opposite me, pointing behind me and shouting something in Bohemian. I whirled round, and there, on one of those dry gravel beds, was the biggest snake I had ever seen. He was sunning himself, after the cold night, and he must have been asleep when Ántonia screamed. When I turned, he was lying in long loose waves, like a letter 'W.' He twitched and began to coil slowly. He was not merely a big snake, I thought—he was a circus monstrosity. His **abominable** muscularity, his **loathsome,** fluid motion, somehow made me sick. He was as thick as my leg, and looked as if millstones couldn't crush the disgusting vitality out of him. He lifted his hideous little head, and rattled. I didn't run because I didn't think of it—if my back had been against a stone wall I couldn't have felt more cornered. I saw his coils tighten—now he would spring, spring his length, I remembered. I ran up and drove at his head with my spade, struck him fairly across the neck, and in a minute he was all about my feet in wavy loops. I struck now from hate. Ántonia, barefooted as she was, ran up behind me. Even after I had pounded his ugly head flat, his body kept on coiling and winding, doubling and falling back on itself. I walked away and turned my back. I felt seasick.

6 Ántonia came after me, crying, 'O Jimmy, he not bite you? You sure? Why you not run when I say?'

7 'What did you jabber Bohunk for? You might have told me there was a snake behind me!' I said petulantly.

8 'I know I am just awful, Jim, I was so scared.' She took my handkerchief from my pocket and tried to wipe my face with it, but I snatched it away from her. I suppose I looked as sick as I felt.

NOTES

9   'I never know you was so brave, Jim,' she went on comfortingly. 'You is just like big mans; you wait for him lift his head and then you go for him. Ain't you feel scared a bit? Now we take that snake home and show everybody. Nobody ain't seen in this kawntree so big snake like you kill.'

10 She went on in this strain until I began to think that I had longed for this opportunity, and had hailed it with joy. Cautiously we went back to the snake; he was still groping with his tail, turning up his ugly belly in the light. A faint, fetid smell came from him, and a thread of green liquid oozed from his crushed head.

11 'Look, Tony, that's his poison,' I said.

12 I took a long piece of string from my pocket, and she lifted his head with the spade while I tied a noose around it. We pulled him out straight and measured him by my riding-quirt; he was about five and a half feet long. He had twelve rattles, but they were broken off before they began to taper, so I insisted that he must once have had twenty-four. I explained to Ántonia how this meant that he was twenty-four years old, that he must have been there when white men first came, left on from buffalo and Indian times. As I turned him over, I began to feel proud of him, to have a kind of respect for his age and size. He seemed like the ancient, eldest Evil. Certainly his kind have left horrible unconscious memories in all warm-blooded life. When we dragged him down into the draw, Dude sprang off to the end of his tether and shivered all over— wouldn't let us come near him.

13 We decided that Ántonia should ride Dude home, and I would walk. As she rode along slowly, her bare legs swinging against the pony's sides, she kept shouting back to me about how astonished everybody would be. I followed with the spade over my shoulder, dragging my snake. Her exultation was contagious. The great land had never looked to me so big and free. If the red grass were full of rattlers, I was equal to them all. Nevertheless, I stole furtive glances behind me now and then to see that no avenging mate, older and bigger than my quarry, was racing up from the rear.

14 The sun had set when we reached our garden and went down the draw toward the house. Otto Fuchs was the first one we met. He was sitting on the edge of the cattle-pond, having a quiet pipe before supper. Ántonia called him to come quick and look. He did not say anything for a minute, but scratched his head and turned the snake over with his boot.

15 'Where did you run onto that beauty, Jim?'

16 'Up at the dog-town,' I answered **laconically.**

NOTES

17   'Kill him yourself? How come you to have a weepon?'

18   'We'd been up to Russian Peter's, to borrow a spade for Ambrosch.'

19   Otto shook the ashes out of his pipe and squatted down to count the rattles. 'It was just luck you had a tool,' he said cautiously. 'Gosh! I wouldn't want to do any business with that fellow myself, unless I had a fence-post along. Your grandmother's snake-cane wouldn't more than tickle him. He could stand right up and talk to you, he could. Did he fight hard?'

20   Ántonia broke in: 'He fight something awful! He is all over Jimmy's boots. I scream for him to run, but he just hit and hit that snake like he was crazy.'

21   Otto winked at me. After Ántonia rode on he said: 'Got him in the head first crack, didn't you? That was just as well.'

22   We hung him up to the windmill, and when I went down to the kitchen, I found Ántonia standing in the middle of the floor, telling the story with a great deal of color.

23   Subsequent experiences with rattlesnakes taught me that my first encounter was fortunate in circumstance. My big rattler was old, and had led too easy a life; there was not much fight in him. He had probably lived there for years, with a fat prairie-dog for breakfast whenever he felt like it, a sheltered home, even an owl-feather bed, perhaps, and he had forgot that the world doesn't owe rattlers a living. A snake of his size, in fighting trim, would be more than any boy could handle. So in reality it was a mock adventure; the game was fixed for me by chance, as it probably was for many a dragon-slayer. I had been adequately armed by Russian Peter; the snake was old and lazy; and I had Ántonia beside me, to appreciate and admire.

24   That snake hung on our corral fence for several days; some of the neighbors came to see it and agreed that it was the biggest rattler ever killed in those parts. This was enough for Ántonia. She liked me better from that time on, and she never took a **supercilious** air with me again. I had killed a big snake—I was now a big fellow.

THINK QUESTIONS

1. Refer to one or more details from the text to describe Jim and Ántonia's relationship before the incident with the rattlesnake. Use evidence that is directly stated and inferences that you draw from clues in the text.

2. Use details from the text to write two or three sentences to describe Jims reaction to the rattlesnake he encounters in the prairie-dog-town.

3. Write several sentences explaining how the incident with the rattlesnake changes the relationship between Jim and Ántonia. Support your answer with specific evidence from the text.

4. Use context to determine the meaning of the word **laconically** as it is used in paragraph 16 of *My Ántonia*. Write your definition of *laconically* and tell how you figured out the meaning of the word. Then verify the meaning in a print or digital dictionary.

5. Noting that the Latin prefix *super-* means "above or beyond" and the Latin root *cilium* means "eyebrow," use the context clues provided in the passage to determine the meaning of **supercilious** in the last paragraph. Write your definition of *supercilious* and tell how you determined the meaning of the word.

CLOSE READ

Reread the excerpt from *My Ántonia*. As you reread, complete the Focus Questions below. Then use your answers and annotations from the questions to help you complete the Writing Prompt.

FOCUS QUESTIONS

1. In paragraph 2, what evidence is there that the natural and historical setting of the American West in the nineteenth century is a source of conflict for the settlers who are looking for a better way of life? Highlight textual evidence. Make annotations to explain the negative effects of the setting on the characters.

2. In paragraph 3, what evidence is there that the setting of the American West offers opportunity for immigrants such as Ántonia's family and Russian Peter? Highlight textual evidence and make annotations to explain your analysis.

3. How does Jim's encounter with the rattlesnake in the prairie-dog-town illustrate the conflict presented by the setting, in paragraph 5? Highlight textual evidence and make annotations to explain your ideas.

4. In what ways does the setting influence Jim's passage into adulthood? Highlight textual evidence in paragraphs 5 and 24. Then make annotations to explain how this evidence supports your analysis.

5. How does Ántonia's status as a girl and an immigrant and Jim's status as a boy and a native-born American create challenges for them as they interact with each other? Highlight textual evidence and make annotations to support your response.

WRITING PROMPT

How does the setting of *My Ántonia* contribute to the challenges Jim faces in his interactions with Ántonia? Use the details you have compiled from examining the setting and characters to

- identify the natural and historical conditions of the setting that help shape the characters and the way they interact.
- identify how and why the characters' interactions change over the course of the story.

Begin with a clear thesis statement. Remember to organize and to support your writing with textual evidence and inferences, using precise language and selection vocabulary. Include transitions to show the relationships among your main ideas, and establish a formal style of delivery. Provide a conclusion that effectively summarizes your key information.

FREAK
THE MIGHTY

FICTION
Rodman Philbrick
1993

INTRODUCTION

studysync tv

Max Kane, a learning-impaired adolescent of giant proportions, is called "Mad Max" and taunted relentlessly about his father, Killer Kane, in jail for murdering Max's mother. Max hates school, and prefers the seclusion of his basement room...until a new boy moves in next door. Self-dubbed "the Freak" due to a genetically malformed body, Kevin is Max's opposite—bright, energetic and curious. Together, they become Freak the Mighty, and embark on a series of

"...this midget kid, this crippled little humanoid, he actually scared you."

FIRST READ

Chapter Three: American Flyer

1   OK, back to the down under, right? My room in the basement. Scuttle into your dim hole in the ground, Maxwell dear. Big goon like you, growing about an inch a day, and this midget kid, this crippled little humanoid, he actually *scared* you. Not the kind of scare that makes your knee bones feel like water, more the kind of scare where you go whoa! I don't understand this, I don't get it, what's going on?

2   Like calling me "earthling." Which by itself is pretty weird, right? I already mentioned a few of the names I've been called, but until the robot boy showed up, nobody had ever called me *earthling,* and so I'm lying on my mattress there in the great down under, and it comes to me that he's right, I *am* an earthling, we're all of us earthlings, but we don't call each other earthling. No need. Because it's the same thing that in this country we're all Americans, but we don't go around to people and say, "Excuse me, American, can you tell me how to get to the nearest 7 Eleven?"

3   So I'm thinking about that for a while, lying there in the cellar dark, and pretty soon the down under starts to get small, like the walls are shrinking, and I go up the bulkhead stairs into the back yard and find a place where I can check it out.

4   There's this one scraggly tree behind the little freak's house, right? Like a stick in the ground with a few wimped out branches. And there he is, hardly any bigger now than he was in day care, and he's standing there waving his crutch up at the tree.

5   I kind of slide over to the chain-link fence, get a better angle on the scene. What's he *doing* whacking at that crummy tree? Trying to jump up and hit this branch with his little crutch, and he's mad, hopping mad. Only he can't really

jump, he just makes this jumping kind of motion. His feet never leave the ground.

6   Then what he does, he throws down the crutch and he gets down on his hands and knees and crawls back to his house. If you didn't know, you would think he was like a kindergarten creeper who forgot how to walk, he's that small. And he crawls real good, better than he can walk. Before you know it, he's dragging this wagon out from under the steps.

7   Rusty red thing, one of those old American Flyer models. Anyhow, the little freak is tugging it backwards, a few inches at a time. Chugging along until he gets that little wagon under the tree. Next thing he picks up his crutch and he climbs in the wagon and he stands up and he's whacking at the tree again.

8   By now I've figured out that there's something stuck up in the branches and he wants to get it down. This small, bright-colored thing, looks like a piece of folded paper. Whatever it is, that paper thing, he wânts it real bad, but even with the wagon there's no way he can reach it. No way.

9   So I go over there to his back yard, trying to be real quiet, but I'm not good at sneaking up, not with these **humongous** feet, and he turns and faces me with that crutch raised up like he's ready to hit a grand slam on my head.

10 He wants to say something, you can tell that much, but he's so mad, he's all huffed up and the noise he makes, it could be from a dog or something, and he sounds like he can hardly breathe.

11 What I do, I keep out of range of that crutch and just reach up and pick the paper thing right out of the tree. Except it's not a paper thing. It's a plastic bird, light as a feather. I have to hold it real careful or it might break, that's how flimsy it is.

12 I go, "You want this back or what?"

13 The little freak is staring at me bug-eyed, and he goes, "Oh, it talks."

14 I give him the bird-thing. "What is it, like a model airplane or something?"

15 You can tell he's real happy to have the bird-thing back, and his face isn't quite so fierce. He sits down in the wagon and he goes, "This is an ornithopter. An ornithopter is defined as an experimental device propelled by flapping wings. Or you could say that an ornithopter is just a big word for mechanical bird."

16 That's how he talked, like right out of a dictionary. So smart you can hardly believe it. While he's talking he's winding up the bird-thing. There's this elastic band inside, and he goes, "Observe and be amazed, earthling," and then he

lets it go, and you know what? I *am* amazed, because it does fly around like a little bird, flitting up and down and around, higher than I can reach.

17 I chase after the thing until it boinks against the scrawny tree trunk and I bring it back to him and he winds it up again and makes it fly. We keep doing that, it must be for almost an hour, until finally the elastic breaks. I figure that's it, end of ornithopter, but he says something like, "All mechanical objects require **periodic maintenance.** We'll schedule **installation** of a new **propulsion** unit as soon as the Fair Gwen of Air gets a replacement."

18 Even though I'm not sure what he means, I go, "That's cool."

19 "You live around here, earthling?"

20 "Over there." I point out the house. "In the down under."

21 He goes, "What?" and I figure it's easier to show him than explain all about Gram and Grim and the room in the cellar, so I pick up the handle to the American Flyer wagon and I tow him over.

22 It's real easy, he doesn't weigh much and I'm pretty sure I remember looking back and seeing him sitting up in the wagon happy as can be, like he's really enjoying the ride and not embarrassed to have me pulling him around.

23 But like Freak says later in this book, you can remember anything, whether it happened or not. All I'm really sure of is he never hit me with that crutch.

Excerpted from Freak the Mighty by Rodman Philbrick, published by Scholastic Inc.

Please note that excerpts and passages in the StudySync® library and this workbook are intended as touchstones to generate interest in an author's work. The excerpts and passages do not substitute for the reading of entire texts, and StudySync® strongly recommends that students seek out and purchase the whole literary or informational work in order to experience it as the author intended. Links to online resellers are available in our digital library. In addition, complete works may be ordered through an authorized reseller by filling out and returning to StudySync® the order form enclosed in this workbook.

Reading & Writing Companion   **401**

THINK QUESTIONS

1. Refer to one or more details from the text to describe how Maxwell (the larger boy) reacts to Kevin (the smaller boy) upon first meeting him—both from evidence that is directly stated and from ideas that you infer from clues in the text.

2. Use details to explain how Maxwell confronts his fear of Kevin. Cite specific evidence from paragraphs 3, 5, and 11.

3. Write two or three sentences explaining how Maxwell and Kevin begin a friendship. Include evidence from the text to support your explanation.

4. Use context clues to determine the meaning of the word **humongous** as it is used in paragraph 9 of *Freak the Mighty*. Write your definition of *humongous* and tell how you determined the meaning of the word.

5. By remembering that the Latin prefix *pro-* means "forward" and the Latin root *pellere* means "to drive," use the context clues provided in paragraph 17 to determine the meaning of **propulsion,** the noun form of the verb *propel,* although in this context it is being used as an adjective: *propulsion unit.* Write your definition of *propulsion* and tell how you figured out the word's meaning. Then verify your definition in a print or digital dictionary.

CLOSE READ

Reread the excerpt from *Freak the Mighty*. As you reread, complete the Focus Questions below. Then use your answers and annotations from the questions to help you complete the Writing Prompt.

FOCUS QUESTIONS

1. Listen to the audio recording of paragraph 3 (1:21–1:42). How does the actor use pacing when saying "walls" to suggest the action of shrinking walls? Highlight textual evidence in paragraph 3 and annotate ideas from the audio recording to show the development of your understanding of media techniques.

2. Listen to the audio recording of paragraph 4 (1:43–2:01). How does the actor use expression when he reads "day care" to convey his impressions of Kevin? Highlight textual evidence in paragraph 4 and annotate ideas from the audio recording to show the development of your understanding of media techniques.

3. Listen to the audio recording of paragraph 5 (2:02–2:28). How does the actor use intonation when he reads, "What's he *doing* whacking at that crummy tree?" and "hopping mad" to convey his attitude toward Kevin? Highlight textual evidence in paragraph 5 and annotate ideas from the audio recording to show the development of your understanding of media techniques.

4. Reread the last two paragraphs of the selection and then listen to the audio recording of the same paragraphs. Use details from the audio version and the printed text to explain what the actor in the audio narration adds to the reader's understanding of the story.

5. In what ways do Maxwell and Kevin experience challenges in their initial interactions? How do they overcome these challenges? Highlight textual evidence and make annotations to support your response.

WRITING PROMPT

Compare and contrast the text and audio versions *of Freak the Mighty.* How are the two versions alike, and how are they different? At what points does the audio version use expression, intonation, or pace to support or interpret the text? In what ways are these interpretations important or unimportant to the development of character, setting, plot, and theme? Begin with a clear thesis statement explaining your topic. Organize and support your writing with evidence from the text and audio file, using precise language, selection vocabulary, and a formal writing style. Include transitions to convey the relationships among your main points or ideas and provide a conclusion that summarizes your key information.

THE RANSOM OF RED CHIEF

FICTION
O. Henry
1910

INTRODUCTION

William Sydney Porter, who wrote under the pen name, O. Henry, was a prolific author, composing more than 600 short stories in his lifetime. An incisive social critic and witty raconteur, O. Henry is most famous for finishing his short stories with comic or ironic twists. This story about two men who pick the wrong boy to kidnap doesn't disappoint.

"Red Chief was sitting on Bill's chest, with one hand twined in Bill's hair."

FIRST READ

1 It looked like a good thing: but wait till I tell you. We were down South, in Alabama—Bill Driscoll and myself—when this kidnapping idea struck us. It was, as Bill afterward expressed it, "during a moment of temporary mental apparition"; but we didn't find that out till later.

2 There was a town down there, as flat as a flannel-cake, and called Summit, of course. It contained inhabitants of as undeleterious and self-satisfied a class of peasantry as ever clustered around a Maypole.

3 Bill and me had a joint capital of about six hundred dollars, and we needed just two thousand dollars more to pull off a fraudulent town-lot scheme in Western Illinois with. We talked it over on the front steps of the hotel. **Philoprogenitiveness**, says we, is strong in semi-rural communities; therefore and for other reasons, a kidnapping project ought to do better there than in the radius of newspapers that send reporters out in plain clothes to stir up talk about such things. We knew that Summit couldn't get after us with anything stronger than constables and maybe some lackadaisical bloodhounds and a diatribe or two in the Weekly Farmers' Budget. So, it looked good.

4 We selected for our victim the only child of a prominent citizen named Ebenezer Dorset. The father was respectable and tight, a mortgage fancier and a stern, upright collection-plate passer and forecloser. The kid was a boy of ten, with bas-relief freckles, and hair the colour of the cover of the magazine you buy at the news-stand when you want to catch a train. Bill and me figured that Ebenezer would melt down for a ransom of two thousand dollars to a cent. But wait till I tell you.

5 About two miles from Summit was a little mountain, covered with a dense cedar brake. On the rear elevation of this mountain was a cave. There we

stored provisions. One evening after sundown, we drove in a buggy past old Dorset's house. The kid was in the street, throwing rocks at a kitten on the opposite fence.

6   "Hey, little boy!" says Bill, "would you like to have a bag of candy and a nice ride?"

7   The boy catches Bill neatly in the eye with a piece of brick.

8   "That will cost the old man an extra five hundred dollars," says Bill, climbing over the wheel.

9   That boy put up a fight like a welter-weight cinnamon bear; but, at last, we got him down in the bottom of the buggy and drove away. We took him up to the cave and I hitched the horse in the cedar brake. After dark I drove the buggy to the little village, three miles away, where we had hired it, and walked back to the mountain.

10   Bill was pasting court-plaster over the scratches and bruises on his features. There was a fire burning behind the big rock at the entrance of the cave, and the boy was watching a pot of boiling coffee, with two buzzard tail-feathers stuck in his red hair. He points a stick at me when I come up, and says:

11   "Ha! cursed paleface, do you dare to enter the camp of Red Chief, the terror of the plains?"

12   "He's all right now," says Bill, rolling up his trousers and examining some bruises on his shins. "We're playing Indian. We're making Buffalo Bill's show look like magic-lantern views of Palestine in the town hall. I'm Old Hank, the Trapper, Red Chief's captive, and I'm to be scalped at daybreak. By Geronimo! that kid can kick hard."

13   Yes, sir, that boy seemed to be having the time of his life. The fun of camping out in a cave had made him forget that he was a captive himself. He immediately christened me Snake-eye, the Spy, and announced that, when his braves returned from the warpath, I was to be broiled at the stake at the rising of the sun.

14   Then we had supper; and he filled his mouth full of bacon and bread and gravy, and began to talk. He made a during-dinner speech something like this:

15   "I like this fine. I never camped out before; but I had a pet 'possum once, and I was nine last birthday. I hate to go to school. Rats ate up sixteen of Jimmy Talbot's aunt's speckled hen's eggs. Are there any real Indians in these woods? I want some more gravy. Does the trees moving make the wind blow? We had five puppies. What makes your nose so red, Hank? My father has lots

of money. Are the stars hot? I whipped Ed Walker twice, Saturday. I don't like girls. You dassent catch toads unless with a string. Do oxen make any noise? Why are oranges round? Have you got beds to sleep on in this cave? Amos Murray has got six toes. A parrot can talk, but a monkey or a fish can't. How many does it take to make twelve?"

16   Every few minutes he would remember that he was a pesky Indian, and pick up his stick rifle and tiptoe to the mouth of the cave to rubber for the scouts of the hated paleface. Now and then he would let out a war-whoop that made Old Hank the Trapper shiver. That boy had Bill terrorized from the start.

17   "Red Chief," says I to the kid, "would you like to go home?"

18   "Aw, what for?" says he. "I don't have any fun at home. I hate to go to school. I like to camp out. You won't take me back home again, Snake-eye, will you?"

19   "Not right away," says I. "We'll stay here in the cave a while."

20   "All right!" says he. "That'll be fine. I never had such fun in all my life."

21   We went to bed about eleven o'clock. We spread down some wide blankets and quilts and put Red Chief between us. We weren't afraid he'd run away. He kept us awake for three hours, jumping up and reaching for his rifle and screeching: "Hist! pard," in mine and Bill's ears, as the fancied crackle of a twig or the rustle of a leaf revealed to his young imagination the stealthy approach of the outlaw band. At last, I fell into a troubled sleep, and dreamed that I had been kidnapped and chained to a tree by a **ferocious** pirate with red hair.

22   Just at daybreak, I was awakened by a series of awful screams from Bill. They weren't yells, or howls, or shouts, or whoops, or yawps, such as you'd expect from a manly set of vocal organs—they were simply indecent, terrifying, humiliating screams, such as women emit when they see ghosts or caterpillars. It's an awful thing to hear a strong, desperate, fat man scream incontinently in a cave at daybreak.

23   I jumped up to see what the matter was. Red Chief was sitting on Bill's chest, with one hand twined in Bill's hair. In the other he had the sharp case-knife we used for slicing bacon; and he was industriously and realistically trying to take Bill's scalp, according to the sentence that had been pronounced upon him the evening before.

24   I got the knife away from the kid and made him lie down again. But, from that moment, Bill's spirit was broken. He laid down on his side of the bed, but he never closed an eye again in sleep as long as that boy was with us. I dozed off for a while, but along toward sun-up I remembered that Red Chief had said

I was to be burned at the stake at the rising of the sun. I wasn't nervous or afraid; but I sat up and lit my pipe and leaned against a rock.

25   "What you getting up so soon for, Sam?" asked Bill.

26   "Me?" says I. "Oh, I got a kind of a pain in my shoulder. I thought sitting up would rest it."

27   "You're a liar!" says Bill. "You're afraid. You was to be burned at sunrise, and you was afraid he'd do it. And he would, too, if he could find a match. Ain't it awful, Sam? Do you think anybody will pay out money to get a little imp like that back home?"

28   "Sure," said I. "A rowdy kid like that is just the kind that parents dote on. Now, you and the Chief get up and cook breakfast, while I go up on the top of this mountain and **reconnoitre.**"

29   I went up on the peak of the little mountain and ran my eye over the contiguous vicinity. Over toward Summit I expected to see the sturdy yeomanry of the village armed with scythes and pitchforks beating the countryside for the dastardly kidnappers. But what I saw was a peaceful landscape dotted with one man ploughing with a dun mule. Nobody was dragging the creek; no couriers dashed hither and yon, bringing tidings of no news to the distracted parents. There was a sylvan attitude of somnolent sleepiness pervading that section of the external outward surface of Alabama that lay exposed to my view. "Perhaps," says I to myself, "it has not yet been discovered that the wolves have borne away the tender lambkin from the fold. Heaven help the wolves!" says I, and I went down the mountain to breakfast.

30   When I got to the cave I found Bill backed up against the side of it, breathing hard, and the boy threatening to smash him with a rock half as big as a cocoanut.

31   "He put a red-hot boiled potato down my back," explained Bill, "and then mashed it with his foot; and I boxed his ears. Have you got a gun about you, Sam?"

32   I took the rock away from the boy and kind of patched up the argument. "I'll fix you," says the kid to Bill. "No man ever yet struck the Red Chief but what he got paid for it. You better beware!"

33   After breakfast the kid takes a piece of leather with strings wrapped around it out of his pocket and goes outside the cave unwinding it.

34   "What's he up to now?" says Bill, anxiously. "You don't think he'll run away, do you, Sam?"

NOTES

35 "No fear of it," says I. "He don't seem to be much of a home body. But we've got to fix up some plan about the ransom. There don't seem to be much excitement around Summit on account of his disappearance; but maybe they haven't realized yet that he's gone. His folks may think he's spending the night with Aunt Jane or one of the neighbours. Anyhow, he'll be missed to-day. To-night we must get a message to his father demanding the two thousand dollars for his return."

36 Just then we heard a kind of war-whoop, such as David might have emitted when he knocked out the champion Goliath. It was a sling that Red Chief had pulled out of his pocket, and he was whirling it around his head.

37 I dodged, and heard a heavy thud and a kind of a sigh from Bill, like a horse gives out when you take his saddle off. A rock the size of an egg had caught Bill just behind his left ear. He loosened himself all over and fell in the fire across the frying pan of hot water for washing the dishes. I dragged him out and poured cold water on his head for half an hour.

38 By and by, Bill sits up and feels behind his ear and says: "Sam, do you know who my favourite Biblical character is?"

39 "Take it easy," says I. "You'll come to your senses presently."

40 "King Herod," says he. "You won't go away and leave me here alone, will you, Sam?"

41 I went out and caught that boy and shook him until his freckles rattled.

42 "If you don't behave," says I, "I'll take you straight home. Now, are you going to be good, or not?"

43 "I was only funning," says he sullenly. "I didn't mean to hurt Old Hank. But what did he hit me for? I'll behave, Snake-eye, if you won't send me home, and if you'll let me play the Black Scout to-day."

44 "I don't know the game,' says I. "That's for you and Mr. Bill to decide. He's your playmate for the day. I'm going away for a while, on business. Now, you come in and make friends with him and say you are sorry for hurting him, or home you go, at once."

45 I made him and Bill shake hands, and then I took Bill aside and told him I was going to Poplar Cove, a little village three miles from the cave, and find out what I could about how the kidnapping had been regarded in Summit. Also, I thought it best to send a peremptory letter to old man Dorset that day, demanding the ransom and dictating how it should be paid.

46   "You know, Sam," says Bill, "I've stood by you without batting an eye in earthquakes, fire and flood—in poker games, dynamite outrages, police raids, train robberies and cyclones. I never lost my nerve yet till we kidnapped that two-legged skyrocket of a kid. He's got me going. You won't leave me long with him, will you, Sam?"

47   "I'll be back some time this afternoon," says I. "You must keep the boy amused and quiet till I return. And now we'll write the letter to old Dorset."

48   Bill and I got paper and pencil and worked on the letter while Red Chief, with a blanket wrapped around him, strutted up and down, guarding the mouth of the cave. Bill begged me tearfully to make the ransom fifteen hundred dollars instead of two thousand. "I ain't attempting," says he, "to decry the celebrated moral aspect of parental affection, but we're dealing with humans, and it ain't human for anybody to give up two thousand dollars for that forty-pound chunk of freckled wildcat. I'm willing to take a chance at fifteen hundred dollars. You can charge the difference up to me."

49   So, to relieve Bill, I **acceded,** and we collaborated a letter that ran this way:

50   Ebenezer Dorset, Esq.:

51   We have your boy concealed in a place far from Summit. It is useless for you or the most skilful detectives to attempt to find him. Absolutely, the only terms on which you can have him restored to you are these: We demand fifteen hundred dollars in large bills for his return; the money to be left at midnight to-night at the same spot and in the same box as your reply—as hereinafter described. If you agree to these terms, send your answer in writing by a solitary messenger to-night at half-past eight o'clock. After crossing Owl Creek, on the road to Poplar Cove, there are three large trees about a hundred yards apart, close to the fence of the wheat field on the right-hand side. At the bottom of the fence-post, opposite the third tree, will be found a small pasteboard box.

52   The messenger will place the answer in this box and return immediately to Summit.

53   If you attempt any treachery or fail to comply with our demand as stated, you will never see your boy again.

54   If you pay the money as demanded, he will be returned to you safe and well within three hours. These terms are final, and if you do not accede to them no further communication will be attempted.

TWO DESPERATE MEN.

Please note that excerpts and passages in the StudySync® library and this workbook are intended as touchstones to generate interest in an author's work. The excerpts and passages do not substitute for the reading of entire texts, and StudySync® strongly recommends that students seek out and purchase the whole literary or informational work in order to experience it as the author intended. Links to online resellers are available in our digital library. In addition, complete works may be ordered through an authorized reseller by filling out and returning to StudySync® the order form enclosed in this workbook.

Reading & Writing Companion   **411**

NOTES

55   I addressed this letter to Dorset, and put it in my pocket. As I was about to start, the kid comes up to me and says:

56   "Aw, Snake-eye, you said I could play the Black Scout while you was gone."

57   "Play it, of course," says I. "Mr. Bill will play with you. What kind of a game is it?"

58   "I'm the Black Scout," says Red Chief, "and I have to ride to the stockade to warn the settlers that the Indians are coming. I'm tired of playing Indian myself. I want to be the Black Scout."

59   "All right," says I. "It sounds harmless to me. I guess Mr. Bill will help you foil the pesky Indians."

60   "What am I to do?" asks Bill, looking at the kid suspiciously.

61   "You are the hoss," says Black Scout. "Get down on your hands and knees. How can I ride to the stockade without a hoss?"

62   "You'd better keep him interested," said I, "till we get the scheme going. Loosen up."

63   Bill gets down on his all fours, and a look comes in his eye like a rabbit's when you catch it in a trap.

64   "How far is it to the stockade, kid?" he asks, in a husky manner of voice.

65   "Ninety miles," says the Black Scout. "And you have to hump yourself to get there on time. Whoa, now!"

66   The Black Scout jumps on Bill's back and digs his heels in his side.

67   "For Heaven's sake," says Bill, "hurry back, Sam, as soon as you can. I wish we hadn't made the ransom more than a thousand. Say, you quit kicking me or I'll get up and warm you good."

68   I walked over to Poplar Cove and sat around the postoffice and store, talking with the chawbacons that came in to trade. One whiskerando says that he hears Summit is all upset on account of Elder Ebenezer Dorset's boy having been lost or stolen. That was all I wanted to know. I bought some smoking tobacco, referred casually to the price of black-eyed peas, posted my letter surreptitiously and came away. The postmaster said the mail-carrier would come by in an hour to take the mail on to Summit.

69   When I got back to the cave Bill and the boy were not to be found. I explored the vicinity of the cave, and risked a yodel or two, but there was no response.

70   So I lighted my pipe and sat down on a mossy bank to await developments.

71   In about half an hour I heard the bushes rustle, and Bill wabbled out into the little glade in front of the cave. Behind him was the kid, stepping softly like a scout, with a broad grin on his face. Bill stopped, took off his hat and wiped his face with a red handkerchief. The kid stopped about eight feet behind him.

72   "Sam," says Bill, "I suppose you'll think I'm a renegade, but I couldn't help it. I'm a grown person with masculine proclivities and habits of self-defense, but there is a time when all systems of egotism and predominance fail. The boy is gone. I have sent him home. All is off. There was martyrs in old times," goes on Bill, "that suffered death rather than give up the particular graft they enjoyed. None of 'em ever was subjugated to such supernatural tortures as I have been. I tried to be faithful to our articles of depredation; but there came a limit."

73   "What's the trouble, Bill?" I asks him.

74   "I was rode," says Bill, "the ninety miles to the stockade, not barring an inch. Then, when the settlers was rescued, I was given oats. Sand ain't a palatable substitute. And then, for an hour I had to try to explain to him why there was nothin' in holes, how a road can run both ways and what makes the grass green. I tell you, Sam, a human can only stand so much. I takes him by the neck of his clothes and drags him down the mountain. On the way he kicks my legs black-and-blue from the knees down; and I've got to have two or three bites on my thumb and hand cauterized.

75   "But he's gone"—continues Bill—"gone home. I showed him the road to Summit and kicked him about eight feet nearer there at one kick. I'm sorry we lose the ransom; but it was either that or Bill Driscoll to the madhouse."

76   Bill is puffing and blowing, but there is a look of ineffable peace and growing content on his rose-pink features.

77   "Bill," says I, "there isn't any heart disease in your family, is there?"

78   "No," says Bill, "nothing chronic except malaria and accidents. Why?"

79   "Then you might turn around," says I, "and have a look behind you."

80   Bill turns and sees the boy, and loses his complexion and sits down plump on the round and begins to pluck aimlessly at grass and little sticks. For an hour I was afraid for his mind. And then I told him that my scheme was to put the whole job through immediately and that we would get the ransom and be off with it by midnight if old Dorset fell in with our proposition. So Bill braced up

enough to give the kid a weak sort of a smile and a promise to play the Russian in a Japanese war with him as soon as he felt a little better.

81   I had a scheme for collecting that ransom without danger of being caught by counterplots that ought to commend itself to professional kidnappers. The tree under which the answer was to be left—and the money later on—was close to the road fence with big, bare fields on all sides. If a gang of constables should be watching for any one to come for the note they could see him a long way off crossing the fields or in the road. But no, sirree! At half-past eight I was up in that tree as well hidden as a tree toad, waiting for the messenger to arrive.

82   Exactly on time, a half-grown boy rides up the road on a bicycle, locates the pasteboard box at the foot of the fence-post, slips a folded piece of paper into it and pedals away again back toward Summit.

83   I waited an hour and then concluded the thing was square. I slid down the tree, got the note, slipped along the fence till I struck the woods, and was back at the cave in another half an hour. I opened the note, got near the lantern and read it to Bill. It was written with a pen in a crabbed hand, and the sum and substance of it was this:

84   Two Desperate Men.

85   Gentlemen: I received your letter to-day by post, in regard to the ransom you ask for the return of my son. I think you are a little high in your demands, and I hereby make you a counter-proposition, which I am inclined to believe you will accept. You bring Johnny home and pay me two hundred and fifty dollars in cash, and I agree to take him off your hands. You had better come at night, for the neighbours believe he is lost, and I couldn't be responsible for what they would do to anybody they saw bringing him back. Very respectfully,

86   EBENEZER DORSET.

87   "Great pirates of Penzance!" says I; "of all the **impudent—**"

88   But I glanced at Bill, and hesitated. He had the most appealing look in his eyes I ever saw on the face of a dumb or a talking brute.

89   "Sam," says he, "what's two hundred and fifty dollars, after all? We've got the money. One more night of this kid will send me to a bed in Bedlam. Besides being a thorough gentleman, I think Mr. Dorset is a spendthrift for making us such a liberal offer. You ain't going to let the chance go, are you?"

NOTES

90   "Tell you the truth, Bill," says I, "this little he ewe lamb has somewhat got on my nerves too. We'll take him home, pay the ransom and make our get-away."

91   We took him home that night. We got him to go by telling him that his father had bought a silver-mounted rifle and a pair of moccasins for him, and we were going to hunt bears the next day.

92   It was just twelve o'clock when we knocked at Ebenezer's front door. Just at the moment when I should have been abstracting the fifteen hundred dollars from the box under the tree, according to the original proposition, Bill was counting out two hundred and fifty dollars into Dorset's hand.

93   When the kid found out we were going to leave him at home he started up a howl like a calliope and fastened himself as tight as a leech to Bill's leg. His father peeled him away gradually, like a porous plaster.

94   "How long can you hold him?" asks Bill.

95   "I'm not as strong as I used to be," says old Dorset, "but I think I can promise you ten minutes."

96   "Enough," says Bill. "In ten minutes I shall cross the Central, Southern and Middle Western States, and be legging it trippingly for the Canadian border."

97   And, as dark as it was, and as fat as Bill was, and as good a runner as I am, he was a good mile and a half out of Summit before I could catch up with him.

THINK QUESTIONS

1. Why do the narrator Sam and his friend Bill Driscoll decide to kidnap the child of Ebenezer Dorset? Cite specific evidence from paragraphs 3 and 4 in your answer.

2. Use details from the text to describe the kidnapped child who comes to be known as Red Chief—based both on stated character traits and on those you infer from details in the text.

3. In his letter, how does Ebenezer Dorset respond to the kidnappers' request for ransom? Draw an inference from the text to explain why he responds in this way. Support your answer with textual evidence.

4. Use context to determine the meaning of the word **acceded** as it is used in paragraph 49 in "The Ransom of Red Chief." Write your definition of *acceded* and tell how you inferred the word's meaning. Then check your inferred meaning in a dictionary to see if it is correct.

5. Remembering that the Greek combining form *phil-* means "loving" and that the base word *progeny* means "children," use the context clues provided in paragraph 3 to determine the meaning of **philoprogenitiveness.** Write your definition of *philoprogenitiveness* and tell how you determined the meaning of this very long word.

Please note that excerpts and passages in the StudySync® library and this workbook are intended as touchstones to generate interest in an author's work. The excerpts and passages do not substitute for the reading of entire texts, and StudySync® strongly recommends that students seek out and purchase the whole literary or informational work in order to experience it as the author intended. Links to online resellers are available in our digital library. In addition, complete works may be ordered through an authorized reseller by filling out and returning to StudySync® the order form enclosed in this workbook.

Reading & Writing Companion   **415**

CLOSE READ

Reread the story "The Ransom of Red Chief." As you reread, complete the Focus Questions below. Then use your answers and annotations from the questions to help you complete the Writing Prompt.

FOCUS QUESTIONS

1. Situational irony occurs when the outcome of a situation contrasts with what was expected to happen. How does the narrator use repetition in paragraphs 1, 3, and 4 to alert readers to the possibility of situational irony? Highlight textual evidence and make annotations to explain your analysis.

2. In paragraphs 1 and 2, explain how the narrator's use of dialect and descriptive language serves to characterize his point of view. Support your response with textual evidence and make annotations to explain your analysis.

3. In paragraph 29, how does the setting suggest that the plot will not proceed as Sam and Bill have anticipated? Highlight textual evidence and make annotations to explain your response.

4. In Sam and Bill's letter to Ebenezer Dorset, they sign "TWO DESPERATE MEN." In what way are these characters desperate as the story begins? How does their sense of desperation change as the plot progresses? Highlight textual evidence and make annotations to support your explanation.

5. In what ways are Sam and Bill challenged by their interactions with Ebenezer Dorset and his son? What do Sam and Bill learn as a result of these interactions? Highlight textual evidence and make annotations to explain your inferences.

WRITING PROMPT

The elements of a story do not exist in isolation. Characters, setting, and plot interact to influence conflict and theme. In "The Ransom of Red Chief," how do the characters, setting, and plot interact to shape the development of the story? Begin with a clear thesis statement to introduce your topic. Use your understanding of story elements, point of view, and inferences to analyze the story. Organize and support your writing with textual evidence, using precise language and selection vocabulary. Include transitions to show the relationships among your ideas, and use a formal style of writing. Provide a conclusion that summarizes your main ideas.

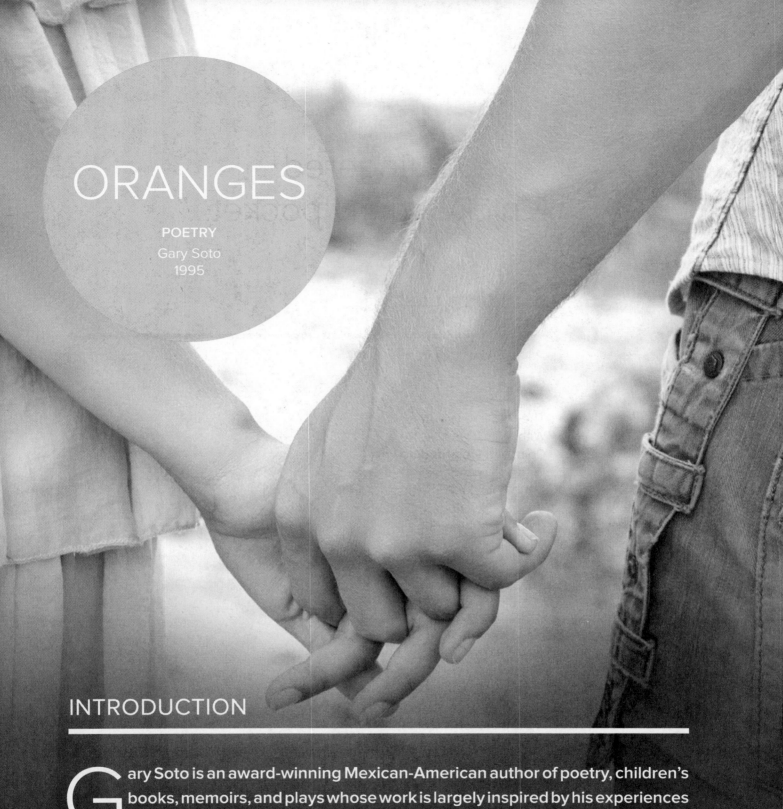

ORANGES

POETRY
Gary Soto
1995

INTRODUCTION

Gary Soto is an award-winning Mexican-American author of poetry, children's books, memoirs, and plays whose work is largely inspired by his experiences growing up among migrant farmworkers in California's Central Valley. Of his poetry, author Joyce Carol Oates has said, "Gary Soto's poems are fast, funny, heartening, and achingly believable, like Polaroid love letters, or snatches of music heard out of a passing car; patches of beauty like patches of sunlight; the very pulse of a life." The poem here, "Oranges," reflects on the emotions of first love

"I fingered
A nickel in my pocket..."

FIRST READ

Oranges

1 The first time I walked
2 With a girl, I was twelve,
3 Cold, and **weighted** down
4 With two oranges in my jacket.
5 December. Frost cracking
6 Beneath my steps, my breath
7 Before me, then gone,
8 As I walked toward
9 Her house, the one whose
10 Porch light burned yellow
11 Night and day, in any weather.
12 A dog barked at me, until
13 She came out pulling
14 At her gloves, face bright
15 With **rouge.** I smiled,
16 Touched her shoulder, and led
17 Her down the street, across
18 A used car lot and a line
19 Of newly planted trees,
20 Until we were breathing
21 Before a drugstore. We
22 Entered, the tiny bell
23 Bringing a saleslady
24 Down a narrow aisle of goods.
25 I turned to the candies
26 **Tiered** like **bleachers,**
27 And asked what she wanted—

28 Light *in* her eyes, a smile
29 Starting at the corners
30 Of her mouth. I fingered
31 A nickel in my pocket,
32 And when she lifted a chocolate
33 That cost a dime,
34 I didn't say anything.
35 I took the nickel from
36 My pocket, then an orange,
37 And set them quietly on
38 The counter. When I looked up,
39 The lady's eyes met mine,
40 And held them, knowing
41 Very well what it was all
42 About.

43   Outside,
44 A few cars **hissing** past,
45 Fog hanging like old
46 Coats between the trees.
47 I took my girl's hand
48 In mine for two blocks,
49 Then released it to let
50 Her unwrap the chocolate.
51 I peeled my orange
52 That was so bright against
53 The gray of December
54 That, from some distance,
55 Someone might have thought
56 I was making a fire in my hands.

From *New and Selected Poems*. Copyright © 1995 by Gary Soto. Used with permission of Chronicle Books LLC, San Francisco. Visit ChronicleBooks.com.

THINK QUESTIONS

1. What do you learn about the speaker, his actions, and the setting in lines 1–11? Cite evidence from the text to support your answer.

2. What happens between the boy and the saleswoman in the drugstore? What does the boy's decision to barter suggest about him? Cite textual evidence to support your response.

3. What happens to the two oranges from line 4 that the speaker had in his jacket? Cite evidence from the poem to support your answer.

4. What does the word **weighted** mean as it is used in the phrase *weighted down* in line 3 of the poem? Use the context clues in lines 3–4 to define the meaning of the word. Write your definition of *weighted* and tell how you figured out the word's meaning.

5. What is the meaning of the word **bleachers** in line 26 of the poem? Use context clues to try to figure out the meaning of *bleachers* as it is used in the simile "Tiered like bleachers." How does the analogy of the candies arranged "like bleachers" help you visualize the meaning of the word? Write your definition of *bleachers* and cite the clues you used in the text to help you determine the word's meaning. Then clarify the precise meaning of the word in a print or digital dictionary.

CLOSE READ

Reread the poem "Oranges." As you reread, complete the Focus Questions below. Then use your answers and annotations from the questions to help you complete the Writing Prompt.

FOCUS QUESTIONS

1. Reread and highlight lines 3–6: "Cold, and weighted down / With two oranges in my jacket. / December. Frost cracking / Beneath my steps . . . ." What image do these lines of the poem create in your mind? Which two of the five senses does the image of "Frost cracking / Beneath my steps" appeal to? Cite specific evidence from the text. Make annotations to record your response.

2. Highlight an example of alliteration in lines 20–23. Why do you think the poet uses alliteration in these lines? What does the use of this poetic element add to the poem? Cite specific evidence from the text. Make annotations to explain your response.

3. Highlight an example of onomatopoeia in lines 43–50. What effect does the use of onomatopoeia have on the mood in these lines of the poem? Make annotations to record specific textual evidence to support your answer.

4. Highlight the analogy (or comparison) the speaker is making in lines 51–56. To what is he comparing the orange he is holding? Why does the orange appear so bright? With what is it being contrasted? Make annotations to explain your analysis.

5. What is the theme of the poem? How does the theme illustrate the challenges of human interactions? Highlight examples of human interactions in the poem. Then make annotations to record your answer. Cite specific evidence from the text as support.

WRITING PROMPT

How do the poetic elements in "Oranges" contribute to both the theme and the emotional impact of the poem? Use the details you have compiled from examining the poem to:

- identify how Gary Soto uses figurative language (similes, metaphors, and onomatopoeia) and alliteration to add a deeper level of meaning to the poem
- identify how the use of figurative language creates strong imagery in the poem
- identify how the poetic elements contribute to your understanding of the theme.

Begin with a clear thesis statement to introduce your topic. Remember to organize and to support your writing with specific textual evidence and inferences, using precise language and selection vocabulary. Include transitions to show the relationships among your ideas, and use a formal style of writing. Provide a conclusion that summarizes your key points or ideas.

EXTENDED WRITING PROJECT

Extended Writing Project Prompt and Directions:

As you've seen in the short stories and novel and play e[...]
interactions are often complicated. Sometimes, we're u[...]
actions not only with other humans but also with the en[...]
should we do about the "invasive alien species" (sound[...]
we've introduced into California—species that are threate[...]
animals? It's your call. Write an argumentative essay in whi[...]
caused by human interaction (interference) with the environm[...]
"Invasive Plant Inventory" to review the issue of invasive species. [...]
an invasive plant or animal, such as the Burmese python that people hav[...]
the Florida Everglades or kudzu, a spreading invasive plant. Research your invasive plant or
animal in at least three print or digital sources, such as books, magazines, or reliable
websites. As you research, ask yourself: Should humans try to solve this problem or let
nature take its course?

Your argument should include:

- an explicitly stated claim about whether or not humans should try to clean up the
  "mess" they started
- persuasive reasons and relevant textual evidence, logically organized
- acknowledgment of opposing claims or other points of view
- citations of your sources in your essay and in a Works Cited page
- a conclusion that restates your claim and summarizes your persuasive evidence

EXTENDED WRITING PROJECT
ARGUMENTATIVE WRITING

ARGUMENTATIVE WRITING

WRITING PROMPT

As you've seen in the short stories and novel and play excerpts in this unit, human interactions are often complicated. Sometimes, we're unaware of the consequences of our actions not only with other humans but also with the environment. For example, what should we do about the "invasive alien species" (sounds like science fiction, doesn't it?) we've introduced into California—species that are threatening the state's native plants and animals? It's your call. Write an argumentative essay in which you explore the challenges caused by human interaction (interference) with the environment. First, reread "California Invasive Plant Inventory" to review the issue of invasive species. Then do research. Choose an invasive plant or animal, such as the Burmese python that people have introduced into the Florida Everglades or kudzu, a spreading invasive plant. Research your invasive plant or animal in at least three print or digital sources, such as books, magazines, or reliable websites. As you research, ask yourself: Should humans try to solve this problem or let nature take its course?

Your argument should include:

- an explicitly stated claim about whether humans should try to clean up the "mess" they started

- persuasive reasons and relevant textual evidence, logically organized

- acknowledgment of opposing claims or other points of view

- citations of your sources in your essay and in a Works Cited page

- a conclusion that restates your claim and summarizes your persuasive evidence

An argumentative essay is a form of persuasive writing. In an argument, the writer makes a claim about a topic and then provides evidence—facts, details, examples, and quotations—to support that claim. After explicitly stating the claim in the opening section of the essay, the writer develops his or her ideas with a specific audience in mind and presents the evidence in the body of the argument, using transitions to link related ideas. The purpose of the argument is to convince readers to accept and agree with the writer's claim.

In order to provide convincing supporting evidence for an argumentative essay, the writer must often do outside research, either because it is assigned or because it is essential to understanding a complex topic. That means the writer must look at print or digital sources of information related to the topic— books, articles, Web pages, blogs, diaries, letters, interviews, and other documents, and incorporate the information that he or she finds into the argument. The writer cites the sources of the evidence that he or she presents in the body of the essay so that readers will know where it came from. (In other Extended Writing Project Lessons, you will learn more about how to select appropriate source material, incorporate your research, and cite your sources.)

The features of an argumentative essay include the following:

- an introduction that states a claim about the topic
- a clearly organized presentation of logical reasoning and relevant evidence
- embedded quotations from credible sources that are clearly cited
- acknowledgment of alternate or opposing claims
- language that clarifies the relationship between the claim and the reasons that support it
- a concluding statement that follows from the argument

As you continue working on this extended writing project, you'll learn more about crafting each of the elements of an argumentative essay with research.

 ## STUDENT MODEL

Before you get started, read this argumentative essay that one student wrote in response to the writing prompt. As you read this Student Model, highlight and annotate the features of an argumentative essay that the student included.

Please note that excerpts and passages in the StudySync® library and this workbook are intended as touchstones to generate interest in an author's work. The excerpts and passages do not substitute for the reading of entire texts, and StudySync® strongly recommends that students seek out and purchase the whole literary or informational work in order to experience it as the author intended. Links to online resellers are available in our digital library. In addition, complete works may be ordered through an authorized reseller by filling out and returning to StudySync® the order form enclosed in this workbook.

Reading & Writing Companion | **425**

What Do We Do About Invasive Alien Species?

How many science-fiction movies have you seen about alien invasions from Mars or elsewhere and the effects that these alien invaders have had on the people and places on Earth? But as the saying goes, truth is often stranger than fiction, and today, humans are facing a real alien invasion, except this time the invaders are not extraterrestrials in the usual sense. They are invasive alien plants and animals that humans have thoughtlessly introduced into areas where they do not belong. What is the effect of this harmful human activity? Nothing less than the extinction of many of the world's native wildlife! But what can be done about this growing problem? Should humans be forced to clean up the mess they started? Or should humans do nothing and let nature take its course? These are the two sides to the issue. This essay will argue that humans need to take action to solve the problem of invasive species before it's too late to save our native wildlife. The question is, how? But first, let's look at the issue.

According to a recent online article, "Invasive Species," published by the National Wildlife Federation, "Approximately, 42% of Threatened or Endangered species are at risk primarily due to invasive species" ("Invasive Species" 1). But what is an invasive species, and why does it pose such a threat to native plants and animals? An invasive non-native species is one that enters a new ecosystem and then settles and reproduces so successfully that it threatens the existence of the area's native species and the balance of the ecosystem itself ("Invasive Species" 1). These invaders, which may not have any natural predators in the new ecosystem, take over an area, destroying the native wildlife that probably have no defenses against them.

Unfortunately, many examples of alien species invasions exist today across the United States. According to the research report in this unit, "California Invasive Plant Inventory," approximately 200 non-native invasive plant species are threatening the state's wildlands—"public and private lands that support native ecosystems"— and these plants can "displace native species" and even "alter ecosystem[s]" ("CIPI" 2). Although these invasive plant species pose a danger to California's wildlands, perhaps no greater threat by an invasive species exists today than that of the Burmese python in the Florida Everglades.

In her article "Snakes on the 'Glades," published online in *U.S. News & World Report*, Laura Bradley explains that "the Burmese python first arrived in Florida as part of the exotic pet trade, and over time made its way into the Everglades as overwhelmed pet owners released the animals into the wild or they escaped" (Bradley 2). As a result of the actions of these irresponsible pet owners, Florida is facing a huge problem today. According to Michael Sarill, in his blog "Burmese Pythons in the Everglades," scientists estimate that "anywhere between 30,000 and 150,000 Burmese Pythons exist in South Florida" (Sarill 1). Because pythons are good at hiding, scientists do not know how many are really out there. Yet according to Sarill, they do know that the population of native species has declined 90 percent in recent years—including 100 percent for rabbits and some other small mammals (Sarill 1). Think of the effects of this over time: The pythons could cause the extinction of every native animal species in the Everglades. Even the alligators are not safe. Pythons have been known to take on alligators and win (Sarill 3)!

But what can be done? After the death of a two-year-old child by one of these pythons, humans began taking steps to slow the growth and spread of these non-native reptiles (Sarill 4). However, some people wonder if this approach is correct or even possible. They say that nature should just take its course. We should do nothing because this is a perfect example of the "survival of the fittest"--the idea that the strongest will survive. Another argument by advocates for doing nothing about the problem is that once the pythons have eaten all the small animals, they might turn on themselves. But if that happens, only the biggest and strongest pythons will survive. Would any human be safe?

There are a couple of flaws in the do-nothing argument. First, it shows a lack of responsibility. People caused the invasion of the Burmese python, so they should do something about it. In addition, nobody knows what might happen when the python has eaten all the animals in the area. Sarill worries that rural communities might be in danger. He states, "As food sources run out, the snakes will grow increasingly desperate in search of a new meal. If a snake is willing to attack a large alligator, household pets are unquestionably vulnerable to attack" (Sarill 4). The problem is really complicated, and given the impact on the environment by invasive species (which were introduced by humans in the first place), we humans really must try to restore nature's balance.

Despite the difficulties, the only way to solve the problem is to remove the pythons from the Everglades. In recent years, Florida has held month-long python hunts.

People came from around the nation to hunt the snakes in 2012, but only 68 were collected (Bradley 3). Although that hunt didn't destroy many pythons, researchers did gather important information about where and how the snakes live, which can help them develop other strategies, but these solutions are far into the future.

In the meantime, the problem of invasive alien species is growing—both ecologically and economically. According to Bradley, the nation "spends more than $120 billion each year dealing with 50,000 introduced species of plants, animals, and microbes" (Bradley 1-2). If we can't control 18-foot-long, 200-pound pythons, how can we even begin to fight against thousands of microbes? Yet we must try, and we must be part of the solution. We humans have had both a positive and negative impact on our environment. When we make a mistake, such as releasing a dangerous predator like the Burmese python into the wild, we must do everything we can to make things right.

Works Cited

Bradley, Laura. "Snakes on the 'Glades." *U.S. News & World Report* 21 July 2014. Web. 9 Dec. 2014. <http://www.usnews.com/news/articles/2014/07/21/invasive-pythons-threaten-florida-everglades>

California Invasive Plant Council. "California Invasive Plant Inventory." 2006. Print.

"Invasive Species." National Wildlife Federation. Web. 9 Dec. 2014 <http:// www.nwf.org/wildlife/threats-to-wildlife/invasive-species.aspx>

Sarill, Michael. "Burmese Pythons in the Everglades." *Baboon* 12 Sept. 2013. Web. 9 Dec. 2014. <http://www.baboongame.com/blog/burmese-pythons-everglades#.Vlc9NVrgA1Q>

THINK QUESTIONS

1. The writer of the Student Model states an opinion (or claim) about whether humans should take action to solve the problem of invasive species. What is the writer's opinion (or claim)? How does the writer support it? What reasons does he or she give? Cite specific evidence from the Student Model in your response.

2. What relevant evidence did the writer include in the Student Model to support his or her opinion (or claim)? Cite the evidence and explain why it is relevant.

3. Write two or three sentences evaluating the writer's conclusion. Cite specific textual evidence from the last paragraph.

4. Think about the writing prompt. Which selections, Blasts, or other resources would you like to use or research to write your own argumentative essay? Give strong reasons for your choice.

5. Based on the selections you have read, listened to, or researched, how would you answer the question, "What are the challenges of human interactions?" What are some ideas that you might consider in the argument you'll be developing for your essay?

NOTES

PREWRITE

WRITING PROMPT

As you've seen in the short stories and novel and play excerpts in this unit, human interactions are often complicated. Sometimes, we're unaware of the consequences of our actions not only with other humans but also with the environment. For example, what should we do about the "invasive alien species" (sounds like science fiction, doesn't it?) we've introduced into California—species that are threatening the state's native plants and animals? It's your call. Write an argumentative essay in which you explore the challenges caused by human interaction (interference) with the environment. First, reread "California Invasive Plant Inventory" to review the issue of invasive species. Then do research. Choose an invasive plant or animal, such as the Burmese python that people have introduced into the Florida Everglades or kudzu, a spreading invasive plant. Research your invasive plant or animal in at least three print or digital sources, such as books, magazines, or reliable websites. As you research, ask yourself: Should humans try to solve this problem or let nature take its course?

Your argument should include:

- an explicitly stated claim about whether humans should try to clean up the "mess" they started
- persuasive reasons and relevant textual evidence, logically organized
- acknowledgment of opposing claims or other points of view
- citations of your sources in your essay and in a Works Cited page
- a conclusion that restates your claim and summarizes your persuasive evidence

Your first step is to think about the problem of invasive species so that you can decide which side you're on. Are you for removing invasive species, or do you think we should leave them alone? Follow the directions in the prompt by reading "California's Invasive Plant Inventory" to explore what an invasive species is. Then use the prewriting strategies you've learned—list making, brainstorming, free writing, concept mapping, sketching, and so on—to figure out which side of the issue you're on.

Try this: Draw a two-column chart. Label one column "Pro" and the other column "Con." Then fill in each column with your ideas about the benefits of taking action against invasive species ("Pro") versus leaving the species alone ("Con"). In the columns, jot down words and phrases or draw pictures. Now look at your responses. Which side of the argument do you seem to be on? Express your opinion in a complete sentence above your chart, based on what you already know. Here's what the writer of the Student Model wrote: "I think humans should try to control the spread of invasive species because we caused the problem, so it's up to us to fix it."

Needless to say, there are still quite a few questions you need to answer before you can take a stand on the issue. First, choose an invasive species to write about. That may take some research. Next, make a list of research questions. You'll want to ask good research questions that will help you make a strong claim and lead you to strong reasons and evidence that will support your claim. The answers you discover during your research will help you build an effective argument about invasive species and whether we should take action against them.

The writer of the Student Model had a great many questions. He or she used a chart to organize them, to record answers based on what he or she already knew, and to identify sources to research the questions and find the answers.

Topic: Invasive species

Claim: "I think humans should try to control the spread of invasive species because we caused the problem, so it's up to us to fix it."

RESEARCH QUESTIONS	ANSWERS BASED ON WHAT I KNOW NOW	POSSIBLE SOURCES FOR MORE RESEARCH
What is an invasive species?	Invasive species are not native to an area. They take over a place by eating the native species, breeding, and spreading.	Print or online newspaper articles, articles in science magazines or journals, wildlife organizations and newsletters, print or online encyclopedias, radio or TV programs, documentaries, websites, including government websites, and blogs
Which invasive species might I want to learn more about?	My grandmother lives in Florida, so I want to know more about Burmese pythons!	Local newspaper and magazine articles and websites, especially government websites, blogs, wildlife organizations, and newsletters
What causes invasive species to come into an area?	Human activity is a major cause because people let exotic pets escape, or introduce plants or animals into an area where they don't belong.	Newspaper articles, newsletters, articles in science magazines or journals, print or online encyclopedias, documentaries, websites, blogs, radio and TV shows about science or the work of wildlife organizations
What are some problems caused by these invasive species?	Burmese pythons have invaded the Everglades and are eating native species in the area, causing some wildlife to become extinct.	Newspaper articles, articles in science magazines, radio programs, websites, especially government websites, blogs, science TV shows, wildlife organizations, and newsletters

RESEARCH QUESTIONS	ANSWERS BASED ON WHAT I KNOW NOW	POSSIBLE SOURCES FOR MORE RESEARCH
What are some solutions to the problems caused by these invasive species?	Removing the pythons from the Everglades is one solution I've heard about.	Newspaper articles, articles in science magazines, radio programs, websites, especially government web sites, blogs, wildlife organizations
How effective are these solutions?	I don't know. I don't think it's going well because the pythons are still a problem in the Everglades.	Newspaper articles, articles in science magazines, radio or TV programs about science, websites, especially government websites, blogs, wildlife organizations, and newsletters
What would happen if we left invasive species alone? Would that be a good or bad thing?	I think the pythons would eat up every other species. That can't be good!	Newspaper articles, articles in science magazines, radio or TV programs about science, websites, especially government websites, blogs, wildlife organizations, and newsletters

Create a similar graphic organizer on your own. Do some research to answer your questions. Then select an invasive species and take a stand on the issue. You can always change your species or your opinion as you do more research and develop your ideas.

SKILL:
RESEARCH AND
NOTE-TAKING

 DEFINE

If you have already completed research presentations for previous units, then you have already learned how to do research. **Research** is how you discover information or double-check facts or ideas. Research can be as simple as scanning social media for current trends, looking up the meaning of an unfamiliar word in a dictionary, tuning in the radio for details about local school closures, going online to learn how to play chess, or trying something new to get firsthand experience.

Unless you have a perfect memory, **note-taking** is essential to effective research. Each time you gather information from a source, you should take notes. A **source** might be a textbook, a newspaper article, a website, an app, an encyclopedia, or an authority on a subject that interests you. Your **notes** should always include the title of the source, its author's name, and the place (print or Web) and date of publication. Once you have that information, you can jot down all the ideas you learned from that source. This might seem like a lot of work, but it's a good practice. For example, you might need to go back later to double-check a fact. Your notes will help save time in finding that source again. You also need this information in order to prepare citations and a Works Cited section at the end of your argumentative essay. Your Works Cited section can help your readers learn more about your topic and ideas. And your readers will be able to use the information about your sources to answer their own questions and do their own research.

Keep your purpose for writing in mind as you do your research. In this unit, you will be writing an argumentative essay. The point of your research is to find facts, details, examples, and quotations that support your claim about why humans should or should not take action against invasive species. Your researched information should help persuade readers to accept your claim and agree with you.

IDENTIFICATION AND APPLICATION

- Before you begin your research, choose a topic. Then do some general reading about it. You might find that the topic doesn't interest you or that you can't find enough evidence to support a claim. If that's the case, choose another topic on which to focus your research.

- Narrow your topic. Some topics are so broad—invasive species around the world, human interactions on Earth—that you could spend years doing research. Try narrowing your topic to one specific aspect—the Burmese pythons in the Everglades, the impact of climbers on Mount Everest— and then look for specific information as you research.

- Ask questions. Remember all those research questions you created in the Prewrite lesson? Keep them in mind as you think about your topic and do your research. As you research, you probably will come up with more questions. That's good. These questions will help you focus your topic even more and determine what you really need to know.

- Use thoughtful key word searches when researching online. Enter specific words and phrases rather than general topics. You will likely have to fine-tune the words and phrases in order to get to accurate and reliable sources.

- Choose your sources carefully. Think about their accuracy and reliability, especially when searching online. Look for well-known sources, such as fact-based newspapers, magazines, and journals. Try to stick to educational and government websites (ending in .edu and .gov instead of .com or .org)—their information is usually more reliable.

- Remember the difference between primary and secondary sources. Primary sources are firsthand accounts written by people who witnessed the events they describe. Autobiographies, diaries, letters, interviews, and memoirs are primary sources. They are good sources for direct quotations. Secondary sources are written after the fact. They combine information from different primary sources. Textbooks, encyclopedia articles, history books, and magazine articles are examples of secondary sources. These are especially good for background information. Go ahead and check *their* sources. They can lead you to helpful primary sources.

- Stay focused when you take notes. Look for the answers to your research questions. Think about your purpose and audience. Don't get distracted by irrelevant information.

- Take careful notes. If you prefer to write your notes on index cards, use one card for each source. Be sure to include the title, author, and publication information on the card. If you need more than one card for the same source, number the cards consecutively. You can also take

Please note that excerpts and passages in the StudySync® library and this workbook are intended as touchstones to generate interest in an author's work. The excerpts and passages do not substitute for the reading of entire texts, and StudySync® strongly recommends that students seek out and purchase the whole literary or informational work in order to experience it as the author intended. Links to online resellers are available in our digital library. In addition, complete works may be ordered through an authorized reseller by filling out and returning to StudySync® the order form enclosed in this workbook.

Reading & Writing Companion   **435**

notes digitally. Use a word-processing program. Open a new document for each source. At the top of the page, identify the title, author, and publication information. Then write your notes. Use bullets or new paragraphs for each new set of facts. There are also note-taking apps and easy-to-use software.

- If you want to quote from a source, write down the words exactly as they appear in the source and place them within quotation marks. Be sure to give credit to the source in your writing. Sometimes you might want to paraphrase, or restate, the ideas. That's a great way to condense ideas. But you still must cite the original source so that readers know where you found the information.

- Citing your sources is very important. It helps you avoid plagiarizing, or presenting other people's words and ideas as your own. Follow this rule: Anytime you use any information from a researched source, give credit to that source.

 MODEL

Consider the following paragraph from the second paragraph of the Student Model, "What Do We Do About Invasive Alien Species?":

> According to a recent online article, "Invasive Species," published by the National Wildlife Federation, **"Approximately, 42% of Threatened or Endangered species are at risk primarily due to invasive species" ("Invasive Species" 1).** But what is an invasive species, and why does it pose such a threat to native plants and animals? **An invasive non-native species is one that enters a new ecosystem and then settles and reproduces so successfully that it threatens the existence of the area's native species and the balance of the ecosystem itself ("Invasive Species" 1).** These invaders, which may not have any natural predators in the new ecosystem, take over an area, destroying the native wildlife that probably have no defenses against them.

The writer presents his or her research in a couple of different ways. First, the writer uses a direct quotation that he or she thinks is relevant to the ideas in the paragraph. Next, he or she introduces the quoted material by identifying its source—a recent online article called "Invasive Species" that was published by the National Wildlife Federation. Then the writer shows the exact words within quotation marks. After the quoted material, he or she provides a citation in parentheses. Because the article doesn't have a stated author, the writer uses the title and page number on which the quoted material appeared.

Copyright © BookheadEd Learning, LLC

The article "Invasive Species" was very helpful to the writer. Later in the paragraph, he or she cites it again. This time, instead of quoting from the source, the writer paraphrases some of the information. This means that the writer uses his or her own words to define what an invasive species is. However, because the definition came from a source, the writer provides a citation.

 ## PRACTICE

Do some research for a quotation about the invasive species you will be writing about in your argumentative essay. Write down the quotation exactly as it appears in the source. Then, for practice, restate the quotation in your own words and cite its source. As always, record the source's title, author, date, and publication information in your notes.

NOTES

SKILL:
THESIS
STATEMENT

DEFINE

The thesis of an argumentative essay takes the form of a claim. A claim is the writer's opinion about the topic of the essay. It is a statement of position, belief, or judgment. A claim might be introduced with certain phrases that make the writer's point of view clear, such as "I believe," "I think," "We should," or "One must." An opinion cannot be proven to be true, but it can be supported with relevant evidence—facts, statistics, quotations from experts, examples, and so on. The claim of an argument typically appears in the introductory paragraph, often as the last sentence.

IDENTIFICATION AND APPLICATION

A thesis statement, or claim, in an argumentative essay

- explicitly states the writer's opinion about the topic of the essay.
- previews the ideas, reasons, and evidence that will be presented in the body paragraphs of the essay.
- addresses all aspects of the argumentative prompt.
- is stated directly in the introductory paragraph.

MODEL

The following is the introductory paragraph from the Student Model essay "What Do We Do About Invasive Alien Species?":

> How many science-fiction movies have you seen about alien invasions from Mars or elsewhere and the effects that these alien invaders have had on the people and places on Earth? But as the saying goes, truth is often stranger than fiction, and today, humans are facing a real alien invasion, except this

time the invaders are not extraterrestrials in the usual sense. They are invasive alien plants and animals that humans have thoughtlessly introduced into areas where they do not belong. What is the effect of this harmful human activity? Nothing less than the extinction of many of the world's native wildlife! But what can be done about this growing problem? Should humans be forced to clean up the mess they started? Or should humans do nothing and let nature take its course? These are the two sides to the issue. **This essay will argue that humans need to take action to solve the problem before it's too late to save our native wildlife.** The question is, how? But first, let's look at the issue.

Notice the boldfaced claim near the end of the essay's opening paragraph. This student's claim responds to the writing prompt by taking a stand on the issue of invasive species: The writer believes that humans need to solve the problem. Instead of using the words "I think," the writer says, "This essay will argue," but the meaning is the same. The writer believes that human intervention is necessary. Notice how in the sentences following the claim, the writer previews the ideas to be discussed in the body of the paper. He or she will explore the issue of invasive species and then talk about how the problem can be solved through human interaction.

 ## PRACTICE

Write a thesis statement for your argumentative essay. It should explicitly state where you stand on the issue of invasive species. You don't need to identify the specific invasive species you chose as your topic, but you can. After writing your claim, exchange it with a partner. Offer each other feedback. How clear is your partner's claim? Is it obvious where he or she stands on the issue of invasive species? Does the claim address all the parts of the prompt? Offer each other suggestions. Make constructive, supportive comments that will help your partner develop an effective thesis.

SKILL:
ORGANIZE
ARGUMENTATIVE
WRITING

 DEFINE

As you have learned, the purpose of argumentative writing is to persuade readers to accept the writer's thesis statement, or claim. To do so, the writer must organize and present his or her reasons and relevant evidence—the facts, examples, statistics, and quotations found during research—in a logical and convincing way. The writer must also select an **organizational structure** that best suits the argument.

Writers of arguments can choose from a number of organizational structures, including **compare-contrast, order of importance, problem-solution, cause-effect, and chronological (or sequential) order,** among others. Experienced writers use **transition words and phrases** to help readers understand which organizational structure is being used. As they plan, writers often use an outline or another graphic organizer to determine the most persuasive way to present their ideas and evidence.

Writers are not limited to using only one organizational structure throughout a text. Within a specific section or paragraph, they might use a different organizational structure. This does not affect the overall organization, however.

 IDENTIFICATION AND APPLICATION

- When selecting an overall organizational structure for an argument, a writer must consider the claim he or she is making. Then the writer must think about the best way to present the evidence that supports it. Do this by asking these questions:

  › To support my claim, should I compare and contrast ideas or details in the text?

  › Is there an order of importance to my evidence? Is some evidence stronger than other evidence? Or does all my evidence support my idea equally well?

> In my claim, have I identified a problem? Do I have supporting evidence that suggests a solution or an answer?

> Does my supporting evidence suggest a cause or an effect?

> To support my claim, does it make sense to retell an event or a series of events in chronological (or time) order?

- Writers often use signal, or cue, words and phrases to help readers recognize the organizational structure of their writing. These words and phrases are also known as transitions:

  > Compare and contrast: *like, and, both, similarly, in the same way* to compare and *unlike, different from, while, but, however, although, on the other hand* to contrast

  > Order of importance: *most, most important, least, least important, first, finally, mainly, to begin with*

  > Problem and solution: *problem, solution, why, how, solve*

  > Cause-effect: *because, therefore, as a result, cause, effect, so*

  > Chronological order: *first, next, then, finally, before, after, now, in the meantime*

 ## MODEL

During the prewriting stage, the writer of the Student Model understood that his or her argument presented a problem—invasive species—and considered two solutions—to take action against invasive species or to do nothing. The ultimate solution, which the writer expressed in the claim at both the beginning and end of the essay, was that it is up to humans to fix any mess they create, especially the control of invasive species. Therefore, the writer of the Student Model decided that the best approach would be to use a problem-solution organizational structure for the argumentative essay.

At several points in the Student Model, the writer uses cue words or phrases to identify problems and a solution:

But what can be done about this growing **problem**?

As a result of the actions of these irresponsible pet owners, Florida is facing a huge **problem** today.

The **problem** is really complicated, and given the impact on the environment by invasive species (which were introduced by humans in the first place), we humans really must try to restore nature's balance.

NOTES

Despite the difficulties, the only way to **solve** the **problem** is to remove the pythons from the Everglades.

In the meantime, the **problem** of invasive species is growing—both ecologically and economically.

Although that hunt didn't destroy many pythons, researchers did gather important information about where and how the snakes live, which can help them develop other strategies, but these **solutions** are far into the future.

Yet we must try, and we must be part of the **solution.**

Once a writer has selected the most appropriate organizational structure for his or her essay, he or she can use an outline or a graphic organizer (for example, a Venn diagram, flow chart, concept map, or timeline) to begin organizing the supporting evidence.

The writer of the Student Model used a graphic organizer during planning to organize the evidence that supported this claim:

This essay will argue that humans need to take action to solve the problem of invasive species before it's too late to save our native wildlife.

 PRACTICE

Use an *Organize Argumentative Writing* graphic organizer such as the one used with the Student Model, or choose one that better suits your organizational pattern. Fill in the organizer with evidence you gathered in the Prewrite stage of writing your argument.

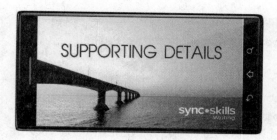

SKILL:
SUPPORTING
DETAILS

 DEFINE

An effective argument provides readers with supporting details in the form of reasons and relevant evidence. Reasons are statements that answer the question, "Why?" They tell why the writer thinks that his or her claim is true. The writer provides reasons to support a claim, which makes it more believable. Relevant evidence includes facts, details, statistics, definitions, quotations from experts, observations, and examples. Evidence that supports the reasons and the claim is often found through research.

Research can be the key to presenting a successful argument. While researching, the writer deepens his or her understanding of the topic and finds evidence that supports the reasons and the claim. (Just as important—if the writer can't find enough evidence that supports the claim, then he or she knows it is time to rethink the claim and the reasons.) Without solid supporting evidence, the writer would simply be stating his or her opinion about a topic—and that's rarely convincing to readers.

Because writers want to convince readers that their claims are true, they carefully select and present the supporting details. A detail is relevant only if it supports the claim and helps build the argument. If the detail does not support the claim or strengthen the argument, it is irrelevant and should not be used.

 IDENTIFICATION AND APPLICATION

Step 1:

Review your claim. In your research, you want to find supporting details that are relevant to your claim. Ask the following question: "What am I trying to persuade my audience to think or believe?" That's what the writer of the Student Model did. Here's that writer's claim:

This essay will argue that humans need to take action to solve the problem of invasive species before it's too late to save our native wildlife.

Step 2:

Ask what a reader needs to know about the topic in order to accept the claim. For example, to accept a claim about whether to take action against invasive species, a reader must first know the kinds of problems that those invaders are causing. Why are invasive species such a problem? Here's the reason the writer gives:

> **According to a recent online article, "Invasive Species," published by the National Wildlife Federation, "Approximately, 42% of Threatened or Endangered species are at risk primarily due to invasive species" ("Invasive Species" 1).**

That's a reason that should make most readers sit up and pay attention! The writer also provides supporting details that back up that reason. They include a definition and some background information:

> • An invasive non-native species is one that enters a new ecosystem and then settles and reproduces so successfully that it threatens the existence of the area's native species and the balance of the ecosystem itself ("Invasive Species" 1).

> • These invaders, which may not have any natural predators in the new ecosystem, take over an area, destroying the native wildlife that probably have no defenses against them.

In the next paragraph, the writer provides another supporting detail—a statistic:

> According to the research report in this unit, "California Invasive Plant Inventory," approximately 200 non-native invasive plant species are threatening the state's wildlands—"public and private lands that support native ecosystems"—and these plants can "displace native species" and even "alter ecosystem[s]" ("CIPI" 2).

All of these supporting details came from the writer's research. The details definitely support the writer's claim that invasive species need to be dealt with before something terrible happens.

Step 3:

You might find a lot of details in your research, and you might want to use them all to support your claim, but it's important to evaluate each detail before you use it to make sure it's relevant. To do this, ask yourself these questions:

- Does this information help the reader better understand the topic?
- Does this information support my claim?
- Does this information help make my argument believable?
- Do I have stronger evidence that makes the same point?

If you can answer *yes* to the first three questions and *no* to the fourth, then definitely use the supporting detail in your argument.

 ## MODEL

The writer of the Student Model used evidence found during his or her research to support the part of the claim that says that people need to take action now against invasive species.

> In her article "Snakes on the 'Glades," published in *U.S. News & World Report,* Laura Bradley explains that "the Burmese python first arrived in Florida as part of the exotic pet trade, and over time made its way into the Everglades as overwhelmed pet owners released the animals into the wild or they escaped" (Bradley 2). As a result of the actions of these irresponsible pet owners, Florida is facing a huge problem today. According to Michael Sarill, in his blog "Burmese Pythons in the Everglades," **scientists estimate that "anywhere between 30,000 and 150,000 Burmese Pythons exist in South Florida"** (Sarill 1). Because pythons are good at hiding, scientists do not know how many are really out there. Yet according to Sarill, they do know that **the population of native species has declined 90 percent in recent years—including 100 percent for rabbits and some other small mammals (Sarill 1).** Think of the effects of this over time: **The pythons could cause the extinction of every native animal species in the Everglades.** Even the alligators are not safe. Pythons have been known to take on alligators and win (Sarill 3)!

What supporting details does the writer use here? Clearly, the writer provides quotations from experts and statistics about the impact of the Burmese pythons on Florida's native wildlife. This evidence highlights the claim that the pythons are a deadly threat to Florida's ecosystem, which invites the reader to ask, what can we do?

PRACTICE

Write the claim you developed in a previous lesson. Below it, write some supporting details for your argumentative essay. Use the research you completed earlier in the Extended Writing Project. Then exchange your work with a partner. Use what you've learned about identifying relevant supporting details to evaluate your partner's work. Offer clear suggestions about the kinds of details you, as a reader, would find convincing.

PLAN

WRITING PROMPT

As you've seen in the short stories and novel and play excerpts in this unit, human interactions are often complicated. Sometimes, we're unaware of the consequences of our actions not only with other humans but also with the environment. For example, what should we do about the "invasive alien species" (sounds like science fiction, doesn't it?) we've introduced into California—species that are threatening the state's native plants and animals? It's your call. Write an argumentative essay in which you explore the challenges caused by human interaction (interference) with the environment. First, reread "California Invasive Plant Inventory" to review the issue of invasive species. Then do research. Choose an invasive plant or animal, such as the Burmese python that people have introduced into the Florida Everglades or kudzu, a spreading invasive plant. Research your invasive plant or animal in at least three print or digital sources, such as books, magazines, or reliable websites. As you research, ask yourself: Should humans try to solve this problem or let nature take its course?

Your argument should include:

- an explicitly stated claim about whether humans should try to clean up the "mess" they started

- persuasive reasons and relevant textual evidence, logically organized

- acknowledgment of opposing claims or other points of view

- citations of your sources in your essay and in a Works Cited page

- a conclusion that restates your claim and summarizes your persuasive evidence

Please note that excerpts and passages in the StudySync® library and this workbook are intended as touchstones to generate interest in an author's work. The excerpts and passages do not substitute for the reading of entire texts, and StudySync® strongly recommends that students seek out and purchase the whole literary or informational work in order to experience it as the author intended. Links to online resellers are available in our digital library. In addition, complete works may be ordered through an authorized reseller by filling out and returning to StudySync® the order form enclosed in this workbook.

Reading & Writing Companion **447**

NOTES

Review the organizational structure and information you used to complete your *Organize Argumentative Writing* graphic organizer. This organized information and your claim will help you create a road map to use for writing your argumentative essay.

Consider the following questions as you develop your main paragraph topics and their supporting details in the road map:

- What invasive species is the topic of your essay?
- What claim (or argument) are you making about this invasive species? (Are you for or against taking action against the invader?)
- What are your reasons for making this claim?
- What specific supporting details and relevant evidence from your research can you use to support your claim?
- How can you best present the evidence so that it persuades your audience to accept your claim?

Use this model to get started with your road map:

Argumentative Essay Road Map

Claim: Humans need to take action to solve the problem of invasive species before it's too late to save our native wildlife.

Paragraph 1 (Introduction) Topic: The problem of invasive species

Supporting Detail #1: Make connection to alien invasions from science-fiction movies

Supporting Detail #2: Explain why invasive species are a problem

State the claim.

Paragraph 2 Topic: What an invasive species is

Supporting Detail #1: Quote definition from National Wildlife Federation

Supporting Detail #2: Explain why invasive species are bad, with facts from NWF article

Paragraph 3 Topic: Invasive species in California

Supporting Detail #1: Use statistics from "California Invasive Plant Inventory" to describe situation in California today

Supporting Detail #2: Transition to invasion of Burmese python in Florida Everglades

Paragraph 4 Topic: Invasion of Burmese Python in Florida

Supporting Detail #1: Quote from *U.S. News & World Report* about how pythons arrived in Florida

Supporting Detail #2: Quote statistics from Michael Sarill's blog to illustrate terrible effects of pythons in the Everglades—30,000 to 150,000 pythons, 100% extinction of rabbits

Supporting Detail #3: Prediction of possible effects in the future

Paragraph 5 Topic: Stopping the pythons

Supporting Detail #1: Pose questions about whether people can stop the spread of pythons

Supporting Detail #2: Raise opposing view that we should do nothing because pythons will eventually turn on themselves

Paragraph 6 Topic: Flaws in the do-nothing argument

Supporting Detail #1: Explain why the argument is not reasonable

Supporting Detail #2: Quote from Sarill about dangers to people and rural communities if we do nothing

Supporting Detail #3: Suggest a solution: We must try to restore nature's balance

Paragraph 7 Topic: Solution to the python invasion

Supporting Detail #1: Paraphrase from *U.S. News & World Report* article about 2012 python hunt

Supporting Detail #2: Make point that researchers learned a lot but can't do much

Paragraph 8 (Conclusion) Topic: Summing Up

Supporting Detail #1: Statistics from *U.S. News & World Report* about how much money invasive species cost the U.S. each year

Supporting Detail #2: Make connection between different types of invasive species

Restate the claim.

SKILL:
INTRODUCTIONS
AND
CONCLUSIONS

 DEFINE

The introduction is the opening paragraph or section of an argumentative essay or another nonfiction text. The introduction of an argumentative essay identifies the topic to be discussed, states the writer's claim, and previews the supporting details (reasons and evidence found during research) that will appear in the body of the text. The introduction is also the place where most writers include a "hook" that engages readers and helps them relate to the topic.

A conclusion is the closing paragraph or section of an argumentative essay or another type of nonfiction text. The conclusion is where the writer brings the argument to a close. The ideas presented in the conclusion follow directly from the claim stated in the introduction and from the supporting details provided in the body of the argument. Therefore, the conclusion is where the writer restates the claim and summarizes his or her evidence and research. Also, the conclusion of an argument might end with a call to action or an insightful comment that will leave the reader with something to think about.

 IDENTIFICATION AND APPLICATION

- In an argument, the introduction is the opening section in which the writer identifies the topic to be discussed and directly states the claim. The claim expresses the writer's opinion (or point of view) about the topic. By presenting the claim at the beginning of the argument, the writer lets readers know his or her position on the topic. This allows readers to form their own opinions, which they can then measure against the writer's as they read the supporting details in the body of the argument—the middle of the essay.

- The introduction is also where the writer provides a preview of the supporting evidence. By providing a preview, the writer can begin to establish an effective argument and increase the likelihood that readers will accept and agree with his or her claim.

- The introduction should also have a "hook." As the word implies, a good hook "grabs" the reader's interest and makes him or her want to read on. A good hook might consist of an intriguing image, a surprising detail, a funny anecdote, a rhetorical question, or a shocking statistic.

- An effective conclusion restates the writer's claim and briefly summarizes the most convincing reasons and researched evidence from the body paragraphs in the essay.

- Some conclusions may offer a compelling insight related to the argument. This insight is the writer's last chance to persuade the audience to accept his or her side of the argument and may even inspire the audience to take action. The insight might be

  › an answer to a question first posed in the introduction.
  › a memorable or inspiring message or quotation.
  › a suggestion that readers learn more.

 ## MODEL

The introduction and conclusion of the Student Model "What Do We Do About Invasive Species?" contains many of the key elements discussed above:

> **How many science-fiction movies have you seen about alien invasions from Mars or elsewhere and the effects that these alien invaders have had on the people and places on Earth?** But as the saying goes, truth is often stranger than fiction, and today, humans are facing a real alien invasion, except this time the invaders are not extraterrestrials in the usual sense. **They are invasive alien plants and animals that humans have thoughtlessly introduced into areas where they do not belong.** What is the effect of this harmful human activity? Nothing less than the extinction of many of the world's native wildlife! **But what can be done about this growing problem? Should humans be forced to clean up the mess they started?** Or should humans do nothing and let nature take its course? These are the two sides of the issue. **This essay will argue that humans need to take action to solve the problem of invasive species before it's too late to save our native wildlife.** The question is, how? But first, let's look at the issue.

The student writer's introductory paragraph **"hooks"** readers by referring to alien invasions in science-fiction movies. The hook is fun and would likely appeal to the writer's classmates, who is his or her most likely audience. The writer moves from imaginary alien invaders to real invasive species, which is the essay's **topic.** By posing a few questions, the writer helps **preview information and details** that he or she will discuss in the body of the essay. Finally, the writer ends the introduction with the **claim,** or statement of opinion:

Copyright © BookheadEd Learning, LLC

". . . humans need to take action to solve the problem of invasive species before it's too late to save our native wildlife."

Now let's look at how the writer ended the argumentative essay:

*In the meantime, the problem of invasive species is growing—both ecologically and economically. According to Bradley, **the nation "spends more than $120 billion each year dealing with 50,000 introduced species of plants, animals, and microbes"** (Bradley 1–2). **If we can't control 18-foot-long, 200-pound pythons, how can we even begin to fight against thousands of microbes?** Yet we must try, and we must be part of the solution. We humans have had both a positive and negative impact on our environment. **When we make a mistake, such as releasing a dangerous predator like the Burmese python into the wild, we must do everything we can to make things right.***

The concluding paragraph does a few important things:

- First, it **reviews the topic**—invasive species are a big and growing problem.
- It **states some final and compelling evidence**—that the U.S. spends billions of dollars each year trying to control invasive species.
- It **asks a question** for the purpose of getting the reader to think about the seriousness of the issue: "If we can't control 18-foot-long, 200-pound pythons, how can we even begin to fight against thousands of microbes?"
- Finally, it **restates the claim:** "When we make a mistake, such as releasing a dangerous predator like the Burmese python into the wild, we must do everything we can to make things right."
- A concluding paragraph should also **restate the most important reasons and evidence** presented in the body of the essay. That's something the writer of the Student Model needs to work on during revision.

 PRACTICE

Write an introduction and a conclusion to your argument. Your introduction should include a "hook," identify your topic, state your claim, and hint at the supporting details (reasons and evidence from your research) that will appear in the body of your essay. Then draft a conclusion that mirrors your introduction by restating your claim and summing up your research. Try to include an insightful comment or interesting question about your topic or claim. Finally, exchange your work with a peer-review partner. Provide helpful feedback about each other's introduction and conclusion.

SKILL: BODY PARAGRAPHS AND TRANSITIONS

 DEFINE

Body paragraphs appear between the introduction and conclusion of an argumentative essay, or any type of nonfiction text. Together, they form the middle section in which the writer of the argument supports his or her claim with relevant reasons and evidence collected during research. Ideally, each body paragraph should focus on one central idea or reason so that the reader can easily follow along. The ideas in each body paragraph should support the claim stated in the introduction and restated in the conclusion.

It's important to structure a body paragraph clearly. Here is one way to structure the body paragraph of an argumentative essay:

- **Topic sentence:** The topic sentence is the first sentence of a body paragraph. It states the central idea of the paragraph. The topic sentence should relate to your claim.

- **Evidence #1:** You should provide evidence that supports your topic sentence. Evidence can include relevant facts, definitions, details, observations, quotations, statistics, and examples.

- **Evidence #2:** Continue to develop your claim with a second piece of evidence.

- **Analysis/Explanation:** After presenting evidence, explain how the evidence helps support your topic sentence—and general claim—about the topic.

- **Concluding sentence:** After presenting your evidence and analysis, restate your claim or main point in a concluding sentence.

As you write body paragraphs, think carefully about how to incorporate your evidence. **Quotations** are an excellent source of evidence, but they need to be integrated into your writing. Be sure to introduce the source of the quotation before you quote it, and place the exact words of the quotations within quotation marks. End the sentence with a citation, so that readers know the source of the quoted material.

Compare these examples of a poorly integrated and a well-integrated quotation:

> **Poorly integrated quotation:** Laura Bradley wrote an article "Snakes on the 'Glades," which appeared in *U.S. News & World Report*. In it she said that "the Burmese python first arrived in Florida as part of the exotic pet trade, and over time made its way into the Everglades as overwhelmed pet owners released the animals into the wild or they escaped" (Bradley 2).

> **Well-integrated quotation:** In her article "Snakes on the 'Glades," published in *U.S. News & World Report*, Laura Bradley explains that " the Burmese python first arrived in Florida as part of the exotic pet trade, and over time made its way into the Everglades as overwhelmed pet owners released the animals into the wild or they escaped" (Bradley 2).

Remember, if a full quotation is too long, you can use **ellipses** (. . .) to show that you left out some words:

> The problem is really complicated, and given the impact on the environment by invasive species (which were introduced by humans in the first place), we humans really must try to restore nature's balance.

> The problem is really complicated, and given the impact on the environment by invasive species . . . we humans must really try to restore nature's balance.

If a quotation is too long or too complicated, you can **paraphrase** it—or any of your evidence. Paraphrasing involves restating the key ideas by using your own words. Here's an example:

> According to Michael Sarill, in his blog "Burmese Pythons in the Everglades," scientists estimate that "anywhere between 30,000 and 150,000 Burmese Pythons exist in South Florida" (Sarill 1). Because pythons are good at hiding, scientists do not know how many are really out there. Yet according to Sarill, they do know that the population of native species has declined 90 percent in recent years—including 100 percent for rabbits and some other small mammals (Sarill 1). Think of the effects of this over time: The pythons could cause the extinction of every native animal species in the Everglades. Even the alligators are not safe. Pythons have been known to take on alligators and win (Sarill 3)!

According to Michael Sarill, scientists estimate that perhaps 30,000 to 150,000 Burmese Pythons exist in South Florida (Sarill 1). As a result, the population of native species has dropped by 90 percent or more (Sarill 1). Think about what that could mean over time: The pythons could cause every native animal species in the Everglades to become extinct—even the alligators (Sarill 3)!

Transitions such as *and, but,* or *or* help writers make connections between words in a sentence, while words and phrases such as *also, in addition to,* and *likewise* help writers establish relationships between ideas in body paragraphs. Transitions help make connections between words in a sentence and ideas in individual paragraphs. Adding transition words or phrases like these to the beginning or end of a paragraph can help a writer guide readers smoothly through a text.

 ## IDENTIFICATION AND APPLICATION

- Body paragraphs are the middle paragraphs that come between the introduction and the conclusion. In an argumentative essay, these paragraphs provide reasons and supporting evidence and focus on one central idea for each body paragraph.
  › A topic sentence clearly states the central idea of a body paragraph.
  › Evidence consists of facts, definitions, quotations, statistics, and examples.
  › Analysis explains how the evidence supports the topic sentence and the claim.
  › A concluding sentence wraps up the central (or main) idea of the paragraph.

- Certain transition words and phrases, such as *for example,* can show the relationship between a main point and its evidence, but transitions can also indicate the organizational structure of a text. Here are some examples:
  › Cause-effect: *because, since, as a result, so, since, therefore, if . . . then*
  › Compare and contrast: *like, also, both, in the same way,* to show comparison and *although, while, but, yet, still, however, on the contrary,* to indicate contrast
  › Chronological (or time) order: *first, next, then, finally, soon, in a few years*

NOTES

- Quotations are an excellent source of evidence. You can use direct quotes from sources, or you can paraphrase a quote in your own words. To avoid plagiarism, be sure to introduce the source of the quotation before you quote it.
  - › Place the exact words of the quotation within quotation marks.
  - › Whenever you paraphrase or provide a direct quote, end the sentence with a citation so that readers know the source of the words or ideas.

ⓠ MODEL

The Student Model uses a body paragraph structure to develop the claim. It also includes transitions to help the reader understand the relationship between (or among) ideas and to indicate the text's organizational structure.

Read the second body paragraph from the Student Model "What Do We Do About Invasive Alien Species?" Look closely at the structure and think about how the writer incorporated his or her research. Notice the transition words in bold. How effective is the paragraph's structure? Does it develop ideas related to the claim? How do the transition words and phrases help you understand the text's organizational structure and the relationships between (or among) ideas?

> *Unfortunately, many examples of alien species invasions exist today across the United States. According to the research report in this unit, "California Invasive Plant Inventory," approximately 200 non-native invasive plant species are threatening the state's wildlands—"public and private lands that support native ecosystems," and these plants can "displace native species" and even "alter ecosystem[s]" ("CIPI" 2).* **Although** *these invasive plant species pose a danger to California's wildlands, perhaps no greater threat by an invasive species exists today than that of the Burmese python in the Florida Everglades.*

The **topic sentence** of this paragraph refers back to the **claim,** which argues that invasive species are a big problem. The sentence is immediately followed by **evidence** in the form of a **quotation** that contains a statistic and a definition. The writer neatly **integrates** the quotation and introduces it by identifying the source. Next follows some analysis. The writer explains that although the threat from invasive species is bad in California, it is worse in Florida. The **transition** word *although* indicates the contrast. This sentence is also the **concluding sentence** of the paragraph and clearly broadcasts to readers that the next paragraph of the argumentative essay will focus on the invasion of the Burmese python in the Florida Everglades.

PRACTICE

Write the body paragraphs of your essay following the format above. Then choose a paragraph to edit. Make sure you have used clear transitions, and check that you have integrated your research smoothly and correctly. When you have finished, exchange work with a partner. Offer each other feedback by answering the following questions:

- How accurate is the topic sentence? Does it state what the paragraph is about? Does it refer to the claim?

- How strong is the evidence used to support the topic sentence?

- Are all quotes and paraphrases integrated well and cited properly?

- Does the evidence thoroughly support the topic sentence—and the claim?

- Does the paragraph include analysis?

- How effective is the concluding sentence?

Please note that excerpts and passages in the StudySync® library and this workbook are intended as touchstones to generate interest in an author's work. The excerpts and passages do not substitute for the reading of entire texts, and StudySync® strongly recommends that students seek out and purchase the whole literary or informational work in order to experience it as the author intended. Links to online resellers are available in our digital library. In addition, complete works may be ordered through an authorized reseller by filling out and returning to StudySync® the order form enclosed in this workbook.

Reading & Writing Companion   **457**

DRAFT

WRITING PROMPT

As you've seen in the short stories and novel and play excerpts in this unit, human interactions are often complicated. Sometimes, we're unaware of the consequences of our actions not only with other humans but also with the environment. For example, what should we do about the "invasive alien species" (sounds like science fiction, doesn't it?) we've introduced into California—species that are threatening the state's native plants and animals? It's your call. Write an argumentative essay in which you explore the challenges caused by human interaction (interference) with the environment. First, reread "California Invasive Plant Inventory" to review the issue of invasive species. Then do research. Choose an invasive plant or animal, such as the Burmese python that people have introduced into the Florida Everglades or kudzu, a spreading invasive plant. Research your invasive plant or animal in at least three print or digital sources, such as books, magazines, or reliable websites. As you research, ask yourself: Should humans try to solve this problem or let nature take its course?

Your argument should include:

- an explicitly stated claim about whether humans should try to clean up the "mess" they started
- persuasive reasons and relevant textual evidence, logically organized
- acknowledgment of opposing claims or other points of view
- citations of your sources in your essay and in a Works Cited page
- a conclusion that restates your claim and summarizes your persuasive evidence

You've already begun working on your own argumentative essay. So far, you've thought about your purpose, audience, and topic. You've researched invasive species and the problems they cause. You've also researched possible solutions, so you should have some solid evidence that supports your claim, or thesis statement, by now. You've decided how to organize your argument and have gathered supporting details in the form of reasons and relevant evidence. You've also thought about and begun to write an introduction, body paragraphs, and a conclusion. What's left to do? It's time to put all your hard work together to write a draft of your argumentative essay.

Use your road map and your other prewriting and planning materials to help you as you write. Remember that an argument begins with an introduction that contains your explicitly stated claim. Body paragraphs then develop your claim by providing supporting details—your reasons and relevant evidence, such as facts, statistics, quotations from experts, and examples. These middle paragraphs also contain an analysis of your evidence, and they include transitions. These transition words and phrases help your readers recognize your organizational structure and the connections between (or among) your ideas. Your concluding paragraph restates or reinforces your claim and summarizes the important points from the argument you've made. Your conclusion may also contain your strongest argument, and it may leave your readers with something intriguing to think about.

When drafting your argumentative essay, ask yourself these questions:

- How effective is my introduction? Will my "hook" grab my reader's interest?
- How can I express my claim more clearly? Will readers understand which side I'm on?
- Which relevant evidence from my research—including facts, quotations, statistics, and examples—best supports my claim?
- How can I use transitions to improve the structure and flow of my argument?
- How well have I integrated quotations and paraphrases from my research into the body of my essay?
- How convincing are my reasons and evidence?
- How effectively do I restate my claim in the conclusion?
- Have I left my readers with something to think about?

Be sure to read your draft closely before you submit it. You want to make sure that you've addressed every part of the prompt.

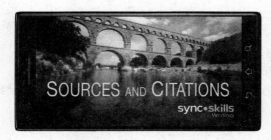

SKILL: SOURCES AND CITATIONS

DEFINE

As you have learned, sources are the texts that writers use to research their writing. A primary source is a firsthand account of events by the person who experienced them. Another type of source is known as a secondary source. This is a source that analyzes or interprets primary sources. Citations are notes that provide information about the source texts. It is necessary for a writer to provide a citation if he or she quotes directly from a text or refers to someone else's ideas. The citation lets readers know who stated the quoted words or originally came up with the idea.

IDENTIFICATION AND APPLICATION

- Sources can be either primary or secondary. Primary sources are firsthand accounts or original materials, such as the following:
  › Letters or other correspondence
  › Photographs
  › Official documents
  › Diaries or journals
  › Autobiographies or memoirs
  › Eyewitness accounts and interviews
  › Audio recordings and radio broadcasts
  › Literary texts, such as novels, poems, fables, and dramas
  › Works of art
  › Artifacts
  › Scientific lab reports and study results

- Secondary sources are usually texts. They are the written interpretation and analysis of primary source materials. Some examples of secondary sources include:
  › Encyclopedia articles
  › Textbooks

> Histories
> Documentary films
> News analyses
> Science books and articles

- Whether sources are primary or secondary, they must be **credible** and **accurate.** This means the information in the sources should be reliable.

- When a writer quotes directly from a source, he or she must copy the words exactly as they appear in the source, placing them within quotation marks. Here's an example from the Student Model:

  According to a recent online article, "Invasive Species," published by the National Wildlife Federation, "Approximately, 42% of Threatened or Endangered species are at risk primarily due to invasive species" ("Invasive Species" 1).

- Writers must cite the sources they're quoting directly. One way to do this is by putting the author's name (or the title, if there is no author) in parentheses at the end of the sentence and the page number on which the quotation appears. Another method is to cite the author's name or source title in the sentence. In the example above from the Student Model, the writer does both because the citation in parentheses does not make clear who actually said the quoted words.

- Writers must also provide citations when borrowing ideas from another source, even when writers are just paraphrasing, or putting the ideas into their own words. Citations serve to credit the source and help readers find out where they can learn more. Furthermore, they help writers avoid **plagiarizing,** or presenting the words and ideas of someone else as their own.

- There are several different styles for citations. Ask your teacher to identify the style he or she prefers.

- Writers who cite sources in the body of their writing need to provide a **Works Cited** section that lists all the sources the writer used. As with citations, there are different styles of Works Cited lists, but the sources are always listed in alphabetical order, by author's last name, or, if the source has no author, then by the title.

 ## MODEL

In this excerpt from the Student Model "What Do We Do About Invasive Alien Species?" the writer quotes from two different sources and identifies each source.

In her article "Snakes on the 'Glades," published online in *U.S. News & World Report*, Laura Bradley explains that **"the Burmese python first arrived in Florida as part of the exotic pet trade, and over time made its way into the Everglades as overwhelmed pet owners released the animals into the wild or they escaped"** (Bradley 2). As a result of the actions of these irresponsible pet owners, Florida is facing a huge problem today. According to Michael Sarill, in his blog "Burmese Pythons in the Everglades," scientists estimate that **"anywhere between 30,000 and 150,000 Burmese Pythons exist in South Florida"** (Sarill 1). Because pythons are good at hiding, scientists do not know how many are really out there. **Yet according to Sarill, they do know that the population of native species has declined 90 percent in recent years—including 100 percent for rabbits and some other small mammals (Sarill 1).** Think of the effects of this over time: **The pythons could cause the extinction of every native animal species in the Everglades. Even the alligators are not safe. Pythons have been known to take on alligators and win (Sarill 3)!**

Notice that only the portions of text taken directly from the source appear in quotations. Paraphrased information should not appear within quotation marks but still must be cited. In each case, the author's last name and the page number on which the information appears are placed in parentheses after the sentence that contains the quoted or paraphrased material.

Here is how the writer's sources appear in the Works Cited section that follows the argumentative essay:

Works Cited

Bradley, Laura. "Snakes on the 'Glades." *U.S. News & World Report* 21 July 2014. Web. **9 Dec. 2014.** <http://www.usnews.com/news/articles/2014/07/21/invasive-pythons-threaten-florida-everglades>

California Invasive Plant Council. "California Invasive Plant Inventory." 2006. Print.

"Invasive Species." National Wildlife Federation. **Web. 9 Dec. 2014** <http://www.nwf.org/wildlife/threats-to-wildlife/invasive-species.aspx>

Sarill, Michael. "Burmese Pythons in the Everglades." *Baboon* 12 Sept. 2013. Web. **9 Dec. 2014.** <http://www.baboongame.com/blog/burmese-pythons-everglades#.Vlc9NVrgA1Q>

Notice how the sources are listed alphabetically by the author's last name, or if the source has no author, then by the title. The author's name is followed by the title of the piece, and the title is followed by the publication information. When the writer uses a source published online, the writer needs to identify its URL and give the date of when he or she accessed it. From this Works Cited section, you can tell that the writer accessed three of the online sources on the same day.

 PRACTICE

If you have not yet written your Works Cited section, you can do that now. Go back to your draft and check that you have cited your sources correctly. Edit your citations, making sure they follow the conventions your teacher recommended. Then exchange your Works Cited section with a partner and provide each other with feedback. Look carefully at how your partner alphabetized, formatted, and punctuated the citations. Edit and provide constructive feedback.

REVISE

WRITING PROMPT

As you've seen in the short stories and novel and play excerpts in this unit, human interactions are often complicated. Sometimes, we're unaware of the consequences of our actions not only with other humans but also with the environment. For example, what should we do about the "invasive alien species" (sounds like science fiction, doesn't it?) we've introduced into California—species that are threatening the state's native plants and animals? It's your call. Write an argumentative essay in which you explore the challenges caused by human interaction (interference) with the environment. First, reread "California Invasive Plant Inventory" to review the issue of invasive species. Then do research. Choose an invasive plant or animal, such as the Burmese python that people have introduced into the Florida Everglades or kudzu, a spreading invasive plant. Research your invasive plant or animal in at least three print or digital sources, such as books, magazines, or reliable websites. As you research, ask yourself: Should humans try to solve this problem or let nature take its course?

Your argument should include:

- an explicitly stated claim about whether humans should try to clean up the "mess" they started

- persuasive reasons and relevant textual evidence, logically organized

- acknowledgment of opposing claims or other points of view

- citations of your sources in your essay and in a Works Cited page

- a conclusion that restates your claim and summarizes your persuasive evidence

You have written a draft of your argumentative essay. You have also received feedback from your peers about how to improve it. Now you are going to revise your draft.

Here are some recommendations to help you revise:

- Review the suggestions made by your peers. You don't have to incorporate every suggestion, but you should carefully consider each one.

- Remember to maintain a formal style. A formal style is appropriate for your purpose—persuading readers to agree with your ideas about a topic. It is also appropriate for your audience—students, teachers, family members, and other readers interested in learning more about your topic.

  › Use standard English in your writing. As you revise, eliminate any informal language, particularly slang, unless it is included in quoted material or is essential to readers' understanding.

  › Review your language. Look for the most persuasive language you can use.

  › Check that you have placed phrases and clauses correctly in each sentence. Now that you know how to use adjective clauses, make sure that you place them logically when you combine sentences.

  › Look for and correct any dangling modifiers by revising a few words. See the following example:

    › **Unclear:** Having finished her homework, a snack was needed.
    › **Corrected:** Having finished her homework, Carla needed a snack.

  › Fix any misplaced modifiers by rearranging your words. See the following example:

    › **Unclear:** Ted ran for the bus in his raincoat, which was ten minutes late.
    › **Correct:** Ted ran in his raincoat for the bus, which was ten minutes late.

  › Incorporate sentence variety in your writing. Check that you aren't beginning every sentence in the same way. Try for a mix of simple, compound, complex, and compound-complex sentences. This will create an interesting structure that will keep readers engaged in your writing.

- After you have revised for elements of style, use these questions to review your argument for how you could improve its organization and supporting details:

  › How explicitly have you stated your claim in the introduction? Could you revise your claim, or thesis statement, to make your position clearer to your readers?

Copyright © BookheadEd Learning, LLC

> Is your organizational structure clear? Is it the best choice for your argument? Would your argument flow better if you used more or different transitions?
> Do you need to add more evidence such as quotations, facts, examples, statistics, or other data to support your claim? Are you missing supporting details that could help your readers better understand your ideas?
> How well have you incorporated your research into your sentences and paragraphs?
> Are your quotations clearly introduced and punctuated properly?
> Have you double-checked your citations to make sure you have correctly cited the source of the quote in the body of the essay and in the Works Cited section of the paper?

EDIT, PROOFREAD AND PUBLISH

WRITING PROMPT

As you've seen in the short stories and novel and play excerpts in this unit, human interactions are often complicated. Sometimes, we're unaware of the consequences of our actions not only with other humans but also with the environment. For example, what should we do about the "invasive alien species" (sounds like science fiction, doesn't it?) we've introduced into California—species that are threatening the state's native plants and animals? It's your call. Write an argumentative essay in which you explore the challenges caused by human interaction (interference) with the environment. First, reread "California Invasive Plant Inventory" to review the issue of invasive species. Then do research. Choose an invasive plant or animal, such as the Burmese python that people have introduced into the Florida Everglades or kudzu, a spreading invasive plant. Research your invasive plant or animal in at least three print or digital sources, such as books, magazines, or reliable websites. As you research, ask yourself: Should humans try to solve this problem or let nature take its course?

Your argument should include:

- an explicitly stated claim about whether humans should try to clean up the "mess" they started

- persuasive reasons and relevant textual evidence, logically organized

- acknowledgment of opposing claims or other points of view

- citations of your sources in your essay and in a Works Cited page

- a conclusion that restates your claim and summarizes your persuasive evidence

NOTES

Now that you've revised your argumentative essay and received feedback from your peers, it's time to edit and proofread your essay to produce a final version. Ask yourself these questions:

- Have I thought about the suggestions from my peers?
- Have I fully supported my claim with strong evidence from my research?
- Have I incorporated my research and cited my sources correctly?
- Would the organizational flow of my argument benefit from more transitions?
- What else can I do to improve my argument and its organization?

Once you are satisfied with the content of your work, proofread it for errors in capitalization, punctuation, grammar, and spelling. Ask yourself these questions:

- Have I used capitalization correctly for names and titles of works?
- Have I placed direct quotations within quotation marks?
- Have I used the proper punctuation for my print and online citations?
- Have I used commas correctly to separate coordinate adjectives in my sentences?
- Have I used commas correctly to separate dependent and independent clauses in compound, complex, and compound-complex sentences?
- Have I corrected any mistakes in grammar or usage?
- Have I checked my spelling and corrected any misspelled words?

Powered by BookheadEd Learning, LLC

Text Fulfillment
Through StudySync

If you are interested in specific titles, please fill out the form below and we will check availability through our partners.

ORDER DETAILS

Date:

TITLE	AUTHOR	Paperback/Hardcover	Specific Edition *If Applicable*	Quantity

SHIPPING INFORMATION

Contact:

Title:

School/District:

Address Line 1:

Address Line 2:

Zip or Postal Code:

Phone:

Mobile:

Email:

BILLING INFORMATION ☐ *SAME AS SHIPPING*

Contact:

Title:

School/District:

Address Line 1:

Address Line 2:

Zip or Postal Code:

Phone:

Mobile:

Email:

PAYMENT INFORMATION

☐ CREDIT CARD

Name on Card:

Card Number: Expiration Date: Security Code:

☐ PO

Purchase Order Number:

StudySync Text Fulfillment, BookheadEd Learning, LLC
610 Daniel Young Drive | Sonoma, CA 95476